Mississippi Valley Traveler

Road Tripping the Great River Road

Volume 1: 18 Trips Along the Upper Mississippi River

(3rd Edition)

by Dean Klinkenberg

Mississippi River Books by Dean Klinkenberg

The Wild Mississippi: A State-by-State Guide
to the River's Natural Wonders (2024)

Mississippi River Mayhem: Disasters, Tragedy,
and Murder on Ol' Man River (2022)

Mysteries by Dean Klinkenberg

Rock Island Lines (Frank Dodge Mystery #1)
Double-Dealing in Dubuque (Frank Dodge Mystery #2)
Letting Go in La Crosse (Frank Dodge Mystery #3)

FREE BOOK! Join my mailing list and get a FREE book:
For a free Frank Dodge mystery, go to: deanklinkenberg.com/free-book

Third edition published in 2024
First published in 2018 by Travel Passages, PO Box 15146, St. Louis, MO, 63110-5146

ISBN: 978-1-7352428-1-1

On the Front Cover: Fountain City, Wisconsin
All photographs by Dean Klinkenberg unless otherwise noted.
Wavy line vector created by starline; available at www.freepik.com/vectors/wavy-line.
Maps by Ryan Wiechmann, Riverwise Publishing (Winona, MN), and Dean Klinkenberg.

TABLE OF CONTENTS

Introduction **5**

Headwaters to Bemidji (Summer) **12**

Ojibwe Cultural Renewal *22*

Wild Rice *23*

Headwaters to Bemidji (Winter) **24**

The Big Lakes of the Mississippi River *27*

Detour: Chippewa National Forest *28*

Snapshot: Curling *31*

Grand Rapids & the Iron Range **32**

The Logging Industry and the Forest *41*

Brainerd to St. Cloud **42**

Sandy Lake Detour *52*

Detour: Saint John's University and the College of St. Benedict *67*

Snapshot: Paul Bunyan *70*

Minneapolis & Fort Snelling **71**

The Summer Minneapolis Burned *91*

Saint Paul **92**

Lake Pepin Tour **108**

Upper Mississippi River National Wildlife & Fish Refuge *127*

Wabasha to La Crosse **129**

Boathouses *139*

Lansing to Guttenberg **160**

Andrew Clemens, Sand Artist *171*

Detour: South of Prairie du Chien *179*

The Architect Priest *183*

Lead Country: Dubuque, Galena & Potosi **184**

Who Was Julien Dubuque? *185*

Dubuque's Historic Churches *195*

More Places to Visit in Lead Country *207*

Dubuque to Clinton **208**

Quad Cities **226**

The Palmers *246*

John Looney *255*

Muscatine to Keokuk & Nauvoo **257**

A Pearl in the Rough *264*

Chief Keokuk *273*

Hannibal & Quincy **300**

Snapshot: Mark Twain Days *314*

Alton to Grafton **315**

Illinois' One Horse Towns *326*

Snapshot: Robert Wadlow *331*

St. Louis **332**

Destroying a City to Save It? *348*

The Great Mississippian City of Cahokia *358*

Kimmswick Detour *368*

French Colonial River **369**

Cape Girardeau & Southern Illinois **381**

Little Egypt *393*

Mississippi River Geology **404**

Floods **410**

Plant and Animal Life **415**

Index **418**

THE USUAL DISCLAIMER (AND THEN SOME!)

Change is a fact of life, especially in the travel industry. Hotels, restaurants, and museums come and go; prices change. Although the information in this book is accurate on the date of publication, I don't have superpowers that allow me to freeze everything in time. I'll keep working on that.

Besides the normal challenges, many small businesses and museums still struggle with hiring enough people to get to full strength. Hours can be variable. Prices are fluid. Please continue to patronize these places, but show up with a reservoir of patience, too.

If you come across something in this book that is wrong, no longer open, or of such terrible quality that you are questioning my judgment, drop me a line and let me know about your experience: www.MississippiValleyTraveler.com/contact.

INTRODUCTION

You're waiting for what?

The Mississippi River has inspired poets, painters, writers, photographers, and thrill seekers, as well as entrepreneurs looking to make a buck off them. The dream of building a road that paralleled this marvelous river is nearly as old as the automobile itself.

While the Mississippi River Parkway Commission marks 1938 as their official birth year, people like Joe Young of Bellevue, Iowa, were advocating for a scenic route along the Mississippi nearly two decades earlier. In 1920, St. Louis' Truman Pierson bragged: "This highway when completed will be not only the most picturesque but also the greatest north and south cross country highway."

A beautiful drive promised a lot of automobile traffic, so advocates were excited by the economic possibilities of all those cars passing through their towns. A 1920 editorial in Iowa's *Bellevue Leader* asserted "If millions are to be spent in the Mississippi Valley by the travelers by automobiles, we must organize to get OUR share."

An early brochure for what was then called The Mississippi River Highway described what tourists could expect:

> "You will marvel at the variety of beautiful scenery, wooded drives, lakes and streams, through America's greatest cattle, rice, sugar, cotton, lumber, grain and ore producing area."

Marvel, indeed. The Great River Road has developed into one of the best drives in the United States. Don't take my word for it. *USA Today* named it one of the "10 Best Bucket List Trips." GoCompare, a British website, listed Highway 61—much of which is the Great River Road—among the best American road trips. Fox News also included the Great River Road as one of the best road trips in the United States.

What can you expect from a drive along the Great River Road today?

Highlights

I find something to enjoy everywhere I go along the Mississippi River, but some experiences and places certainly stand out. For me, the main draws of the Mississippi Valley are the river's natural beauty, its deep history, and the river towns.

The single best reason to visit the Mississippi is the river itself. Catch a sunrise or sunset, whichever suits your lifestyle. They are spectacular. Experience migration season, when millions of birds are flying north or south along the river. Look for (or listen for) songbirds in the spring or tundra swans in fall. Linger at one of the many overlooks and soak in the expansive views. Get outside and hike, bike, paddle, or picnic along the river.

We are lucky to have so many parks and public lands along the river, but if you twisted my arm and made me choose which ones shouldn't be missed, I'd pick these:

- Itasca State Park near Bemidji, Minnesota
- Wyalusing State Park near Prairie du Chien, Wisconsin
- Trail of Tears State Park near Cape Girardeau, Missouri

People have lived along the Mississippi for thousands of years, and there are places along the river that preserve much of that history. Earthen mounds and sites of ancient communities line the Mississippi. If you have limited time, don't miss Effigy Mounds National Monument near Marquette, Iowa and Cahokia Mounds State Historic Site near St. Louis.

Descendants of the original inhabitants still live and work along the river today. Check out a powwow if there's one going on, which is one way to connect with Native American communities. The Wacipi Celebration in July at the Prairie Island Indian Community near Red Wing, Minnesota, would be a good choice.

The flashiest museums may be in the biggest cities, but nearly every small town has a museum of its own and I love them all. Please show them some love, too. Here are a few essential museums and historic sites that shouldn't be missed:

- Forest History Center; Grand Rapids, Minnesota
- Mill City Museum; Minneapolis, Minnesota
- Science Center of Minnesota; Saint Paul, Minnesota
- National Eagle Center; Wabasha, Minnesota
- Minnesota Marine Art Museum; Winona, Minnesota
- National Mississippi River Museum and Aquarium; Dubuque, Iowa
- Muscatine History and Industry Center; Muscatine, Iowa
- Nauvoo, Illinois
- Mark Twain Boyhood Home and Museum; Hannibal, Missouri
- National Blues Museum; St. Louis, Missouri
- City Museum; St. Louis, Missouri
- Sainte Genevieve National Historical Park; Sainte Genevieve, Missouri

River towns, especially the smaller ones, are laid back places with main streets that are lined with beautiful buildings. Stop into a cafe and crash the local coffee klatch. Grab a pint at a local craft brewery or a glass of wine from a nearby vineyard. Save room for pie. River towns also throw some fun festivals. Check these out if you're in the area at the right time:

- Saint Paul Winter Carnival (Jan.); Saint Paul, Minnesota
- Grumpy Old Men Days (Feb.); Wabasha, Minnesota

- Soulard Mardi Gras Pet Parade (Feb.); St. Louis, Missouri
- Tugfest (Aug.); Port Byron, Illinois and LeClaire, Iowa
- Oktoberfest (Sept./Oct.); La Crosse, Wisconsin

You'll notice that there are a lot of locks and dams along the upper Mississippi River. Virtually all have viewing areas to watch boats lock through. A few also offer public tours. Visiting one lock is probably enough for most people. The locks on Arsenal Island in the Quad Cities (#15) and south of Alton, Illinois, (Mel Price) also have exhibits about river shipping.

A Few "Best of" Lists

I like lists. Every now and then I publish a new list of the best this or best that along the Mississippi River. Here are a few that you might find helpful:

- Best **places to eat with river views**: https://MississippiValleyTraveler.com/naz4
- Best places to **get outdoors**: https://MississippiValleyTraveler.com/outdoors
- The most important **books** about the Mississippi River: https://MississippiValleyTraveler.com/books

Driving the Great River Road

The Great River Road is a signed route, not a specific highway—a road map rather than a road. Each of the ten river states picks the specific roads that they want to be a part of the signed route in their state. Whatever the route, it passes through dramatic scenery, magnetic small towns, and diverse big cities.

The road follows a single route through northern Minnesota, but from the Twin Cities to New Orleans, there are signed routes on both sides of the river. This gives you about 3,700 miles of pavement to drive, so you might want to get going now.

For the most part, the roads stick close to the Mississippi River, but in many places, you won't see the river at all, except for a few fleeting moments here and there or when you cross on a bridge. You'll find the best views of the river along these stretches:

- Wisconsin Highway 35, especially between La Crosse and Lynxville
- US Highway 61 between La Crescent and Red Wing, Minnesota
- Illinois Highway 100 between Alton and Grafton
- Illinois Highway 96 between Hamilton and Nauvoo

Even when you're not right next to the river, the Great River Road passes through the very heart of the United States. The best stretches are the two-lane highways that meander near the river. It's a great way to get to know (or to get reacquainted with) the country. People are friendly, and you're rarely further than a forks-length from a good slice of pie.

You probably don't have the time to drive the entire Great River Road in a single trip, so I've created the chapters in this book that would be ideal for weekend getaways. Any of these chapters could be stretched into a longer stay, of course. In addition, you could easily extend a trip by moving on to another chapter. The more time you allow, the more satisfying the experience will be.

In this volume, all of the trips are along the upper Mississippi, which stretches from northern Minnesota to Cairo, Illinois.

I don't have space to include every community along the Mississippi River, but don't fret! My website includes profiles of every Mississippi River community in Minnesota, Wisconsin, and Iowa, plus most of Illinois. I add new profiles regularly. Go to the river towns section at MississippiValleyTraveler.com.

The Great River Road is easy to **explore in an RV.** The US Army Corps of Engineers maintains many RV-friendly campgrounds along the Mississippi, including some that are right next to the river. In addition, state and local governments (counties and cities) also maintain campgrounds along the Mississippi that have room for RVs. Most of these campgrounds aren't set up to offer full hook-ups but many will at least have power available. Roads can be narrow in some places and may not have a shoulder, and there are still a few older bridges you may want to avoid. In small towns, you may have to park your RV a block or two off the main street.

Exploring Without a Car

You can tour the Mississippi River without driving. If you prefer a bicycle, the Mississippi River Trail follows a signed route along the Great River Road from Minnesota to Louisiana. Some sections are on separate paved paths, but many follow highway shoulders. The best guide is Bob Robinson's 2008 book *Bicycling Guide To The Mississippi River Trail: A Complete Route Guide Along The Mississippi River*, although it is a bit dated now.

Paddling on the Mississippi is also a great experience, whether you're interested in getting out for a few hours or a few days. Throughout the book I've included outfitters who can set you up for a day trip or a few days. Some, such as Big Muddy Adventures in St. Louis, take people on guided tours. For a list of paddling outfitters, head to: wp.me/pwgfk-1XA. For a list of **water trails**, go to wp.me/pwgfk-3ss

If you prefer to let someone else do the work, cruises on the Mississippi River are popular and new boats hit the river nearly every year. Most of the cruises stick to the lower Mississippi River for much of the year, then head north in late summer and through the fall. They aren't cheap, but all serve great food and include lectures on the river's history and culture. It's a relaxing way to get to know the river and its river towns.

Unfortunately, it's not easy to travel the Great River Road with public transit. Amtrak trains follow the river from La Crosse to St. Cloud but nowhere else. Some Burlington Trailways buses serve river towns, but they don't often follow the river. If you don't own a car, I'd suggest renting one if you want to visit more than one community.

When Should You Visit?

Now! There isn't a bad time of year to visit. Each season presents its own rewards and challenges. The weather can vary widely from northern Minnesota to southern Illinois, although the differences are less extreme in summer. Some places (museums and lodging) close in the winter, but you won't have to deal with mosquitoes, either. Peak travel along the upper Mississippi is usually in July, August, and October.

SPRING

Songbirds and snowbirds migrate north along the Mississippi River in spring and a succession of wildflowers begin to bloom. It's a pleasant time of year for a hike, with few bugs. Days can be pleasant and nights cool, with strong thunderstorms possible. Spring can be in full force by early April in southern Illinois, but it might not take hold until mid-May in northern Minnesota.

SUMMER

The most active time of year for wildlife, insects, and outdoor enthusiasts. In the southern reaches, summer days are hot and humid, and the nights don't always provide relief, unless you're next to the river. In the north, days are usually warm but not hot and daylight can linger well past 10pm. Wild rice ripens in northern Minnesota in late August, and a succession of wild berries keeps home canners busy.

FALL

Autumn is the busiest time of year for many spots along the upper Mississippi River, especially north of the Quad Cities. Fall colors can be dramatic, and a layer of fog or mist often develops over the river in the morning, which adds a romantic touch to the scenery. Fresh farm products are abundant, especially apples and gourds. Waterfowl migrate south along the river, like the tundra swans that stop along the Mississippi River for a few weeks before it freezes. Days can be pleasant in southern Illinois, while northern Minnesota typically experiences its first frost in mid-September.

WINTER

You may think winter is a bad time of year to visit the upper Mississippi River. You'd be wrong. Winter sports are popular in the northern reaches, places where you can learn how to play broomball or perfect your ice skating. Saint Paul's Winter Carnival is reason enough to travel north in winter. Besides that, bald eagles migrate south and put on a heck of a show in places where there's open water, like just below dams. Many communities host festivals with a bald eagle theme.

About This Book

I do all I can to make sure that I spend my money at **owned businesses**. When I do, I know that most of every dollar I spend will stay in that community, which makes the whole place better off. And I know that many of those businesses are run by people who are passionate about what they do, which often means they have a depth of knowledge and commitment to service that chain stores can never match.

Sure, you can find national brands along the Great River Road but why not take a chance and try something that hasn't been focus-grouped and mass-marketed to the lowest common denominator? Why not sample some local flavor with a hand-crafted beer or treat yourself to the homey atmosphere of a bed-and-breakfast? Relax, slow down, hang out, talk to people. That's my prescription for enjoying travel anywhere, and it will be especially rewarding along the Mississippi Valley.

I also love history, which you'll soon discover as you read this book. I do my best to tell stories that represent the broad swath of people who lived (and still live) there. Some of the histories run several pages. If you aren't interested, just skip ahead to the next section where you'll find information on what to see and do in each place.

> There's no shortage of stories about the Great River, which is why I started the **Mississippi Valley Traveler podcast**. In each episode, I go deep into a topic about the river's culture, history, and natural world. It helps the miles fly by as you drive the Great River Road. Find it everywhere podcasts are available, including Spotify, Apple podcasts, and YouTube.

ABOUT MY PICKS

This book has no advertisements and no paid listings. The recommendations are, for better or for worse, based upon my judgment of what is good, interesting, or just worthy of your time. I prefer to visit **locally owned businesses**, as I wrote earlier, where you can get a feel for the community rather than fulfilling a corporate marketing department's idea of what puts you in the mood to part with your money.

FOOD AND LODGING

Restaurants get on my radar through recommendations from residents and visitors. I also pay attention to the places that are always busy. I try to find places that serve food that is a little bit different from the norm or that are popular with locals, even if the food isn't exactly cutting edge. If I don't eat at a particular restaurant, I stop by anyway to check out the visuals and to look over a menu. If a restaurant is busy and locals speak highly of it, I'll put it in the book, even if I don't get a chance to taste their food personally. The restaurants I list in this book will therefore offer either a great place to get a taste of local life or a great meal, or both. You may find other places that offer the same benefits. Feel free to let me know if you do.

I also include listings for **farmers markets**. If you are traveling on a budget or if you like to cook for yourself as you travel, farmers markets often offer bargains, plus they are great places to buy from local farmers and to get seasonal fruits and vegetables. In many communities, the farmers market may also be a social event, so it can be an easy way to meet people who live in the area.

When it comes to lodging, I focus on–you guessed it!–**locally owned places** that offer either a great deal or a personalized experience you won't get at a Holiday Inn. My bias is to support independent motels, inns, and bed-and-breakfasts. I only provide listings for chain hotels that have an especially cool property on the river. Further, I rarely visit or review single-unit vacation rentals. If that's what you're looking for, search sites such as Airbnb.com or VRBO.com. Some river towns will have multiple listings. If you disagree with my recommendations, feel free to drop me a line and let me know why I'm wrong.

If you're going to camp at a state park in Minnesota or Wisconsin, you must buy a vehicle permit to enter the park. You can purchase a day pass, but if you're going to be in the area for more than three or four days, you're better off buying an annual pass. You'll pay another fee to stay at a campsite.

Tip #1: Many smaller towns still support meat markets and butcher shops. I love stopping in to pick up freshly made sausage or other locally processed meats. A few shops might even make sandwiches to go.

Tip #2: Most campsites can be reserved in advance (even at state and federal campgrounds) but expect an additional charge for the convenience. I recommend reserving sites in advance on weekends, especially at the busier parks (such as Itasca State Park). If you're a penny pincher like I am, you can take your chances by waiting to get a campsite until the day you need it. If the park has an attendant on duty, you can get a spot without the fee. Some places also let you call and book a same-day spot without charging a fee.

The Upper Mississippi River

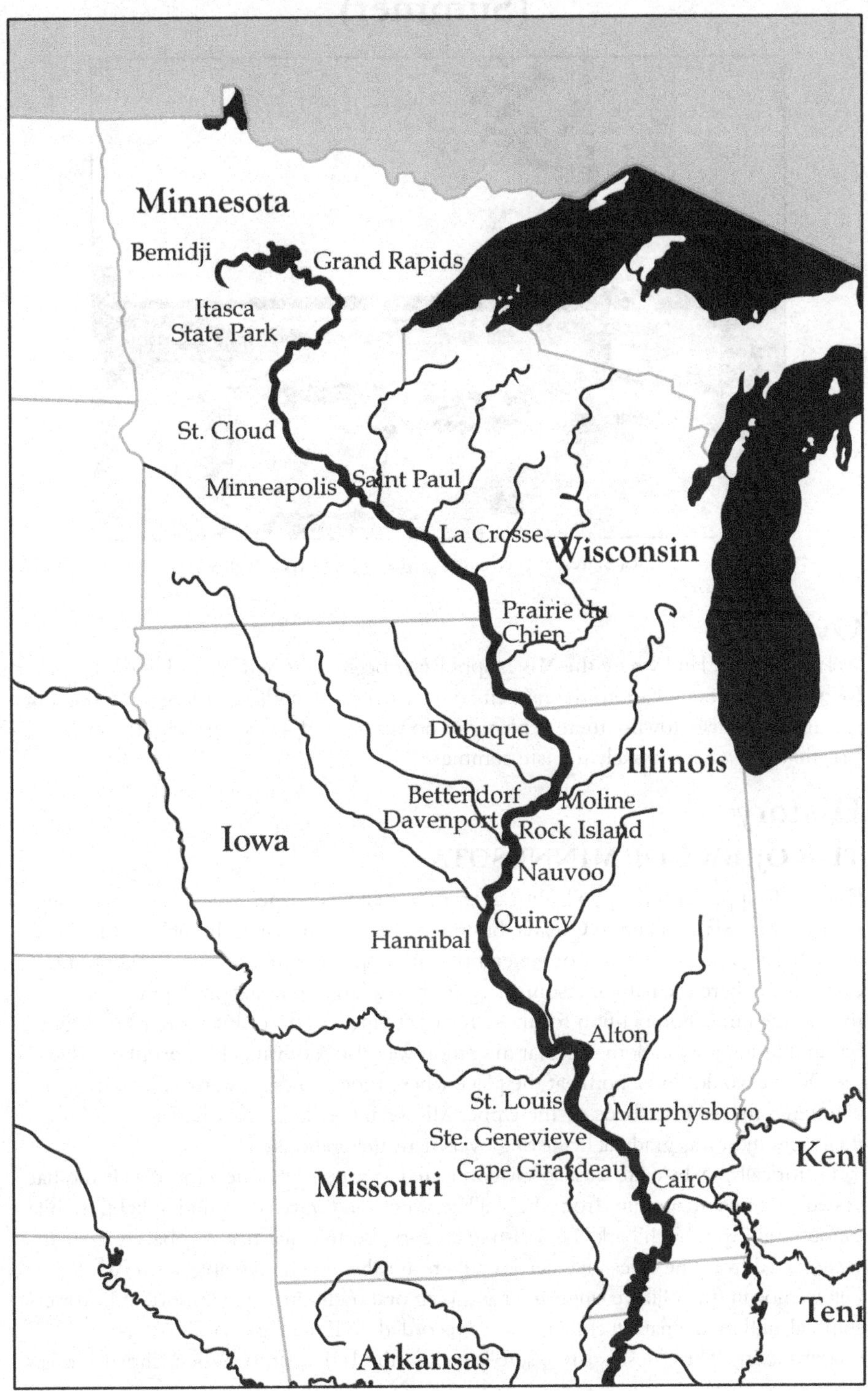

Minnesota
Bemidji
Grand Rapids
Itasca
State Park
St. Cloud
Minneapolis
Saint Paul
La Crosse
Wisconsin
Prairie du
Chien
Dubuque
Illinois
Bettendorf
Moline
Davenport
Rock Island
Iowa
Nauvoo
Quincy
Hannibal
Alton
St. Louis
Murphysboro
Ste. Genevieve
Cape Girardeau
Cairo
Missouri
Kent
Tenn
Arkansas

HEADWATERS TO BEMIDJI
(Summer)

Itasca State Park: Where the Mississippi River Begins

Overview

Welcome to the land where the Mississippi River begins! From deep within the boreal forest at Itasca State Park to the first city on the river—Bemidji, an energetic and culturally diverse college town—there is plenty to do year-round. Let's start with the time of year that you are most likely to visit: summer.

History

THE OJIBWE OF MINNESOTA

Ojibwe (Chippewa) Indians, who speak an Algonquin language, have deep roots along the upper Mississippi and in Canada, but there was also an eastern branch that had lived along the St. Lawrence River for generations. As population density increased on the east coast (where the natural resources supported a larger population than western Europe at the time), competition for those resources increased, so small groups of Ojibwe began migrating west. Some of that migration was also motivated by a prophecy that the Ojibwe would find a home at the place where food grows on water. When they encountered the wild rice beds of the Upper Midwest, they knew they had arrived. Still, their migration was gradual, occurring over many generations.

Historically, Ojibwe life was closely connected to water. They ate a lot of fish and harvested wild rice (manomin) from the shallow waters and traveled around in light, mobile canoes built from birch bark. They also grew corn, beans, squash, and tobacco and harvested food from the forest like berries, tubers, mushrooms, and maple sugar. While Ojibwemowin (the Ojibwe language) has a long oral tradition, some important historical, spiritual, and mathematical concepts were recorded on birch bark scrolls (wiigwaasabakoon). The oldest existing scrolls date to the 16th century. When Christian missionaries encountered the Ojibwe, they considered the scrolls to be objects of pagan worship, so they destroyed many of them.

The fur trade transformed life for the Ojibwe. Their standard of living expanded. Their population and territorial influence grew. They gained knives and guns made from steel and iron but transitioned from a fully self-sufficient life to one that relied more heavily on trade with Europeans. Marriages between fur traders and Ojibwe women were common, which is why one-third of Ojibwe people in Minnesota today have French surnames.

The fur trade also changed the relationship between the Ojibwe and their Dakota (Sioux) neighbors. After some initial conflict, the Dakota and Ojibwe negotiated a deal in which the Dakota hunted and lived in much of the territory where beaver were plentiful, while the Ojibwe served as middlemen to bring Dakota pelts to the French. This arrangement worked well for over 50 years. Intertribal marriage was relatively common, and prominent leaders in both nations often were of mixed Ojibwe-Dakota ancestry.

The dynamics began to shift when the French tried to reassert their dominance over the fur trade in the 1720s, which triggered several decades of conflict with the British and between Indian nations allied to one side or the other. One casualty was the peace between the Dakota and the Ojibwe. In 1736, a conflict erupted that split their alliance and triggered several decades of intense fighting. While some Dakota were already migrating south and west when the conflict erupted, the battles with the Ojibwe would push the Dakota out of northern Minnesota for good.

The fur trade was enormously consequential for indigenous Americans. Guns transformed intertribal battles, escalating small and localized conflicts to new, more lethal levels (more like European wars). In addition, contact with Europeans brought waves of epidemics to which Native Americans had no immunity. Between the 1730s and 1820s, epidemics of smallpox flared up regularly. The epidemic of 1782 was especially devastating, killing up to 60% of Ojibwe and Dakota people in Minnesota.

The crash in the fur trade coincided with the arrival of new groups of Europeans who were moving into the upper Mississippi region looking for permanent homes instead of opportunities to trade. These events put great pressure on Native communities.

For the Ojibwe, like many Indian nations before them, one response to the crisis was to sell rights to their traditional lands. The Ojibwe signed their first land cession agreement with the US government in 1837, giving up territory along the St. Croix River. The agreement was supposed to guarantee the Ojibwe continued access for hunting and fishing, but that was later denied to them. The land sales accelerated a downward economic spiral as the cash they raised was used to prop up a troubled economy. There was nearly another option.

As late as 1842, the US Congress considered a treaty that would have created a territory of self-rule in what is now the southern portion of Minnesota. The treaty would have prohibited White settlement in the area and would have given self-governance and eventual US citizenship to Native Americans living there. The idea had a lot of prominent supporters, including President John Tyler, the War Department, and Henry Sibley, one of the most influential figures in early Minnesota history. Congress refused to back the treaty, however, and within a few years, as the US acquired new territory in the Southwest and West, US leaders embraced the ideology of Manifest Destiny and dreamed of a United States that stretched from ocean to ocean. That vision did not have room for a state run by Native people.

Instead of creating a territory of self-governance, the US flip-flopped and created the Territory of Minnesota, then ramped up pressure on the Ojibwe and other Native Americans to sign away most of their lands. At the time Minnesota became a territory in 1849, fewer than 5,000 Europeans lived there, and quite a few of them were of mixed Native American and European ancestry. In contrast, at least 25,000 Indigenous people lived in the same area. Less than ten years later when Minnesota became a state, the population had jumped to 150,000 people of European descent, and the Ojibwe had sold rights to most of their traditional territory and were living on reservations.

For the Ojibwe, life just got more difficult. Reservations were governed by Washington-appointed bureaucrats instead of tribal chiefs. Most of their traditional religious practices were banned, while Christian missionaries were invited to reservations. Many children were sent away to boarding schools that aggressively pushed assimilation. Their clothing was burned and their hair cut to conform to American styles. They weren't allowed to speak their own language and were given Christian names. Captain Richard Henry Pratt, a superintendent of the Carlisle Indian Industrial School, summed up the larger purpose when he said "Our goal is to kill the Indian in order to save the man."

With the Ojibwe and and other Native Americans confined to reservations, Whites moved into Minnesota in big numbers. The state's population grew from 150,000 at statehood to over a million in the 1880s and just kept growing. In short order, new towns would be carved out of the forests near lumber and mining companies, and cities would be built on the prairies as centers of commerce for farmers. The Ojibwe, meanwhile, would continue (and still continue) to fight US government efforts to chip away at their land, as well as fighting the bigger battles for self-determination and preservation of their cultural identities.

ITASCA STATE PARK

The landscape of the Headwaters region was shaped by Pleistocene-era glaciers. The last ice sheets receded about 20,000 years ago, leaving behind thousands of lakes like Itasca. The Mississippi River emerges from the north arm of Lake Itasca at an elevation of 1,475 feet above sea level and flows north—yes, north!—to Lake Bemidji before it changes direction.

The area around Lake Itasca has a long history of human activity, at least 8,000 years. The first settlers hunted large game with stone-tipped spears and traveled in small family groups (maybe 25-100 people) with a pet dog, moving around with the seasons. They lived around Lake Itasca in the spring, fishing and collecting turtles, then went west to the grasslands in the summer. In the fall, they returned to Itasca to hunt bison and collect acorns, hazelnuts, and berries. In winter, they stayed in caves and forests to the east of Lake Itasca.

Subsequent generations of people moved around with the seasons like their ancestors had, harvesting food and relying heavily on fish and game. Wild rice has probably been a food staple for thousands of years. Later communities developed distinctive styles of pottery, and some buried their dead in elaborate graves covered with mounds of dirt. Effigy mounds, those in the shapes of animals like birds or bear, became more common about 2,000 years ago.

While Europeans had been searching for the source of the Mississippi for a long time, the Ojibwe already knew where it was. Henry Schoolcraft is credited with making the definitive find in 1832, although it's doubtful that he would have found it without the help of his Ojibwe guide, Ozaawindib.

The Ojibwe called the lake Omashkoozo-zaaga'igan (Elk Lake). Schoolcraft, though, wanted a grander sounding name for the source of the Mississippi, so with the help of William Boutwell, he coined a Latin phrase that means true head and simply took the middle letters from the phrase for the lake's name: *veritas caput* became Itasca.

Much of the credit for the park's creation goes to Jacob Brower, who conducted surveys of the area. He nursed the enabling legislation through a disinterested Minnesota Senate, and became the first and arguably most influential commissioner when the park was created in 1891.

The early years were challenging. At one point, commissioner Mary Gibbs had to stare down logging companies that were operating illegally in the park. Besides that, the park was a low priority for the state. Unwilling to purchase the land from timber companies that demanded a high price, most of what is now Itasca State Park was logged before 1920.

In the 1930s, the tide began to turn. During the Depression, men working for the Civilian Conservation Corps remade the park, building roads, fire towers, and campgrounds, and planting thousands of trees. Within a generation, the park became a popular destination, which it remains today.

The park has grown to protect 30,000 acres of mostly second-growth forest. Its forests are home to 13 species of birds of prey (including bald eagles), black bear, and gray wolves. Loons call out from the lakes. Itasca State Park has maintained a wild character in spite of dramatic changes to its landscape over time and is truly one of the special places along the Mississippi River.

BEMIDJI

The city takes its name from the Ojibwe word for the lake: Bay-me-ji-ga (where the current cuts across, named because of the way the Mississippi River passes through). The town was initially known as "Bermidji." The "r" was officially dropped in 1898.

The first settler in the area was Shay-Now-Ish-Kung (Rattler, later also known as Chief Bemidji) who lived on the south shore of Lake Bemidji with his wife Kah-ge-gay-ah-nah-quod-oke (Eternal Cloud Woman) and family and a small community of fifty people. In 1890, Merian Ellsworth Carson established a trading post on the Mississippi River between Lakes Irving and Bemidji.

Bemidji is one of the few towns along the Mississippi that doesn't owe its origins directly to the river. The primary reasons the town took off were logging and the Great Northern Railroad. Even though logging surveys began in the 1870s, few trees were cut before the railroad arrived because the rivers in this part of the state were not a reliable means of transporting cut timber.

Bemidji benefited from being near a lot of logging camps (20,000 lumberjacks worked in the surrounding woods), but the city also had several mills. The largest was the Crookston Lumber Mill, which operated from 1903 until it burned down on November 8, 1924. At its peak, 2,000 men and boys worked there. When the mill was operating and the doors were open, the noise was so loud that folks in Bemidji had a hard time getting a good night's sleep. After the mills closed, a few lumber-related businesses survived, primarily those that manufactured wood products, but people probably slept a lot better.

Bemidji also got a boost when it became the county seat, the result of intense lobbying in which the town proprietors donated plots for a county courthouse and elementary and high schools. The leading town proprietor, Tams Bixby, was a friend of the president of the Great Northern Railroad, James Hill. The railroad initially had no plans to build a line through Bemidji, but the land donations and Bixby's close ties to Hill helped persuade the railroad to reroute through town, which in turn made Bixby's land far more valuable. The economy today is largely based on education (Bemidji State University is a major employer), health care, and tourism.

Explore

ITASCA STATE PARK

Attractions

Most visitors start (and many end) their experience in the park with the short walk from the parking lot to the **Headwaters**. In summer, that selfie at the headwaters will probably include a lot of strangers. If you don't want to be part of a large crowd, try visiting early or late in the day or sometime other than mid-summer. The **Mary Gibbs Mississippi Headwaters Center** has interpretive panels about the Mississippi River, including one describing the many names we've attached to it.

There's so much more to the park than the Headwaters, though, such as 30 miles of hiking trails, wildlife viewing, and water recreation. **Wilderness Drive**, an 11-mile one-way loop through some of the remote areas of the park, is a great place to explore leisurely by bike or car. It's also a good way to escape the crowds, especially if you get out of the car and hike. Some highlights:

- The **Bohall Trail**: a short hike through an old-growth stand of white and red pine (be prepared for mosquitoes).
- The **bison kill site**: a location that yielded a treasure-trove of artifacts left behind by humans some 8,000 years ago.
- **Aiton Heights Fire Tower**: a vigorous climb to the top that is rewarded with great views of the forest from 100 feet high.

While you're in the park, check the schedule for **ranger-led activities**, such as guided nature walks.

Getting On the River

The **Mississippi River State Water Trail** begins at Itasca State Park and runs to the Iowa border. The trail is divided into ten segments, and each one has been mapped in detail, so paddlers know what to expect. There are campsites at regular intervals, and many are accessible only from the water, so it's unlikely you'll have company. Some of the sites also have drinking water. You can download the most current versions of the maps from the Minnesota Department of Natural Resources (www.dnr.state.mn.us/watertrails/mississippiriver/index.html).

Drinking and Dining

Douglas Lodge has a full-service restaurant that serves breakfast, lunch, and dinner in season. You can also get cafeteria-style food at the **Mary Gibbs Mississippi Headwaters Center**.

Where to Stay

Spend at least one night in the park, which offers a range of accommodations from camping to simple motel-style rooms to housekeeping cabins. Most are open from Memorial Day weekend to mid-October, but the **Four Season Suites** are open all year. Whether you're looking for a cabin or a campsite, reserve in advance for stays in July or August (reservemn.usedirect.com/MinnesotaWeb or 866.857.2757).

Camping

The park has two main **campgrounds** with over 200 sites between them. They tend to fill up on summer weekends. There are also 11 backpack sites that require a one- to five-mile hike to reach. They are available all year.

Lodging

The **Douglas Lodge Guest Rooms** offer an affordable rate in a modest-sized room for one or two people.

Itasca State Park rents several modern log cabins with up to three bedrooms. Most are near Douglas Lodge, but the **Housekeeping Cabins** are by the Bear Paw Campground and the **Lake Ozawindib Cabin** is by itself near the boat ramp at Lake Ozawindib. **Bert's Cabins at Itasca** range from one to three bedrooms and come with a full kitchen. Cabins are generally open May to October.

The rooms at the **Douglas Lodge Four-Plex** are spacious and equipped with a fireplace and screened porch. The **Four Season Suites** feature a kitchenette with a small fridge and 2-burner cooktop. They sleep up to four people and are the only units open in winter.

BEMIDJI

Attractions

Take your time driving to Bemidji along the **Great River Road**. The route passes over the Mississippi River in a few places. You will hardly recognize it.

Take a selfie with **Paul and Babe** (Visitors Center, 300 Bemidji Ave. N; 218.759.0164) and wave to your friends via the live stream (www.bemidji.org/webcams). There's a delay of a couple of minutes. The tall statues of Paul Bunyan and Babe the Blue Ox were built in 1937 as a tribute to the local logging industry. Inside the visitors center, you'll find a fireplace built using stones from each Minnesota county, all US states, all Canadian provinces, and each national park. Adjacent to the center, you'll find a statue of Shay-Now-Ish-Kung (Chief Bemidji).

The **Beltrami County History Center** (130 Minnesota Ave. SW; 218.444.3376) features a number of displays highlighting the region's characters and events from the past, as well as a good research library.

Watermark Art Center (505 Bemidji Ave. N; 218.444.7570) hosts exhibits in the visual arts that often feature local and regional artists.

The **Headwaters Science Center** (413 Beltrami Ave. NW; 218.444.4472) has a hands-on policy that will interest the kids, as well as exhibits about native wildlife.

The Bemidji region is awash with opportunities to get outside and recreate. One of the best options is **Lake Bemidji State Park** (3401 State Park Rd. NE; 218.308.2300), which has a nice beach and good hiking. Check out the Bog Walk and look for orchids (in June, usually.)

Bemidji Woolen Mills (301 Irvine Ave. NW; 218.751.5166) has been a fixture in town since 1920 and still manufactures many of its products in Bemidji. They can help outfit you for that winter visit I know you want to make.

Gallery North (310 4th St. NW; 218.444.9813) sells jewelry, beautifully crafted wood pieces, and other hand-crafted art, and sometimes carries books by local writers.

Gifts O' the Wild (47974 US 71; 218.751.4914), an eccentric gift shop south of Bemidji, stocks a range of Minnesota-themed items. The store sells wild rice, jams from local producers, art and crafts from local Native Americans, and shot glasses embossed with the name Minnesota. The store sells a lot of junk, too, but there's plenty of good stuff at reasonable prices.

Headwaters to Bemidji Route Map

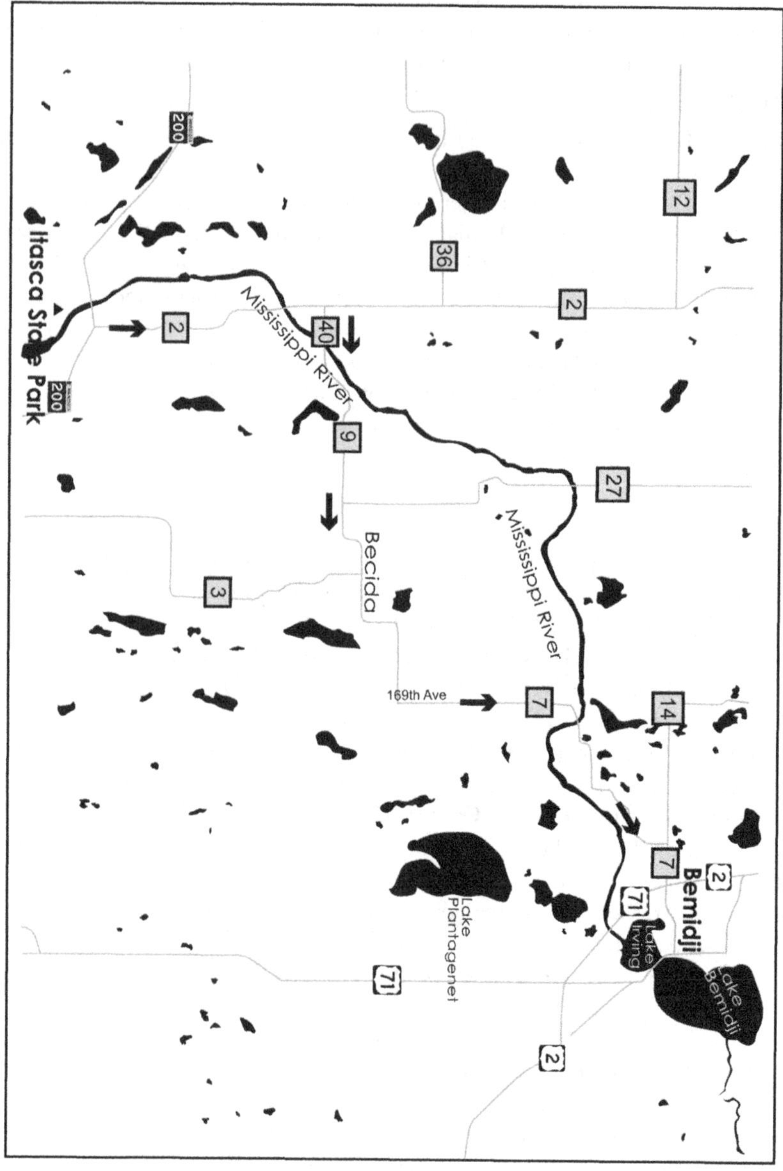

Begin at Itasca State Park and drive 34 miles along the back roads to Bemidji:

- From the north entrance of Itasca State Park, go north on Clearwater County 2
- Head east on Clearwater County 40, which becomes Hubbard County 9
- After Becida, go north on 169th Avenue, which becomes Hubbard County 3
- Continue north as the road becomes Beltrami County 7 and follow it into Bemidji where it becomes Division Street, then 5th Street into downtown
- To continue on the Great River Road out of Bemidji, follow Paul Bunyan Drive to the southeast

Bemidji Map

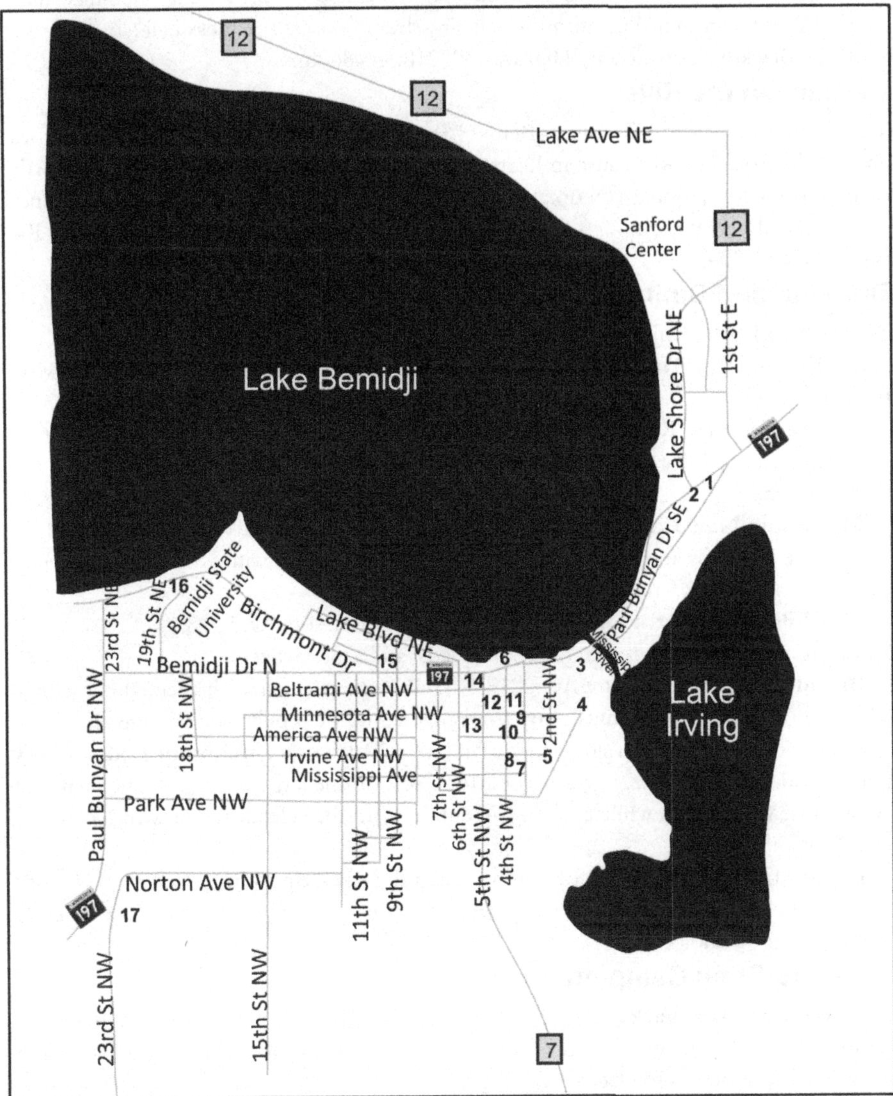

Attractions
4. Beltrami County History Center
17. Bemidji Curling Club
7. Bemidji Woolen Mills
10. Gallery North
12. Headwaters Science Center
17. Neilson-Reise Arena
6. Paul and Babe Statue
6. Visitors Center
14. Watermark Art Center

Where to Eat and Drink
5. Bemidji Brewing
3. Bemidji Farmers Market
11. Brigid's Pub
8. Minnesota Nice Café
9. Raphael's Bakery Café
2. Sparkling Waters
13. Wild Hare Bistro/Coffeehouse

Where to Sleep
15. Lake Bemidji Bed & Breakfast

Other
1. Jefferson Bus Lines stop/Holiday Station
16. Jefferson Bus Lines stop/ Bemidji State University, Walnut Hall

The **Rabideau CCC Camp** (30 minutes northeast of Bemidji) is one of the few remaining camps from the 1930s-era Civilian Conservation Corps. Fifteen buildings still stand. Visitors can tour the education building, bunkhouses, and mess hall (six miles south of Blackduck on County Highway 39; 218.335.8600).

Getting On the River

The **Outdoor Program Center** at Bemidji State University (218.755.2999) rents canoes and kayaks from the boathouse in Diamond Point Park (Birchmont Dr. NE), just north of the university campus. You don't have to be affiliated with the university to rent one.

You can also rent a canoe or kayak at **Lake Bemidji State Park** (3401 State Park Rd. NE; 218.308.2300).

Drinking and Dining

AUTHOR'S PICK: Enjoy a tasty beer or snack at **Bemidji Brewing** (211 America Ave. NW; 218.444.7011). They typically have at least six beers on tap and do a great job with them all.

For over 30 years, **Raphael's Bakery Café** (319 Minnesota Ave. NW; 218.444.2867) has been pleasing folks with made-from-scratch baked goods, hearty breakfasts, and tasty lunches.

Minnesota Nice Café (315 Irvine Ave. NW; 218.444.6656) lives up to its name. They serve delicious and hearty food, especially for breakfast, with Northwoods friendliness. I'm a big fan of their wild rice pancakes.

The **Wild Hare Bistro and Coffeehouse** (523 Minnesota Ave.; 218.444.5282) is known for tasty made-from-scratch soup, salads, and sandwiches.

Brigid's Pub (317 Beltrami Ave.; 218.444.0567) is a popular Irish-themed bar with a lot going on, including live music and trivia nights; the Irish pub food is quite tasty.

For dining with a view, head to the restaurant at **Ruttger's Birchmont Lodge** (7598 Bemidji Rd. NE; 218.444.3463) and look for a seat on the large lakefront patio. You can enjoy those good views while enjoying an entrée from the eclectic menu with Northwoods-inspired items.

Located on the narrow strip of land between the lakes, **Sparkling Waters** (824 Paul Bunyan Dr. S; 218.444.3214) serves up fine dining in a casual but classy setting. Walleye is always a good choice.

Where to Stay: Camping

Lake Bemidji State Park (3401 State Park Rd. NE; 218.308.2300) has nearly 100 campsites in a heavily wooded area on the north side of the lake. The sites are large and about half have access to electricity.

Where to Stay: Bed and Breakfasts

Lake Bemidji Bed and Breakfast (915 Lake Blvd. NE; 218.556.8815) rents three rooms in a turn-of-the-20th-century Victorian house that is near the university. Rates include a hot breakfast, and each room has a private bath.

Where to Stay: Lodging

Ruttger's Birchmont Lodge (7598 Bemidji Rd. NE; 218.444.3463) is a historic resort on the north side of the lake that has been thoroughly updated. They offer rooms in the original lodge building, as well as cabins of varied sizes and suites, many with lake views.

Bemidji has several chain motels, as well. Rates tend to be higher than similar communities and can fill up quickly when there are special events. Most are along Paul Bunyan Drive northwest of downtown.

Special Events

The **First Friday Art Walk** is a good excuse to explore downtown Bemidji and to check out the work of local and regional artists.

The Bemidji **farmers market** sets up in a parking lot on the south end of downtown (200 Paul Bunyan Dr. S). Look for it Saturdays, Sundays, Tuesdays, and Thursdays during the day from July through October.

In early August, **dragon boat races** on Lake Bemidji are great fun to watch.

Ojibwe people in the area host **powwows** on major holidays, including Memorial Day, July 4, and Labor Day. Also check the event schedules for the area's **tribal colleges**, such as Leech Lake Tribal College in Cass Lake (6945 Little Wolf Rd. NW; 218.335.4200) or Red Lake Nation College in Red Lake (15480 Migizi Dr.; 218.380.7100).

Getting There

Jefferson Lines offers long-distance bus service to Bemidji. Buses stop at a Holiday Station store (1106 Paul Bunyan Dr. SE) and on the campus of Bemidji State University (Walnut Hall, 331 19th St. NE).

For More Information

There are practical limits to how much I can include in a book, but not with a website! Check out the city profiles on my website to see if they include listings that I couldn't fit in this book.

Itasca State Park: MississippiValleyTraveler.com/Itasca-State-Park
Bemidji: MississippiValleyTraveler.com/Bemidji

There's no shortage of stories about the Great River, which is why I started the **Mississippi Valley Traveler podcast**. In each episode, I go deep into a topic about the river's culture, history, and natural world. It helps the miles fly by as you drive the Great River Road. Find it everywhere podcasts are available, including Spotify, Apple podcasts, and YouTube.

Ojibwe Cultural Renewal

Decades of federal programs aimed at forcing assimilation have taken a toll on Ojibwe identity and cultural life (and contributed to high poverty rates and poor health), but a resurgence is underway for the 50,000 Ojibwe in Minnesota. Some of it is a response to the challenges in contemporary life, but there is also a desire to preserve Ojibwe traditions while it is still possible. Schools for Ojibwe youth are an important part of these efforts.

Few Native American children have had or will have a teacher who is also Native. Few will see positive images (or any images) of indigenous people in their studies. Exposure to positive cultural images is critical for developing a positive sense of self, as well as for imagining a future. Schools like Bug-O-Nay-Ge-Shig, a magnet school for Native American children on the Leech Lake Reservation, are working to address these issues by implementing educational programs taught by native teachers that are grounded in traditional cultural practices.

Cultural revitalization is happening in other ways, as well. Powwows, a recent innovation that draws from many different Native traditions, provide opportunities for Native people to come together. While dancing and singing are the most visible activities, reuniting with family and friends and forging new connections are just as important. Many Ojibwe continue to harvest wild rice, maple syrup, and to hunt and trap animals, carrying on the traditions of their ancestors. Perhaps the most ambitious sign of cultural revitalization is the growing interest in breathing new life into Ojibwemowin (the Ojibwe language).

Language is a core component of identity. It shapes how we see and interpret the world. In Ojibwemowin, for example, the word for an older woman, mindimooyenh, translates as "one who holds things together," which communicates a very different place in society than when we call someone an old woman. The word for an older man, akiwenzii, means a caretaker of the earth.

The number of speakers of Ojibwemowin has been declining for a while, pushed to the edge of extinction by US policies that tried to eliminate native languages. By the beginning of the 21st century, there were fewer than a thousand fluent Ojibwemowin speakers in Minnesota. Language renewal efforts have worked well in New Zealand for the Maori and in Hawaii for native Hawaiians and coincided with decreases in drug and alcohol abuse. These efforts have inspired Ojibwe leaders in Minnesota who hope to replicate their successes.

It's a big effort, one that includes founding immersion schools for Ojibwe youth, creating dictionaries, and recording and transcribing conversations between fluent Ojibwemowin speakers. Another effort is the Ojibwe Language Project, which is advocating for bilingual signs (English and Ojibwe) around Bemidji. Since it began in 2005, the effort has grown to include many businesses, government offices, and public schools (nearly 20% of the students at Bemidji public schools are Ojibwe). This is quite a contrast to a time not too long ago when many places in Bemidji had signs that read "No Indians allowed."

Wild Rice

Wild rice is central to the diet and culture of Native Americans of the Upper Midwest, less defining than language but far more than just something to eat. When the Ojibwe migrated to the upper Midwest, a prophecy foretold that they would know they had reached their new home when they found the land where food grows on water. When the Ojibwe saw wild rice growing in the region, they knew they were home.

Wild rice—manomin in Ojibwe and psin to the Dakota—is not actually rice but an annual grass (*Zizania aquatica*). Early French explorers called it Folle Avoine or "False Oat." It sprouts from seeds after the water has warmed above 45°F, preferring the shallows of lakes and rivers where the water has a little movement. Ribbon-like leaves shoot to the surface by June and eventually grow to two feet above the water, forming thick patches that resemble a wheat field. The kernels ripen from late August into early September.

Harvesting wild rice efficiently takes the effort of two skilled people: one to keep a canoe moving with a long pole that gently propels the boat forward, and another to remove the ripe kernels via a technique called knocking. Some kernels will inevitably miss the canoe and fall into the water, which is fine; it provides the seeds for next year's rice. Unripened kernels remain attached to the stalks, so fields can be harvested a second time a few days later.

Raw kernels have to go through several steps of processing. In the end, less than half of the raw harvest will turn into edible rice. Freshly harvested wild rice is damp and smells like freshly cut grass. It has to be dried right away or it will rot. Once dry, it has to be roasted so the kernels pull away from the hulls. The roasted rice is then crushed or vibrated to sort the hulls from the kernels, then it is all tossed about in a process called winnowing that removes the hulls, leaving just the edible kernels.

Wild rice has historically provided a food safety net for people of the region. It is high in protein and carbohydrates and, as long as it is kept dry, it will keep indefinitely. In the middle of winter, if all other food sources are scarce, at least there is rice.

Tips for Buying Wild Rice: Prices vary depending upon how and where it is harvested. If you see "wild rice" that is under $4 a pound, it was grown commercially, then harvested and processed mechanically. At the top end, typically $9 a pound and up, is rice that actually grew in the wild and was harvested by hand using traditional methods, often by Native Americans. Some of this rice is also processed by hand, but most of the rice you'll see for sale was processed mechanically. Many people consider the commercially grown version to be an inferior product with a less satisfying flavor. You will also see bags labeled "broken" that are kernels that split apart during processing. This is still quite tasty to eat but it is less desirable than intact kernels, so you will pay less for it. Moose Lake Wild Rice sells a good range of locally harvested wild rice through their online store (www.mooselakewildrice.com).

HEADWATERS TO BEMIDJI
(Winter)

The Headwaters of the Mississippi River in winter

Overview

There's no such thing as too cold, just bad clothing, so there's no excuse to avoid northern Minnesota in winter. Just get the right clothing! You can't know Minnesota without visiting in winter. While it's true that some nights can be dangerously cold, those nights are rare. Take your cue from the locals: dress in layers and don't let a little cold weather stop you from getting outside to enjoy the wonders of winter.

The Route

Follow the route described earlier (p. 18) for Bemidji in summer. You may encounter occasional patches of snow or ice, so take your time.

Explore

ITASCA STATE PARK

Attractions

In winter, the **Jacob Brower Visitor Center** stays open 24 hours a day to provide a predictable and accessible place to warm up.

Visit the **Headwaters**. In winter, you'll probably have the place to yourself.

Put on a pair of **snowshoes** and go explore a trail, enjoying the remarkable silence. You can rent snowshoes at the Jacob Brower Visitor Center.

If you have your own skis, explore the park's 13 miles of **cross-country skiing** trails.

Drinking and Dining

Bring your own food and **dine in your suite**. The park's restaurants are closed in winter. The nearest one, **Lobo's Bar and Grill** (28453 State Highway 200; 218.266.3611), is just outside of the park; otherwise, you'll have to drive to Bemidji or Park Rapids.

Where to Stay

Several **campsites** are available in winter for those who enjoy winter camping. For the rest of us, the **Four Season Suites** are open all year.

BEMIDJI

Attractions

Take your time driving to Bemidji along the **Great River Road**. The road passes over the Mississippi River in a few places, although it will be probably be frozen.

Take a selfie in front of **Paul and Babe** by the Visitors Center in Bemidji (300 Bemidji Ave. N; 218.759.0164) and wave to your friends via the live stream (www.bemidji.org/webcams). There's a delay of a couple of minutes.

Check to see if the **Bemidji Curling Club** is in action at Neilson-Reise Arena (1230 23rd St. NW; 218.751.1123). You are welcome to watch and you may even get a lesson.

Ever heard of **broomball?** It's a winter sport that incorporates many of the rules of hockey but with a bit of soccer flair. Teams of six (three forwards, two defenders, and a goalie) race around an ice rink trying to outscore each other. Instead of ice skates, players wear boots or shoes with a spongy sole and strike at a small ball with a stick that has a broom-shaped head (or is an actual broom). You can watch broomball in a few places around town, and if you're nice, you might even be able to join a game. The Parks and Recreation Department sometimes organizes open broomball nights. Give them a call (218.759.3560) to find out what's going on.

Sharpen your skates and go for a spin on an indoor or outdoor **ice skating** rink. Many parks around town maintain outdoor rinks, but if you prefer to be sheltered from the weather, head to **Neilson-Reise Arena** (1230 23rd St. NW; 218.751.4541). Call to find out when open skates are scheduled.

Cross-country skiing isn't just good exercise, it's a great excuse to spend some time outdoors in winter. (See the next page if you need to rent skiing gear.) You can explore a hundred miles on the nine groomed trails around Bemidji. If you don't have much (or any) experience, the Montebello Trail is a good place to start, a mostly flat path that covers nearly three miles. Half of the trail is lit up after dark, which you won't find in many places. Access it from the south end of the parking lot at **Neilson-Reise Arena**. You can find a full list of cross-country skiing trails at: www.visitbemidji.com/things-to-do/in-the-snow/cross-country-skiing.

Go **ice fishing**. I don't know if this is the most popular winter activity, but it seems like it. As soon as the ice on area lakes is thick enough, villages of ice fishing houses pop up and roads are plowed to them. You can fish without a house (but not without a fishing license). For a taste of ice fishing—with or without the house—contact **Dick Beardsley Fishing Guide Service** (218.556.7172; dickbeardsleyfishingguide.com).

> **TIP**: To enjoy the cross-country ski trails in state parks and forests, you must purchase The Great Minnesota Ski Pass. You can buy one on-line at www.dnr.state.mn.us/skiing/skipass/index.html

Minnesota has over 14,000 miles of **snowmobile trails**, and many of them run close to Bemidji. There's a 37-mile trail, for example, between Bemidji and Itasca State Park. If you are interested in exploring the winter wonderland by snowmobile, you'll find a good overview here: www.visitbemidji.com/things-to-do/in-the-snow/snowmobiling. No one rents snowmobiles in the area, but if you make a new friend in Bemidji, who knows? Maybe they will know someone who knows someone who will help you out.

Buena Vista Ski Area (19600 Irvine Ave. NW; 218.243.2231) is an epicenter of winter sports, with hills for skiing, snow tubing, and snowboarding, and trails for cross-country skiing. They also offer rides in a two-horse open sleigh.

If you need to outfit yourself with appropriate winter clothing, check out the **Bemidji Woolen Mills** (301 Irvine Ave. NW; 888.751.5166), which still manufactures some of its products in Bemidji.

Equipment Rentals

If you didn't come equipped for winter sports, the **Outdoor Program Center** at Bemidji State University (218.755.2999) can probably set you up with what you need. They rent equipment for winter sports, including cross-country skis, snowshoes, fat bikes, and gear for ice fishing. You don't have to be affiliated with the university to rent equipment.

Drinking and Dining

Bemidji's restaurants are open all year; see the listings above for Bemidji in summer.

Where to Stay: Bed and Breakfasts

Lake Bemidji Bed and Breakfast (915 Lake Blvd. NE; 218.556.8815) rents three rooms year-round in a turn-of-the-20th-century Victorian house that is near the university. Rates include a hot breakfast, and each room has a private bath.

Where to Stay: Lodging

Ruttgers Birchmont Lodge (7598 Bemidji Rd. NE; 218.444.3463) offers lodge rooms and suites in winter at their resort on the northern side of Lake Bemidji.

You'll find the usual chain motels in Bemidji, as well. Rates tend to be higher than similar communities and can fill up quickly when there are special events. Most are along Paul Bunyan Drive northwest of downtown.

Special Events

Check the event schedules for the area's **tribal colleges**, such as Leech Lake Tribal College in Cass Lake (6945 Little Wolf Rd. NW; 218.335.4200) or Red Lake Nation College in Red Lake (15480 Migizi Dr.; 218.380.7100).

For More Information

There are practical limits to how much I can include in a book, but not with a website! Check out the city profiles on my website to see if they include listings that I couldn't fit in this book.

Itasca State Park: MississippiValleyTraveler.com/Itasca-State-Park/
Bemidji: MississippiValleyTraveler.com/Bemidji/

> Go deeper into the world of the Mississippi with my other guide: *The Wild Mississippi: A State-by-State Guide to the River's Natural Wonders*. The *Wild Mississippi* describes the river's main ecosystems, the plant and animal life supported in them, and lists 166 places (public lands) to be near the river.

The Big Lakes of the Mississippi River

For the first 300 miles of its existence, the Mississippi River is a small stream, sometimes swampy, whose flow passes directly through several lakes: Irving (613 acres), Bemidji (6,420 acres), Stump (290 acres), Big Wolf (1,107acres), Andrusia (1,600 acres), Cass (15,596 acres), Winnibigoshish (56,470 acres), Little Winnibigoshish (945 acres), Blackwater (674 acres), Jay Gould (537 acres), Blandin Reservoir (449 acres), and Rice (322 acres).

Stump Lake and Blandin Reservoir are the only artificial lakes in the bunch; retreating glaciers created the others. Incidentally, the Mississippi River reaches its most northerly point about one mile west of Stump Lake.

These lakes—except for Stump Lake and Blandin Reservoir—have been around a long time, although many have water levels that are artificially high because of the Mississippi Headwaters Dam Project. From 1884 to 1912, the US Army Corps of Engineers built dams at six northern Minnesota lakes (Winnibigoshish, Leech, Pokegama, Big Sandy, Gull, and Cross Lake/Pine River), hoping the resulting reservoirs would stabilize water levels on the Mississippi River below Saint Paul. The dams did give a bit of a boost to the Mississippi through the Twin Cities but not further south, a point that became irrelevant after the lock and dam system was built in the 1930s. Even though the dams failed to achieve their original purpose, they are still maintained today, primarily because they improve recreational use of these lakes.

The higher water levels, however, had some serious, negative consequences. Not only did the higher water submerge thousands of acres of Ojibwe land, it also damaged fish populations and the wild rice fields that grew around the edges of the lakes. A century of negotiations and lawsuits was finally resolved (mostly) at the end of the 20th century. The Army Corps of Engineers now manages water levels in a way that is more favorable for wild rice and for fish.

The Ojibwe called Cass Lake Gaa-miskwaawaakokaag (place of red cedar), but early Europeans named it for Lewis Cass, who led a group of explorers to this spot in 1820 when he was governor of the Michigan Territory. Cass believed, incorrectly, that this lake was the source of the Mississippi River. On the western side of the lake, Star Island is an island within a lake that has its own lake: 199-acre Lake Windigo. The island has been a sacred spot to Native Americans for at least 1,500 years and was the site of an Ojibwe village well into the 19th century. Today, most of the island is part of the Chippewa National Forest.

The Ojibwe must have felt deep affection for Lake Winnibigoshish, given that its name translates as something like "miserable dirty water lake." Winnie (or Big Winnie) can have its own weather. Minor winds can stir up water into waves that can easily capsize a small boat. Wind patterns can change without warning. Don't underestimate its power if you go on the lake in a boat. Keep your life jackets on and, if you are in a canoe, paddle near shore instead of trying to cross open water. But don't take my word for it. Ask the people who live around the lake.

Detour: Chippewa National Forest

Chippewa National Forest takes up a big chunk of north-central Minnesota and intersects three major ecosystems: boreal forest (mostly aspen, birch, spruce, fir, and pines), hardwood forest (dominated by maple and basswood), and prairie. The national forest has a lot to offer visitors today, but it was once the homeland of the Ojibwe people, and they didn't give it up willingly.

History

The US Congress sold the Dawes Act of 1887 as a way to reduce poverty among native peoples and to encourage assimilation into mainstream US culture. The major feature of the act was a policy called allotment, which was a mandate to force Indian nations to shift from collective ownership of reservation lands to individual ownership. The Nelson Act of 1889 brought the policy to Minnesota. It aggressively encouraged Ojibwe onto the White Earth reservation. Reservation lands were surveyed and individual tribe members could receive an 80-acre parcel (or 160 acres for a family). Land that wasn't claimed for individual ownership was sold on the open market—to anyone, even non-Indians. In practice, the act was about taking more land from Native Americans. By the time allotment officially ended in 1934, the amount of land owned by Native Americans in the US fell from 138 million acres to 48 million.

In Minnesota by 1934, the Leech Lake Ojibwe owned just 4% of land on their reservation. Other Ojibwe bands weren't much better off: the Mille Lacs Ojibwe owned 7% of their reservation and the White Earth Ojibwe 10%. The Red Lake Ojibwe agreed to sell off big portions of their reservation but they resisted allotment, so their reservation land is still owned collectively.

The availability of so much land triggered a battle over whether to sell it off for commercial use or preserve it. With so many northern forests clearcut and reduced to wastelands of stumps and slash, advocates from the Minnesota Federation of Women's Clubs waged a campaign to preserve what was left.

In 1902, Congress passed a bill creating the 225,000-acre Minnesota National Forest, which was renamed the Minnesota National Forest in 1908 when it was expanded to 1.6 million acres. In 1928, it acquired its current name, Chippewa National Forest.

Most of the national forest land came from what had been the Leech Lake Reservation. For the Ojibwe who lived there, the creation of the national forest meant that they no longer had legal access to 80% of their land, as well as hundreds of lakes where they had traditionally fished and harvested wild rice. For a time, forest rangers rigidly enforced the bans, seizing wild rice that had been harvested within the forest boundaries.

While conservation was a primary goal, the bill created a managed forest, which meant logging was still allowed. Cleared sections were to be replanted. Over time, 90 percent of the national forest has been logged, with just a few strips of old growth trees preserved. Every year, the Forest Service allows 64 million board feet of lumber to be harvested from about 1% of the land in the forest. Just five percent of the original red and white pine remains.

Over time, management practices have evolved, so there is less clearcutting and the Forest Service now must consult with the Leech Lake Ojibwe to ensure that their management doesn't interfere with treaty rights. Through litigation, the Ojibwe have regained access for hunting, fishing, and ricing.

Attractions

Within the forest boundaries, there are 440,000 acres of wetlands, much of it lakes and river miles. The forest has 21 developed campgrounds, but you can pitch your tent pretty much anywhere you want. You can explore the area on the 22 miles of paved bike trails, 160 miles of hiking trails, 20 miles of horse trails, or 400 miles of snowmobile trails. The forest sustains a wide range of wildlife, including nearly 200 nesting pairs of bald eagles and 70 species of fish.

The **Supervisor's Office** for Chippewa National Forest (200 Ash Ave. NW; 218.335.8600) is a good place to get information on the forest, but the building itself—constructed in 1935 from native materials like red pine—is a beauty and is worth a tour.

The 980-acre **Star Island** sits in the middle of Cass Lake. Most of it is managed by the US Forest Service as part of Chippewa National Forest, but there is some private property. One of the unique features is Lake Windigo—a lake on an island within a lake. The Forest Service maintains six miles of hiking trails and a campground. You'll need a boat to get there.

Chippewa National Forest maintains about 300 miles of trails, most of which offer flat hikes through dense forest. The **Norway Beach Interpretive Trail** is an easy 1½ mile hike that has a number of signs to help you understand the forest a little better. The **Cut Foot Sioux Trail** is a popular one and for good reason. Its 18 miles wind through dense forest along old forest service roads and are used by hikers, mountain bikers, and horseback riders. In winter, it's a good trail for cross-county skiing and snowshoeing.

There are also over 80 miles of biking trails, about half of which are paved. The **Migizi Trail** circling Pike Bay is a mostly flat 19-mile loop that passes by old-growth red and white pine. In winter, roads become snowmobile trails at Chippewa National Forest, and many hiking trails make for good cross-country skiing and snowshoeing. The Migizii Trail is also popular for cross-country skiing.

A surveyor's error left a 40-acre section of virgin forest untouched by the logging industry. This tract is preserved today as **The Lost Forty**. You can hike through the tract and explore the varied ecosystem where a few old red and white pines mix in with deciduous trees and lush undergrowth of ferns and Solomon's seal. The tract is northwest of Wirt, about two miles north of the intersection of county roads 29 and 26. It takes about an hour to drive to it from Bemidji.

The **Edge of the Wilderness National Scenic Byway** runs 47 picturesque miles from Grand Rapids to Effie along Minnesota Highway 38. Most of the drive passes through the Chippewa National Forest. Along the way, you'll cross the **Laurentian Divide**. Water on one side of the divide goes to the Mississippi River and down to the Gulf of Mexico via the Mississippi River, while water on the other side flows into one of the streams that feed Hudson Bay.

The hike to the **Joyce Estate** on Trout Lake is an enjoyable stroll through second growth deciduous forest. Built by industrialist David Joyce, whose family made part of its fortune from logging in northern Minnesota, the 4,500-acre escape was the family retreat from Chicago for over 50 years. At its peak, the estate included 40 buildings, a golf course, and a hangar for a seaplane. It takes about 25 minutes to drive to the trailhead from Grand Rapids, followed by a three-mile hike (one-way) through the woods to reach the estate.

Where to Stay: Camping

Chippewa National Forest maintains several campgrounds (218.335.8600). All sites are basic (pit toilets and no electricity or showers), unless otherwise noted. You can reserve a site in advance through www.recreation.gov or by calling 877.444.6777.

- **Knutson Dam** (5 miles north of US Highway 2 on County Road 10): 14 sites in a quiet area.
- **Norway Beach** (US Highway 2, four miles east of Cass Lake village): four loops of forested, moderately sized sites, including some lakeside sites in the Wanaki and Cass Lake loops, but the only electric sites are in the Chippewa loop; all loops have showers.
- **Winnie Campground** (on Forest Road 2168, about 18 miles from Cass Lake): off the beaten path on the western shore of Lake Winnie in deep woods, but it is one of the few campgrounds with a blacktop road all the way to it; the sites are large and rustic, and some are on the water.
- **Star Island** (southwest shore): can only be accessed by boat; bring water and pack out all your trash.

The campgrounds below are located north of Deer River on Highway 46 and are on the south or east side of Lake Winnibigoshish.

- **Tamarack Point Campground** (go 13 miles on County Road 9 from Deer River, then take Forest Service Rd. 2163): 31 attractive sites on Lake Winnie in wooded areas with room to spread out.
- **Winnie Dam Recreation Area** (County Road 9 at the Mississippi River): 22 large, wooded sites with electricity.
- **Deer Lake** (Forest Road 2198, about 20 miles from Deer River): two campground loops and a swimming beach.
- **East Seelye Point** (Forest Road 2198, about 20 miles from Deer River): a small campground, but most of the sites are near the water; it has a swimming beach.
- **Mosomo Point** (Forest Road 2190, about 19 miles from Deer River): several sites with water views.
- **O-Ne-Gum-E** (State Highway 46, about 18 miles from Deer River): a popular campground right next to the highway; some sites have electricity.
- **West Seelye Bay** (Forest Road 2198, about 20 miles from Deer River): 22 wooded sites.
- **Williams Narrows** (County Road 148, about 15 miles from Deer River): 17 sites and a swimming beach.

Snapshot: Curling

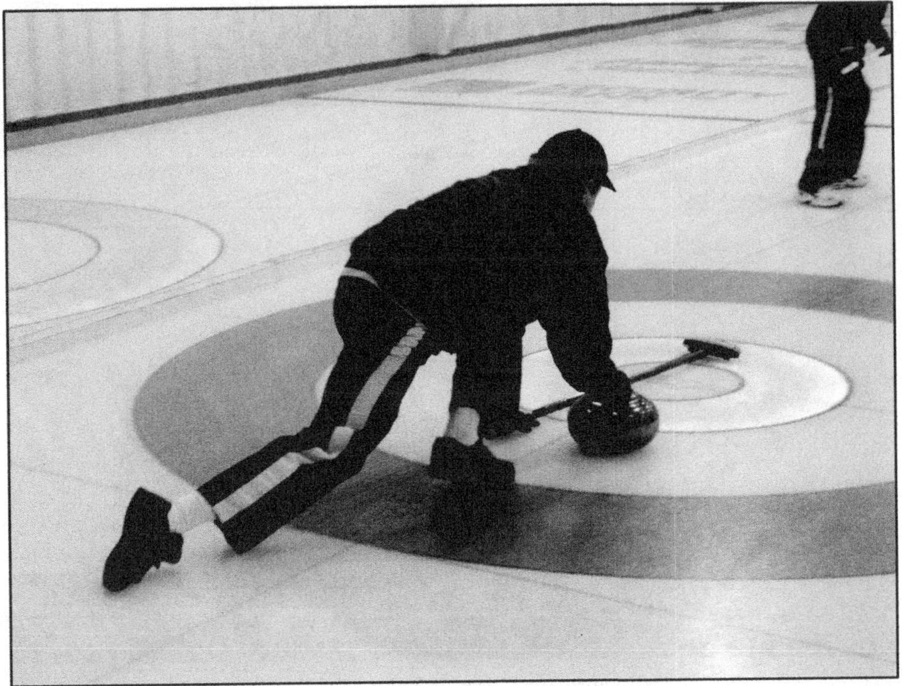

Curling in Bemidji, Minnesota

In a place where politeness isn't just a social norm but an extreme sport, curling is a perfect fit. There is no referee. Players police themselves and proper etiquette is perhaps the most highly valued strategy. In New York, you may need a mediator to order a bowl of soup, but in Minnesota, folks play a sport without an unbiased observer and no one gets punched or cursed at.

The sport gets its name from the way the rock is thrown or curled. Players release the rock with a gentle twisting motion that causes it to rotate slightly as it glides down the ice. The rotation imparts some control on the direction the rock goes; for an ideal throw, the rock curls 2-3 revolutions. Sweeping creates a smoother surface that impacts speed more than direction. Players do two miles worth of sweeping during a game, which is two miles further than the average American walks in a day.

Scoring is pretty simple. The rock closest to the tee (center) scores a point. Additional points are added if the team has other rocks that are closer to the center than any of their opponent's rocks, but most of the time only one point is scored per end (round). In theory, it is possible to score eight points on one turn, but that almost never happens.

Bemidji is a curling hotbed. Leagues run from November to March and attract a wide range of folks. You are likely to find a first grader teamed up with her grandparents on one team and a family of four on another. Bemidji has produced a number of champion curlers, including four of the six men on the 2006 Olympic team.

GRAND RAPIDS & THE IRON RANGE

Ironman Memorial; Chisholm, Minnesota

Overview

Grand Rapids forms the hub of a fascinating area: on the southwestern edge of the Mesabi Iron Range, in the middle of dense forests and the northern Minnesota resort scene, and along the Mississippi River where it turns south. Grand Rapids is also the seat of government for Itasca County, which—at 2,844 square miles—is bigger than two US states. Stay in Grand Rapids and use it as a base to explore the Mesabi Iron Range and other nearby sites, then lose yourself in the forest for a few days.

History

GRAND RAPIDS

Grand Rapids was founded at the foot of 3½ miles of rapids. When WW Winthrop passed the rapids in 1857, he named them Pokegama and wrote:

> "Pokegama is the most interesting and romantic point on the Mississippi above St. Anthony. The river rushes through a narrow pass, with a bold, rocky bank on the northern side, and over a rocky bed, and with a roar audible at a considerable distance. There is no distinct fall, but continuous rapids for about a quarter of a mile capable of furnishing very great water power for future mills."

In 1858, the year Minnesota became a state, the *North Star* (later rechristened the *Anson Northup*) became the first steamboat to navigate to the rapids, carrying sightseers on an excursion from Fort Ripley. While there were too many obstacles in the river for steamboats to travel the entire route from the Twin Cities to Grand Rapids, boats ran regular service for decades between Aitkin and Grand Rapids.

Logging began in the late 1860s, and the town grew into the main supply point for logging camps within a hundred miles. The jobs in the logging industry attracted a lot of immigrants from northern Europe. In the 1905 census, a quarter of Itasca County residents were born in Sweden, Norway, or Finland; another 10% were from Canada.

Grand Rapids won the county seat in 1892 but not without some of the usual hijinks. Rivals at the village of La Prairie looked to have the upper hand, helped by a newspaper that acted as a strong voice for the community. Advocates for Grand Rapids, though, managed to convince the owner to move the paper to their town and switch sides. The *La Prairie Magnet* therefore became the *Grand Rapids Magnet* and immediately argued that the county seat belonged in the paper's new home.

When it came time to vote on the county seat, some outlying areas reported more votes than residents. A clerk in one remote precinct, when asked who voted in his area, replied, "Everything with hair on it." On a ballot, the name of an ox often appeared next to its owner's surname. Oxen wanted their voices heard, too! Then again, maybe it was just hard to tell the man from the ox in winter.

The Itasca Paper Mill opened in 1901 and produced 30-40 tons of paper a day right out of the gate. The plant is still operating, though it is now owned by the Finnish company UPM. Grand Rapids today relies on tourism, logging, health care, and light manufacturing. Education is also an important player in the local economy. Itasca Community College is consistently rated as one of the best in the country.

COHASSET

Cohasset spreads out along Jay Gould Lake, Pokegama Lake, and the Mississippi River. The city was named after a town in Massachusetts; the name comes from an eastern Native American language meaning something like "long rocky place." The Ojibwe called the area Ushigunikan (the place of bass).

The Duluth and Winnipeg Railroad extended from Grand Rapids to Cohasset in 1892. The trip took 15 minutes and cost 30 cents. The village of Cohasset was laid out in 1893 and incorporated in 1901. When the village council held its first session in 1902, one of their first actions was to force saloons to close for a few hours on Sunday nights instead of the usual practice of staying open 24/7. The council also banned the abuse of "dumb animals." Some wondered if this was meant to protect the village council.

Around the time that Cohasset became an official place, it was largely a big lumber camp full of saloons that catered to lumberjacks. In the 1900 census, residents listed occupations including teamster, blacksmith, log watchman, woodsman, farm laborer, prostitute, log driver, shingle sawyer, boat builder, and steamboat captain.

The village's location on the Mississippi River was a big plus. The Itasca Rail Road ran 18 miles from Cohasset into the woods to collect trees, then dropped them into the Mississippi River where teams of men drove them downriver to mills. Logs were often piled so thick on the river that you could walk across them without getting wet. When the railroad couldn't reach agreement with a lumber company to buy more land along the Mississippi River, though, the railroad shifted its operations to Deer River, and Cohasset saw a predictable decline in its economy.

In those early years, there weren't enough local farmers, so food had to be brought in by railroad. Much of the forested land was eventually turned into farms but only after stumps were cleared, a laborious task that could be sped up with a little dynamite. Potatoes were the most common crop at first, but many farmers later converted to dairy.

This part of the state has a long history as a vacation destination. Summer resorts began opening as early as 1909 not far from Cohasset. A few old-time resorts persist, but most have been replaced by privately owned summer homes.

Although the center of iron ore mining was further northeast, the Western Mining Company operated for a while near Cohasset. From 1955 to 1961, the company excavated some three million tons of iron ore from Tioga Mine Number Two.

In 1951, voters chose Edna Comstock as their new mayor, the first woman in the state to win election at that level of government. She was also a tough, no-nonsense person. If word got around that a fight had broken out—say, at the liquor store—she'd grab a gun and head down there to break it up.

In 1975, Cohasset disincorporated, but in 1990 the whole township incorporated as a city. Tourism remains a big business in the area, but some logging continues, as well.

THE MESABI IRON RANGE

Minnesota's Iron Range is actually three distinct areas: the Vermillion Range, the Mesabi Range, and the Cuyuna Range. The Mississippi River touches two of those: the Mesabi and Cuyuna Ranges.

The Merritt brothers built the first mining operation in the Mesabi Range in 1890 near today's city of Mountain Iron, and within a short time mining ignited a boom economy. The first iron ore mine opened in 1892, and just 20 years later, there were 150 operating mines. The Merritts eventually lost all their holdings to John Rockefeller, but the mining economy kept growing bigger, anyway.

The industry did well in the early years because the iron ore required little processing and was close to the surface, so it was cheap to extract. It also helped that there was a vast pool of cheap labor from the thousands of immigrants who poured into the area (70% were from Finland, Sweden, Slovenia, and Croatia).

Railroads ran along the spine of the Mesabi Range, bringing the iron ore from the mines to the ports of Lake Superior, where it was shipped to the big industrial cities of the Great Lakes, like Pittsburgh and Cleveland, where huge mills turned iron ore into steel and Andrew Carnegie into a very rich man.

From 1900 to 1980, 60% of the US supply of iron ore came from the Mesabi Range. Three-quarters of the iron used in World War II came from just one mine—the Hull Rust Mine near Hibbing. Much of that iron ended up underground again because of the war. Production of iron ore peaked during the war years, then gradually declined until the supply of high-grade iron ore was essentially depleted by the 1960s.

In the 1970s, a new process was employed that made it economical to process rock with a lower percentage of iron ore including taconite, which usually has a 15-35% iron ore content. While high-grade iron ore could just be dug out and shipped directly to steel mills, taconite has to be crushed, ground, screened, and baked to turn it into pellets that are about 67% iron. These pellets are then shipped to the steel mills.

The mines still provide good-paying jobs, although far fewer than they used to. Mining today accounts for less than 10% of total employment in the Iron Range. The largest sectors are in health care, government, and service industries like tourism.

Explore

COHASSET

Attractions

Schoolcraft State Park (County Road 74; 218.743.3362) borders the Mississippi River 25 minutes west of Grand Rapids. It has a couple of miles of hiking trails and a boat ramp and is typically a quiet place (vehicle permit required).

Pokegama Recreation Area (34385 US Highway 2; 218.326.6128) is right on the Mississippi River and is a popular place to picnic and fish.

Bass Brook Wildlife Management Area (County Road 63 at Lake St.) has several hiking and cross-country ski trails through woods and swamp that sometimes parallel the Mississippi River. Enter by walking across the dam at Pokegama Recreation Area.

The **Tioga Recreation Area** (23946 Tioga Beach Rd.; 218.328.6225), a former mine, now offers 30 miles of trails for mountain biking and snowshoe adventures, plus swimming beaches and lots of water to explore by paddling.

Drinking and Dining

Florio's Grill and Tavern in Cohasset (105 NW Main St.; 218.999.7077) serves the usual sandwiches, but you can also get a gyro. They offer a tasty selection of steak and seafood entrées, too.

Where to Stay

Camping

Schoolcraft State Park (County Road 74; 218.743.3362) has 28 rustic, spacious campsites among tall trees; sites 6-14 are closest to the river.

Pokegama Recreation Area (34385 US Highway 2; 218.326.6128) has 19 attractive sites with water and electric and two tent sites off by themselves on the other side of the park. Most sites have a good view of the Mississippi River.

Sugar Bay Campground and Resort (21812 Moose Point Rd.; 218.326.8493) is in a scenic location on Pokegama Lake. They rent 10 sites with full hookups and cater to seniors (60 years old and up). They do not accept credit cards.

GRAND RAPIDS

Attractions

AUTHOR'S PICK: The **Forest History Center** (2609 County Road 76; 218.327.4482) offers visitors a taste of life in logging camps, thanks in part to the efforts of living-history actors. Inside the main building, naturalists offer tips to help identify the critters we share the woods with, like recognizing tracks and scat. For a more vigorous experience, you can climb a 100-foot-tall fire tower for a wide view of the area.

MacRostie Art Center (405 NW 1st Ave.; 218.326.2697) features the work of local and regional artists with rotating exhibits.

Grand Rapids State Bank (523 NW 1st Ave.; 218.326.9414) hosts an impressive collection of taxidermy, thanks to the Wilcox family who are avid hunters. Some of the animals in the bank include jackal, cape buffalo, warthog, and kafue lechwe.

When Paul Bunyan passes through town, he can kick back for a rest in the **oversized Adirondack chair** built by artist Doug Heiken (southeast corner of 4th St. NE/US Highway 2 and Pokegama Ave./US Highway 169).

Grand Rapids Map

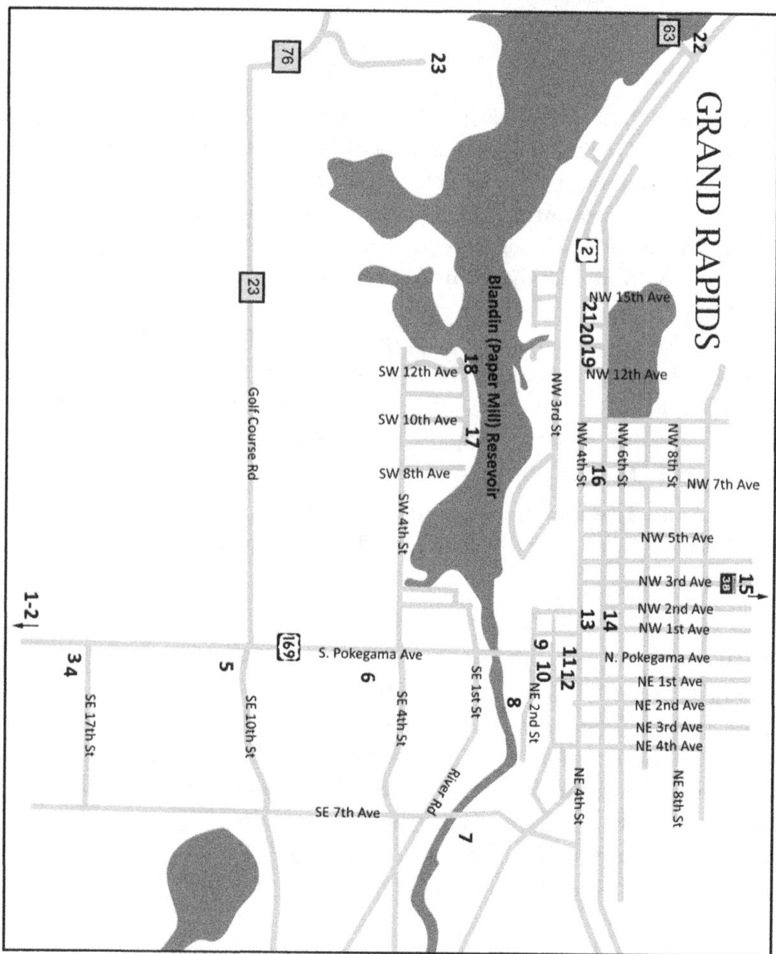

Attractions

15. Edge of the Wilderness National Scenic Byway
23. Forest History Center
14. Grand Rapids State Bank
9. Itasca County Historical Society
2. Judy Garland Museum
13. MacRostie Art Center
22. Paddle Hoppers
11. Paul Bunyan's Chair
8. Riverfront Trail Park
17. Skogebo Park
18. Sylvan Landing
7. Veterans Memorial Park

Where to Eat and Drink

12. Brewed Awakenings
19. Forest Lake Restaurant
16. Grand Rapids Farmers Market
5. Klockow Brewing Company
21. Pasties Plus
10. Rapids Brewing Company
1. Zorbaz

Where to Sleep

20. Forest Lake Motel
6. Itascan Motel
4. Timberlake Lodge Hotel

Other

3. Jefferson Lines Bus Stop

Mesabi Iron Range Map

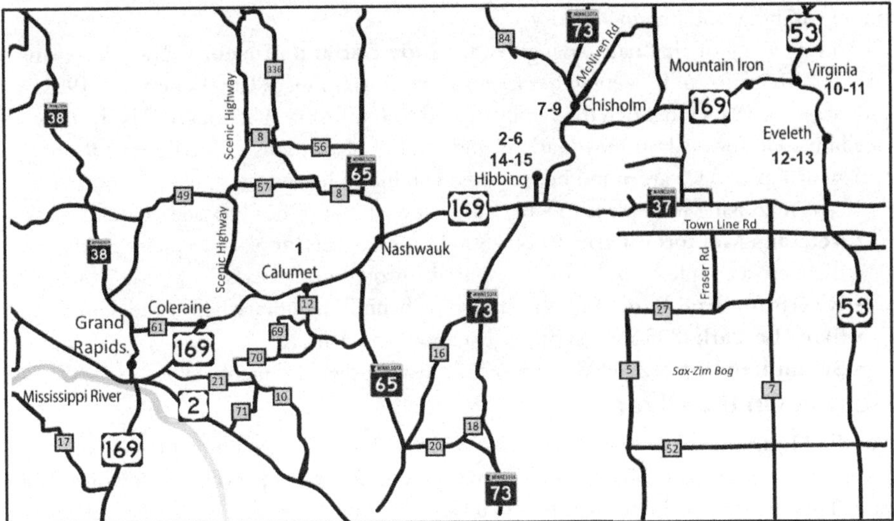

Attractions

Calumet

1. Hill Annex Mine State Park

Hibbing

2. Dylan childhood home
3. Greyhound Bus Museum
4. Hibbing High School
5. Hibbing Public Library
6. Hull Rust Mine View

Chisholm

7. Iron Ore Miner Statue
8. Minnesota Discovery Center
9. Minnesota Mining Museum

Virginia

10. Ginny the Loon
11. The Sawyer

Eveleth

12. The Big Stick & Puck
13. US Hockey Hall of Fame Museum

Where to Eat and Drink

14. BoomTown Brewery/Woodfire Grill
15. Sunrise Deli

DRIVING DIRECTIONS

If you follow the Great River Road into Grand Rapids from the west, you'll arrive on Itasca County 76. The route from there follows:

- Itasca County 23 eastbound (Gold Course Rd.)
- US Highway 169 (Pokegama Ave.) to the north
- Itasca County 3 (River Road) southeast

To get to the Mesabi Range from Grand Rapids, follow U.S. Highway 169 (4th Street) east from Grand Rapids. Hibbing is 35 miles from Grand Rapids; Virginia is 24 miles from Hibbing.

The **Itasca County Historical Society** (201 N. Pokegama Ave.; 218.326.6431) hosts exhibits on native daughter Judy Garland, as well as woolly mammoth and the area's fur trading, mining, and logging history.

And speaking of that native daughter, the **Judy Garland Museum** (2727 Pokegama Ave. S; 218.327.9276) is keeping her legacy alive. Born Frances Ethel Gumm in 1922, Judy was two years old when the family moved to California. The museum is the only one in the US focused on Judy Garland and is a fun place to visit. You'll find a thorough review of her movie career and her restored childhood home.

If you're looking for a place to hang out next to the river, head to one of these parks:

- **Veterans Memorial Park** (10 NE 8th Ave.) is a pleasant place to picnic, and there are a couple of miles of hiking trails through the woods.
- **Riverfront Trail Park** (140 NE 2nd St.) is behind the library below the dam.
- **Skogebo Park** (805 SW 1st St.) is just above the dam.
- **Sylvan Landing** (1225 SW 1st St.) has a fishing pier and picnic tables.

Getting On the River

Paddle Hoppers (17 County Road 63; 218.326.5853) can set you up with a canoe, kayak, or stand-up paddleboard for an hour or several days, depending upon your ambition. They also sell paddling gear that you can take home with you.

Drinking and Dining

Klockow Brewing Company (36 SE 10th St.; 218.999.7229) produces an impressive range of tasty beer which you can enjoy in a spacious setting. On Saturday evenings, they host live music.

Rapids Brewing Company (214 N. Pokegama Ave.; 218.999.9712) is another good choice for local craft beer. New beers roll out regularly and you can enjoy them with a meal (pizza, sandwiches, salads, soups) in a converted theater.

For a good breakfast, lunch, or cup of coffee, check out the organic offerings at **Brewed Awakenings** (24 NE 4th St.; 218.327.1088).

Pasties Plus (1405 NW 4th St.; 218.326.2234) continues a local tradition by preparing hand-sized pastries filled with meat and vegetables. Pasties fed miners on the job for generations. Get one to go and enjoy it as part of a picnic.

For dinner, **Forest Lake Restaurant** (1201 NW 4th St.; 218.326.3423) is a popular choice. You'll find everything from steaks and walleye to sandwiches and good cocktails.

Zorbaz on Pokegama Lake (32946 Crystal Springs Rd.; 218.326.1006) makes good pizza and is a popular place for a drink; they can be very busy on weekends.

Where to Stay: Bed and Breakfasts

For a relaxing getaway, stay in one of the two rooms at the **Green Heron Bed and Breakfast** (2810 Meyers Bay Rd.; 218.999.5795). Less than ten minutes from central Grand Rapids, the B&B offers a sandy beach on Lake Pokegama, use of kayaks or a canoe, a private modern room with en suite bathroom, and a full breakfast.

Lodging

The **Forest Lake Motel** (1215 4th St. NW; 218.326.6609) rents spacious and well-kept budget rooms that come equipped with coffee, microwave, and a small fridge.

Rooms at the **Itascan Motel** (610 Pokegama Ave. S; 218.326.3489) evoke a vintage 1960s feel and are also budget-friendly and in good shape. They also rent kitchenettes.

Timberlake Lodge Hotel (144 SE 17th St.; 218.326.2600) is a Northwoods-themed hotel with beautiful rooms in an uninspiring part of town.

Special Events

See what's fresh at the **farmers market** (701 NW 4th St.; May-Oct, Sat).

The **Northern Cruisers Weekend of Wheels Car Show** draws a big crowd in July.

Grand Rapids celebrates its past and present with **Tall Timber Days** on the first weekend in August.

Getting There

Jefferson Lines runs bus service to Grand Rapids (1702 S. Pokegama Ave.).

THE MESABI IRON RANGE

The **Mesabi Trail** (www.mesabitrail.com) runs 132 miles on a paved path from Grand Rapids to Ely. The trail is open to non-motorized use all year (biking and hiking in summer; cross-country skiing and snowshoeing in winter). Purchase a pass to use it.

CALUMET

Volunteers at **Hill Annex Mine State Park** (880 Gary St.) lead 90-minute tours of the former open pit mine that operated from 1912 to 1978. Call the park for tour times and to make a reservation (218.247.7215) for the fossil hunting or the historic mine tour.

CHISHOLM

The **Minnesota Discovery Center** (1005 Discovery Dr.; 218.254.7959) preserves the history of mining in the Iron Range. Think of it as a mining theme park, complete with mini-golf, an amphitheater, a 19th-century village, museum, and archives. The museum has a number of good displays, including the Hall of Geology with lots of cool rocks, and an informative video that shows the whole mining process. Across the highway, the **Iron Ore Miner Statue** (US Highway 169) is dedicated to all those who labored in the mines. At 81 feet tall, it is the third tallest freestanding sculpture in the US (behind the Arch and the Statue of Liberty). Sculptor Jack Anderson created it from Corten steel and covered it with brass, copper, and bronze. Each miner's boot weighs 220 pounds.

The **Minnesota Mining Museum** (701 W. Lake St.; 218.254.5543) has an impressive collection of large mining equipment like the 1910-era Atlantic Steam Shovel. Check out the railroad diorama in the depot crafted by renowned artist Francis L. Jaques.

HIBBING

Attractions

The views at the **Hull Rust Mine View** (611 McKinley St.; 218.262.4166; free; open May-Sept.) are jaw dropping, plus you get a closeup view of the massive trucks and shovels used to extract iron ore from one of the world's largest open pit mines.

The Mesaba Transportation Company began service by transporting miners and their families between home and work in Hibbing. You know the business today as the Greyhound Bus Company. Learn about their history at the **Greyhound Bus Museum** (1201 Greyhound Blvd.; 218.263.5814). One highlight is the collection of restored buses from different eras. If you have any memories of long-distance bus travel—like I do—this place will stir up nostalgia, like the time I took a 30-hour ride to bowling camp.

Bob Dylan graduated from Hibbing High School in 1959 when he was still known as Bobby Zimmerman. Pick up a guide for a **walking tour of Dylan sites** from the **Hibbing Public Library** (2020 5th Ave. E; 218.362.5959; https://hibbingmn.gov/

217/Bob-Dylan-Walking-Tour) Highlights include the house where he grew up (2425 7th Ave. E) and the Dylan collection at the library.

Tour the magnificent **Hibbing High School** (800 E. 21st St.). Mining companies spent $4 million in 1923 to build the grand structure as payback for displacing residents from North Hibbing. The 1,805-seat auditorium is unbelievably ornate for a high school. Go in the main entrance, then to the office to pick up a brochure and to let them know you're not a creep who likes to wander around high schools (Sept-May, 9a-2p.; guided tours in summer).

Drinking and Dining

Sunrise Deli (2135 1st Ave.; 218.263.5713; open M-F) has a nice selection of take-out food, including regional specialties including sarma.

For a sit-down meal paired with a locally brewed beer, head to Hibbing's **Boom-Town Brewery and Woodfire Grill** (531 E. Howard St.; 218.440.1710). The menu is loaded with comfort food favorites, and the taps dispense an impressive range of beer.

Virginia

Artists Gareth Andrews and Byron Kesanen crafted **The Sawyer** (Rotary Park; 4th St. N at 6th Ave. W) from Corten steel, a material that takes on a rust color as it ages. The sculpture depicts a sawyer sharpening an impressive blade.

Minnesota's state bird is the loon, and the biggest one you'll ever see sits in the middle of Silver Lake (9th Ave. W across from Mesabi Range College). **Ginny the Loon** is 21-feet long and calls the lake home when it's not frozen.

Eveleth

Fans of frozen sports will want to detour to Eveleth to tour the **US Hockey Hall of Fame Museum** (801 Hat Trick Ave.; 218.744.5167), which is chock full of memorabilia on the sport in the US.

Stop for a photo op at **The Big Stick & Puck** (Grant Ave. at Monroe St.), the world's largest hockey stick, quite possibly used by Paul Bunyan.

Getting There

Jefferson Lines offers bus service to Hibbing (Country Kitchen, 2520 E. Beltline).

For More Information

There are practical limits to how much I can include in a book, but not with a website! Check out the city profiles on my website to see if they include listings that I couldn't fit in this book.

Grand Rapids: MississippiValleyTraveler.com/Grand-Rapids
Cohasset: MississippiValleyTraveler.com/Cohasset
Mesabi Iron Range: MississippiValleyTraveler.com/Mesabi-Iron-Range

There's no shortage of stories about the Great River, which is why I started the **Mississippi Valley Traveler podcast**. In each episode, I go deep into a topic about the river's culture, history, and natural world. It helps the miles fly by as you drive the Great River Road. Find it everywhere podcasts are available, including Spotify, Apple podcasts, and YouTube.

The Logging Industry and the Forest

In 1870, dense forests of old red and white pine and spongy peatlands covered the northern third of Minnesota from Lake Superior to the Dakotas. Red pine favors drier sites that burn frequently, while white pine prefers sites with more moisture and less intense fires.

By 1890, Deer River, Grand Rapids, and Bemidji had been carved from the forest and built over swamps. Thousands of men worked in nearby logging camps. Pine was soft, easy to cut, and floated well, all while remaining durable and resistant to rot. Twenty years later, the great pine forests were essentially gone.

The growing US West had a nearly insatiable appetite for wood to build houses, stores, and railroad tracks, and as a fuel source until coal became widely used. Wood from the pine forests of Wisconsin and Minnesota met much of the demand, building Minneapolis, Fargo, Omaha, and St. Louis.

By the early 1900s, thousands of square miles of towering pines had been replaced by a barren landscape of stumps and debris that spread to the horizon. The debris was kindling for massive fires that swept away towns and people. One of these, the Cloquet Fire of 1918, burned 1,500 square miles southwest of Duluth, destroying ten towns and killing 453 people.

As the trees disappeared, the logging companies moved west. Some of the denuded land in Minnesota was cultivated for agriculture. Before the land could be farmed, the stumps had to be cleared, sometimes with backbreaking labor, sometimes with back-saving dynamite.

Early farmers had some success with root vegetables like potatoes and rutabagas, but farming in northern Minnesota was not the path to wealth. The soil was sandy and the growing season short, just 100-120 days on average from the last frost in mid-May to the first frost in mid-September.

In some places, the forests began to regenerate. Aspen and birch were the first to reestablish, followed by white spruce, then oak, then maple, basswood, and ironwood, before white pine slowly reemerged. If left alone, the pine forests could fully recover in a couple of centuries. But we still need wood.

Folks began to figure out other models for logging that ensured a more consistent harvest without devastating the landscape. Land management rules were established that allowed only a percentage of the available trees to be logged in any given year. Remaining stands of old growth forest were protected in places like the Lost Forty and at Itasca State Park. Today, trees grow faster than they are being cut, and nature is slowing restoring the forests that we have left alone.

Logging is still central to the economy of northern Minnesota. There aren't a lot of other options. Many small landowners make much-needed extra cash by selling their trees, and a few communities still have mills that provide jobs, like the paper mills in Grand Rapids and International Falls. In today's forests, the mature trees—aspen, balsam fir, and spruce—are being harvested for pulpwood and wafer board instead of pine for framing and furniture. The white and red pine that once dominated northern Minnesota's forests are now pretty scarce.

BRAINERD TO ST. CLOUD

Paul and Babe welcome you to Brainerd, Minnesota

Overview

A drive from Brainerd to St. Cloud is a trip through a landscape in transition and one that has been highly altered by human activity. Just east of Brainerd, the former Cuyuna Iron Range boomed with iron ore mining for a generation. Brainerd sits in the middle of lake country, a busy place where summer vacationers flock to spend weekends in waterfront cabins in second-growth forests. Just past Brainerd, the forests and lakes recede into prairie and farmland. This guide extends a few miles east of Brainerd to include the Cuyuna Iron Range and Aitkin. St. Cloud anchors the southern end of this route, a place where visitors can get a taste of city life and sample a mix of cultural attractions.

History

AITKIN

Aitkin owes its early growth to the logging industry. When it was founded in 1871 (when the Great Northern Railroad built a station here), it was the northern-most settlement on the Mississippi River. The town's primary industry was supplying the nearby logging camps that housed upwards of 2,000 men. All of those men needed a place to relax, which explains why the small city had over a dozen saloons and several brothels in the early years. For about 40 years, an average of 226 million board feet of lumber moved down the Mississippi past Aitkin, peaking in 1904 at 500 million board feet before ending just six years later when there were no more trees to cut down.

The city is named for William Alexander Aitkin (1785-1851), a man of Scottish descent who worked his way down from Canada in the early 1800s to work in the fur trade. Aitkin was, by all accounts, a man well-adapted to life as a backwoodsman, even though his family in Scotland seemed quite worried about his well-being in the wilderness (he was from the big city of Edinburgh). By 1831, he was put in charge of an American Fur Company trading post at the confluence of the Sandy and Mississippi Rivers. After his post was sold, Aitkin had a spat with his new bosses and got fired in 1838, so he set up a rival post. When Aitkin died in 1851 (he was probably in his early 60s), he left behind at least two dozen children. He had been married six times (or more), all to Native American women.

James Warren Tibbets was one of the first settlers, getting started with a 160-acre homestead grant after the Civil War. He served as the first sheriff and the first postmaster. He and his family were quite hospitable; they often provided temporary lodging at their house for men who were making their way to a logging camp. It wasn't always an ideal place to live, though. One summer, he had to send his family to live in Elk River because the mosquitoes were so bad in Aitkin.

The distance from Grand Rapids to the City of Aitkin is less than 50 miles as the crow flies, but if you travel by the Mississippi, you'll cover 120 miles. That's because the Mississippi meanders through the soft soil left behind by glacial Lake Aitkin. Fifty years of regular steamboat service began on this route in 1871 with the sternwheeler *Pokegama*. The steamboats' primary mission was to supply the area's logging camps, but they also provided passenger service. The route had 25 regular stops, but locals could flag down a boat at any point. There wasn't much river traffic downriver of Aitkin, just occasional trips to Brainerd or Pine River.

The area has always been prone to flooding. Following a major flood in 1950, the US Army Corps of Engineers built a six-mile canal north of Aitkin that diverts water when the river is high. The canal has kept the City of Aitkin from being inundated, although surrounding areas still flood.

CUYUNA IRON RANGE

Henry Pajari, a surveyor for the Van Hise Company, located iron ore belts in the north and south Cuyuna Range in 1882 and tried to map the deposits but failed because the ore was deeper than he could dig. A few years later, Cuyler Adams arrived and finished the job. He founded the Orelands Mining Company and opened an underground mine. Adams is also responsible for naming the range, which, in spite of how it may sound, is not derived from a Native American word for this or that. Adams just combined letters from his first name and the name of his St. Bernard (Una) to come up with Cuyuna.

The first shipment of ore went out in 1911: 147,649 tons from the Kennedy Mine shipped via the Soo Line railroad. By 1910, there were more than a thousand miners at eleven active mines. In 1919, the nineteen active mines employed over 2,700 miners and shipped over two million tons of ore.

Workers at the Armour and Kennedy mines organized a major strike that began on April 12, 1913. The 900 miners advocated for an eight-hour workday, overtime pay, a minimum wage, and health benefits. The strike was settled in about two weeks when workers and management sat down at the same table and negotiated directly with each other. The miners received improved working conditions and a minimum wage.

The prevailing view among folks today is that relations between management and the miners were generally good when everyone (including managers) was local. Eventually, though, the big companies started bringing in out-of-town managers who imported heavy-handed oversight of the workers. Conflict between labor and management escalated after that.

The Cuyuna Range didn't have the lasting power of the other ranges. The Kennedy Mine closed in 1925. The last underground mine in Minnesota (Inland Armour Number 2) closed June 1, 1967. The Cuyuna Range's last open pit mine closed in 1982. The towns lost some residents, and the folks who stayed either worked at small manufacturing plants in the area or had to commute to work in other places.

Those abandoned open pit mines and piles of discarded rock have provided an unexpected benefit, however. Many of them have been turned into recreation areas, with deep blue lakes and challenging mountain biking trails that attract visitors from across the country. While tourism hasn't replaced the old mining economy, it has helped to stabilize many Cuyuna Range communities.

BRAINERD

Brainerd came into existence because a landowner downriver at Crow Wing made a bad decision. When the Northern Pacific Railroad was looking to complete a line through the area, it initially planned on bridging the Mississippi at Crow Wing. Clem Beaulieu, however, demanded too much money for his land, thinking the railroad bosses were bluffing about building somewhere else. They weren't.

The bridge was completed in 1871 at a location first known as Omamagua (a swift movement across a river) or The Crossing. The city was christened Brainerd by J. Gregory Smith, then president of the Northern Pacific Railroad. He chose the name to honor his wife, Eliza Brainerd Smith and her father, Lawrence Brainerd.

Brainerd was literally cut out of the forest. In 1872, HL Bridgeman described the main street as "a long row of everlasting wooden fronts, peculiar to western railroad towns, and hiding cheaper and poorer structures behind." Six years later, a traveler marveled at the beauty of those wooden houses, most of which were painted white and sat amid tall pines.

Among the town's many saloons and gambling halls was an establishment called the Dolly Varden Club. The first room you entered was roughly 40' by 20', with whitewashed walls and a sawdust floor. It was filled with gaming tables tagged with names like chuck-a-luck, high dice, and mustang, while the back room was reserved for higher class games like rouge-et-noir and faro. You couldn't buy alcohol at the Dolly Varden—the terms of their deed didn't allow it—so most patrons were quiet and well-behaved, so the story goes.

Lyman White was perhaps the person most responsible for getting Brainerd started. He was an agent for the Lake Superior and Puget Sound Land Company, which specialized in platting towns and selling lots. He was president of Brainerd's first city council and was elected its second mayor. In his spare time, he organized the First National Bank and the first school district.

By 1873, Brainerd had 21 stores, 18 hotels and boarding houses, and 15 saloons. In that same year, the Lake Superior and Puget Sound Company spent $7,000 in Brainerd on buildings, sidewalks, and streets to attract more residents. In 1874, you could buy a ten-room house for $550 or, for a couple hundred dollars less, buy a nice house on Laurel Street between 5th and 6th Streets. If you felt like splurging, $700 would buy property on South 5th Street that came with a house, bathroom, cellars, furniture, stove, chickens, and pigs.

In 1873, the railroad moved its offices to Saint Paul, and half of the city's residents left with it. The town struggled until 1879, then boomed again in the 1880s when the railroad brought jobs back: Brainerd grew from 1,864 residents in 1880 to 7,110 just five years later. For decades, Brainerd was heavily dependent on the railroad for jobs, which accounted for upwards of 90% of the jobs in the 1920s.

Brainerd was never an especially busy place for steamboat traffic on the Mississippi. The downstream rapids weren't easy to navigate, and the dam built in 1888 didn't help much, either. Brainerd saw a few excursion boats like the *Lotta Lee* but not much else.

Brainerd had a tough time in 1875. In that year, the railroad bridge over the Mississippi River collapsed as a train passed over it, killing the engineer and three others. That same year, Thomas Lanihan was elected mayor after the previous one had resigned. His election was not appreciated by folks in power, however. He was a garbage man whose name had apparently been put on the ballot as a protest and joke. Even though his victory was completely legal, the city council refused to recognize him, opting instead to dissolve the city. For six years, the city was governed by the township board.

Other businesses besides the railroad kept local folks busy. The Brainerd Lumber Company's sawmill provided work for hundreds of men until 1905. Since then, a paper mill has provided steady employment for many. Brainerd also benefited from its proximity to the Cuyuna Iron Range, partly as a rail transfer point for ore being shipped to Missouri and Illinois.

Baby Face Nelson visited Brainerd on October 23, 1933, not for a fishing vacation but to rob the First National Bank. He withdrew $32,000 and deposited a few bullets in the facade of the building (201 S. 6th St.). The holes are still visible today.

Brainerd suffered a terrible loss during World War II. After US forces surrendered to the Japanese in the Philippines on April 9, 1942, some 75,000 American and Filipino soldiers were forced to walk 65 miles to a prison camp through intense heat and brutal treatment from Japanese guards. The Bataan Death March, as it became known, took the lives of 43 men from Brainerd. Most died from disease or were killed for not keeping up with the group.

A few random facts about Brainerd:

- City sidewalks were made of wood until 1900; the last plank walk was replaced in 1907.
- Paul Bunyan set up an amusement park in 1950.
- Brainerd got fluoride in its water in 1980 after a long legal battle.
- Brainerd was one of the locations in the movie Fargo, but no scenes were shot in the city; the movie did not receive an enthusiastic response from locals.

Brainerd suffered a major economic blow in the 1980s when the railroad closed much of its operation and transferred workers to other places. The resort and service industries provide a lot of jobs, but most don't pay anywhere close to what the railroad did. Brainerd has struggled to chip away at its unemployment rate, which is all the more reason to stop at a locally owned business and spend some dollars.

BAXTER

Baxter was founded in 1904 and named for Luther Loren Baxter, a lawyer for the Northern Pacific Railroad. Baxter was a small village for much of its existence, even after the entire township incorporated in 1939. By the 1970s, though, new subdivisions were popping up like zits on a teen's face. Baxter today is a bedroom community of residential subdivisions and strip malls and a lot of open space between them.

FORT RIPLEY

In 1848, the US government coaxed members of the Ho Chunk (Winnebago) nation to move from a reservation in Iowa to a new reservation in northern Minnesota. The government directed them to a strip of land between feuding Ojibwe (Chippewa) and Dakota (Sioux) communities. US authorities hoped their presence would serve as a buffer. The military opened a fort in the area in 1849 to keep an eye on everyone, eventually landing on the name Fort Ripley (the fort's third name in two years), in honor of General Eleazar W. Ripley, a veteran of the War of 1812.

Soldiers cleared a space in the middle of the forest and built a fort, a simple square design with a blockhouse at each corner and one side facing the Mississippi. The first soldiers moved in on May 13, 1849. The nearest community of any size was seven miles upriver at Crow Wing or 15 miles downriver at Little Falls, but Samuel Baldwin Olmstead lived across the Mississippi River from the fort and kept the soldiers supplied with meat and veggies.

In order to support the fort, the military established a reservation on both sides of the Mississippi River. Most of the 57,000 acres was on the east side of the river and set aside for logging and farming. By 1857, land in northern Minnesota had become available to Euro-American settlers after land cessions by the Ojibwe and after the Ho Chunk had been moved again (to land along the Minnesota River this time). Spurred by the arrival of new people, the military decided it only needed one square mile on the west bank where the fort was located, so the 57,000 acres east of the river went on the market. The land was divided into 40-acre sections and listed at $1.25 an acre.

The military let a few individuals buy land before the auction, primarily because they had land claims that pre-dated the arrival of the military. They registered and paid for their claims the day before the auction on October 19. The rest of the land was auctioned off the next day, but it turned out that the lots sold for far less than the asking price: just one to twenty-four cents per acre. Some of the auction winners got certificates, while others were told to wait until the report was submitted and approved by the bosses in D.C. On November 11, 1857, the land sales were canceled by the Secretary of War, John Floyd, because the prices were too low.

Secretary Floyd's actions set off a legal battle that lasted twenty years. All of the bidders had paid for their claims on the day of the auction, but no one had received a refund. Some claimants were awarded certificates of ownership, but it wasn't clear if those certificates meant anything. The military kept control of the land, but pressure kept growing to dispose of it. Congress authorized sale of the military reservation in 1873, but not much happened until 1877 when the fort itself was badly damaged by a fire. At that time, the military decided to abandon the fort and prepare to sell the land, but again, the process was slow. In 1880, Congress passed a bill that transferred the land from the military to the Department of the Interior, which finally got the land on the market, minus a few portions set aside for a railroad and to appease squatters.

That was a lot of fuss over land that the military never really did much with. Back in 1857, when the military was first trying to sell off the reservation on the east side of the river, they had decided to close the fort. On July 8, 1857, the troops were pulled out and reassigned. Unfortunately, trouble between some Ojibwe and new Europeans in the area soon broke out and threatened to evolve into a major fight, so the military had to re-garrison the fort. By early September, just two months after shutting down Fort Ripley, a new detachment arrived to occupy it.

The following summer (1858) was an unusually cool one, with plant-killing frosts on June 11, July 12, and August 28. On the plus side, that cold weather probably did a fine job of keeping the mosquito population in check. The fort was quiet most of the time but did see increased activity during the Dakota Conflict of 1862, then again as a staging area for troops sent to fight Dakota people in 1863-64. The fire that badly damaged the fort erupted in January 1877. The fort was entirely abandoned within a year after that.

CAMP RIPLEY

Long after Fort Ripley closed, the Minnesota National Guard was looking for a new home to replace a base at Lake City that it had outgrown. In 1931, they bought 12,000 acres along the Mississippi River near the site of the old Fort Ripley. Out of respect for the old fort, the new camp took its name. Camp Ripley would eventually grow to over 50,000 acres, with facilities to house 12,000 troops at any given point in time. From 1934-1942, men employed by the Works Progress Administration built the impressive stone entrance gate, towers, walls, and a building called Valhalla, which is the governor's residence during official visits.

THE VILLAGE OF FORT RIPLEY

Besides the old fort and the National Guard camp, there is a small village called Fort Ripley that was first inhabited by Europeans in 1880. It was a stop along the new railroad to Brainerd. The village wouldn't be much without the efforts of the Tucker family. John Tucker ran the depot for 34 years. His son, Claude, served as postmaster for 35 years. Fort Ripley had a grain elevator and was home to potato wholesalers in the early 1900s, which was most of its industry. Local folks incorporated it as a city in 1927, although the place never attracted that many residents. In 2010, the official population was just 69, down from 92 residents twenty years earlier.

LITTLE FALLS

The Mississippi River passes over a small series of waterfalls here that the Ojibwe called Kakabikans (the little squarely cut off rock, or small falls). A dam now obscures the falls, but there are still plenty of cut-off rocks strewn about.

There was once an important Ojibwe village just north of town where the Little Elk River meets the Mississippi. It was a crossroads for generations and the residence of renowned Chief Pugona Geshig (Hole-in-the-Day), who is buried on a nearby bluff. There was also a fur trading post at that junction for a while.

Euro-American settlement of the area began in 1848 when James Green staked out a squatter's claim on the east bank of the Mississippi River at a site that is within the current city limits. He built a sawmill that was powered by water from the river, but he didn't have a chance to do much more. He contracted cholera in 1850 and died.

Much of the town's initial growth was fueled by the Little Falls Manufacturing Company, which built a dam and sawmill in the late 1850s. When the dam failed in 1859, it was repaired, then was destroyed again the next year by a flooding Mississippi. The town languished for the next decade.

A new dam was finally completed in 1888 as part of a hydroelectric power plant. The completion of the plant triggered a bit of a boom. Several new businesses were built, including a couple of flour mills, a sash factory, a paper pulp mill, and an iron foundry.

Sawmills were the biggest business in the early years, however, and the Pine Tree Lumber Company was one of the busiest. It was founded by Frederick Weyerhaeuser and Peter Musser in 1891 but managed by their sons, Charles Weyerhaeuser and Drew Musser. The two families also lived in neighboring houses on the Mississippi River.

The best-known native is a guy named Charles Lindbergh. He was born in Detroit but spent most of his childhood in a house next to the Mississippi River in Little Falls. As a child, he spent a fair amount of time swimming and playing around the river, experiences which contributed to his passionate views about conservation.

Lindbergh wasn't a fan of classrooms, at least until he enrolled in flight school. He built his piloting credentials first as a barnstormer, then by flying mail around the country. He became the first person to fly solo from New York to Paris on May 21, 1927, and quickly became one of the most famous people in the world.

Lindbergh was not comfortable in the public eye, though, a feeling that only intensified after his 20-month-old son was kidnapped and murdered in 1932. The case was in the news so often that Lindbergh and his family moved to Europe for a while after Bruno Hauptmann was convicted of the crime. After returning to the US, Lindbergh spoke out against US intervention in Europe as Germany was blitzkrieging its way across the continent—something he was heavily criticized for—but he switched his views after the attack on Pearl Harbor. He continued to reinvent himself throughout his life. He became a respected writer and a passionate conservationist as he got older.

Little Falls is also the hometown of accomplished author Louise Erdrich (*Love Medicine, The Bingo Palace)*. In 2021, she won a Pulitzer Prize for *The Night Watchman*. Little Falls today is a scenic small town with more to do than you might expect.

SARTELL

Joseph Sartell, the city's namesake, arrived in 1854. He was an east coast transplant with root in Massachusetts. Sartell was a millwright who, true to his background, went about opening up mills over the next few decades. In 1884, he and sons started a lumber mill, the Sartell Brothers Lumber Company, that stayed open until the 1930s. For most of the city's existence, a member of the Sartell family was on the City Council.

The two main industries that sustained the early city were a paper mill and a valve plant. The completion of the dam in 1907 provided power for the Watab Pulp and Paper Company mill that opened the same year. The company changed hands a few times, but it was owned by VERSO on May 28, 2012 when an explosion at the mill killed 50-year old Jon Maus and injured four others. The ensuing fire took several days to extinguish. The plant later closed permanently, eliminating jobs for the 259 employees (down from 500 just three years earlier). The mill had been losing money anyway, but the explosion and fire made it too expensive to repair and keep it open. The average wage at the time of the plant closing was $26.35/hour. The building has since been demolished.

The DeZurik Valve Company opened in 1925, founded by Matt DeZurik, who had once worked at the paper mill. One of their innovations was the "eccentric valve" that could go from closed to fully open with just a 90 degree turn. It is still operating today.

During Prohibition, Sartell had an active cottage industry making liquor. Over a dozen of the towns hundred or so houses were unofficial "beer farms" where home brew was sold to visitors. The feds occasionally cracked down and even managed to send a few residents to the federal prison in Leavenworth, Kansas.

The housing market boomed beginning around 1960 and the city's population exploded as it grew quickly into a bedroom community. In 1960, Sartell had a population under 800; in 2010 it was almost 16,000.

SAUK RAPIDS

The origin of the Sauk name is not entirely clear. The Sauk nation never lived this far north, but there is a story that five Sauk Indians fled here after killing someone. Another source suggested that the name comes to us from the Ojibwe language, where Sauk means "a meeting place," which could be a reference to the mouth of the Sauk River at the Mississippi, or maybe it's just that this area had significance as a meeting grounds for the Ojibwe. I've checked a couple of sources, though, and I have yet to find one that says "Sauk" means "a meeting place" in Ojibwe. Guess I'll keep digging.

Europeans first came to the area to establish a trading post. Phillip Beaupre established a post near the mouth of the Sauk River in 1845 that changed hands a few times. The village was platted in 1854 by a group that included Jeremiah Russell, who is sometimes called the Father of Sauk Rapids. Russell was from the Northeast US, like many of the first Euro-American settlers. Before he came to Sauk Rapids, Russell worked as a clerk to the sutler at Fort Snelling and as a trader.

The little village saw some steamboat traffic from Minneapolis (62 boats reached Sauk Rapids in 1858), but the city was pretty much the end of the line because of the rapids. Sauk Rapids also had ferry service across the river, a stage coach stop, and a railroad station. The village was named the Benton County seat in 1859, but calls for a more central location were eventually heeded. County government offices were moved to Foley in 1901.

The sawmill was the first major industry; it processed timber coming down river from the pine forests. Granite mining was an important local industry beginning around 1880. For decades, big plans were floated to build a dam for water power, but they failed to materialize. The first dam in the area was eventually built upriver at Sartell in 1907.

Sauk Rapids is perhaps best known for a natural disaster that nearly wiped it off the map. On April 14, 1886, a tornado ripped through the area, destroying property in St. Cloud before destroying nearly every business in Sauk Rapids. Thirty-eight people died and twice as many were injured. Some witnesses claimed the Mississippi was sucked dry by the winds. While many people claim the tornado was the reason that St. Cloud became the commercial center of the region instead of Sauk Rapids, the reality is that St. Cloud already had a larger population and more industry. The failure to build a dam on the Mississippi to generate power was a bigger factor in the town's slow early growth than the tornado.

The town center has been redeveloped many times over the city's history, so there aren't a lot of original buildings left. Sauk Rapids eventually got the growth it desired, but it came about 100 years later than expected and has been primarily residential. From 1960 to 2010 the city's population tripled from 4,038 to 12,773.

ST. CLOUD

St. Cloud was built on tallgrass prairie where it opens up at the edge of hardwood forest. Deep ravines divided early communities from each other. Upper Town was above the northern ravine along the Mississippi River. Lower Town was below the southern ravine. Middle Town was right between them, naturally. All three communities got started between 1853 and 1855.

The first area to pop up was Upper Town. In 1853, Sylvanus B. Lowry, a transplant from Tennessee, claimed land above the northern ravine. He brought enslaved laborers with him, even though slavery was supposed to be off-limits in Minnesota Territory.

Even as he developed a city, which he named Acadia, he managed fur trading posts at Watab and Sauk Rapids and worked as an interpreter. In short order, other wealthy Southerners followed Lowry to Acadia. When the Civil War began, however, Southerners abandoned the town, and the city became an isolated residential community.

At the opposite end of town (and the opposite end of the cultural spectrum), George Fuller Brott (a New Yorker) bought a claim from squatter Martin Wooley and built Lower Town. He platted the site as St. Cloud City and attracted Euro-American settlers from New England, most of whom were committed abolitionists and temperance advocates. By 1857, the city had a hundred buildings, including the Stearns Hotel, which was a favorite location for Southerners who headed north to escape the summer heat at home. Development of lower town was slowed by disputes over land claims, however, as some of the city's land was deeded to the St. Paul & Pacific Railroad before the official city plat was completed, which created a bit of confusion over who owned what. Rather than wait out the uncertainty, many businesses just moved to Middle Town, with some taking their buildings with them. Like Upper Town, Lower Town was mostly residential.

Which brings us to Middle Town. John Lyman Wilson bought the 320-acre claim of Ole Bergeson (another squatter) for $100 and commenced building a town. Wilson was a millwright from Maine who arrived in the area in 1851 and built sawmills at other places in Minnesota. Wilson had read a lot about Napoleon Bonaparte. When Wilson platted Middle Town, he reportedly chose a name that was inspired by a story from Napoleon's life. Josephine, Napoleon's wife, was in residence at their summer home in Saint-Cloud when messengers arrived to deliver news from France. Napoleon asked, "And how are things in Saint-Cloud?" That was apparently enough to make an impression on Wilson.

And who was the St. Cloud that the Paris town is named for? Clodoald was one of four sons of Clovis, the King of the Franks. When Clovis died in 511, it triggered a battle for the throne that left three of Clodoald's brothers dead. Clodoald barely escaped death. He fled to the sanctuary of a hermit life where he studied under St. Severinus and renounced any claims to his father's throne. Clodoald, which became Cloud in French, was eventually ordained a priest and established a shrine at Nogent-sur-Seine where his relics are now kept in a church called St. Cloud. The village of Nogent-sur-Seine later changed its name to St. Cloud, as well. If your profession involves manufacturing nails or if you suffer from carbuncles, he is your patron saint.

Back to Middle Town, which was located more or less where today's downtown St. Cloud is situated. Middle Town was settled primarily by German Catholics, many of whom were part of a settlement society from Evansville, Indiana, that was led by John W. Tenvoorde (who was Dutch). As late as 1858, Middle Town had only about a dozen families in residence, including some Germans who had moved from Sauk Rapids because they weren't allowed to brew beer there.

These three cities were united into one by an act of the Minnesota Legislature in March 1856, with the name St. Cloud winning the day. St. Cloud developed rapidly, which may have prompted an anonymous—and jealous—neighbor to call it "… a small but pretentious suburb of Sauk Rapids." Sylvanus Lowry began ferry service across the Mississippi River in 1856; Wilson and Brott soon followed suit. St. Cloud had some steamboat traffic from Minneapolis before the Civil War, but water levels on the river varied too widely for dependable service.

While river traffic was somewhat limited, St. Cloud was strategically located on one of the main overland stops for oxcarts traveling the Red River Trail, which was probably the catalyst for a booming freight business that later took off in St. Cloud. Brothers James Crawford and Henry Clay Burbank established a freight business that employed coaches and a steamboat to move goods around.

All was not peachy keen between folks in town, however. Jane Grey Swisshelm arrived in St. Cloud in 1857 and founded the *St. Cloud Visitor*, a paper that regularly condemned slavery and its supporters. As you might guess, she and Lowry—the first mayor of a unified St. Cloud—had a hard time getting along. While she lauded his intellectual and leadership abilities, she attacked his support of slavery, writing: "his life spent among Negroes and Indians made him feel his superiority and assert it with the full force of honest conviction." Her office was ransacked at least once, but support from the community helped her rebound. Swisshelm left St. Cloud when the Civil War started. She first worked as a nurse tending wounded Union soldiers, then as an adviser to President Lincoln.

St. Cloud boomed after the Civil War, growth that was fueled in part by the arrival of railroads and the rise of the granite quarrying industry. Granite quarrying began around 1863, but really picked up after 1865. By 1920, there were twenty active quarries employing 2,500 men, including many Scots and Swedes. Granite from these quarries helped build the Cathedral of Saint Paul and the Minnesota State Reformatory for Men at St. Cloud. The latter is surrounded by a granite wall that is 1,700 yards long, 4½ feet thick at the base, and 22 feet high.

You'll also notice that many streets that dead end at the Mississippi have granite walls. These were built by the Works Project Administration in the 1930s using granite donated by local companies. Granite quarrying, however, was rough on the health of quarry workers. Many developed silicosis from breathing the dust. Methods to protect workers from silicosis were not perfected until 1970.

The Great Northern Railroad erected a rail yard after the Civil War that grew into the largest employer in town. The community around the yard incorporated as Waite Park. Today it houses a repair facility for Burlington Northern. Other early businesses included breweries, sash and door manufacturing, a cigar shop, iron works, and flour mills.

The Pantown Neighborhood Historic District occupies part of the west side of the city (8th Street North from 33rd Avenue North to 29th Avenue North). The craftsman-style homes were built between 1917 and 1919 for employees of Samuel Pandolfo's Pan Motor Company. The company produced a few hundred cars beginning in 1918 but was hardly a success. It didn't help when Pandolfo was convicted of mail fraud in 1919 and sent to federal prison for three years. The Pan Motor Company chugged along for a couple more years by making parts for other auto companies, then shut down in 1922.

While politicians of the past may have promised a "chicken in every pot," during Prohibition they could have pledged "a still in every home." Those stills provided a second income for many folks in the St. Cloud region, including quite a few farmers. Law enforcement was usually willing to look the other way for local moonshiners. Most folks produced the mash by fermenting a hybrid corn called Minnesota 13 that was developed at the University of Minnesota, which is why that moonshine became known as Minnesota 13 and even gained an international fan club.

St. Cloud's largest employer today is St. Cloud Hospital (3,300 people), followed by the State of Minnesota, Electrolux Home Products, Coborns, St. Cloud State University, and Gold 'n Plump Poultry. As you drive around, you may notice a few unfamiliar fast-food chains. That is because St. Cloud is a favored testing ground for those businesses.

Explore

AITKIN

Attractions

The **Aitkin County Historical Society** (20 Pacific St. SW; 218.927.3348) maintains a museum in the old rail depot that includes a telegraph switchboard, an early hair salon, and a lot of material on the local steamboat industry.

The city's former Carnegie library now houses the **Jaques Art Center** (121 2nd St. NW; 218.927.2363), named for Frances Lee Jaques, who attained a fair amount of fame with his nature-inspired paintings. The Art Center has several of his works and also hosts rotating exhibits.

Drinking and Dining

Enjoy a locally crafted pint of beer and live music at **Block North Brew Pub** (302 Minnesota Ave. N; 218.928.8090). Stick around for dinner and you'll be treated to an impressive range of options that includes grilled ribeye, wild rice risotto, and ratatouille.

Where to Stay: Camping

The **Aitkin Campground** (814 4th Ave. NW; 218.927.7364) has nine sites with electric on a high bank next to a boat ramp on the Mississippi River; campground amenities include drinking water, a shower house, flush toilets, and a dump station.

Special Events

The **Aitkin County Fair** (632 Minnesota Ave. N) has been a tradition since 1891. Look for it in early July and hop on a ride at the midway, check out a grandstand show like stock car races, and grab a scoop of ice cream.

In August, Aitkin celebrates it watery past with **Riverboat Days**. Events include a parade, a marathon, and opportunities to canoe and kayak on the Mississippi.

If you're in the area the day after Thanksgiving, don't miss the **Fish House Parade**, one of the region's most unique (and eccentric) events and a chance for visitors to see the creativity that goes into building a structure that fishing fanatics will eventually set on a frozen lake and escape to as often as possible during the long winter.

Getting There

Jefferson Lines offers long-distance bus service to Aitkin (City Hall, 109 1st Ave. NW).

CUYUNA IRON RANGE

DEERWOOD

Deerwood was the first village founded in the area. Originally called Withington, the name was changed in 1882 because it sometimes was confused with Worthington, Minnesota. Deerwood is located along an old portage route that connected the Mississippi River to Mille Lacs.

The loamy soil wasn't too good for most types of farming, but it was well-suited for fruit crops like apples, grapes, and raspberries, as well as potatoes. By the Depression years, though, few people were left who raised those crops. The area around Deerwood had a lot of resorts in the early years but, like at Sandy Lake, many were eventually sold and replaced by private lake homes.

Where to Stay: Lodging

Ruttgers Bay Lake Lodge (25039 Tame Fish Lake Rd.; 218.678.2885) may be one of the oldest resorts in Minnesota (it opened in 1898), but the lodging is entirely modern; choose from a range of options including condos, cottages, and lodge rooms.

CROSBY

The village's namesake and founder, George Crosby, chose this site for a town at least in part because there were no known iron ore deposits underneath. The explosive growth of the mining industry created an early housing crunch as miners flooded into the newly developing towns. Some boarding houses rented "hot beds," which were shared by two men, just at different times of day. Joe slept in the bed during the day, while Boris used it at night. George Crosby built houses in the village that he leased to the mining companies, who in turn rented them to miners. As miners gained seniority, they could move up to a bigger house for the same rent.

Many of the first residents were immigrants from the Balkans, Italy, Germany, Finland, Sweden, and Norway. Crosby's early residents settled into ethnic neighborhoods, just like in bigger cities. The northeast part of town was Scandinavian; Lakeview was home for the Finns; and further west was Balkan Street. If you walked along Main Street on a Saturday night, you might feel like you had just arrived at a meeting of the United Nations.

In winter, coal dust from the mines and home stoves coated the snow black. The town would also take on a red hue at times because of iron ore-tinted dust. If you hung your clothes out to dry, you had to check the wind direction first or risk having them dyed against your will. In 1933, in the midst of the Depression, Crosby's residents elected a communist mayor, Emil Nygard. He was the first communist mayor in the US. At the time he was elected, Nygard, whose father worked as a miner for 51 years, was 26 years old and unemployed.

Attractions

The **Soo Line Depot Museum** (101 1st St. NE; 218.546.6178; open Memorial Day to Labor Day) is housed in the old railroad depot and features a vintage Scorpion snowmobile from 1964 that was built in nearby Ironton, a birch-bark canoe, and displays on the area's mining history. The museum also has a replica of the first Man High Project module, an experimental flight in 1957 in which Major David G. Simons spent 32 hours in a three-foot by five-foot capsule attached to a balloon that reached 100,000 feet above the surface. It started its ascent 500 feet deep in the Portsmouth Mine.

The museum features exhibits about the Milford Mine disaster, which is memorialized at **Milford Mine Memorial Park** (26351 Milford Lake Dr.; 218.824.1067). In 1924, 41 men drowned when Foley Lake flooded the underground mine. Only seven miners escaped alive. The peaceful park was built at the former mine site. There is a short trail lined with markers, including memorials to each of the men who died. To get there, follow Minnesota Highway 6 north from Crosby, go left on Crow Wing County Road 30, then take the first left onto Milford Lake Drive.

The **Cuyuna Lakes State Trail** runs eight miles from Crosby to Riverton. You'll find trailheads and parking in Crosby (follow 2nd St northeast, then go left at the T intersection) and in Riverton (on Rowe Road near County Road 128).

If you need to rent equipment to enjoy the outdoors, **Red Raven** (2 3rd Ave. SW; 218.833.2788) rents bicycles, snowshoes, and cross-country skis. **Cuyuna Outfitters** (10

Sandy Lake Detour

Some places are special and have been for a long time, maybe because they have a reliable and diverse supply of food and offer predictable shelter, or perhaps because the place is imbued with supernatural qualities. Or maybe it's just the food and shelter. Regardless, Sandy Lake is one of those special places that emits an irresistible pull to stay put and call it home.

History

Sandy Lake, whose name is derived from the Ojibwe word Kah-me-tah-wung-a-guma (lake of the sandy waters), is rich with life, from the abundant population of fish in its depths to the beds of wild rice that line its edges. It is at the southwest end of an ancient travel route that connected the Great Lakes to the Mississippi River. Copper artifacts found along the trail suggest that this was a trade route for thousands of years. It was a busy place during the fur trading era (mid-18th century to mid-19th century), too, but the Savanna Portage, as voyageurs called it, was hardly a beloved passage.

The primary route followed the St. Louis River to the East Savanna River, followed by a land portage to the West Savanna River and on to Sandy Lake. The Sandy River connects Sandy Lake to the Mississippi River via a short channel. The land portage was about 6 miles long or 12 "poses" as the French called each leg of the trip. Goods were usually hauled from one point to another to make the effort manageable. One complete move from point to point was called a pose. Much of the portage was through a tamarack swamp, which, as I'm sure you can guess, could be an unpleasant experience. Lieutenant James Allen, who traveled with Henry Schoolcraft on the 1832 expedition to find the headwaters of the Mississippi, was no fan of the portage: He wrote:

"No idea can be formed of the difficulty of this portage without witnessing it. The men, with heavy loads, are sometimes forced to wade through a swamp of half a mile, full of roots and bushes, and over their knees in mire at every step. And where the road is dry, it is generally over a hill, or across a gully, the steep banks of which are worse to pass than the swamps."

Given the importance of the transit route that passed through the lake, it's no surprise that folks built settlements here. In fact, archaeological evidence suggests that people have been living next to Sandy Lake for thousands of years. In more recent centuries, the Dakota had a village at the lake for generations, then, as the Ojibwe moved into Minnesota, one of their first and most important village sites was at Sandy Lake.

In 1794, the Northwest Fur Company built a trading post at the lake. An exhausted Zebulon Pike reached the post on January 8, 1806, and stayed for a life-saving 12 days. While that trading post closed in 1816, the American Fur Company operated a post at Sandy Lake for a few years beginning in 1826.

By the mid-19th century, the world was changing for Native Americans east of the Mississippi River. In 1850, President Zachary Taylor ordered all Ojibwe in Michigan, Wisconsin, and Minnesota removed to Sandy Lake. They were told that once they were all gathered at the lake, they would get the annuity payments due to them. Thousands of Ojibwe traveled to Sandy Lake in the fall, only to discover that US agents and Minnesota's Territorial Governor Ramsey refused to pay them. Food rations ran low; much of it was tainted, anyway. Hundreds died from dysentery and other diseases, and the surviving Ojibwe had to travel back to their communities in the middle of winter. In spite of many attempts over the years to move them out, a community of Ojibwe has continued to live at Sandy Lake, today on a 32-acre tract officially recognized as reservation land.

At the end of the 19th century, Congress authorized construction of a dam at Sandy Lake as part of the Headwaters Dam Project. The first dam, a wooden structure, was completed in 1895 and included a lock so steamboats supplying the logging camps in the Sandy Lake area could get through. A concrete dam replaced the wooden one in 1911. By the early 20th century, Sandy Lake became the scene of a vibrant vacation industry, with many small, family-run resorts around the lake.

Sandy Lake today still has that dam, a small community of Ojibwe, lots of fish and wild rice, but those small resorts are gone, replaced by expensive vacation homes that now surround the lake. This place, even in the 21st century, continues to have a certain magic that compels people who visit to stick around for a while. Go for a day or stick around for a quiet night or two.

Attractions

You can get a taste of the old overland route at **Savanna Portage State Park** (55626 Lake Pl.; 218.426.3271) where several hiking trails follow parts of the portage. The park has a number of other trails, historic sites, and swimming beaches.

Sandy Lake Recreation Area (22205 531st Ln.; 218.426.3482), near the dam, has a range of activities for visitors to pass the time, including a swimming beach, fishing, and an interpretive center in the original lock house.

Where to Stay

If you'd like to stay a night, **Savanna Portage State Park** (55626 Lake Pl.; 218.426.3271), a 10-minute drive from the lake, has 61 sites in a wooded area, plus backpacker sites. They also rent a rustic cabin and a one-bedroom guesthouse.

Sandy Lake Recreation Area (22205 531st Ln.; 218.426.3482) has about 60 sites in an attractive, shaded if rather compact setting. There are electric and nonelectric sites and many are right on the lake.

Aitkin Lake Resort (21607 - 537th Ln.; 218.426.3327) has been pleasing visitors since 1926. The resort offers five sites with water and electric in a bucolic resort setting, complete with shower house and paddleboats. They also rent a few well-kept housekeeping cabins in a beautiful lakeside location far from the road and the rest of the world. Bring towels and a willingness to chill.

Big Sandy Lake Lodge and Resort (20534 - 487th St.; 218.426.5040) is a modern, full-service resort on the southeast side of the lake. They rent 18 rooms in the lodge, plus cabins and townhouses.

Brainerd to St. Cloud Route Map

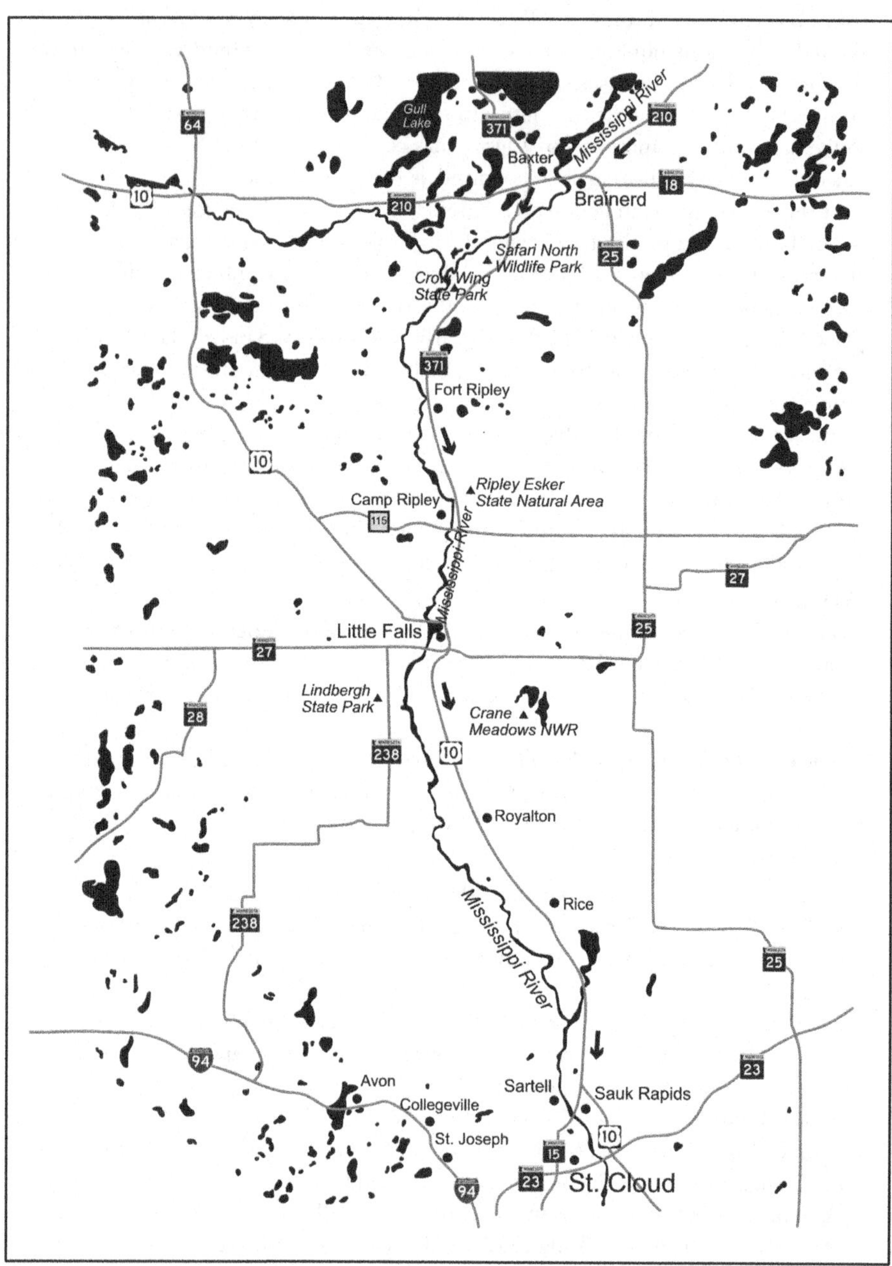

State Highway 210 connects the Cuyuna Iron Range with Brainerd. In Brainerd, State Highway 210 becomes Washington Street. Follow it west to Minnesota Highway 371 and go south to get to Fort Ripley and Little Falls. At Little Falls, continue on US Highway 10 to St. Cloud. The total distance from Brainerd to downtown St. Cloud is 65 miles.

Cuyuna Iron Range Map

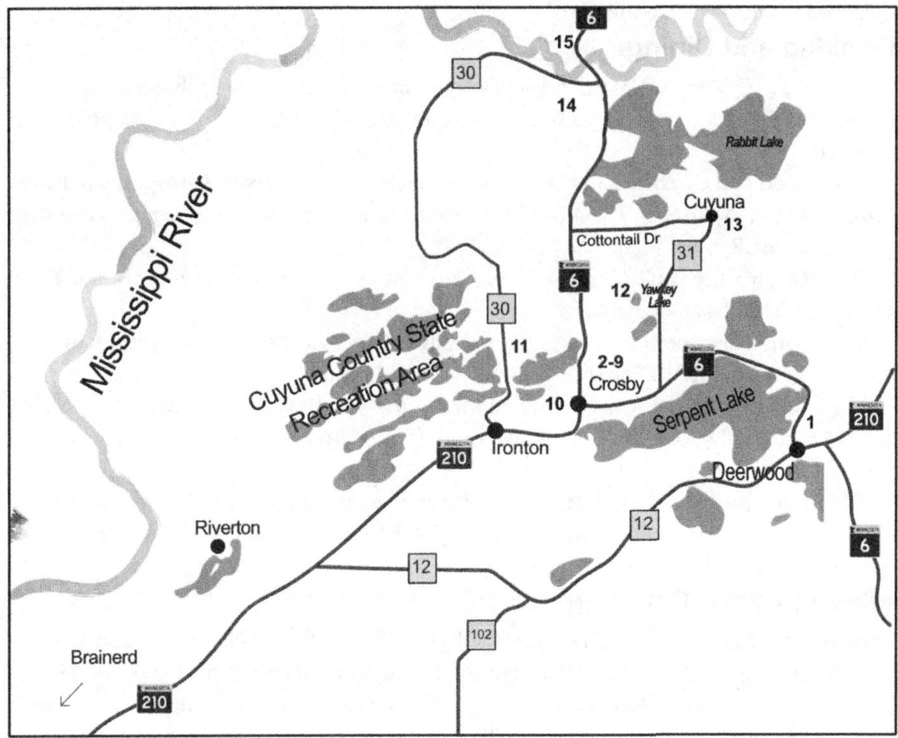

Attractions

2. Cuyuna Outfitters
14. Milford Mine Memorial Park
3. Red Raven
4. Soo Line Depot Museum
13. Wood Tick Inn

Where to Eat and Drink

5. Cuyuna Brewing Company
6. Mixed Company, A Kava House
7. North Country Café
8. Red Raven Bike Café
15. The Bridge Tavern
9. Victual

Where to Stay

1. Crosby Lofts
11. Portsmouth Campground
10. True North Basecamp
12. Yurts at Cuyuna Country State Recreation Area

In 1921, 41 men died in an accident at the Milford Mine near Crosby. Read all about the tragic event in *Mississippi River Mayhem: Disasters, Tragedy, and Murder on Ol' Man River*. Find a copy wherever books are sold.

3rd Ave. SW; 218.838.1982) rents kayaks (including tandem crystal kayaks) and standup paddleboards for use on area lakes. They will deliver a boat to your starting point and meet you when you are done.

Drinking and Dining

Victual (124 W. Main St.; 218.545.1000)—a boutique store serving high quality ice cream, cheese, meats, and specialty liquors—can satisfy your desire for a taste of the good life.

For a good cup of coffee and breakfast or lunch, head to **Mixed Company, A Kava House** (128 W. Main St.; 218.545.1010), owned and run by a fourth-generation resident of the Cuyuna Range.

Red Raven Bike Café (2 3rd Ave. SW; 218.833.2788) is another option for coffee and a light breakfast or lunch.

Relax with a tasty craft beer with the friendly folks at the **Cuyuna Brewing Company** (1 E. Main St.; 218.866.0914).

If you're in the mood for something heartier, the **North Country Café** (12 W. Main St.; 218.545.9908) should be able to take care of you with homestyle dishes at affordable prices.

For a tasty meal next to the Mississippi River, head five miles north of Crosby to **The Bridge Tavern** (26969 Highway 6; 218.546.5219). If the weather's nice, enjoy a burger or walleye dinner on the big patio.

Where to Stay: Camping

True North Basecamp (825 1st St. SW; 218.833.2267) offers 23 lakeside campsites close to the Cuyuna trails. They also rent six mining camp-inspired steel and wood cabins that offer a comfier place to rest than a tent. The cabins have heating and air conditioning but don't have a kitchen, so you'll still need to make your own arrangements to cook or go into town to a restaurant. Bring your own bedding.

For something completely different, there are also three **yurts** available for overnight stays at the **Cuyuna Country State Recreation Area** (218.546.5926); all are on the west side of Yawkey Mine Lake. Each comes equipped with a wood-burning stove, bunk beds, tables and chairs, and windows that open. You'll still need to bring bedding, and you'll cook outside with our own equipment, just as if you were camping.

The **Portsmouth Campground** at Cuyuna Country State Recreation Area has 18 electric and 15 non-electric sites. The campground is on the northwest shore of Portsmouth Mine Lake, just off County Road 30 (Irene Ave. in Ironton).

Lodging

The 16 rooms at **Crosby Lofts** (30 W. Main St.; 218.325.3317) occupy the upper floors of a historic building in central Crosby. Some rooms lean Spartan and come with bunk beds, while others offer tasteful, private spaces for couples or friends traveling together. All rooms are modern and clean and within an easy bike ride of Cuyuna's trails.

IRONTON

Attractions

The mining companies left behind a dramatically altered landscape, with deep holes in the ground and tall piles of cast-aside rocks. Over time, ground water seeped into the pit mines, creating deep blue lakes, while vegetation grew atop those piles of rocks. The end result is a reclaimed landscape that is now the **Cuyuna Country State Recreation**

Area (218.546.5926). Lakes are named after the mines that created them (Alstead Mine Lake, Pennington Mine Lake, Yawkey Mine Lake, etc.), and those rock piles are now crisscrossed with challenging mountain biking trails. There's a swimming beach at the Portsmouth Campground; some lakes are popular for fishing; many are popular places for scuba diving; and the lakes are a good place to paddle around in a canoe or kayak.

The **Cuyuna Mountain Bike Trail System** encompasses 25 miles of popular mountain biking trails that range from easy to very difficult, riding through thick forest and next to deep blue lakes and up to scenic overlooks. In winter, some trails are maintained for fat biking, which has nothing to do with your BMI but rather the way bikes are adapted for riding in snow.

Special Events

The Woodtick Inn in Cuyuna (County Road 31; 218.772.0252) hosts hotly contested **Woodtick Races** on the second Saturday in June,a tradition that began around 1970.

BRAINERD AREA

Attractions

Upriver of Brainerd Airport, the **Mississippi River Northwoods** (State Highway 210) covers 2,000-acres with nearly three miles of undeveloped shoreline along the Mississippi River, giving the Brainerd area nine miles of wild shorelines along the Mississippi. Follow State Highway 210 about five miles east of Brainerd to the entrance.

Just east of town, there are several hiking trails, some moderately difficult, around the **French Rapids access**. In winter, you can cross-country ski on the same trails. Get to it by taking Crow Wing County 142 at the Brainerd Airport.

Crow Wing County Historical Society Museum (326 Laurel St.; 218.829.3268) is the best place to get oriented to the area's history, with exhibits on the railroad, logging, mining, 19th-century home life, baseball, and much more.

Kiwanis Park (1101 East River Rd.), next to the Mississippi River, has a playground, a dog park, and room to spread out for a picnic lunch.

For a walk on the quiet side, explore the 400 acres and 16 miles of trails through native plants at the **Northland Arboretum** (14250 Conservation Dr.; 218.829.8770).

Northwoods-themed **Paul Bunyan Land** (17553 State Highway 18; 218.764.2524; open Memorial Day to Labor Day) is full of kitschy fun, especially for the kids, like the 26-foot-tall talking Paul Bunyan; he might even address you by name. The theme park has several rides, plus Pioneer Village and its antiques.

For a bit of mindless fun, head to the visitors center on Highway 371 and pick up a list of the **Paul Bunyan and Babe statues** around the area, then find them. There are many, including the one by the visitors center, and the talking one at Paul Bunyan Land.

Next to one of those statues in the center of Brainerd (6th St. and Washington St.), you'll find one of the more unique **water towers** in the US. Built from 1919 to 1922, it looks a lot like a flashlight, like one that Paul Bunyan might have used. It was also the first all-concrete water tower used in the US, for those of you who are into such things. It was taken out of service in 1958 but is maintained to preserve Brainerd's history.

The **Paul Bunyan State Trail** connects Brainerd to Bemidji on 112 miles of paved off-road path that cuts through forest and around lakes.

South of Brainerd, **Safari North Wildlife Park** (8493 Highway 371; 218.454.1662) showcases hundreds of animals from around the world, including some endangered species such as snow leopards.

Crow Wing State Park (County Road 27; 218.825.3075; vehicle entry fee) is another treasure along the Mississippi River. Within the park's 3,291 acres, you'll find several miles of riverfront hiking and trails that cut through prairie and hardwood forest. Interpretive signs tell the story of the ghost town of Crow Wing that once prospered here. Crow Wing State Park is nine miles south of Brainerd.

In winter, **Mount Ski Gull** near Nisswa (9898 County Road 77 SW; 218.963.4353) is the place for downhill skiing, tubing, and snowboarding.

Easy Riders Bicycle and Sportshop (415 Washington St.; 218.829.5516) rents winter gear, including snowshoes and ice skates.

Getting On the River

You can rent a canoe or kayak from **Easy Riders Bicycle and Sportshop** (15 Washington St.; 218.829.5516). Shuttle service is available, but schedule it in advance.

Crow Wing State Park (County Road 27; 218.825.3075) rents canoes and kayaks.

Drinking and Dining

Every time I visit Brainerd, I look forward to a tasty cup of coffee, a fresh pastry, and good conversation at **Coco Moon** (601 Laurel St.; 218.825.7955).

Knotty Pine Bakery (707 Laurel St.; 218.454.2470) offers tasty treats and go, including cinnamon buns, coffee cakes, kronuts, and other tasty baked goods.

Enjoy a craft beer in the bright and spacious tasting room of **Jack Pine Brewery** in Baxter (15593 Edgewood Dr. N.; 218.270.8072). Guys can relieve themselves in urinals built from kegs–the cycle of (water) life, you know!

Check out the **Last Turn Saloon** (214 S. 8th St.; 218.829.4856) for bar food with atmosphere, a place that pays homage to a tavern of the same name that was the last stop on the way out of town for loggers heading to the woods. Located in the basement of a historic building, the interior is decked out with art glass and finely carved wood.

Sage on Laurel (606 Laurel St.; 218.454.7243) offers a touch of fine dining with a Minnesota accent. If you're lucky, maybe they'll still have chicken wild rice pot pie when you visit.

Where to Stay

There's a wide range of lodging options around Brainerd, from rustic camping to luxury resorts and from chain motels to private homes. The options below focus on independently run places in Brainerd proper or near the Mississippi River. It can be difficult to find a room in the area during the NHRA Nationals at Brainerd International Raceway in August, so book in advance.

Camping

The campground at **Crow Wing State Park** (County Road 27; 218.825.3075) is in a lovely wooded area on a high bank near the river.

PleasureLand RV VIP Campground at Brainerd International Raceway (5523 Birchdale Rd.; 218.824.7223) offers 164 RV sites with full hookups, as well as an open area for basic camping that is close to bathrooms and a showerhouse.

Gull Lake Recreation Area (10867 E. Gull Lake Dr.; 218.829.3334), run by the Army Corps of Engineers, offers spacious sites in a wooded area next to Gull Lake ten miles northwest of Brainerd.

Lodging

Niemeyer's Rugged River Resort (12241 Stallman Rd.; 218.829.4587) rents six updated cabins on the Mississippi River just northeast of Brainerd.

Shady Hollow Resort (1009 Shady Hollow Rd.; 218.828.9308) is ten miles southwest of Brainerd on Hardy Lake, which is very near the Mississippi River. They have eight comfortable cabins equipped with modern amenities, including air conditioning.

Special Events

The **Lakes Area Growers Market** sets up on Tuesday mornings at the Franklin Arts Center (1001 Kingwood St.) and Friday mornings in Baxter at Westport Shopping Center (14091 Baxter Dr.)

Brainerd International Raceway (5523 Birchdale Rd.; 218.824.7223) draws huge crowds for its annual **drag races**. If you've got some spare cash, you can attend the **Performance Driving School** and learn the art and skill of race-car driving. They host their biggest event, the **National Hot Rod Association Nationals** (NHRA), around the third week of August. Book your lodging well in advance.

The **Crow Wing County Fair** (2000 SE 13th St.; 218.829.6680) brings together farm animals, tractor pulls, motocross racing, and live music in early August.

Getting There

Brainerd Lakes Regional Airport (16384 Airport Rd.; 218.825.2166) is just east of the city. Delta offers daily service to Minneapolis/Saint Paul International Airport.

Jefferson Lines offers long-distance bus service to Baxter (Westgate Mall, 14136 Baxter Rd.).

CAMP RIPLEY

Attractions

Everyone in your vehicle will need to show a valid ID to enter Camp Ripley. Once you are through security, visit the **Minnesota Military Museum** (15000 Highway 115; 320.616.6050), which has a good collection of guns (machine guns, Lugers, rifles, grenade launchers), war memorials, and outdoor exhibits with heavy equipment like tanks, helicopters, and troop movers.

The **Minnesota State Veteran's Cemetery** (State Highway 115) is just east of the main entrance to Camp Ripley.

Northwest of the base, Ripley Esker snakes across the landscape for seven miles, a long ridge built up from sand and gravel deposited by a stream beneath a glacier. You can walk across a three-quarter- mile segment at **Ripley Esker State Natural Area** (County Road 282; 651.259.5800). There are no maintained trails, but there is an old footpath you can follow. The views are best in spring and fall. From Camp Ripley, go north on State Highway 371 and exit at County Highway 48; after 0.7 miles, turn north on County Road 282 and go 1½ miles to a parking space on the east side of the road.

LITTLE FALLS

Attractions

The **Charles A. Lindbergh House and Visitor Center** (1620 S. Lindbergh Dr.; 320.616.5421) offers guided tours of the Lindbergh family home with stories about their lives. The center is typically open Fridays and Saturdays from Memorial Day to Labor Day, as well as a few days in late November.

The Morrison County Historical Society runs the **Charles A. Weyerhaeuser Memorial Museum** (215 S. Lindbergh Dr.; 320.632.4007), which has some interesting exhibits in multiple rooms on the county's history.

St. Cloud Regional Map

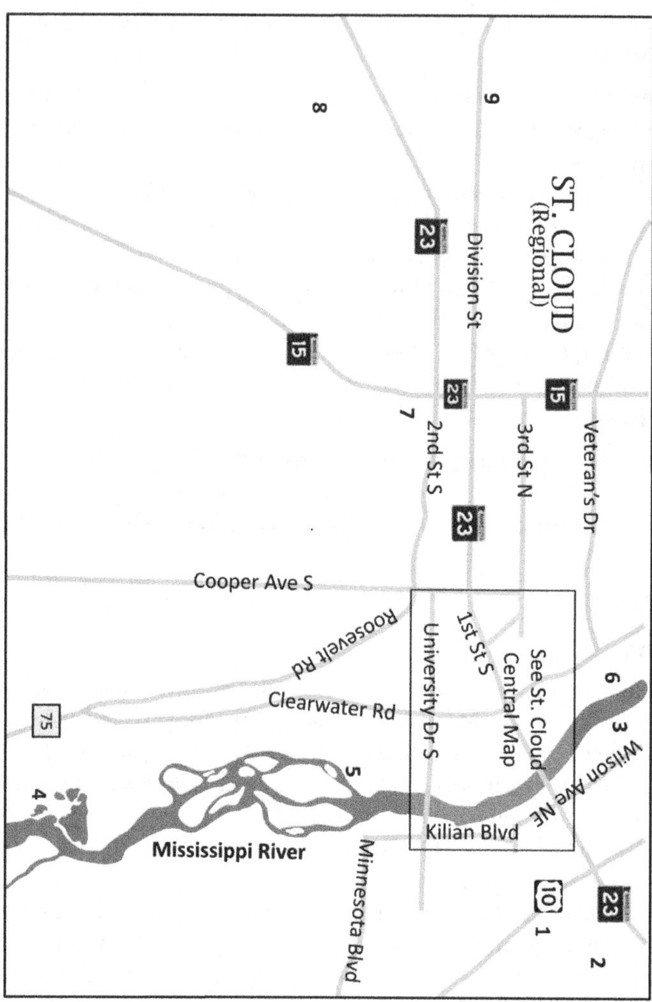

Attractions

5. Beaver Island Park
6. Hester Park
8. Quarry Park
4. River Bluffs Regional Park
7. Stearns County History Center
3. Wilson Park

Where to Eat and Drink

9. Anton's

Where to Stay

2. St. Cloud Campground & RV Park
1. The Night's Inn

In 1886, a tornado swept through St. Cloud and leveled most of Sauk Rapids. Read all about the devastation in *Mississippi River Mayhem: Disasters, Tragedy, and Murder on Ol' Man River*. Find a copy wherever books are sold.

St. Cloud Central Map

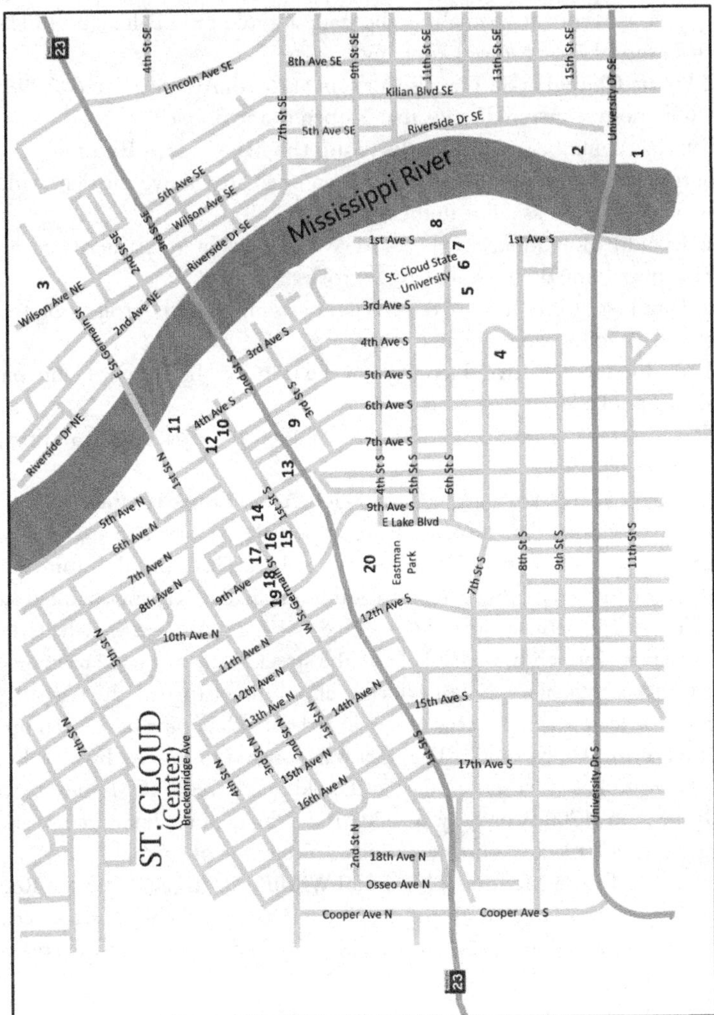

Attractions

4. Barden Park
15. Cathedral of St. Mary
2. Clemens/Munsinger Gardens
20. Eastman Park
11. Minnesota Baseball Hall of Fame
18. Paramount Center for the Arts
12. Pioneer Place on Fifth
1. Riverside Park

At St. Cloud State University

7. Jefferson Lines Bus Stop SCSU
8. Kiehle Visual Arts Center
6. Outdoor Recreation
5. Performing Arts Center

Where to Eat and Drink

9. Beaver Island Brewing Company
13. Farmers Market
19. Jules Bistro
14. Pickled Loon
16. Arroy
12. Veranda Lounge
17. White Horse

Other

3. Amtrak station
10. Jefferson Lines Bus Stop Downtown

If there's a fishing enthusiast in your family, you'll want to visit the **Minnesota Fishing Museum** (304 W. Broadway; 320.616.2011) and check out the displays on spearing, decoys, replicas of record fish caught in the state, and old motors like the 1902 6v submersible from the Electric Motor Company.

Sacred Heart Chapel at St. Francis Convent (116 8th Ave. SE; 320.632.2981) is a gorgeous Romanesque-inspired space that is open to the public.

Little Falls has a number of **city parks along the Mississippi River**:

- LeBourget Park (Larson Memorial Dr.) is an open area above the dam with plenty of places to toss a line in the river
- Maple Island Park (Kidder St. SE at 3rd Ave. SE) has pretty gardens and places to picnic near some of those square-cut rocks
- Green Park (1st St NE at 8th Ave NE) is a pleasant place to stroll along the river and chat with folks, especially in the evening
- Mill Park (Lindbergh Drive) incorporates the ruins of the former Hennepin Paper Mill as public art

Great River Arts (122 1st St. SE; 320.632.0960) has three galleries featuring the work of local and regional artists.

If you're a fan of large-scale art, you're in luck. Artist **Frank Gosiak** painted three **murals** around town that depict scenes from Little Falls history: two are on the exterior of the Hennepin Paper Company (W. Broadway at 1st St. NW), while a third is on a building at E. Broadway and 2nd Street. In addition, Charles Kapsner painted two frescoes at Lindbergh Elementary School (102 9th St. SE). *The Stewardship*, which depicts the life of Charles Lindbergh, is visible from the street, but you'll need to contact the school to arrange a tour of *Beginnings*, which is about the history of the region.

On the west side of town, 57 aces of virgin red and white pine have been preserved at **Pine Grove Park** (Highway 27). The tract was donated to the city by local lumber barons. Walk around to get a sense of what the old pine forests of Minnesota were like.

Pine Grove Zoo (1200 Broadway W; 320.616.5595), next to Pine Grove Park, is a walkable and pleasant place to show your kids a nice range of animals.

South of town, **Crane Meadows National Wildlife Refuge** (19502 Iris Rd.; 320.632.1575) preserves large swaths of wetlands. Expect good birding and pleasant hiking. Besides migrating birds, several pairs of sandhill cranes nest in the area.

Tours

Take a guided tour through the mansions built for the Charles Weyerhaeuser and Drew Musser families at the **Linden Hill Historic Mansions** (608 Highland Ave.; 320.616.5580). Tours are offered from Memorial Day through Labor Day.

You can also tour the **Burton-Rosenmeier House** in Little Falls (606 1st St. SE). The Classical Revival house was built in the early 1900s—with an abundance of porches—and has been home to two prominent local families. Today, it serves as the home of the Little Falls Convention and Visitors Bureau.

Take a **walking or driving tour** around the historic core of Little Falls. You can pick up a guide at the visitors center.

Drinking and Dining

Wet your whistle with a craft beer at **Starry Eyed Brewing Company** (16757 11th St. NE; 320.232.0382) and enjoy it out on the spacious grounds when the weather's nice.

Three generations have run **Thielen Meats** (300 13th St. NE; 320.632.2821), where you can get a variety of fresh house-made sausages and cook them next to the river.

Stop at **Little Falls Bakery and Deli** (121 E. Broadway; 320.632.6388) for fresh pastries and bread or for a light lunch.

A.T. The Black and White (116 1st St. SE; 320.632.5374) offers affordable gourmet food (burgers to salmon with Cajun shrimp) with a casual feel in a downtown building that has housed a restaurant since 1931.

Where to Stay

Camping

Charles Lindbergh State Park (1615 S. Lindbergh Dr.; 320.616.2525) offers about 40 campsites in a heavily wooded area that was once part of the Lindbergh family estate.

Lodging

Clifwood Motel (1201 Haven Rd.; 320.632.5488) rents 18 clean budget rooms in decent shape.

If you are traveling with a group, you may be able to arrange lodging at the **Linden Hill Historic Mansions**; give them a call to inquire (320.616.5580).

Special Events

Little Falls hosts a **farmers market** on Wednesday and Saturday mornings (Boys and Girls Club, 505 W. Broadway).

The **Morrison County Fair** assembles in early August (15575 Hawthorn Rd.; 320.632.1040), with grandstand events such as motocross and a demolition derby, plus animal-judging contests and ice cream treats.

The **Little Falls Arts and Crafts Fair** (320.632.5155) in September attracts thousands of visitors to the city's downtown streets. It's probably best to park at the fairgrounds (15575 Hawthorn Rd.) and take a shuttle to the fair.

Getting There

Jefferson Lines stops in Little Falls at a local McDonalds (104 Lemieur St.).

ST. CLOUD

Attractions

The **Stearns County History Center** (235 33rd Ave. S; 320.253.8424) is the place to research local or family history or just to leisurely take in the extensive exhibits on the region's history, including the local granite industry. New exhibits are added regularly.

The **Cathedral of St. Mary** (25 8th Ave. S; 320.251.1840) was completed in 1931. The original Gothic-revival church from 1864 was destroyed by fire in 1920. Construction for the replacement began in 1921 but took a decade to complete. Services were held in the basement until the sanctuary was ready. The church you see today is Romanesque in design. As part of a major renovation in 1980, the baldachin was removed and installed over an altar at Assumption Cemetery.

The **Minnesota Amateur Baseball Hall of Fame Museum** (320.252.8227) honors the state's best amateur baseball players. You'll find it on the second floor of the River's Edge Convention Center downtown (10 4th Ave. S).

Clemens/Munsinger Gardens (1515 Riverside Dr. SE) is a lovely group of formal gardens along the riverfront. In season, a succession of blooming plants turns the riverfront into a Technicolor paradise. The six gardens that comprise Clemens Gardens include one for roses and another for perennials. Just below it, Munsinger Gardens is a showcase for plants that grow and flower in shade.

St. Cloud has several **riverside parks**:

- Wilson Park (625 NE Riverside Dr.) and Hester Park (1020 N. 6th Ave.) are neighborhood parks on opposite sides of the river.
- Riverside Park (1725 Kilian Blvd.) was established in 1915 on the site of a former sawmill.
- Beaver Island Park (1503 S. 3rd Ave.) has 25 acres of scenic and serene riverfront property.

The paved **Beaver Islands Trail** winds five miles along the west side of the Mississippi from 1st Street North to Clearwater Road at Montrose Road.

Popular **Quarry Park and Nature Preserve** (1802 County Road 137; 320.255.6172) was formed from a reclaimed granite quarry. In summer, enjoy four miles of unpaved trails for hiking and mountain biking. In winter, those trails are great for cross-country skiing.

River Bluffs Regional Park (3822 Clearwater Rd.) on the south end of town has a few miles of wooded hiking trails and access to the river.

The **Paramount Center for the Arts** (913 W. St. Germain St.; 320.259.5463) is a multi-faceted arts venue, with an auditorium for live theater and music, as well as exhibits of visual arts in its Gallery St. Germain and the theater lobby.

Pioneer Place on Fifth (22 5th Ave. S; 320.203.0331) hosts several shows a year (drama, musicals, etc.), as well as concerts in an intimate setting that began life as an Elks Club in 1913.

The **Veranda Lounge** at Pioneer Place (320.203.0340) hosts live music on weekends and jazz on Thursday nights.

The **St. Cloud Municipal Band** (320.308.3223) has been performing for the locals for over 110 years. Look for summer performances in **Barden Park** (720 5th Ave. S), the city's oldest park.

St. Cloud State University has several cultural activities that are open to the public. Students and faculty stage live theater and musical events at the **Performing Arts Center** (620 3rd Ave. S; 320.308.3229). Also on the SCSU campus, the **Kiehle Visual Arts Center** (580 1st Ave. S; 320.308.0121) hosts a gallery on the main floor that showcases the works of student artists.

Getting On the River

Outdoor Recreation at St. Cloud State University (Student Recreation Center, 1111 3rd Ave. S.) rents canoes, kayaks, and camping gear for summer fun, as well as winter gear like snowshoes, sleds, and a portable ice house. You don't need to be affiliated with the university to rent equipment.

Twenty minutes south of St. Cloud, **Clear Waters Outfitting Company** (Clearwater: 100 Pine St.; 320.558.8123) can set up up with a canoe, kayak, or stand-up paddleboard; shuttle service is available.

Stop by Clear Waters Outfitting and check out the **replica** of the swing-cable ferry used in the 19th century. Carpenter and Clearwater resident Steve Houle built it.

Drinking and Dining

Beaver Island Brewing Company (216 6th Ave. S; 320.253.5907) serves tasty craft beer in a canoe-themed taproom.

The **Veranda Lounge** (22 5th Ave. S; 320.258.0254), which is adjacent to Pioneer Place on Fifth, is primarily a wine bar, but they also serve snacks and flatbreads.

Detour: Saint John's University and the College of St. Benedict

Benedictine monks from Pennsylvania (via Germany) established **Saint John's University** as a men's college in 1857. They first set up around Lower Town (St. Cloud) but moved to their current location west of St. Cloud in 1865. The campus is a model for balancing the demands of a 21st-century educational institution with land stewardship. The campus is about a 25-minute drive from downtown St. Cloud via Division Street, County Road 75, and Interstate 94. There are several sites worth visiting:

St. John's Benedictine Abbey Church, completed in 1961, is a stunning modernist building designed by renowned architect Marcel Breuer; the open interior is decorated with the world's largest stained-glass window.

The **HILL Museum & Manuscript Library** was founded in 1965 to preserve old European manuscripts. What you'll really want to see, though, are pages from the **Saint John's Bible**—a remarkable work of art completed in 2011 after 13 years of work. It is the first illuminated Bible completed in 500 years and is worth the short drive from St. Cloud. Pages from the Bible are displayed in the lower level of Alcuin Library (M-F 10-4; some Saturdays Noon-4).

Richard Bresnahan is a renowned potter and artist-in-residence at St. John's University. Stop in to his pottery studio to learn about his art and mission to create sustainable pottery (St. Joseph Hall, 2810 Saint John's Rd. in Collegeville; 320.363.2930).

The **Stephen B. Humphrey Theater** (320.363.5777) hosts performing arts and live music.

The **St. John's Boys Choir** (320.363.2558) performs several times a year throughout the region, primarily during the school year.

Benedictine sisters settled down the road in St. Joseph in the early 1860s. They established the **College of St. Benedict** for women in 1913 to educate future teachers. The monastery (104 Chapel Ln.) and adjacent college are a 20-minute drive from downtown St. Cloud via Division Street and County Road 75.

The **Sacred Heart Chapel** is a beautiful baroque structure. Built from 1912 to 1914 (and renovated in the early 1980s), it blends traditional design with modern touches. The copper-clad dome rises 135 feet high and is supported by granite columns inside.

The **Whitby Gift Shop and Haehn Museum** have exhibits on the past and present of the Benedictine sisters of St. Joseph (320.363.7098; open from early April until Christmas).

The **Benedicta Arts Center** (320.363.5777) hosts three concerts a year performed by the Minnesota Orchestra and four annual performances of the St. Cloud Symphony Orchestra (320.257.3114).

Jules Bistro (921 W. St. Germain St.; 320.252.7125) prepares an impressive variety of pastries and baked goods, from scones to macarons to tarts. They also serve fresh soups, salads, sandwiches, and flatbreads if you're looking for a good meal. Try shakshuka for breakfast.

The **White Horse** (809 W. St. Germain St.; 320.257.7775) specializes in freshly prepared meals that draw inspiration from many cuisines, especially for dinner. The food is complemented by a fine selection of craft beer and adult beverages.

Arroy (800 W. St. Germain St.; 320.240.1454) serves tasty Filipino and Thai food, including a few catfish preparations that you've probably never had before.

The **Pickled Loon** (715 W. St. Germain St.; 320.281.3581) serves an impressive range of lighter fare and entrées that sample a variety of international cuisines; the menu changes with the seasons.

Anton's in nearby Waite Park (2001 Frontage Rd. N; 320.253.3611) is the place for fine dining in a casual setting, if you consider a hybrid log cabin/covered wagon décor to be casual. The popovers are beloved (for good reason), but they do a good job with the whole menu. There are some seats that have a nice view of the Sauk River, and they have a pretty darn good selection of Scotch.

For something completely different, detour 20 miles to Avon and check out **Fisher's Club** (428 Stratford St.; 320.356.7372). Once owned in part by Garrison Keillor of *Prairie Home Companion* fame, the restaurant is beloved for its outstanding walleye dinners, charming ambiance, and views of Middle Spunk Lake. Reservations for dinner are strongly recommended.

Where to Stay: Camping

St. Cloud Campground & RV Park (2491 2nd St. SE; 320.251.4463) is located just east of St. Cloud on the outskirts of town and can accommodate anything from tent camping to RVs.

Lodging

The Night's Inn (720 Highway 10 South; 320.255.1274) is an older mom-and-pop budget motel along US Highway 10; the rooms are in good shape and each has a microwave and a small fridge.

Downtown has a few chain motels but the highest concentration is around the intersection of Highways 15 and 23 west of downtown.

Special Events

Find the St. Cloud **farmers market** on Saturday mornings at the Lady Slipper parking lot (198 7th Ave. S.)

Quarterly Art Crawls give folks a chance to wander around downtown St. Cloud and check out the works of local artists. The events take place on a Friday in March, June, August, and November, but the August event is so much bigger than the rest that it gets its own name: **The Sizzling Summer Art Crawl**.

In June, St. Cloud celebrates its existence with **Granite City Days** (320.255. 7201), a long weekend of fun that includes a singing competition, canoe trips around the Beaver Islands, the Lemonade Art Fair, and the requisite parade.

Summertime by George brings live music and a festival atmosphere to the shores of Lake George in **Eastman Park** (St. Cloud: 425 E. Lake Blvd.) on Wednesday evenings from mid-June to late August; free shuttles run from downtown to the park.

Getting There

St. Cloud is one of the stops along **Amtrak**'s *Empire Builder* route (555 E. St. Germain St.; 800.872.7245). Westbound trains headed for Seattle have a scheduled departure time of 1:09am. Eastbound trains depart early in the morning (6:32am) for Mississippi River towns Saint Paul, Red Wing, Winona, and La Crosse before continuing on to Chicago. The *Empire Builder* trains often run late.

St. Cloud's **MetroBus** offers a Northstar Link service (Route #887) that runs from the downtown transit center (510 1st St. S) to the **Northstar commuter rail station** at Big Lake. It primarily serves commuters to Minneapolis, but many people also use it to got to and from Twins baseball games and Vikings football games.

Allegiant Air and Sun Country Airlines operate flights from **St. Cloud Regional Airport** (1550 45th Ave. SE; 320.255.7292).

Jefferson Lines offers long-distance bus service to St. Cloud, with two stops: downtown (501 1st St. S.) and at St. Cloud State University's Atwood Center (651 1st Ave. S.).

For More Information

There are practical limits to how much I can include in a book, but not with a website! Check out the city profiles on my website to see if they include listings that I couldn't fit in this book.

Aitkin: MississippiValleyTraveler.com/Aitkin
Cuyuna Iron Range: MississippiValleyTraveler.com/Cuyuna-Iron-Range
Sandy Lake: MississippiValleyTraveler.com/Sandy-Lake
Brainerd: MississippiValleyTraveler.com/Brainerd
Baxter: MississippiValleyTraveler.com/Baxter
The Ripleys: MississippiValleyTraveler.com/The-Ripleys
Little Falls: MississippiValleyTraveler.com/Little-Falls
Sartell: MississippiValleyTraveler.com/Sartell
Sauk Rapids: MississippiValleyTraveler.com/Sauk-Rapids
St. Cloud: MississippiValleyTraveler.com/St-Cloud

You may also want to visit these places I didn't have room for:
Clearwater: MississippiValleyTraveler.com/Clearwater
Monticello: MississippiValleyTraveler.com/Monticello
Elk River: MississippiValleyTraveler.com/Elk-River

Snapshot: Paul Bunyan

Affection for Paul Bunyan runs deep in the Northwoods, which is why you'll find many different monuments to pose with, including the ones above. Clockwise starting from the top left: downtown Brainerd, MN; Akeley, MN; Pequot Lakes, MN; Brainerd Lakes Visitor Center; Bemidji, MN.

So you think you know Paul Bunyan? Ha! I investigated the legendary character a few years ago. What I learned surprised me. Read about it at https://mississippivalleytraveler.com/bunyan.

MINNEAPOLIS & FORT SNELLING

The Mississippi River at Minneapolis

Overview

Minneapolis has a spirit that sets it apart from many other American cities. It's a place with a lively downtown, a diverse arts scene, great food, nice people, and a surprising range of outdoor activities for a big city, including the best public riverfront along the Mississippi. You could spend a year here and not come close to experiencing all that the city offers. Alas, this is a weekend guide and one focused on the sights along the Mississippi River, so you'll have to come back to see the rest.

History

THE DAKOTA OF MINNESOTA

In the Dakota (Sioux) language, a place where two rivers meet is called bdote. One bdote is revered above all others, the place where life began according to Dakota legend: the bdote of the Minnesota and Mississippi Rivers. For generations of Dakota, the area around this bdote was the place where they gathered for councils, religious ceremonies, and burials. As Europeans moved into Dakota lands, this bdote would also witness great tragedies.

The Dakota people have deep roots in northern Minnesota, at least since the 17th century but probably much earlier. They were traditionally divided into seven groups known collectively as the Oceti Sakowin (Seven Council Fires). There were four groups of Santee or Eastern Dakota: Mdewakanton (the Spirit Lake People), Wahpekute (the Shooters Among the Leaves People), Wahpeton (the People Dwelling Among the

Twin Cities Route Map

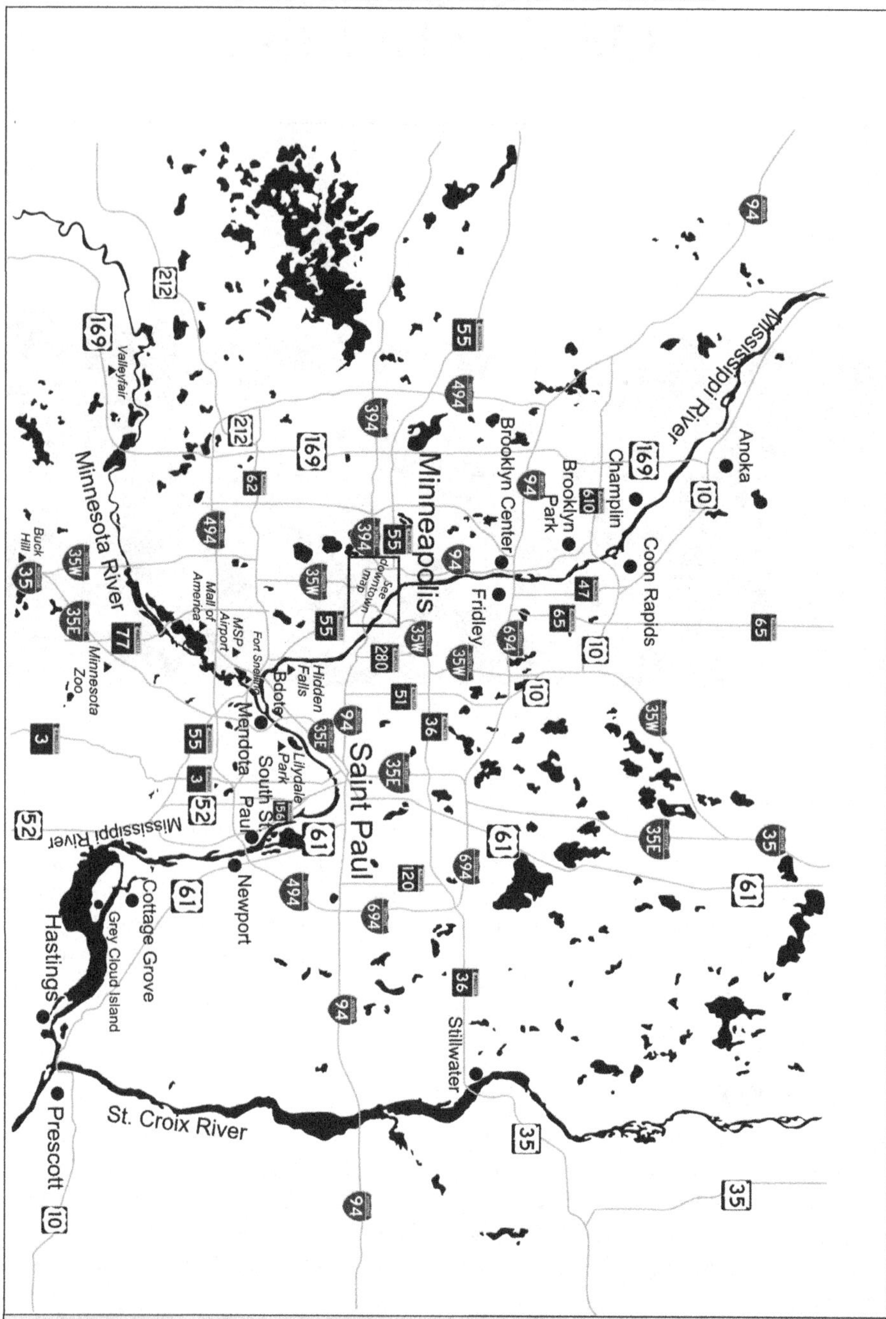

During rush hour on August 1, 2007, the I-35W bridge over the Mississippi River collapsed, sending dozens of commuters spiraling down toward the water. Read all about it in *Mississippi River Mayhem: Disasters, Tragedy, and Murder on Ol' Man River*. Find a copy wherever books are sold.

Great River Road Driving Directions in Minneapolis

If you want to stick to the Great River Road in Minneapolis, follow the route below. It begins at the I-694 Bridge and heads south to at the Fort Road Bridge that connects Saint Paul with Fort Snelling on Minnesota Highway 5. The total distance for this route is about 36 miles.

SOUTH ON THE WEST BANK

- Go east on I-94 (which actually heads south)
- Exit at W. Broadway Avenue and go east
- South on W. River Road (it becomes W. River Parkway)
- West on Godfrey Parkway
- South on Minnesota 55 (Hiawatha Ave.)
- North on Minnesota Highway 5 to cross the river

NORTH ON THE EAST BANK

- North on South Mississippi River Blvd., which becomes East River Parkway
- North on 14th Ave. SE
- West on SE 4th St.
- South on SE 6th Ave.
- North/west on SE Main St., continuing on Marshall St. NE (which then becomes East River Rd.)

MISSISSIPPI RIVER BRIDGES IN MINNEAPOLIS

- The I-694 Bridge connecting Brooklyn Center with Fridley
- The Camden Bridge connecting 42nd Ave. North and /37th Ave. NE
- The Lowry Avenue Bridge
- The Broadway Avenue Bridge
- The Plymouth Avenue Bridge
- The Father Louis Hennepin Bridge for Hennepin Avenue
- The Third Avenue Bridge (Minnesota Highway 65)
- The Stone Arch Bridge (bicycles and pedestrians only)
- The Saint Anthony Falls Bridge for I-35W
- The 10th Avenue Bridge
- Washington Avenue Bridge (Minnesota Highway 122)
- The Dartmouth Bridge for I-94
- FW Cappelen Memorial Bridge for Franklin Avenue

BRIDGES CONNECTING MINNEAPOLIS AND SAINT PAUL

- The Lake Street Bridge (aka Marshall Ave. Bridge) connecting Lake Street in Minneapolis with Marshall Avenue in Saint Paul
- Intercity Bridge (aka Ford Parkway Bridge) connecting 46th Street in Minneapolis with the Ford Parkway in Saint Paul
- The Fort Road Bridge connecting Saint Paul with Fort Snelling on Minnesota Highway 5
- The Lexington Bridge connecting Saint Paul and Lilydale via I35E

Leaves), and Sisseton (the People of the Fish Villages); two groups of Western Dakota: Yankton (the Dwellers at the End) and Yanktonai (the Little Dwellers at the End); and the Teton (the Dwellers of the Plains). The various bands of Dakota were governed by councils that ruled by consensus.

Dakota life in northern Minnesota centered around Mde Wakan (Spirit Lake; today called Mille Lacs). Dakota lived in family groups called tiyospaye. While they often traveled by foot, they also navigated rivers and lakes in canoes (dugouts and bark). The Dakota had a reputation as exceptional archers. Pierre-Charles Le Sueur witnessed a Dakota man shoot a bird out of the air with a bow and arrow!

In Dakota culture, men hunted game, while women gathered berries, nuts, roots, and maple sugar. Wild rice (psin in Dakota) was also a staple. After the wild rice harvest in late summer, they moved to the woods of northeast Minnesota where game like deer and elk were more plentiful. In spring, they returned to the villages (which housed as many as a thousand people) near lakes and rivers where fish and birds were abundant.

In the mid-17th century, some Indian nations were pushed west by the Haudenosaunee (Iroquois), a migration that triggered near constant warfare for a while in the upper Midwest. None of the new nations could dislodge the Dakota, however. The Ojibwe (Chippewa) got a different reception. As they moved into northern Minnesota, the Dakota welcomed the Ojibwe, who probably fought alongside the Dakota in some battles against other groups trying to settle along the upper Mississippi. The Dakota and Ojibwe formed a partnership in the fur trade that lasted for fifty years.

The peace between the Dakota and the Ojibwe broke down when the French tried to reassert their dominance over the fur trade in the 1720s, which triggered several decades of intense conflict. While some Dakota were already migrating south and west when the conflict erupted, the battles with the Ojibwe would push the Dakota out of northern Minnesota.

As the fur trade crashed in the early 1800s, groups of Europeans began moving into the upper Mississippi region looking for permanent homes instead of just opportunities to trade. Their arrival put great pressure on native communities.

The Dakota, like many Indian nations before them, dealt with the crisis in part by selling rights to their traditional lands. Their first land treaty was negotiated in 1805 with Lieutenant Zebulon Pike. Although the agreement was not legally binding for many reasons, the US government claimed it had granted them 100,000 acres at the confluence of the Minnesota and Mississippi Rivers.

FORT SNELLING

Lieutenant Zebulon Pike led an expedition of 20 men tasked with exploring the upper Mississippi River in the wake of the Louisiana Purchase. Pike's group left Fort Bellefontaine (near St. Louis) in 1805 and entered a territory that was familiar but still full of mysteries. Pike's expedition didn't have the success of Lewis and Clark, but he did get one thing done: he secured the spot where Fort Snelling would later be built, land that included the bdote of the Mississippi and Minnesota Rivers.

The US didn't do anything with the former Dakota land until 1819, when Colonel Henry Leavenworth led 200 troops upriver from Prairie du Chien to establish a presence in the area to protect the interests of American fur traders. The troops initially set up camp where the village of Mendota is today, at a place they called the Cantonment of New Hope. They had a rough start. In the first winter, at least 40 soldiers died, most from scurvy.

In the spring, they moved a mile north to the current site of the fort to a place they called Camp Coldwater. Colonel Josiah Snelling replaced Leavenworth in August 1820 and got to work almost immediately building a new fort. When completed in 1825, the rhombus-shaped fort had a tower at each angle and stone walls around the barracks. The fort was first called Fort St. Anthony but was renamed for Colonel Snelling in 1824.

Life at the fort was maddeningly dull from most accounts. Colonel Snelling apparently drank a lot of whiskey to pass the time. Desertion grew into such a problem in the early 1820s that fort commanders paid Native Americans a bounty of $20 for each deserter they brought back to the fort.

Fort Snelling was a remote outpost, but it became less isolated in 1823 when the *Virginia* reached the fort, the first steamboat to travel that far north on the Mississippi. In the next three years, 14 more steamboats landed at the fort.

Colonel Snelling was transferred to Jefferson Barracks (at St. Louis) in 1827. Zachary Taylor (later the 12th US President) was fort commandant in 1828-29 when the fur trade was still going strong. He wasn't fond of the monopoly that controlled the trade, calling the American Fur Company "the greatest set of scoundrels the world ever knew." Another post commander was Seth Eastman; he would later achieve fame for his paintings.

Dr. John Emerson was transferred to Fort Snelling around 1836. He brought with him an enslaved man named Dred Scott. Slavery in the territory was prohibited by the Missouri Compromise of 1820, but there had been enslaved people in the territory before the legislation passed and the legislation didn't change that fact. Colonel Snelling and other officers also owned enslaved Africans.

While living at the fort, Scott met Harriet Robinson, an enslaved woman owned by Indian agent Lawrence Taliaferro. The two were married at the fort, by Taliaferro, who then passed ownership of Harriet to Emerson. In 1840, the Emersons moved to St. Louis, minus the doctor, who was sent to Florida to serve during the Seminole War. After the doctor's death in 1843, the Scotts sued his widow for their freedom. They based their suit on the doctrine of "once free, always free," a claim they believed they could make because of the time they had lived in territories where slavery was outlawed. That strategy had, in fact, been used successfully to free more than a hundred other enslaved people. A St. Louis jury awarded the Scotts their freedom in 1850, but the US Supreme Court ruled in 1857 that the Scotts were personal property and must remain enslaved. The infamous decision inflamed the debate about slavery in the United States and made civil war nearly inevitable.

Treaties with the Ojibwe and Dakota people in 1837 opened up land between the St. Croix and Mississippi Rivers to Euro-American settlement. Thousands of people moved into the area, not always respecting the legal boundaries set by the treaty. In 1840, Major Plympton ordered soldiers to drive out squatters who were living below the fort on military land. Many of those folks moved on to form Saint Paul.

Fort Snelling was closed in 1858 but not for long. Three years later it was reactivated to prepare troops for the Civil War. In August 1862, a major conflict erupted with the Dakota who lived along the Minnesota River. The outbreak of hostilities was triggered primarily by Dakota frustrations with the failure of the US government to live up to its treaty obligations and with traders who were stealing money from the treaty payments. By the summer of 1862, many Dakota were starving and growing increasingly desperate. When a group of young Dakota men raided a farm and killed several Euro-American settlers on August 18, the Dakota who lived along the lower Minnesota decided to launch a full assault against the Americans, in spite of the advice of leaders such as Taoyatedute (Little Crow) who believed it would be a fatal mistake. Even those reluctant leaders went along in the end, though.

During the conflict, Colonel Henry Sibley, the state's first governor, organized soldiers at Fort Snelling. Initially, the Dakota were on the offensive and had the American forces in disarray, but when the Dakota assaults on the city of New Ulm and Fort Ridgely fell just short, the Dakota lost their advantage. By mid-September, the last major battle was over, and the Dakota had surrendered.

In the aftermath of the hostilities, 38 Dakota men were hanged in a public square in Mankato (on December 26)—the largest mass execution in US history. The area around Fort Snelling was turned into a concentration camp. Some 1,600 Dakota—mostly women and children—were interred until they could be permanently moved out of Minnesota. They wintered below the fort (at present-day Fort Snelling State Park) in horrid conditions. Many were attacked by nearby civilians, and disease and starvation ran rampant. Upwards of 300 Dakota died before spring arrived, when they were shipped out to reservation land in South Dakota.

The Dakota—all Dakota—paid dearly for the conflict. Roughly a thousand Dakota actively fought, but all 6,300 Santee Dakota were punished. The US canceled treaties, seized all their land in Minnesota, and expelled them from the state.

In 1864, Sakpedan (Little Six) and Wakanozhanzha (Medicine Bottle), two leaders of the Dakota uprising, were captured and returned to the fort, probably illegally as they had been living in Canada at the time of their capture. They were tried and convicted of killing civilians during the Dakota Conflict and sentenced to be hanged.

According to legend, as the two men were standing on the platform on November 11, 1865, a train whistle sounded in the distance and Sakpedan, hearing the sound, said: "As the white man comes in, the Indian goes out."

That prophecy, though, didn't come true. While Americans and Europeans soon dominated the state, Dakota and other Indigenous people didn't go away. Some Dakota returned to Minnesota and established reservations at Upper Sioux, Lower Sioux, Shakopee, and Tinta Wita (Prairie Island), where their descendants live today.

Fort Snelling was officially decommissioned in 1946, but some buildings on the grounds are still being used by reservists. In the 1960s, the State of Minnesota approved funds to restore and preserve the fort as a historic site.

MENDOTA

The first Euro-Americans to move into the area were the soldiers at the Cantonment of New Hope, who wintered here before Fort Snelling was built. They were followed by folks who were involved in the fur trade, primarily discontented French Canadians and Métis who had left Selkirk's colony at Fort Garry (Winnipeg).

Among those early Euro-American settlers was Alexis Bailly, who ran a trading post for eight years beginning in 1826. The new settlement, first called St. Peter but changed to Mendota in 1837, would eventually attract nearly 250 refugees from Fort Garry, although many didn't stay long. Discontent with Selkirk motivated many folks

> **RANDOM FACT:** The first Minnesota State Fair was held at Fort Snelling in 1860; they had a booth selling pemmican on a stick. (Just kidding.)

to resettle, but others were driven away by the Red River flood of 1826 or by the drought and grasshopper plagues that had made farming so difficult.

The American Fur Company set up a trading center at Mendota in 1834. Henry Hastings Sibley, then just 23 years old, managed it. He had left his native Detroit five years earlier in search of a more exciting life on the frontier. In 1839, while living at the post, he married a Dakota woman known as Red Blanket Woman. They had a daughter, Helen (also called Wahkiyee, or Bird). Few details about his relationship with Red Blanket Woman were written down, but it apparently ended around 1842. He placed Helen with a missionary family but remained part of her life until she died in 1859. Henry went on to marry Sarah Jane Steele in 1843, the daughter of Fort Snelling's commander, General James Steele, and brother of Minneapolis' Franklin Steele. Sibley would later serve as the state's first governor.

The trading post was built in a strategic location. It benefited from the protection provided by Fort Snelling and from being the early terminus of the Red River Ox Cart Trail. The post moved a lot of pelts. In 1835 alone, they acquired 289,000 muskrat pelts, far and away the most of any animal. As the primary settlement outside of Fort Snelling, Mendota was also the social center for the region and was the only place to get supplies like meat, tea, and flour.

Mendota's early prospects were cut short as Saint Paul rose to prominence. The trading post was moved to Saint Paul in 1849, shifting the terminus of the oxcart trail to that city. Mendota nearly got the state capital, but when they lost that battle, the village lost much of its population and social life.

A small community endured, however. Mendota served as county seat from 1854 to 1857 before it was moved to Hastings. A ferry operated across the river from 1825 to 1926. During the Civil War, Mendota was a popular party town for soldiers and their friends, something that was annoying enough to entice some residents to move away.

Esdras Bernier ran a large onion farm for some 30 years beginning in the 1880s, which earned him the nickname "Bernie the Onion King." He used Sibley's old fur trading complex to warehouse his crop. In 1910, the Daughters of the American Revolution (DAR) purchased the Sibley property and began restoration work. For years, the DAR ran a popular restaurant and teahouse in the building.

MINNEAPOLIS

We're told that we're better off not knowing how sausage and legislation are made, but maybe starting a city from scratch should be on that list, too. Before there was a Minneapolis, there was land where the Dakota people lived, home to a sacred place known as Owamniyomni (eddy whirlpool) or HaHa Tonka (big waterfall). We know it today as St. Anthony Falls. In 1806, the US government claimed 100,000 acres of Dakota land around the falls based on a mostly illegitimate treaty negotiated by Zebulon Pike. For 30 years, the only official development that occurred was the construction of Fort Snelling.

In 1838, some of those 100,000 acres were officially opened for private development, which sparked an influx of folks eager to get rich. Officers from the fort were officially prohibited from making claims, but that didn't stop Major Joseph Plympton and Captain Martin Scott from trying. They were out-sneaked, though, by Franklin Steele, the sutler at the fort, who crossed the river in the middle of the night and built a small cabin to stake out a claim.

Steele hired a series of voyageurs to maintain and guard the cabin, but even with that help, he still had to pay off a claim jumper. It all worked out in his favor in the end, as he and his good friend, Pierre Bottineau, a former trader for the American Fur Company, gained control of the land around St. Anthony Falls.

Steele didn't have much money to develop his land, so in 1847 he sold 90% of the water power rights for $10,000 and used the money to build a dam and a sawmill to process timber coming down river. His mill opened in September 1848 but was plagued by a number of problems, like the fact that he built on government land that had not yet been surveyed, which is less of a problem when you have political connections like he did. Once the land was surveyed, Steele quickly gained ownership of the prime lots by paying some people to make claims on his behalf and buying many others. He used his holdings to plat a village on the east bank of the Mississippi River that he named St. Anthony (after the falls), giving a name and shape to a community that already had nearly 300 residents, most of them from Maine and other parts of New England.

St. Anthony's early growth was haphazard and sprawling, with almost every structure built of wood (there was plenty of it, after all). In the early years, Saint Paul was the more prosperous city, growing more quickly and having better transportation connections. St. Anthony tried to claim the "head of navigation" title from Saint Paul but didn't succeed, even after the development of shallow-draft boats in the early 1850s that allowed river traffic to travel north of the falls on the Mississippi River to St. Cloud. Another early Euro-American settler, hotel-owner Anson Northup, tried to get the state capital moved from Saint Paul to St. Anthony. He lost that argument but won the state university for St. Anthony as a consolation prize.

Milling was at the center of the city's economy from the beginning. The first mill went into operation around 1823 to grind flour for Fort Snelling. It failed. The bread from the milled flour turned out to be unfit to eat. Nearly 30 years passed before RC Rogers opened the next mill.

By the end of the 1860s, flour mills lined both sides of the Mississippi River. Part of the boom was due to an innovation that dramatically increased the portion of a grain of wheat that could be processed, leading to a highly sought-after brand of flour that Minneapolis shipped around the world. This innovation made Minneapolis the preeminent milling center in the Midwest. The mills were dangerous places, though. On May 2, 1879, the Washburn "A" Mill exploded. At least 18 people died, and a fire ignited that destroyed many neighboring buildings.

Land on the west bank of the Mississippi River developed more slowly because it was either part of the military reservation or Dakota land. Claims for land on the military reservation had to be approved by officers at Fort Snelling, a situation that bred corruption. Some officers at the remote fort charged a fee for their permission. Buyers who didn't agree to the terms would have their claim denied, and soldiers would march in and destroy whatever work they had done to build on the land.

Many names were proposed for the settlement on the west bank. The *Minnesota Pioneer* suggested the name "All Saints" might be a good fit, considering the highly pious nature of early Euro-American settlers, but the first name that was officially entered into the records was Albion. It was unpopular. In the November 5, 1852, edition of the *St. Anthony Express*, Charles Hoag, a teacher, suggested the name "Minnehapolis," a fusion of "Minnehaha" ("waterfall" in Dakota) with the Greek "polis." It struck a chord, and the name was adopted, after dropping the "h."

When the government finally decided to reduce the size of the military reserve and sell land, it first proposed to auction lots to the highest bidder, which was the standard practice. The folks who were already living there weren't too happy with that idea, so they made plans to keep the eastern speculators at bay, by any means necessary. When the planned sales were delayed, the squatters had time to send a representative to DC to plead their case. After some effort, they convinced Congress to sell them the land they had been occupying illegally for the standard $1.25/acre, far below what the land would have actually fetched if the auction had been held. Many then quickly sold their claims at the higher, prevailing rate. So the west bank of Minneapolis was basically settled by folks who got special favors because they were connected or had paid bribes, then those folks went to DC to stave off competition for their not-yet-legal claims and Congress gladly complied, handing handsome profits to those Euro-American settlers. Bratwurst.

In 1854, that Steele guy founded the Minneapolis Bridge Company to connect the growing villages on the east (St. Anthony) and west (Minneapolis) banks. The first bridge was completed in December 1854, a single arch span with a wood plank deck supported by cables—the first bridge to span the Mississippi River anywhere. The toll was 10 cents, paid by brave folks who walked across the temporary and loose planks that formed the deck. The bridge was re-engineered after storm damage in March 1855 and officially opened on July 4. The bridge spurred development on the west bank in an area that became known as Bridge Square, at the junction of Nicollet Avenue (the road south to Fort Snelling) and Hennepin Avenue (the road to communities north of Minneapolis). Nicollet Avenue would eventually become the retail center for the city, while Hennepin Avenue would attract offices and banks.

By 1856, both St. Anthony and Minneapolis were doing well, each having about 4,000 residents. Franklin Steele considered founding a city downriver near Fort Snelling. He was going to call it Minnesota City, but the financial panic of 1857 killed his plans. He bought sheep instead.

Economic growth slowed during the Civil War, but the region still managed to build a rail connection between Saint Paul and St. Anthony that opened in 1862. The connection across the Mississippi River to Minneapolis took another three years. After the war, Minneapolis and St. Anthony boomed. Local mills processed more lumber than they could use locally. Much of the excess harvested timber was shipped down the Mississippi River (as far as St. Louis) for processing.

Sawmills lined the riverfront from Hennepin Avenue to Camden Place. Nearby, lumberjack restaurants around Hennepin and Washington (the City Market District) served the mill workers. One of those merchants eventually got fed up with the number of customers who didn't pay, so he dispensed his soup through a syringe. If a customer refused to pay, he would use the syringe to remove the soup from the bowl. (I'm guessing that was a lot easier to do for something like split pea than chicken noodle!)

In 1866, voters defeated a plan to merge Minneapolis and St. Anthony (by 85 votes), but the two cities were finally merged by an act of the Minnesota Legislature on February 28, 1872. The newly merged city grew quickly, especially as immigrants from Sweden, Norway, and other northern European countries flooded in to work in the mills.

Lumber production in Minnesota peaked around 1899 when 594 million board feet were processed. Twenty years later, nearly all the lumber mills were closed. As lumber milling waned, though, flour milling grew. In 1885, Minneapolis was the world's largest producer of flour. By 1900, Minneapolis overtook Saint Paul as the primary wholesaling market in the upper Midwest and also grew into the financial and banking center for the region. As transportation costs and competition increased in the 20th century, flour milling declined in Minneapolis, although many of the companies based there owned a big share of new mills that opened in places like Buffalo and Kansas City.

Minneapolis has also been an innovator in retail sales. As late as 1894, no stores (anywhere) sold "ready-to-wear" clothing. Men's suits were tailor made and women went to dressmakers and millinery shops. In 1894, Elizabeth Quinlan and her partner Fred Young opened a boutique at 513 Nicollet that sold ready-to-wear women's clothing. It was just the second such store in the country. Quinlan was also the only female clothing buyer in the US at the time. In 1926, her company built an elegant new Italian Renaissance building at 9th and Nicollet for its expanded operations.

Minneapolis and Saint Paul were fiercely competitive, often in silly ways. For much of the latter part of the 19th century, both cities fudged census figures as they fought over which city had a bigger population. In 1890, the federal government intervened and demanded a do-over when they discovered that Minneapolis was counting a lot of dead people, and that Saint Paul's dime stores, barber shops, and depots had a booming population. The new count showed that Minneapolis was the more populous city, a title it has held ever since.

In the early half of the 20th century, Minneapolis embraced the urban renewal craze. In less than a generation, one-third of downtown buildings were razed for new development, including the original heart of the city around Bridge Square. By the early 1900s, the area had a rapidly growing population of very poor folks, including many unemployed loggers, but at least they had plenty of entertainment options, with 30 brothels and 110 bars nearby. The city cleared the area beginning in the late 1950s.

As early as the 1980s, immigrants from Somalia moved to Minneapolis, but the pace quickened in the 1990s on the heels of the Somali civil war. Tens of thousands found a new home in Minnesota, with many settling in the Cedar-Riverside neighborhood.

Minneapolis today has a diverse economy, home to the headquarters of several big corporations like General Mills and Target. The city is a regional center for retail sales and health care. Minneapolis is also home to what is probably the largest college campus that spans a major river: the University of Minnesota is adjacent to downtown Minneapolis and has buildings on both banks of the Mississippi River.

Explore

MINNEAPOLIS

Attractions

Minneapolis is a busy city, which means that parking can sometimes be challenging, especially if you expect to park next to your destination. In some areas, you may have to park a block or two away. Downtown has a number of garages and some spots on the street, but it is more expensive than other parts of the city. If any of that concerns you, consider alternate ways of getting around, such as the light rail lines or car services such as Uber or Lyft.

Northwest of downtown, the **Minnesota African American Heritage Museum & Gallery** (1256 Penn Ave. N.) celebrates the art, culture, and lives of African Americans in Minnesota with exhibits (free) and live programs. The gallery is on the fourth floor of the building; free parking is available in the building's garage.

There's no shortage of activities in Minneapolis, regardless of the time of year. There are miles and miles of **paved walkways and bikeways** along the river, so ditching the car for a while is a good idea. **Nice Ride** bike rental stations are located in several areas along the river. I recommend paying for a day pass, which buys unlimited 30-minute rides for 24 hours. There are a lot of stations around the city, so there's never really a need to ride longer than half an hour. You can purchase a pass on your smartphone or at one of the kiosks near the bike racks.

AUTHOR'S PICK: Walk the **Stone Arch Bridge** across the river at downtown. It has great views of St. Anthony Falls and the now-closed Upper St. Anthony Lock. You can access it from both sides of the river. The Stone Arch Bridge is part of the **St. Anthony Falls Heritage Trail**, a 1.8-mile route that loops from First Bridge Park to Father Hennepin Park in historic **St. Anthony Main**, crossing the Stone Arch and Father Hennepin Bridges.

On the West Bank of the Falls

Footpaths and bridges wind through the remains of a 19th-century flour mill at **Mill Ruins Park** below the Stone Arch Bridge.

When the **Upper St. Anthony Lock** (1 Portland Ave.; 952.303.2706) opened in 1963, Minneapolis thought it had finally achieved its dream of becoming the head of navigation on the Mississippi River. Alas, the lock never attracted the traffic that city leaders had hoped for. The lock was closed in 2015, largely because there was so little commercial navigation, but also to help halt the spread of invasive carp to the lakes of northern Minnesota. The National Park Service operates a visitors center at the lock and leads periodic guided tours of the structure (10a, 11a, 3p daily).

Tour the **Mill City Museum** (704 S. Second St.; 612.341.7555), built into the ruins of the old Washburn "A" Mill along the Mississippi River. The upper balcony has spectacular views.

Even if you don't have time to take in a show, visit the **Guthrie Theater** (818 S. 2nd St.; box office: 612.377.2224), the striking blue building just south of the Mill City Museum. The building was designed by famed architect Jean Nouvel and opened in 2006. The Guthrie offers guided tours (a Backstage Tour and an Architecture Tour; check times before visiting), but you are welcome to walk around when it is open. Make sure to check out the views from the Endless Bridge, a balcony overlooking the river.

On the East Bank of the Falls

Boom Island Park (724 Sibley St. NE), which hasn't been an island for a while, has hiking trails, spots to picnic, and good views of the river and Minneapolis. The park has both **Nice Ride** (see page 89) and **Paddle Share** (see page 83) stations, from which you can rent a bike or a kayak.

Water Power Park has great views of the falls and of Minneapolis. The **Lower Trail** winds through thick vegetation and old industrial ruins next to the river. Access it across the street from the old Pillsbury "A" Mill on Main Street.

The **Weisman Art Museum** (333 E. River Parkway; 612.625.9494) overlooks the Mississippi River from the east bank of the University of Minnesota campus. The building, designed by celebrity architect Frank Gehry, houses a mostly modern collection.

South of Downtown

Minnesota is home of the largest community of Somalis in the US, so it's a natural that Minneapolis is where you'll find the **Somali Museum of Minnesota** (2925 Chicago Ave.; 612.886.3723). The collections feature hundreds of objects of traditional Somali arts, and the museum also hosts cultural programs.

You'll find the 53-foot-tall **Minnehaha Falls** in Minnehaha Park (4801 S. Minnehaha Park Dr.; 612.230.6400), which were featured in Henry Wadsworth Longfellow's *The Song of Hiawatha.* There are walkways that descend to the bottom of the falls, and a dirt trail that leads to the Mississippi River.

Coldwater Spring (5601 Minnehaha Park Dr. S.) is a restored oak savanna and prairie complex that has long been sacred to area Native Americans (the Dakota call it mni sni). The spring also supplied drinking water to For Snelling for about a hundred years. The site has several walking trails that weave through the prairie.

Other Minneapolis Attractions

Minneapolis has a great music scene. See what's going at famed **First Avenue** (701 N. 1st Ave.; 612.332.1775) or one of the hundreds of other places that host live music.

The **Foshay Tower** (now the W Hotel; 821 S. Marquette Ave.) is an Art déco masterpiece that bankrupted its namesake. Multi-millionaire Wilbur Foshay built the 32-story tower to celebrate his success in the utilities business. Foshay's design was inspired by the Washington Monument. For the grand opening in 1929, Foshay threw a lavish three-day party that attracted dignitaries from around the country, at least in part because he paid for their travel. Two months later, the stock market crashed, the Depression began, and Foshay went broke. He was eventually convicted of securities fraud and served time in federal prison. After he left prison, he got a job working for the Chamber of Commerce of Salida, Colorado, for $1,800 a year and was quite happy to do it. He died in a Minneapolis nursing home on the 28th anniversary of the tower's dedication. The building is a gem, accented with Italian marble, African mahogany, gold-plated knobs, and many other features. You are welcome to wander around the lobby, and there's an observation deck ($) at the top with great views of the area.

The **Basilica of St. Mary** (1600 Hennepin Ave.; 612.333.1381) is a grand Beaux Arts structure southwest of downtown. Ground was broken in 1907 and the first mass held in 1914, but the structure wasn't completed until 1926. The imposing square dome rises about 280 feet above street level.

The **Walker Art Center** (725 Vineland Pl.; 612.375.7600) is a nationally known museum that showcases contemporary art. Don't miss the adjacent **Minneapolis Sculpture Garden**, where you can see the famous spoon and cherry sculpture.

The **Minneapolis Institute of Arts** (2400 3rd Ave. S; 888.642.2787) has an expansive collection that you won't see in a day, but you should try, including the special exhibits that cycle in and out.

Just down the street from the Minneapolis Institute of Arts, the **Hennepin County History Museum** (2303 3rd Ave. S; 612.870.1329) has several rooms of exhibits on the region's history and a good research library.

The **American Swedish Institute** (2600 Park Ave.; 612.871.4907) showcases Swedish cultural heritage. The museum is housed in the historic, gorgeous Turnblad Mansion and hosts rotating art and cultural exhibits.

See a show at the **Guthrie Theater** (818 S. 2nd St.; 612.377.2224), **In the Heart of the Beast Theatre** (1500 E. Lake St.; 612.540.5385), or one of the other local theaters.

Birchbark Books (2115 W. 21 St.; 612.374.4023) is an independent bookstore that specializes in offering its customers an intimate experience. They have a good collection of fiction and books by/about Native Americans. The store is owned by Pulitzer Prize-winning author Louise Erdrich.

AROUND FORT SNELLING

The reconstructed **Fort Snelling State Historic Site** (200 Tower Ave.; 612.726.1171) offers a glimpse at life for soldiers stationed there and tells the stories of the Dakota and early Europeans who moved into the area. On some days, actors in period clothing chat with visitors and answer questions.

Fort Snelling State Park (Post Road; 612.725.2389), located below the fort itself, is a wild place with multiple hiking and biking trails (or skiing in winter) spread across its 3,000 acres. The park includes Wita Tanka/Pike Island , which sits at the confluence of the Minnesota and Mississippi Rivers (the place called Bdote by the Dakota people). There is also a moving memorial to the Dakota who were placed in a concentration camp at this site after the Dakota Conflict of 1862.

MENDOTA

Just past Fort Snelling, the **Sibley House Historic Site** in Mendota (1357 Sibley Memorial Highway; 651.452.1596) pays homage to the fur trade era by preserving the old trading post and private residences from that era, including Sibley's home.

High above the confluence of the Mississippi and Minnesota Rivers, **Oheyawahi** (a hill much visited), is a place where native peoples—Dakota, Ojibwe, and Ioway—assembled for ceremonies that celebrated life and marked death. In 1851, the Dakota signed a treaty at this site that ceded much of their land west of the Mississippi River. Today, the spot is known also as **Pilot Knob** (2044 Pilot Knob Rd.) and is a preserve with great views where oak savanna restoration is progressing nicely.

Getting On the River

You can rent a kayak through the **PaddleShare** program operated by the National Park Service and its partners (Friday-Sunday). In Minneapolis, you can rent from North Mississippi Regional Park and paddle 3.9 miles to Boom Island or rent at Mississippi Watershed Management Organization and paddle 1.7 miles to Boom Island.

Paddle Bridge (www.paddlebridge.com) offers guided kayak tours on the Mississippi. They run tours on different segments of the river, each one lasting 2-3 hours.

Day cruises on the **Minneapolis Queen** (952.474.8058) depart from Bohemian Flats Park (2150 W. River Parkway S.) for 90-minute sightseeing cruises through Minneapolis. They also offer cruises with a pizza, happy hour, and Mexican food theme.

Take a ride on the solar-powered **Minneapolis Water Taxi** (612.801.1921). Call ahead to schedule a one-hour tour on the river above St. Anthony Falls.

Drinking and Dining

The Twin Cities have their fair share of distinct foods, such as the juicy lucy: a hamburger stuffed with cheese. They've been serving them here for decades, while the rest of us are Johnny-come-latelies. Food writer Jess Fleming recommends **Matt's Bar** (3500 Cedar Ave. S.; 612.722.7072) for a taste of the original (with American cheese) or the **Blue Door Pub** (1514 Como Ave. SE; 612.367.4964) if you're more adventurous (they have many cheese options, including blue cheese). You'll find the juicy lucy on many menus, though. A few other foods you might come across, if you're lucky:

- **Hotdish**, which is a baked casserole that usually includes a meat (ground beef, typically), a paste-like cream of something soup, and a crispy topping, preferably tater tots. You're more likely to eat it at potluck than a restaurant, but you will see it on some menus.

Downtown Minneapolis Map

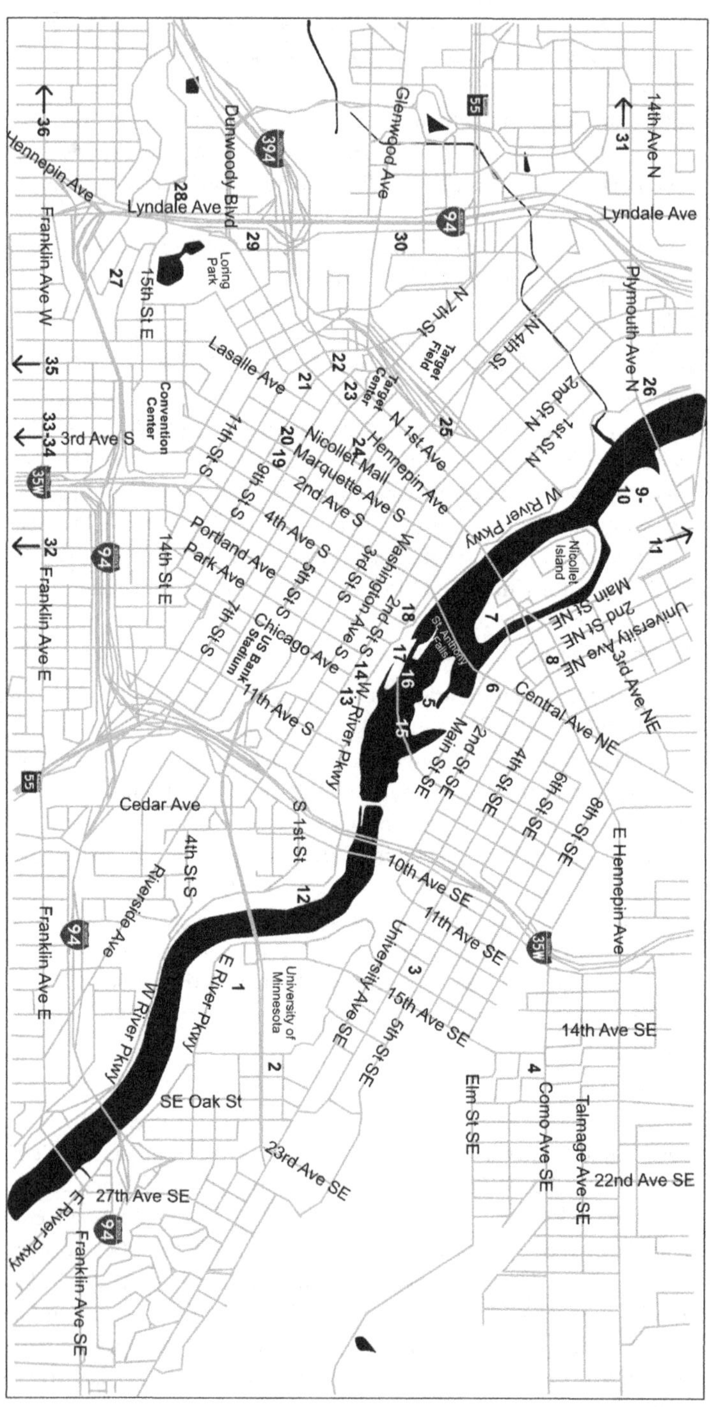

Downtown Minneapolis Map Index

Attractions

32. American Swedish Institute
29. Basilica of St. Mary
36. Birchbark Books
10. Boom Island Park
23. First Avenue
19. Foshay Tower
13. Guthrie Theater
33. Hennepin County History Museum
14. Mill City Museum
17. Mill Ruins Park
34. Minneapolis Institute of Arts
12. Minneapolis Queen dock
28. Minneapolis Sculpture Garden
9. Minneapolis Water Taxi
31. Minnesota African American Heritage Museum & Gallery
6. St. Anthony Main
15. Stone Arch Bridge
16. Upper St. Anthony Lock
28. Walker Art Center
5. Water Power Park
1. Weisman Art Museum

Where to Eat and Drink

3. Al's Breakfast
4. Blue Door Pub
34. Fika Café
11. Food Building
20. Hell's Kitchen
19. Keys at the Foshay
8. Kramarczuk's East European Deli
30. Lyndale Farmers Market
24. Murray's Steakhouse
7. Nicollet Island Inn
18. Owamni by The Sioux Chef
35. Pho Tau Bay
19. Prohibition Bar
26. Pryes Brewing Company

Where to Stay

27. 300 Clifton Bed & Breakfast
21. Chambers Hotel
2. Graduate Minneapolis
7. Nicollet Island Inn

Other

22. Greyhound/Jefferson Lines Depot
25. Megabus Stop

- **Bars**, which are deep-dish sweets that can be as simple as chocolate chip or complex layers of flavors. They are also more common at pot lucks and bakeries than on restaurant menus. Check out the selection at **Sarah Jane's Bakery Northeast** (2853 Johnson St. NE; 612.789.2827).
- **Swedish dishes** like lefse, which are thin potato pancakes that are usually sweet but can be savory, and Swedish meatballs. You can treat yourself to meatballs and other delicious Swedish dishes at the upscale **Fika Café** at the **American Swedish Institute** (2600 Park Ave.; 612.871.4907).
- Minneapolis and Saint Paul have large Vietnamese communities, which translates into a wealth of good **Vietnamese restaurants**. In Minneapolis, you'll find several along the stretch of Nicollet Avenue known as Eat Street, especially from the 2500 block south. **Pho Tau Bay** (2837 Nicollet Ave.; 612.874.6030) is a great choice, with 20-some pho options, as well as vermicelli dishes and other traditional options.
- And let's name the tinned meat in the room: **SPAM**. It's a Minnesota invention and still produced at a plant south of the Twin Cities (in Austin). Many Chinese apparently call it "Meaty Juicy Satisfaction," according to the folks at the SPAM Museum. It's really versatile (just ask Monty Python!) but it's not for everyone (like vegetarians and vegans). I find it quite salty. You may see it show up on a few menus. If so, go for it! If you don't like it, you can always get a juicy lucy.

The food scene in Minneapolis is exciting, dynamic, and delicious. For an overview, check out *Mpls.St.Paul Magazine*. Here are some places that are either long-time favorites or offer a predictably good experience:

Go **brewery hopping** around the city! (But don't drive yourself around; use taxis or a ride share service such as Lyft or Uber.) Scan through the on-line guide (discoverthecities.com/st-paul-minneapolis-breweries) for a list of places you might want to sample from. **Pryes Brewing Company** (1401 W. River Rd. N; 612.787.7937) is right on the Mississippi just upriver of downtown and is a fun place to enjoy a good beer with good views. The pizzas are delicious and you can work off those calories with a game of feather bowling, which I bet you've never done before.

Get a drink at **Prohibition Bar** (W Hotel, 27th floor; 821 Marquette Ave. S; 612.597.2413), the former penthouse of riches-to-rags utilities baron Wilbur Foshay.

Keys at the Foshay (114 S. 9th St.; 612.339.6399) serves up creative comfort food, especially for breakfast, in Art déco elegance.

Family-owned **Murray's Steakhouse** (26 S. 6th St.; 612.339.0909) offers classic Minnesota fine dining that has been pleasing locals since the end of World War II.

AUTHOR'S PICK: **Hell's Kitchen** (80 S. 9th St.; 612.332.4700) serves food that is fun and creative and won't break the bank. For a taste of Minnesota, try the walleye hash or mahnomin (wild rice) porridge.

AUTHOR'S PICK: Sean Sherman and Dana Thompson offer a dining experience that is both familiar and eye-opening. **Owamni by The Sioux Chef** (420 1st St. S.; 612.444.1846) prepares food made from ingredients that are indigenous to Native America. You won't find wheat flour or dairy but instead they feature ingredients such as pheasant and berries. The menu changes regularly. Reservations are a good idea.

Dining at the **Nicollet Island Inn** (95 Merriam St.; 612.331.1800) is a sumptuous affair, complete with white tablecloths, top-notch service, and succulent food. Lunch is also excellent and more affordable.

Ukrainian-born Wasyl and Anna Kramarczuk founded a bakery and sausage shop that is still going strong 50 years later. **Kramarczuk's East European Deli** (215 E. Hennepin Ave.; 612.379.3018) specializes in dishes from eastern Europe, including pierogi and Ukrainian sausage. I love the garlicky Krakowska sandwich. You can dine in the restaurant or visit the deli counter to take something with you.

The **Food Building** in northeast Minneapolis (1401 Marshall St. NE) is a dream come true for foodies who live for quality items from small producers. Wander the halls to watch artisan cheese makers, bakers, and salami makers at work.

Al's Breakfast (413 14th Ave. SE; 612.331.9991) in Dinkytown is a tiny place with a big reputation for hearty breakfasts. Don't show up starving, as you'll likely have to wait a bit for one of the few seats.

Where to Stay: Lodging

Downtown hotels are convenient and put you within walking distance of most everything you'll want to see, but they can be expensive. Most also charge extra for parking, which can run an extra $20-$30 a day. The places below offer a different experience from standard chain hotels.

Located in Minneapolis's theater district, the **Chambers Hotel** (901 Hennepin Ave.; 612.767.6900) rents modern rooms in a historic building. Rooms tend to be better a bargain than other downtown hotels.

The **Graduate Minneapolis** (615 Washington Ave. SE; 612.379.8888), rents affordable rooms with a modern and whimsical twist. The hotel sits in the middle of the University of Minnesota campus and along the METRO light rail Green Line.

The historic **Nicollet Island Inn** (95 Merriam St.; 612.331.1800) offers luxury accommodations on the island of the same name within walking distance of downtown.

If you'd prefer a higher end experience, **300 Clifton Bed & Breakfast** near Loring Park (300 Clifton Ave.; 612.281.1550) rents four rooms in a historic mansion in a neighborhood of historic mansions near the Walker Art Center. Rooms include a continental breakfast, but you can upgrade to a four-course gourmet breakfast.

Regional Attractions

You will probably want to wander away from the river at some point, and there are plenty of reasons to do so. Here are a few of the major attractions in the metro region:

- **Valleyfair Amusement Park** in Shakopee (952.445.6500)
- The **Minnesota Zoo** in Apple Valley (13000 Zoo Boulevard; 952.431.9200)
- The **Mall of America** in Bloomington (60 E. Broadway), the largest mall in the US
- The **Minnesota Vikings** football team (US Bank Stadium downtown)
- The **Minnesota Twins** baseball team (Target Field; 1 Twins Way)
- The **Minnesota Timberwolves** basketball team (Target Center; 601 N 1st Ave.)
- The **Minnesota Wild** hockey team (Xcel Energy Center in Saint Paul)
- The **Minnesota Lynx** of the Women's National Basketball Association (Target Center downtown)
- **Minnesota United FC** of Major League Soccer play at Allianz Field in Saint Paul
- The **Minnesota Roller Derby** (Roy Wilkins Auditorium in Saint Paul, 175 W. Kellogg Blvd.)
- The **Saint Paul Saints** of the American Association of Independent Professional Baseball (CHS Field in Saint Paul)
- Head to **Buck Hill (**Burnsville) for skiing, snowboarding, and snow tubing

Special Events

Farmers markets are popular in Minneapolis. These are your best bets:

- Lyndale Market (312 E. Lyndale Ave. North): Daily 6am-1pm
- Government Center Market (300 S. 6th St.): Tuesdays 9am-3pm
- Nicollet Mall between 6th and 9th Streets (downtown): Thursdays 6-2

Minneapolis hosts a bunch of festivals, many of which celebrate the area's water wealth. Here are a few to consider checking out:

- The eccentric **May Day** celebration led by In the Heart of the Beast Theatre.
- The **Stone Arch Bridge Festival** in mid-June, which features musical performances and the works of local artists.
- The **Minneapolis Aquatennial** is a city-wide celebration of the region's water riches (July). Highlights include a parade after dark, professional waterskiers, and canoe rides.

Getting There

BY AIR

Minneapolis-Saint Paul International Airport is located south of downtown Minneapolis in the suburb of Bloomington. The airport is connected to downtown via the METRO Blue Line light rail service. You can ride the light rail between terminals 1 and 2 for free. It's an airport with the usual amenities, like taxis, car rental services, domestic and international departures/arrivals, crappy food, and overzealous security.

BY TRAIN

The Twin Cities are served by **Amtrak's** *Empire Builder* and *Borealis* trains. The *Empire Builder* connects Chicago to the Pacific Northwest, while the *Borealis* trains connect Saint Paul and Chicago. The only station in the region is Saint Paul's **Union Depot** (240 Kellogg Blvd.). See page 107 (the Getting There section in the Saint Paul chapter) for more information.

BY BUS

Both **Greyhound** and **Jefferson Lines** offer long-distance bus service to the Twin Cities. Both have stations in downtown Minneapolis (950 Hawthorne Ave.), as well as several other spots around the Twin Cities; check their websites for details.

Megabus also serves Minneapolis (318 3rd Ave. S.). You must buy tickets in advance through their website.

Getting Around

BY CAR

Interstate 94 connects the two downtowns. If it's not rush hour, you can get from one to the other in 15 minutes; otherwise, well, queue up Prince on your favorite music device, and you won't care how long it takes (it will take a while). In spite of all the limited access highways around the Twin Cities, roads are frequently busy and getting from one place to another will probably take longer than you think. Give yourself extra time.

BY RAIL

The Twin Cities region has an expanding light rail system and decent bus routes. **Metro Transit's** Blue Line (formerly the Hiawatha Line) offers light rail service from the Mall of America to downtown Minneapolis (Target Field Station), with stops at the airport and Fort Snelling. The Green Line connects downtown Saint Paul (beginning at Union Station) with downtown Minneapolis, with stops at the University of Minnesota.

The **Northstar Line commuter rail** (612.373.3333) runs trains from downtown Minneapolis (Target Field Station) with stops at several Mississippi River towns (Elk River, Anoka, Coon Rapids, and Fridley); riding the entire distance takes about 50 minutes.

BY BICYCLE

The Twin Cities have hundreds of miles of bike lanes and trails, many of them along both sides of the Mississippi River. Minneapolis and Saint Paul are among the most bicycle-friendly cities in the US, so don't be surprised when you see many devoted bicyclists doggedly continue to ride through the brutal winter months.

You don't even need to bring a bicycle with you. From spring through fall (July 3-5—just kidding! It's actually April through November), you can rent a bicycle from one of the 170 **Nice Ride** stations strategically positioned around the area. Each station has a vending machine that accepts credit cards. You pay a daily fee (or an annual membership, if you wish) and then you'll get a code to unlock a bike. Pick a bike, enter the code, and you're off. (Note: You won't find any helmets at the stations. You don't have to wear one, but if you prefer to do so, you should bring your own.) Now here's the great part. You can ride the rest of the day without paying again, as long as you limit each segment to 30 minutes or less. Each ride under 30 minutes is free, and there's no limit on the number of times you can turn in a bike and get another one. All you need to do is know where the stations are, so when you get near the 30 minute mark you can return the bike you're on and get another one. You don't have to do it his way, of course, but the rental price increases sharply the longer you keep one bike. This might seem like an odd pricing system, but it's meant to ensure that bicycles stay in circulation throughout the day.

In downtown, you can even hire a bicycle taxi (pedicabs) to take you around. The pedicabs are plentiful downtown, especially in the evening and into the early morning hours, a fun and easy way to get back to where you're staying after a night of exploring the clubs. There are no set fares; it's up to you to negotiate a rate with your driver.

DOWNTOWN SKYWAYS

You can explore much of downtown Minneapolis or Saint Paul without ever having to go outside, something that you might appreciate more in January than July. Most of the downtown buildings and parking garages are connected via skyways. It's easy to get lost, but there are plenty of maps, and you can always ask someone for directions.

For More Information

There are practical limits to how much I can include in a book, but not with a website! Check out the city profiles on my website to see if they include listings that I couldn't fit in this book.

Twin Cities: MississippiValleyTraveler.com/Twin-Cities-Overview
Minneapolis: MississippiValleyTraveler.com/Minneapolis
Fort Snelling: MississippiValleyTraveler.com/Fort-Snelling
Mendota: MississippiValleyTraveler.com/Mendota

An Urban National Park

You won't find another national park quite like it: The Mississippi National River and Recreation Area stretches for 72 miles in Minnesota from Ramsey and Dayton to Hastings, right through the heart of the Twin Cities metro area. It's the only national park solely dedicated to the Mississippi River and a rare national park in the heart of a major city.

And what a stretch of river to designate as a national park. At the upper reaches of the park, the Mississippi is emerging from the prairies and farms of north-central Minnesota. Soon, it hits the only waterfall on the Mississippi (St. Anthony Falls), passes through the river's only gorge, turns and merges with the Minnesota, and then makes a sharp turn south and into the beautiful, bluff-lined valley of the Driftless Area. The river alternately passes through suburbs, industrial corridors, big city downtowns, and even a few spots that remain mostly rural.

When Congress established the recreation area in 1988, it represented a new model for the NPS. Instead of buying land and managing it, the park service partners with local governments and land owners. (Of the 57,000 acres within the park's boundaries, the Park Service only owns 67.) Mississippi Park Connection, a nonprofit based in the Twin Cities, also works with the Park Service on programs that get people to the river and on some habitat restoration efforts.

The park serves something like a cheerleader and clearinghouse for recreation opportunities along the river. They compile a lot of information, which you can access at one of the visitor centers (at the Minnesota Science Center and, in summer, at the Upper St. Anthony Lock) or through their website (www.nps.gov/miss/index.htm).The park also manages the PaddleShare stations along the river, which allows folks to rent a kayak for a couple of hours and paddle on part of the Mississippi.

So stop into one of the visitor centers and learn about all there is to do along the Mississippi in the Twin Cities.

The Summer Minneapolis Burned

On May 25, 2020, George Floyd bought a pack of cigarettes from a small Minneapolis grocery store. An employee then called 911 to report Floyd for purchasing the cigarettes with a counterfeit $20 bill. When police arrived a few minutes later, Floyd was in a car with two other people. Police forced him out of the car, handcuffed him, and tossed him on the street. Officer Derek Chauvin put a knee on Floyd's neck to restrain him. Two other officers helped keep Floyd down, and a fourth kept onlookers at a distance. Chauvin kept his knee on Floyd's neck for 9 minutes and 29 seconds, even after Floyd pleaded that he couldn't breathe and even for a minute and 20 seconds after paramedics arrived to help Floyd. The paramedics pronounced Floyd dead at the scene. The four police officers were fired the next day.

Bystanders recorded the murder on their cellphones, and the video quickly spread over traditional and social media, which ignited protests in hundreds of cities around the world against police use of force and racial injustice. Protests turned violent in a few places. In Minneapolis, a small group of people spray painted a district police station and vandalized a police car, which ignited several days of rioting. Daytime protests—when the crowds were much larger—remained non-violent (but still contentious), but at night, smaller groups of people looted and burned buildings in the area around where the officers murdered Floyd. In Minneapolis alone, rioting caused an estimated $500 million in damages, much of that to small businesses owned by immigrants and people of color.

The murder and subsequent protests triggered a mea culpa moment in much of the US. The discussions have been difficult and often harsh. The tone demoralized some police officers. Some quit. Some police departments have confronted the issues directly and have taken steps to address historical wrongs, even if those efforts are often under the radar. In other communities, not much changed at all.

In 2021, a jury found Chauvin guilty of murder. He was sentenced to 22 years in prison. The other three officers were convicted of violating Floyd's civil rights in early 2022. The area where the riots were centered is now marked by empty lots and businesses that are still trying to recover.

SAINT PAUL

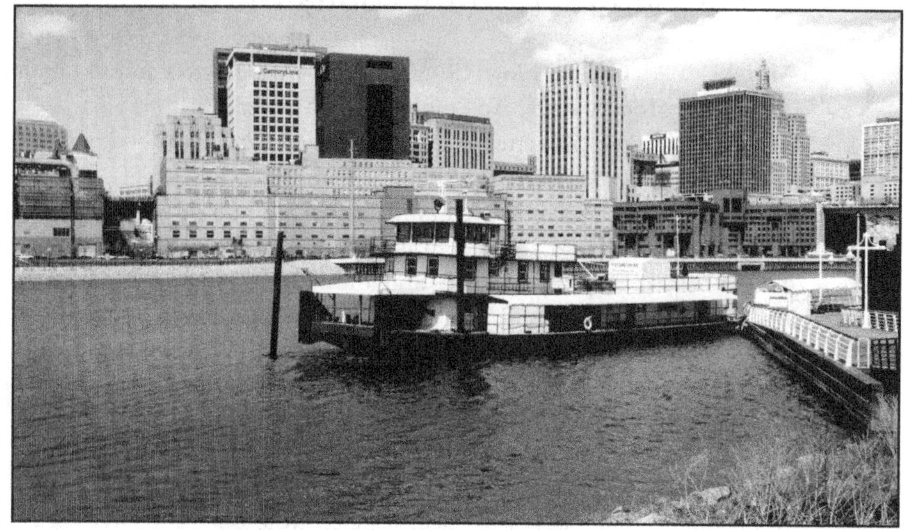

Saint Paul on the Mississippi River

Overview

Saint Paul has a reputation for being the more staid half of the Twin Cities, and it's not entirely unfair. Not that there's anything wrong with that. Downtown Saint Paul may lack the nightlife and glitz of downtown Minneapolis, but Saint Paul has strong neighborhoods, plenty of good restaurants, a diverse community, and a continually evolving riverfront that keeps getting better.

History

SAINT PAUL

Prior to the arrival of Europeans, this stretch of the Mississippi River was home to a number of Dakota sacred sites and seasonal settlements. The area around wakan tipi (spirit cave), in particular, was an important area where Dakota came together to trade and connect with each other and remains sacred to Dakota people today.

French Canadians and Métis from Fort Garry (today's Winnipeg) were among the earliest Europeans to arrive. Unhappy with life at the settlement, they were attracted to this area by Fort Snelling and the stability it promised. The fort's commander, Colonel Snelling, gave them permission to live on the military reserve on the west side of the river at an abandoned military camp. Some began to farm, while others worked the fur trade. Over time they were joined by a few retired voyageurs and discharged soldiers.

One of the early Euro-Americans in the area was Pierre Parrant, a former voyageur who made a claim in 1832 along the Mississippi River near Fountain Cave. Parrant was about 60 years old when he moved to the area, and the voyageur lifestyle had taken on a toll on his physical appearance. Then again, maybe he was never all that pretty. He was blind in one eye, an eye that was "marble-hued and crooked, with a sinister white ring glaring around the pupil, giving a kind of piggish expression to his sodden low features." Because of that defining feature, Parrant was better known as Pig's Eye, a nickname that he never warmed up to. The area around his claim also took on the name "Pig's Eye," thanks to Edmund Brisset:

> "I looked up inquiringly at Parrant and, seeing his old crooked eye scowling at me, it suddenly popped into my head to date it [a letter he was writing] at Pig's Eye, feeling that the place would be recognized, as Parrant was well known along the river. In a little while an answer was safely received, directed to me at Pig's Eye."

Parrant hoped to use his claim as a base for selling booze, something that didn't sit well with the military officials, but he proved to be his own worst enemy. Within a few months of getting settled in, he borrowed money from William Beaumette and used his claim as collateral. When Parrant failed to pay back the loan, Beaumette foreclosed. Parrant continued to make other claims in the area—and to sell alcohol—finally disposing of his last parcel to Benjamin Gervais in 1844. He died not long after than while en route to Sault St. Marie, Michigan.

Minnesota's capital city might still be known as Pig's Eye were it not for Father Lucien Galtier. He built a log church in 1841 on a high bank on the east side of the river. On November 1, he blessed it and dedicated it to Saint Paul. Galtier had been living downriver at St. Peter (now called Mendota) and thought Paul and Peter were so connected that he should name the new church after Paul. After he completed the church, he lobbied for the settlement to adopt the same name. He got his way. The new steamboat landing that developed nearby became known as Saint Paul's Landing, then just Saint Paul. Parrant's nickname didn't disappear entirely, though; it lives on with Pig's Eye Lake and Saint Paul-based Pig's Eye Brewing Company.

Throughout much of the 1830s, the small group of Euro-Americans co-existed with the military at Fort Snelling, but by 1838, supplies were growing scarce and the military was increasingly unhappy with liquor sales coming from the area. The officers eventually cracked down and forced everyone to move off of military property. Most just moved downriver a few miles. In 1840, the military extended the boundaries of the reservation but folks again refused to move, so in May soldiers marched in and forcefully evicted everyone, destroying their cabins in the process. Most of the Euro-American settlers from that group moved into what is now downtown Saint Paul, an area where development was legal after the 1837 treaty with the Dakota.

The earliest residents of Saint Paul were mostly French Canadian, but there were also Euro-American settlers who were Swiss, Danish, Swedish, some Native Americans (Dakota, mostly), and even a formerly enslaved man, James Thompson. Germans arrived beginning in the late 1840s, including many who were Jewish. Mount Zion Hebrew Congregation was founded in 1856.

Irish immigrants were among the early residents of Saint Paul, too. Three hundred people marched in the city's first St. Patrick's Day parade in 1851. Even though the city had a wide range of ethnic groups in its neighborhoods, the Irish and Germans dominated much of the city's social and civil life for decades. (Nine of the ten mayors between 1932 and 1972 had Irish ancestry.)

The early success of Saint Paul hinged largely on its role in the transportation network—at the end of the 400-mile Red River Ox Cart Trail and at the northern end of navigation on the Mississippi River. Throughout the mid-1800s, two-wheeled carts pulled by oxen traveled between Fort Garry (Winnipeg) and Saint Paul via Pembina (North Dakota). Caravans of carts, sometimes hundreds of them, moved fur and bison pelts from the northern plains to markets in Saint Paul. From there, the furs were then shipped down the Mississippi River. On the trip back north, the ox carts carried supplies like food and clothing. Railroads eventually made oxcarts obsolete.

Minnesota officially became a US Territory on March 3, 1849, but it took a month for the news to reach Saint Paul because the frozen river had slowed mail delivery. Congress designated Saint Paul as the temporary capital, leaving residents of the territory to choose a permanent site. It took more than a little trickery and deal-making for Saint Paul to remain the seat of government. Saint Paul faced competition for the capital from Stillwater and St. Anthony (now Minneapolis). In 1851, the issue was settled by good old-fashioned horse trading: Saint Paul kept the capital, but St. Anthony got the state university and Stillwater the state prison.

In 1857, the territorial legislature passed a bill that would have moved the capital to St. Peter (now Mendota). Not everyone thought that was a good idea. Joseph Rolette was a successful fur trader from a prominent family. Rolette had been instrumental in starting the Red River Ox Cart Trail. Jolly Joe, as he was known, served in the legislature as a representative for the village of Pembina. As chair of the Enrolled Bills Committee, it was his job to oversee certification of the bill, so it could be passed on to the governor for his signature. The bill reached his committee on February 28, and Rolette, rather than stealing the bill as the story is commonly told, simply went AWOL. Without him present at the meeting, the committee couldn't take any action.

For the next week, Rolette hid out (in plain sight, it seems) at a hotel (or maybe a brothel; there are variations in the story) where he played cards and enjoyed a few adult beverages each day. A week later as the legislative session was ending, Rolette resurfaced and the committee reported that it had been unable to certify the bill, thus killing it. Or so it seemed. During Rolette's absence, the legislature passed a duplicate copy of the bill that was promptly signed by the governor. A court later threw out the duplicate bill, ruling that the second bill hadn't been approved through the required channels. Saint Paul kept the capital and Jolly Joe became a folk hero. As far as I know, there is no statue of Rolette in Saint Paul (just a couple of portraits), but there should be, preferably one showing him with a drink in one hand and cards in the other.

Steamboats kept Saint Paul well-stocked and its residents connected to the outside world. The arrival of the first steamboat of the season was therefore a welcome moment that was often greeted with a big party. Early Saint Paul had two good steamboat landings: the Lower Landing at Jackson Street (today's Lambert Landing) and Upper Landing at Chestnut Street.

Saint Paul incorporated as a city with three wards in 1854 and was doing pretty well, at least until rampant land speculation drove prices artificially high in the 1850s and slowed things down for a bit. When the financial panic of 1857 hit, it took a heavy toll on Saint Paul, as it lost half its population and 80% of its businesses.

That early city was no thing of beauty, by the way. There were no parks. The streets were muddy and narrow and lined with wooden buildings. Trash piled all over the place, and the city stunk to high heaven thanks to the slaughterhouses and rendering plants. Early residents needed good boots and a strong stomach to get through a typical day.

In 1862, the St. Paul and Pacific Railroad built a line connecting Saint Paul to St. Anthony. The railroad grew into a national force after the Civil War, solidifying Saint Paul's role as a transportation hub for the Upper Midwest and the gateway to the Northwest. In 1888, an astonishing eight million people passed through Saint Paul's Union Depot on 150 daily trains. The railroad grew to dominate the transportation network, because it didn't have to shut down for half the year, like the Mississippi River did.

Saint Paul's population growth picked up again after the Civil War, with a wide range of ethnic groups settling in. City residents could read newspapers that were printed in English, German, Swedish, Norwegian, Danish, and French. Chinese immigrants began arriving in the 1870s.

In 1863, Robert Hickman arrived in Saint Paul on a raft with 176 fugitive African Americans fleeing the south. Other formerly enslaved people followed. By 1900, Saint Paul was home to five African American churches. Minnesota gave voting rights to Black men in 1868, two years earlier than the US government, and passed a civil rights act that prohibited discrimination based on race in 1898. The African American community was centered around Rondo Street, an area that was largely sacrificed for the construction of Interstate 94.

The West End attracted immigrants from Italy's Abruzzi-Molise region in the early 1900s. They settled near the Upper Landing below the High Bridge but were forced to move after severe flooding in the 1950s. Many of the businesses ended up on 7th Street.

Immigrants from Mexico began arriving in the mid-1910s. Many were recruited by companies to work in the sugar beet industry because of labor shortages caused by World War I. Immigrants from Southeast Asia, many of them from the Hmong ethnic group, began settling in Saint Paul in the late 1970s in the aftermath of the Vietnam War. Saint Paul also had a small wave of migration of Russian Jews in the 1980s.

During World War I, antipathy to Germany and Germans led to some remarkable efforts at renaming common objects:

- Sauerkraut became liberty cabbage
- Dachshunds became liberty hounds
- German fried potatoes became American fries
- Hamburger became Salisbury steak

On at least two occasions, Saint Paul officials were unwilling to go along with laws that restricted the sale of alcohol. In 1852, the Territorial Legislature outlawed the sale of alcohol and banned liquor dealers from juries. Saint Paul refused to enforce the law, which was eventually thrown out by the courts. During Prohibition, the Green Lantern (a speakeasy on Wabasha Street that was a popular place with the gangster set) was perhaps the only place in town where you could get a beer that had alcohol, although other types of alcohol were easy enough to come by.

In the early part of the 20th century, crime was endemic in Saint Paul, so police chief John O'Conner came up with a unique way to fight back. Under the O'Conner Layover System, criminals were left alone within the city limits as long as they followed three rules: 1) non-resident criminals had to let the police know they were in town; 2) they had to refrain from criminal activity within the city limits, and 3) they had to pay a service fee (just don't call it a bribe!). The system worked well, at least for Saint Paul, as crime rates in the city dropped dramatically. Neighboring areas weren't quite as lucky.

O'Conner kept tight control of the system, but he retired in 1920 and his successors weren't as adept. The whole system unraveled after Prohibition was repealed, depriving the criminal networks of a major revenue stream. Looking for new opportunities, some of the criminals broadened their activities into kidnapping. In 1933, William Hamm, Jr. (president of Theodore Hamm's Brewery) was held for ransom, and the next year Edward Bremer (heir to the Schmidt Brewery estate) was also kidnapped. Federal agents got involved in the cases and began poking around Saint Paul police offices. Most of those involved in the O'Conner system ended up in jailed or shown the door. O'Conner, who had a reputation as being one of the best detectives in the country, seemed to have had the best of intentions. From all indications, he sincerely believed that this system would be good for the city. He wasn't entirely wrong, either.

Downtown Saint Paul has lost much of its historic architecture. From 1963 to 1975, 240 of the 400 retail stores that had once lined the streets were razed for urban renewal projects, including almost all of the neighborhoods around the state capitol. Twelve square blocks in the heart of downtown were replaced by bland modernist buildings connected by skyways that protect folks from the cold weather but take foot traffic off the streets and away from storefronts. Today, downtown Saint Paul is on the upswing again. Renewed interest in the riverfront has spurred new housing and an ambitious city plan to spruce up its river-facing neighborhoods.

SOUTH SAINT PAUL

Today's South Saint Paul is a city divided into two distinct geographic locations: the residential areas and town center sit high atop the bluffs, while the industrial zone that gave birth to the city rests in the floodplain down below.

Charles Wilbur Clark founded a city he called South Park in 1886, along the Mississippi River. It now forms the north end of South Saint Paul. Clark gave 27 acres to Alpheus Stickney's Minnesota and Northwestern Railroad Company (later called the Chicago Great Western) to build maintenance shops. Heavy industry developed quickly, and the city of South Saint Paul was incorporated in 1887.

Stickney didn't rest after building the rail yards. In the late 1880s, livestock from the area had to be transported to Chicago for processing, a long and costly trip. In 1886, Stickney formed the Saint Paul Union Stockyards Company to make that trip unnecessary. The new stockyards attracted hundreds of men to the area who were looking for work, with many taking up temporary quarters in boarding houses near the yards. As the stockyards grew, packing houses began to open nearby, even though the area flooded regularly. The first hog slaughtering plant opened in 1888, and soon big companies moved in, including Cudahy Packing Company (1894-1954), Swift (1897-1969), and Armour (1919-1975).

Thousands of people worked in the plants processing pigs, sheep, and cows. They were a diverse group but mostly immigrants: Irish, Poles, Serbs, Croats, Romanians, Germans, Swedes, Hungarians, Russians, plus some African Americans. The Armour plant was once the largest building in Minnesota. At its peak, it employed 4,000 people and turned 2,000 animals an hour into bacon, steaks, chili, hot dogs, and by-products like leather, lard, and Dial soap. Work at the plants was disrupted by major strikes in 1904, 1921, and 1948 as workers rallied for better working conditions and higher wages.

At one time, every sixth-grade class in South Saint Paul toured the Armour plant. Many of those children were not exactly happy with the experience of walking across floors covered with blood and among dead animals hanging upside down. Many got sick during the tour, but I bet it was an experience they never forgot!

The children weren't the only ones sickened by the factories. Every packinghouse used the Mississippi River as a sewer. They dumped untold amounts of waste into the river, fouling it so bad that nothing could live in it. In 1926, a survey of the Mississippi between Saint Paul and Hastings found three fish alive—not three species, but three fish, total. There was no effort to deal with the pollution until Lock and Dam 2 was built at Hastings, and it became obvious that the pollution would no longer just flow downriver to sicken someone else.

In the 20th century, the South Saint Paul Stockyards were the largest in the world. All those workers needed a place to unwind, so there were dozens of bars along Concord Street (places like the Hook-em Cow). But nothing lasts forever. The industry began to change as livestock farms grew larger and sold directly to packinghouses, bypassing stockyards. Soon after that, the packinghouses began relocating to rural areas. Swift closed in 1969, leaving behind a toxic mess that required an expensive cleanup before the land could be redeveloped as an industrial park. The Armour plant closed in 1979 and was razed in 1989. One of the few visible reminders of the packinghouse era is the Livestock Exchange Building (Concord St. at Grand Ave.) that was built in 1887. South Saint Paul today has transformed from a center of industry into a bedroom community.

One of the notable South Saint Paul natives was Jane Muckle Robinson. From 1885 to 1921, she lit kerosene lamps on the Mississippi River between Dayton's Bluff and the stockyards to help boats navigate after dark. She tended four lights, lighting them by sunset and extinguishing them after sunrise. The lamps had to be cleaned and filled every day. At the end of her career as a post light keeper, she estimated that she had covered 50,000 river miles in her rowboat. Jane's life inspired Charlie Maguire, the one-time "Singing Ranger" for the National Park Service, to write a song about her (*Light the River*).

INVER GROVE HEIGHTS

The McGroarty family, the first of many immigrants from Ireland to settle in the area, arrived in 1848. The family included 24-year-old John, Bridget, his wife, their two-year-old son Bryan, and John's 23-year-old brother, William. Their trip from New York City to St. Paul took four years, probably because they walked most of the way. When John made his 300-acre claim in 1853, most of his neighbors were Dakota people.

In the early years, ethnic groups clustered in different parts of town: Americans along the river, Germans in the north central section, and Irish and French in the west. The Germans and Irish were the most numerous, and they apparently found a rather clever way to compromise on the name of the village, combining the names of an Irish village in County Donegal (Inver) and a German town in Schleswig-Holstein (Grove). Inver Grove Village incorporated in 1909 with just one square mile of land, although the village appeared on township maps as early as the 1880s.

The village had an active community along the Mississippi River from early on, mostly folks who made a living through farming, logging, and fishing. In the early 1900s, Joseph Mrozinski made a pretty good living as a commercial fisherman. In the first half of the 20th century, many younger residents commuted to work in the South Saint Paul stockyards and packinghouses.

The Minnesota and North Western Railroad Company reached Inver Grove in 1886. The South St. Paul Beltline Railroad built a swing bridge over the Mississippi in 1894; it later became part of the Rock Island Railroad. Railroads employed a lot of men in the area, and many of them lived in boarding houses in town.

Twin Cities Route Map

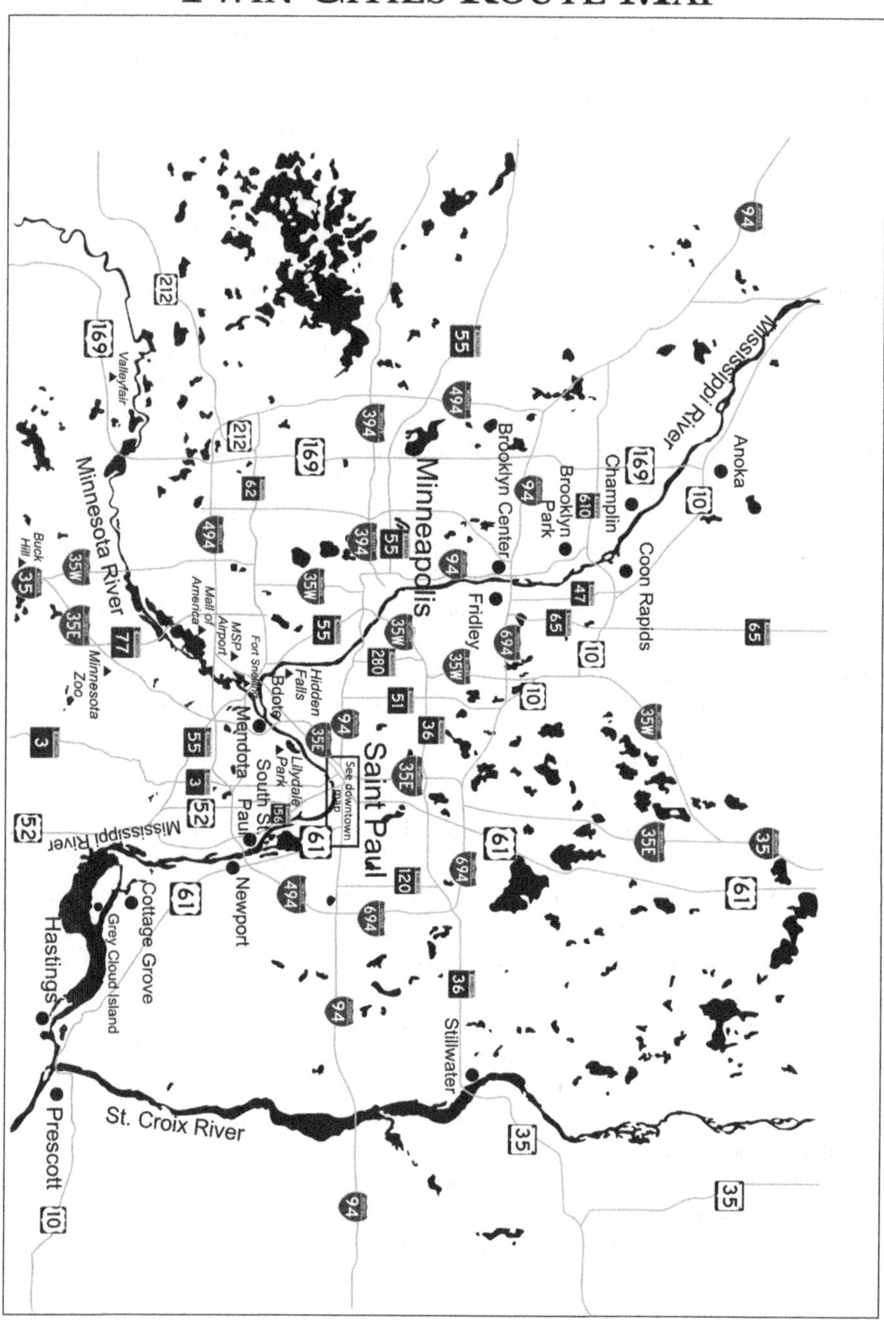

Random Fact: Charles Schultz, the creator of the Peanuts comic strip, was born in Saint Paul.

Great River Road Driving Directions in Saint Paul

If you'd like to follow the Great River Road through Saint Paul, take the route below. It begins at the Fort Road Bridge connecting Saint Paul with Fort Snelling on Highway 5 and goes downriver on the west bank. The total distance for this route is about 30 miles. At the Wakota Bridge connecting South Saint Paul and Newport via I-494, it crosses the river and heads upriver on the east bank:

DOWN THE WEST BANK

- South on Minnesota 55 (Hiawatha Ave.)
- East on Sibley Memorial Highway (Highway 13)
- North/east on Lilydale Road (Highway 45); it becomes W. Water St. (Highway 40)
- East on Plato Boulevard
- South on Wabasha St. South, which becomes Cesar Chavez St., then Concord St.; hop on I-494 eastbound to cross the river and continue back to Saint Paul

UP THE EAST BANK

- North on US 61
- West on Warner Road (becomes Shepard Rd.)
- North on South Mississippi River Blvd., which becomes East River Parkway. This loop ends at Highway 5 and the Fort Road Bridge, but you can continue on East River Parkway into more of Saint Paul and then into Minneapolis.

BRIDGES CONNECTING SAINT PAUL AND MINNEAPOLIS

- The Fort Road Bridge connecting Saint Paul with Fort Snelling on Minnesota Highway 5
- The Lexington Bridge connecting Saint Paul and Lilydale via I-35E

MISSISSIPPI RIVER BRIDGES IN SAINT PAUL

- The Smith Avenue High Bridge (Minnesota Highway 149)
- The Wabasha Street Bridge
- The Robert Street Bridge
- The Lafayette Bridge for US Highway 52
- The Wakota Bridge connecting South Saint Paul and Newport via I-494

Central Saint Paul Map

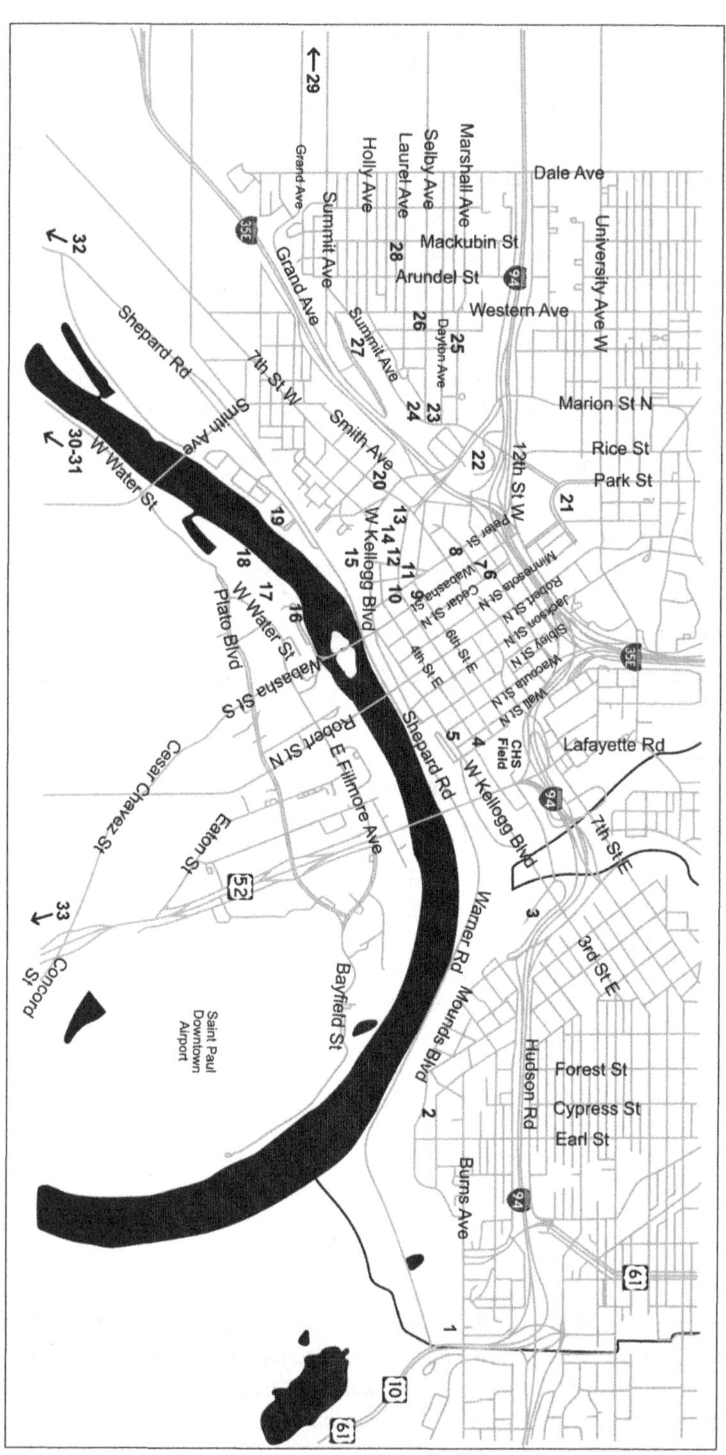

Saint Paul Map Index

Attractions
33. Air Force/WWII Museum
23. Cathedral of Saint Paul
7. Fitzgerald Theater
17. Harriet Island Regional Park
2. Indian Mounds Regional Park
24. James J. Hill House
11. Landmark Center
30. Lilydale Regional Park
22. Minnesota History Center
21. Minnesota State Capitol
15. Mississippi River Visitors Center
12. Ordway Center for the Performing Arts
18. Padleford Cruises
9. Palace Theatre
14. RiverCentre
15. Science Museum of Minnesota
3. Wakan Tipi/Vento Nature Sanctuary
13. Xcel Energy Center

Where to Eat and Drink
31. Buon Giorno Deli
20. Cossetta Italian Market and Pizza
19. City House
4. Downtown Farmers Market
1. Obb's Sports Bar
8. Ruam Mit Thai
32. Summit Brewery
26. W.A. Frost
29. Wuollet Bakery

Where to Stay
6. Celeste of St. Paul
16. Covington Inn
27. Davidson Hotel
28. Historic District B&B
25. New Victorian B&B
10. Saint Paul Hotel

Other
5. Union Depot/Amtrak/Buses

There's no shortage of stories about the Great River, which is why I started the **Mississippi Valley Traveler podcast**. In each episode, I go deep into a topic about the river's culture, history, and natural world. It helps the miles fly by as you drive the Great River Road. Find it everywhere podcasts are available, including Spotify, Apple podcasts, and YouTube.

The village maintained its own offices for 56 years, until the whole township incorporated as the City of Inver Grove Heights in 1965 (the "Heights" added apparently to give the city a more elevated reputation!). In the last 20 years, the city's population nearly doubled as the city grew into a mid-sized suburb.

GREY CLOUD ISLAND

Grey Cloud Island has a long history of human habitation. The island has dozens of mounds, and archaeological surveys have found evidence of settlements that date roughly to the early Woodland period (about 2,100 years ago). In the early 1830s, Medicine Bottle led a small group of Dakota from Kaposia and built a village on the island, but they later had to move to comply with the Treaty of 1837.

Fur trader Hazen Mooers and his son-in-law, Andrew Robertson, moved into the houses abandoned by the Dakota. Robertson named the island after his mother-in-law, Margaret Aird Mooers, aka Marpiyahotawin (Grey Cloud Woman). She was the granddaughter of the famed Dakota leader Wabasha.

Joseph Renshaw Brown built a house on the southern end of the island in 1838. He set up a dairy farm, grew wheat and veggies, had a trading post, supplied wood to steamboats, and served as Justice of the Peace, presumably in his spare time. But he didn't stop there. Brown also made a decent amount of money selling whiskey to the soldiers at Fort Snelling and would later play a role in the founding of Stillwater before helping to write the state constitution and serving as Indian agent.

A small community grew on the island, many of whom were former voyageurs with Dakota wives. Grey Cloud City was platted in 1856, but there were few takers and the 1857 economic panic pretty much finished it off. It is still largely rural today, even after Cottage Grove annexed the southern part of the island in the 1980s.

Explore Down the West Bank

LILYDALE

Attractions

Lilydale Regional Park (950 Lilydale Rd.; 651.632.5111) spreads across the lowlands next to the river. The park includes the ruins of a kiln from the former brick works that was located on this site. In the winter, water seeping from the bluff faces freezes, forming really cool ice waterfalls.

Drinking and Dining

Step inside **Buon Giorno Deli** (981 Sibley Memorial Highway; 651.905.1080) and you won't walk out empty-handed. Pick up prepared pasta or get a made-to-order sandwich, then finish it with a cannoli or bar. They also stock Italian-themed grocery items and have a full-service deli counter stocked with cheese and cured meats.

SAINT PAUL: WEST BANK

Attractions

Harriet Island Regional Park (200 Dr. Justus Ohage Blvd.) is everyone's backyard. The park has plenty of room to spread out and picnic or throw a Frisbee around. It's the site of many festivals and is the home base for the Padleford river cruises.

SOUTH SAINT PAUL

Attractions

Volunteers at the **Commemorative Air Force & World War II Museum** (310 Airport Rd, Hangar #3; 651.455.6942; open W, Sa 9:30-5:30) carefully preserve aircraft from the second world war. You can walk around the planes (tightly packed into an old airport hangar) for a close-up look and read exhibits about the equipment and experiences of people on the front lines. If you've got a few hundred bucks in spare cash, they also arrange flights in many of the aircraft. Twice a year, they host swing dances in the hangar.

Kaposia Park (1028 Wilde Ave.) commemorates the last location of the Dakota village called Kaposia.

Wildflower Levee Park is a small park along the Mississippi just north of the Wakota Bridge that is only accessible from the riverfront trail.

Grandview Park (Grand Ave. W) has plenty of benches to sit and enjoy good views of the river and South Saint Paul from the top of a bluff.

INVER GROVE HEIGHTS

Attractions

The **Rock Island Swing Bridge** (4465 66th St.) opened in 1894 as a double-deck bridge for buggies on top and the South St. Paul Beltline Railroad below. The bridge was closed in 1999 and ten years later most of the bridge, except for the approach from Inver Grove Heights, was demolished. The remaining section has been turned into a walkway that extends into the river and offers great views.

Drinking and Dining

The **Mississippi Pub** at River Heights Marina (4455 66th St. E; 651.455.4975) is a fine place to enjoy a drink and pub food while watching the river and boats come and go.

Explore Up the East Bank

GREY CLOUD ISLAND

Attractions

Grey Cloud Dunes Scientific and Natural Area (110th St.; 651.259.5800) covers over 200 acres of sand dunes that rise 50 to 100 feet above the east bank of the river. The trails wind up and down across the dunes and through some minor ecosystem changes. The area is popular with hikers and birders. Bring a hat and sunscreen.

SAINT PAUL: EAST BANK

Attractions

Sitting atop Dayton's Bluff (Imnizaska to the Dakota), **Indian Mounds Regional Park** (10 Mounds Blvd.) is a pleasant place to walk around, to take in the views atop the bluffs and to contemplate the past while looking at the preserved Hopewell-era mounds.

Wakan Tipi/Vento Nature Sanctuary (265 Commercial St.; 651.260.6260) grew out of an abandoned industrial area near a cave that the Dakota people called Wakan Tipi (Spirit Cave). You can explore the sanctuary via an easy stroll on the walking trails that wind through restored wetlands and next to the bluffs. The cave, however, was greatly altered when the railroad chopped off a big chunk of rock face to build tracks and closed off the entrance.

The warehouses and old buildings of the **Lowertown** neighborhood, just east of downtown, have come back to life with artists' residences, galleries, and hip dining. It is also where you'll go to watch the **Saint Paul Saints** of the American Association of Professional Baseball (**CHS Field,** 360 Broadway; 651.644.6659).

The historic **Fitzgerald Theater** (10 East Exchange St.; 651.370.2953), owned by Minneapolis' First Avenue, hosts live shows, music mostly. The **Palace Theatre** (17 W. 7th Pl.) is another beautiful, historic performance venue.

The **Landmark Center** (75 W. 5th St.), built in 1902 as a US Post Office, Court House, and Custom House, hosts a visitors information center and several historical and art displays. Inside you'll also find the **American Association of Woodturners Gallery** (651.484.9094) that showcases exceptional examples of wood carving skills, as well as the **Schubert Club Museum** (651.292.3267) that has a large collection of keyboards and musical instruments from around the world. For a touch of local history, check out the **Heritage Organization of Romanian Americans in Minnesota** (Room 319; open Sundays).

The **Ordway Center for the Performing Arts** (345 Washington; 651.224.4222) hosts live performances from Broadway musicals and drama to well-known musicians.

The **Science Museum of Minnesota** (120 W. Kellogg Blvd.; 651.221.9444) has a whole gallery dedicated to the Mississippi River, as well as great views of the river from inside and out.

In the lobby of the Science Center, you'll find the **Mississippi River Visitor's Center** (651.290.4160), which is staffed by National Park Service (NPS) rangers who are eager to answer your questions about the 72-mile long **Mississippi National River and Recreation Area** (MNRRA; see page 90), the only NPS unit whose central mission is related to the Mississippi River (www.nps.gov/miss).

The **Minnesota History Center** (345 Kellogg Blvd. West; 651.259.3000) has a number of fun and interesting exhibits on the state's history (climb inside the grain elevator at Grainland!) and a fantastic research library.

The **Minnesota State Capitol** (75 Rev. Martin Luther King Blvd.; 651.296.2881) is a magnificent piece of architecture. Designed by Cass Gilbert and opened in 1905, the building is Renaissance Revival in style and style it has aplenty. You can explore the building on your own or take a 45-minute guided tour.

The imposing **Cathedral of Saint Paul** (239 Selby Ave.; 651.228.1766) is the fourth built for the archdiocese. Construction began in 1906 and wasn't completed until nine years later. The Renaissance-style building feels massive in scale, but the interior is open and softened by several archways. Visitors are welcome to wander around when no mass is in progress. You can pick up a print guide for a couple of bucks.

James J. Hill built the railroad (the Great Northern Railroad) that helped build the Great Plains and the Northwest. This made him a very wealthy man, so he built a very big house to call home. The Richardsonian Romanesque mansion has 22 rooms, a two-story art gallery, rich woodwork, and much more spread throughout its 36,000 square feet. The Minnesota Historical Society conducts tours of the **James J. Hill House** throughout the year (240 Summit Ave.; 651.297.2555).

Hidden Falls Regional Park (1313 Hidden Falls Dr.), named for a spring-fed waterfall that oozes from the bluff, has nearly seven miles of paved trails along or near the Mississippi River, plus many spots to spread out and relax. There is also a **PaddleShare** station in the park.

Other Saint Paul Attractions

The **Bell Museum** (2088 Larpenter Ave. W; 612.626.9660) has a nice collection of engaging exhibits about natural history, from displays about the origins of the universe to ecosystem dioramas with taxidermied critters.

Como Park (1225 Estabrook Dr.; 651.266.6400) is among the best urban parks in the country. Among its 384 acres, you'll find a small zoo, a Victorian conservatory, the 100-year old Cafesjian's Carousel that was saved from auction in the 1980s, kayaks and paddle boats you can rent for a spin on Lake Como, and plenty of room to spread out and take a walk or enjoy a picnic.

Getting On the River

Padleford Riverboats (651.227.1100) offers daily sightseeing and dinner cruises on the Mississippi River from Harriet Island.

You can rent a kayak from Hidden Falls Regional Park and paddle 6.3 miles to Harriet Island Regional Park (Friday-Sunday), thanks to the **PaddleShare** program operated by the National Park Service and its partners.

Tours

Take a tour of the **Summit Brewery** (910 Montreal Circle; 651.265.7800), and you'll be rewarded with samples at the end.

Create your own two-mile **loop tour**. Walk or bike by the big houses of Summit Avenue and the businesses of Grand Avenue. The streets parallel each other. Use Lexington Parkway and Dale Street to connect them on either end.

Drinking and Dining

For an overview of local food specialties, see the Minneapolis chapter (see pages 83 and 86) and check out *Mpls.St.Paul Magazine*. Below are a few places that are long-time favorites or offer a predictably satisfying experience:

Like Minneapolis, Saint Paul has a booming **craft beer** scene. Take an evening and sample what they have to offer but consider letting someone else do the driving for you. Get a complete list of craft breweries at: discoverthecities.com/st-paul-minneapolis-breweries. Put **Summit Brewery** (910 Montreal Circle; 651.265.7800) on your list.

Wuollet Bakery (1080 Grand Ave.; 651.292.9035) has been satisfying locals cravings for sweet things since 1944. Take your time browsing the selection of cakes, tortes, and donuts, but don't skip the tasty bars!

La Boulangerie Marguerite (1279 Randolph Ave.; 651.699.9292) is another great option for baked goods, especially for French-inspired ones. The cozy retail store offers fresh bread, croissants, macarons, and other beautiful pastries.

For 40 years, **W.A. Frost** (374 Selby Ave.; 651.224.5715) has been turning out excellent, contemporary food from its home in a gorgeous historic building near the Cathedral. They source many ingredients from local producers, and the fine dining menu includes vegetarian options. They also serve a very satisfying brunch on weekends.

For good and affordable Thai food, check out downtown's **Ruam Mit Thai** (367 Wabasha St. N; 651.222.7871), where you'll also find delightful surprises such as Pha Ram Long Song, a red curry dish served on a bed of steamed spinach.

Cossetta Italian Market and Pizza (211 7th St. W; 651.222.3476) began as a small market in 1911 to serve residents of the Upper Levee neighborhood but has since grown into something of an Italian food megaplex. You can still browse Italian food products in the market (including many ready-to-eat meals), then grab a pizza or traditional Italian entrée at the cafeteria-style restaurant. Finish the experience with a delectable pastry such as cannoli or maybe a cup of tasty gelato. When the weather is nice, you can enjoy your food on the rooftop patio.

Enjoy lunch or a snack with great views at **City House** (258 Mill St.; closed in winter), a converted grain elevator next to the river. It's conveniently located on a bike trail.

For a traditional Friday night fish fry (and you have many choices in Saint Paul), check out **Obb's Sports Bar** (1347 Burns Ave.; 651.776.7010).

Where to Stay

Like Minneapolis, downtown hotels are convenient, but they can be expensive. For something different from the standard chain hotels, consider the options below.

Bed and Breakfasts

AUTHOR'S PICK: The **Covington Inn** (100 Harriet Island Rd.; 651.292.1411) is an experience unlike any other along the Mississippi. A converted tow boat anchored to Harriet Island, the inn rents four unique suites, each with a stellar view. Downtown is a short walk away, and breakfast is delicious.

The **Historic District B&B** (483 Ashland Ave.; 763.360.3717) rents four rooms and a carriage house in a 19th century home just a few minutes from downtown in the Ramsey Hill neighborhood. Rooms are updated and immaculate and within walking distance of restaurants and shops. A full gourmet breakfast is included with the price.

Another beautiful old mansion has been converted into the **New Victorian B&B** (325 Dayton Ave.; 651.321.8151). Built in 1881 in the Cathedral Hill neighborhood, the massive house is filled with exquisite woodwork and other details and has a lot of room to spread out. Two of the four rooms come with a balcony. The house is on a lovely tree-lined street and within walking distance of places to eat and shop.

Lodging

Housed in a former convent and arts conservatory, **Celeste of St. Paul** (26 Exchange St. E.; 651.222.0848) dazzles with beautiful, open spaces. Walls are decorated with fine art and stained glass windows cast colored light. Guest rooms are sleek and modern. The price is reasonable for the location in the heart of downtown (a few steps from the Fitzgerald Theater) and includes a hot breakfast. Parking is available at a nearby garage.

The historic **Saint Paul Hotel** (350 Market St.; 800.292.9292) has hosted Charles Lindbergh, the gangster Leon Gleckman, and Lawrence Welk. You could be next. The 254-room hotel blends the classic architecture of the past with modern luxury touches.

The **Davidson Hotel** (344 Summit Ave.; 651.560.2009) offer nine luxury suites in a century-old mansion built for a railroad executive. The hotel is located among a row of other mansions near the Saint Paul Cathedral and overlooks the Mississippi.

Regional Attractions

See the summary of regional attractions in the Minneapolis chapter (pages 87-88).

Special Events

Looking for a **farmers market**? Here are some options:

- Downtown Farmers Market (290 E. 5th St.; 651.227.8101): Saturdays 6am-1pm, Sundays 8am-1pm
- South Saint Paul (12th Ave. & Southview Blvd.): Wednesday afternoons
- Inver Grove Heights (8055 Barbara Ave.): Sundays 8a-1p

AUTHOR'S PICK: It may seem odd to stand outside in January in Saint Paul to watch a parade, but I found it exhilarating. Folks up here have been throwing a **Winter Carnival** since 1886. If standing outside for the festivities doesn't appeal to you, you can grab a viewing spot from one of the skywalks, or just check out the ice and snow sculptures or one of the myriad concerts and special events over the two weekends.

Saint Paul celebrates its ethnic diversity with the **Festival of Nations** at downtown's RiverCentre in May. Head to Harriet Island in August for the **Irish Fair of Minnesota.**

The **Minnesota State Fair** (1265 Snelling Ave. N) is arguably the major social event of the season (late August), a granddaddy of an event that is part county fair (complete with livestock judging), part amusement park (with a busy Midway), part gustatory challenge (think deep-fried bacon or hotdish on a stick), and part music festival (much of it included in the standard admission price).

Getting There/Getting Around

Amtrak's *Empire Builder* and *Borealis* trains stop in Saint Paul. The *Empire Builder* runs between Chicago and Seattle, with stops along the Mississippi River at La Crosse, Winona, Red Wing, Saint Paul, and St. Cloud. The *Empire Builder* often runs late. Westbound *Empire Builder* trains (to Seattle) have a scheduled departure time of 11:13pm, while eastbound *Empire Builder* trains (to Chicago) have a scheduled departure time of 8:50am. *Borealis* trains connect Saint Paul and Chicago, with stops along the Mississippi at La Crosse, Winona, Red Wing, and Saint Paul. Northbound trains have a scheduled arrival time of 6:29pm, while southbound trains have a scheduled departure time of 11:50am. Fares are based on the number of available seats and therefore vary considerably; in general, the earlier you book, the cheaper the ticket will be. Amtrak's only stop in the Twin Cities is at Saint Paul's Union Depot (240 Kellogg Blvd.).

Union Depot is also the place to catch a long-distance bus. **Greyhound, Jefferson Lines, and Megabus** all arrive at and depart from the depot.

For tips about getting around, see the Minneapolis chapter (page 89).

For More Information

There are practical limits to how much I can include in a book, but not with a website! Check out the city profiles on my website to see if they include listings that didn't fit here:

Twin Cities: MississippiValleyTraveler.com/Twin-Cities-Overview
Lilydale: MississippiValleyTraveler.com/Lilydale
Saint Paul: MississippiValleyTraveler.com/St-Paul
South Saint Paul: MississippiValleyTraveler.com/South-St-Paul
Grey Cloud Island: MississippiValleyTraveler.com/Grey-Cloud-Island
Inver Grove Heights: MississippiValleyTraveler.com/Inver-Grove-Heights

And don't miss these places I didn't have space to include in this book:
Hastings: MississippiValleyTraveler.com/Hastings
Prescott: MississippiValleyTraveler.com/Prescott

How much food on a stick can one guy eat? **FIND OUT** how I did at the Minnesota State Fair: mississippivalleytraveler.com/a-day-at-the-minnesota-state-fair/

LAKE PEPIN TOUR

Sailing on Lake Pepin

Overview

A wide expanse of water framed by golden limestone bluffs. Attractive small towns serving up delicious food. Painters and poets creating fine art. Vigorous hikes up the bluffs rewarded with breath-taking views. Leisurely strolls on paved trails to wind down. Wineries and craft breweries in scenic settings. Sunsets to calm the most savage of beasts (or sunrises, if you're an early bird). The area around Lake Pepin is special for all this and more.

It's tempting to take one day to drive the hundred miles around Lake Pepin, but once you realize how much there is to see and do, you're going to wish you'd given yourself more time to explore. Take a full weekend and enjoy the sights at a reasonable pace. Even after a weekend, you'll be making plans to come back to experience what you missed the first time, or just come back to do all again.

If you want to hit the road on a whim, you can explore the area just fine, but weekends often require some advance planning, especially when fall colors are blooming. If you're looking for a place to base, Red Wing is a good choice. It offers a variety of lodging and dining options. For a quieter time, the Wisconsin communities at the downriver end of the lake (Pepin, Stockholm, Maiden Rock) have beautiful homes and inns that are perfect for a relaxing getaway.

Whatever you decide to do, whether it's a day trip or a long weekend, do it slowly. Don't spend the whole trip as a drive-by tourist. The roads are mostly two lanes and the towns small. Get out of the car and walk around. Breath in the air. Say hi to folks. And give yourself plenty of time to sit and watch one of those sunsets.

The Lake

Lake Pepin is a 25,000-acre widening of the main channel of the Mississippi River formed by the Chippewa River delta. The Chippewa River deposits more silt than the Mississippi can carry away, so a natural dam has formed. For 22 miles, the river spreads out and slows down, widening as much as 2 ½ miles. The water is 20–30 feet deep in much of this stretch. It is a popular place for sailing in summer and ice boating in winter. Lake Pepin is usually the last place on the upper Mississippi River where the ice clears out; when the lake ice melts away, navigation season begins.

Father Louis Hennepin tried to name it Lake of Tears, maybe because he was captured by a small group of Dakota in 1680 near its southern end. French explorers who did not have the kidnapping experience called it Lac Bon Secours or Lake of Good Hope, so they obviously had a different feeling for the lake. Ultimately, the name that stuck is probably derived from Charlemagne's son, Pepin the Short (cousin of Pepin the Wide), who ruled France from 740 to 768.

The Lake is a popular recreation area, but it is facing significant threats. Ten times the normal amount of silt is being dumped into the lake—most of it coming down the Minnesota River—a pace that would fill the 10,000-year-old lake completely in about three hundred years. All that excess silt is already filling in some side channels. Modern farming practices are largely responsible for the increased silt load.

Those same farming practices are also sending high amounts of nitrogen and phosphorous into the river and Lake Pepin. Large-scale corn and soybean production require heavy applications of fertilizers, and much of that runs off into rivers. When the levels of nitrogen and phosphorous get too high, they can trigger rapid growth of algae that quickly consume oxygen, which kills fish and sometimes encourages the growth of toxic microorganisms.

Those threats may sound scary, but the lake is perfectly fine to swim in. Siltation is a threat to the long-term health of the river, not your well-being today. As for the fertilizer runoff, just stay out of the water if you see patches of algae.

Lake Pepin is a special place. Enjoy it today and please advocate for its health, so future generations get to enjoy it, too.

History: Minnesota Communities

PRAIRIE ISLAND INDIAN COMMUNITY

Following the US-Dakota Conflict of 1862, all Dakota were forced from Minnesota and removed to reservations, first in South Dakota, then in Nebraska. By 1880, squalid conditions prompted many Dakota to go back home. Some walked the entire distance from Nebraska. They ended up at a place they called Tinta Wita but we know today as Prairie Island. Europeans considered the land on the island unsuitable for farming, so it attracted little interest. The Dakota, however, knew how to live off the land at Prairie Island and used many of the native plants in traditional medicine. The relative isolation of life on Prairie Island helped this Dakota community maintain traditional aspects of life.

The US government first recognized the Prairie Island Indian Community in 1886 when it granted reservation status. In 1936, the reservation was expanded from 120 to 534 acres, and a community council form of government was adopted that functions like a state government. The construction of Lock and Dam 3 in the late 1930s flooded low-lying sections of the island and reduced the number of habitable acres on the reser-

Lake Pepin Route Map

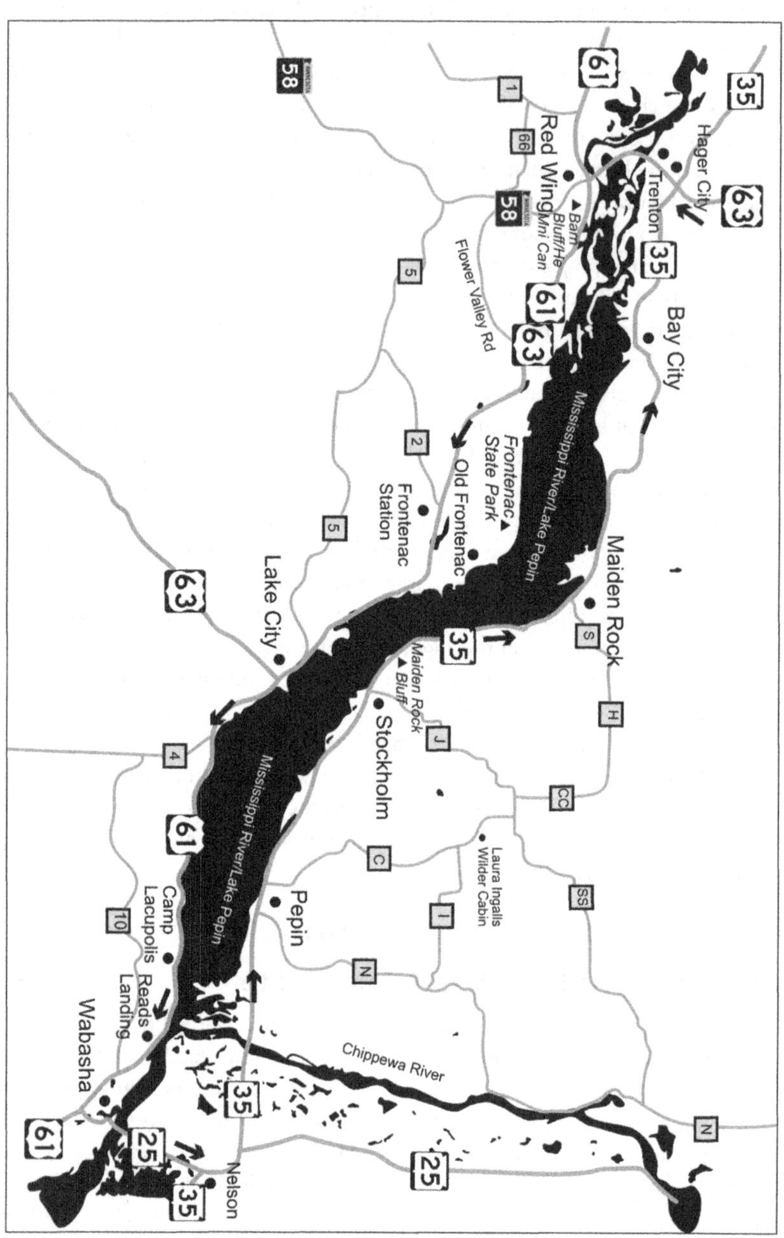

Getting around Lake Pepin couldn't be simpler. The entire route is about 100 miles.

- On the west side (Minnesota), follow US 61 from Red Wing to Wabasha
- Follow State Highway 60 into Wabasha and over the Mississippi River
- On the east side (Wisconsin), follow State Highway 35 from Nelson to Hager City
- Follow US 63 back into Red Wing

vation to 300. Until the 1980s, Dakota people living on the reservation had limited economic opportunities. Poverty was common. Community members had no input when a nuclear plant was built adjacent to the reservation in 1968.

In 1984, the Prairie Island Indian Community opened a bingo room with seating for 1,400 gamers. Five years later, the community jumped into the gaming world with both feet when they built their first casino. The casino employs some 1,500 people. Gaming revenues have been used to build a community center, a health center, to improve sewer and water facilities, and to fund a wide range of charitable causes throughout the region. The revenues also help the community support a herd of buffalo on reservation land.

RED WING

The largest city on this route, Red Wing takes its name from a respected Mdewakanton Dakota leader who established a village here. Red Wing was born about 1750 and was probably the nephew of Chief Wabasha I. Red Wing was a spiritual leader and a successful military leader of the Mdewakanton Dakota in the latter part of the 18th century. In Dakota, his name was Tatankamani (Walking Buffalo). French explorers, for reasons that are not well documented, called him L'Aile Rouge (Red Wing). He broke from Wabasha's band and lead a group to a new home near the mouth of the Cannon River.

Red Wing led an active life in the midst of changing times. He chatted with the explorer Zebulon Pike in 1805 and fought for the British in the War of 1812 but later switched sides. He traveled to Portage des Sioux (Missouri) in 1815 to sign a treaty of friendship with the Americans. When he was older, he gave the name Red Wing to his oldest surviving son, Wakute, and called himself Shakea (The Man Who Paints Himself Red). He died in 1829 while hunting.

The land around the Cannon River was not open to legal settlement until 1853, but a few Euro-Americans still found a way to move in. Two families of Swiss missionaries arrived first: Samuel and Persis Denton in 1837 and Daniel and Lucy Gavin in 1838. They stayed until 1845 and, by all accounts, didn't convert anyone.

When Minnesota became a territory in 1849, another group of Presbyterian missionaries arrived. The new group of missionaries included Joseph Hancock and his wife Maria Houghton Hancock. Joseph built good relationships with the Dakota community and learned their language. In 1850, Maria died during childbirth, and the next year his son died, too. Distraught, he left Red Wing for several years.

John Day moved from Wisconsin—illegally—into the abandoned mission house and tried to establish a claim on land that was still Dakota territory. The Dakota tore the house down. Day built a new house and the Dakota tore that one down, too. This process repeated itself about a dozen times before Day finally gave up.

The Dakota ceded rights to their lands with the 1851 Treaty of Mendota and were forced from Minnesota by the 1860s. With the Dakota gone, Euro-Americans flooded in and reshaped the area, most of them from the eastern US, but many Scandinavian and German immigrants also migrated in. Red Wing was platted in 1853 and became the county seat. Joseph Hancock eventually returned and played a central role in the city's development. He served as postmaster and wrote the first county history.

Hotels were built to house new arrivals, including tuberculosis-stricken Henry David Thoreau who came for a four-day health respite in June 1861. While in Red Wing, he climbed Barn Bluff and was so moved he wrote of the river valley: "Too much could not be said for the grandeur and beauty." Thoreau died a year later.

Red Wing counted 1,251 residents in 1860 and over 4,000 just ten years later, including a small community of African Americans. Much of Red Wing's early growth was fueled by wheat. In 1873, Red Wing had a warehouse that could store one million bushels of the grain. The wheat trade declined in importance by 1880, but Red Wing had a strong, diversified economy with businesses that included shoe manufacturing, sorghum processing, the Red Wing Iron Works, cigar factories, brewing, brick manufacturing, lumber, and quarrying.

Pottery makers have been mainstays in the local economy for generations. Local clay was plentiful and high quality. The industry began with German immigrant Joseph Pohl in 1861; he later decided that farming was a better fit for him. William Philleo founded a terra cotta business in 1870 and had a nice run. He moved his company to Saint Paul in 1880 and renamed it, but some of his former employees stayed in town and founded the Red Wing Stoneware Company. In 1906, the three existing pottery companies merged to form the Red Wing Union Stoneware Company, which produced pottery until 1967. In 1984, the Red Wing Pottery brand was brought back to life.

Red Wing's economy today is a mix of light manufacturing, healthcare, and tourism; the Red Wing Shoe Company—founded in 1905—employs the most people.

OLD FRONTENAC AND FRONTENAC STATION

Rene Boucher established Fort Beauharnois in 1726 and brought two Jesuit missionaries who founded the Mission of St. Michaels the Archangel, possibly the first church in Minnesota. They abandoned the fort by 1763 when the French were forced to cede their North American lands to Great Britain.

In 1857, Brigadier General Israel Garrard bought 4,000 acres from Jean Baptiste Faribault and later established a village he named Frontenac in honor of Louis de Buade de Frontenac, a governor general of New France who commissioned several explorations of the Mississippi Valley. While the village of Frontenac attracted some industry, its main claim to fame was the resort at the northeast end of town. Garrard converted a warehouse into the Lakeside Hotel, then turned a general store into a hall with a theater, billiards, and tavern. He also built nine cottages for summer guests. For 70 years, Frontenac was a favored summer vacation spot for the genteel on holiday.

After the resort waned in popularity, Methodists bought the former Lakeside Hotel and ran it as a retreat center for decades. Many of the buildings later fell into decline until a gradual effort to restore them began in 1987, largely through the efforts of Bill and Linda Flies. What makes Frontenac unique today is not so much the number of Civil War-era buildings but that an entire community from that period remains essentially intact. The former resort buildings are now private residences.

Neighboring Frontenac Station came to life in the 1870s when the railroad built tracks that bypassed Old Frontenac. The decision was made at least partly because Israel Garrard didn't want trains rumbling through his bucolic resort community.

Frontenac Station developed into a solid, small community whose businesses served the local agricultural industry. By 1900, the village had a quarry, a grain elevator, a saloon, general stores, and blacksmiths. Stone from a nearby quarry was used in the construction of the Cathedral of St. John the Divine in New York City.

Frontenac Station is also home to the oldest government building in continuous operation in Minnesota. The Florence Town Hall was completed in 1875 and is still serving the local community.

Villa Maria opened in 1880 by Ursuline nuns as a boarding school for girls. The school was a big success, which required new buildings. Israel Garrard donated a large tract and the new school and dormitory buildings opened in 1890. The school did well for decades but came to an abrupt end when the school was struck by lightning in 1969 and burned to the ground. The sisters decided not to rebuild and closed the school. The sisters then ran a retreat center on their campus for 45 years. It closed in 2016.

LAKE CITY

Jacob Brody arrived in 1853 and was joined by his brother Philip and others the next year, most of whom came from New England. Before Lake City amounted to much, the towns of Florence and Central Point were attracting development, but those communities faded away as it became clear that Lake City had the superior steamboat landing. In 1858 alone, Lake City counted 1,500 steamboat dockings.

The population exploded from 300 in 1856 to 2,500 in 1870 and business boomed. For a brief time, Lake City was busy with clamming, button manufacturing, and grain shipping. The railroad arrived in 1872, and the grain elevators were moved from the lakefront to the railroad tracks. With the decline in steamboat traffic, Lake City grew into a commercial center for local farmers. During the Depression, all three banks in town closed. Only one eventually reopened.

Lake City residents have witnessed two major disasters on Lake Pepin. The *Sea Wing* excursion boat sank near Lake City on July 13, 1890, killing 98 of 215 passengers. On December 15, 1944, a B-24 Liberator crashed in Lake Pepin during a snowstorm. The four-engine prop plane was a long-range bomber being moved from Saint Paul to Kansas City. It exploded on impact and sank. The bodies of the three crew members could not be recovered until the lake ice melted six months later.

CAMP LACUPOLIS

A small village was founded here in 1861 with the catchy name Lake-Opilis. The name is derived from Greek and means something like "Camp Lake City." It never got big enough to justify a post office, but it once had a stagecoach stop, so that's something. Overland visitors from the west would stop for the night, then continue on to Lake City by boat in the morning. It is now a village of log cabins and campers.

READS LANDING

Reads Landing peaked early. The village of Reads Landing is on the site of a former trading post known as Waumadee that was operated by successive generations of the Rocques family beginning around 1810. They sold the land to Edward Hudson, so naturally this spot became known as Hudson's Landing. After he died, Englishman Charles Read purchased Hudson's claim.

Read emigrated to the US at age ten with his brother's family. He served with the American army that invaded Canada in 1837. The 17-year-old Read was captured by the British and sentenced to hang. Luckily for Mr. Read, Queen Victoria pardoned him and let him return to the US.

In 1844, he settled in Nelson's Landing (Wisconsin), then later moved across the river to establish a trading post, even though Alexis Bailly already ran a trading post near Hastings. Read platted the village in 1856 and incorporated it in 1868 with a great deal of optimism. Reads Landing thrived as a bustling steamboat port that served the logging trade. Logs came down the Chippewa River and were assembled into large rafts, then those rafts floated downriver for processing. Several hundred raftsmen would stay in town, awaiting their turn to assemble and go.

Reads Landing was one of the lumbermen's favorite places for R&R—with nearly two dozen hotels and saloons to pick from! —which led to the inevitable "scenes of violence and lawlessness staged on its streets," as described in a county history book. As the lumber trade declined, Reads Landing descended into irrelevance. The village disincorporated in 1896.

From 1882 until the 1950s, trains crossed the river via a 2,900-foot pontoon bridge. A 400-foot pontoon section would swing open to let boats pass through. The pontoon sank 14 inches when a train crossed. The bridge was a maintenance headache. In 1951, ice and high water caused severe damage to the bridge, and the railroad shut it down rather than fix it again.

WABASHA

Wabasha claims to be Minnesota's oldest city, and it's hard to argue the point. Europeans first arrived in 1826. Duncan Campbell and a few others trickled into the area in the 1840s. A small community developed, many of them of mixed Native American and European ancestry.

The city was named Wabashaw in 1843 for the Dakota chief who lived in the area. The last "w" was dropped in 1858 when the city incorporated. The early population included a mix of French Canadians, Native Americans, English, and Americans who were later joined by German, Irish, and Scandinavian immigrants.

Wabasha had a few lumber mills and companies that produced finished lumber pieces. Many people also made a living directly from the river through fishing, clamming, ice harvesting, and boat building. Between 1860 and 1870, the city's population nearly doubled from 894 to 1,739. Wabasha was among the many communities that served as a transit spot for local wheat, at least until wheat farming ended in the 1880s. The St. Paul and Chicago railroad reached Wabasha from Saint Paul in 1871. This ensured Wabasha's future and ended Reads Landing's.

Wabasha's first highway bridge opened in 1931, ending nearly 70 years of ferry service. The ramp into town had an s-curve that bent to Pembroke Avenue so traffic would flow through the commercial district. It was replaced in 1989 with one that has a ramp that goes right over the top of the commercial district, so traffic now bypasses it. (You now know better and should detour to downtown.)

Wabasha served the retail needs of the local farming community until the availability of automobiles made it easier for folks to drive to bigger cities to shop. The city also suffered from consolidation in the farm economy. In recent years, the city has had modest growth in light industry, and those grain mills are still operating.

History: Wisconsin Communities

NELSON

Englishman James Nelson settled near the mouth of the Chippewa River in the 1840s, so naturally the area was called Nelson's Landing. The area had a ferry connection to Read's Landing for a while, although the sloughs on the Wisconsin side could make for a challenging trek.

Madison Wright arrived in the township in 1848 and is generally acknowledged as the first Euro-American settler. He lived in the bottomlands but did most of his trading in

Wabasha. When he died, Wabasha sent a bill for his burial to the Fairview-Nelson Town Board. They replied that if Wright had died poor, it was because he spent all his money in Wabasha, so Wabasha should bury him.

Nelson's Landing was a busy place for a while. A lot of people passed through on the way to or from the logging camps. More new residents arrived in the mid-1850s, but the village wasn't platted until 1884 when the railroad surveyed a depot site.

PEPIN

John McCain built the first home in the township in 1846. He was involved in the logging industry and piloted boats on the Chippewa and Mississippi Rivers. He bought hundreds of acres of land and platted a village he called Lakeport.

The first claim at the present site of Pepin was made by McCain's cousin, William Boyd Newcomb, thus supplying the village's first name, Newcomb's Landing. Like his cousin, he worked initially in the lumber industry, and then became a river pilot. When the village was platted in 1855, it was called North Pepin. Virtually all of the village's initial growth was driven by the logging industry.

North Pepin didn't have the best steamboat landing, however, so the village lost business to the Beef Slough rafting operation in Alma, then lost the county seat to Durand. The village later found new life catering to farmers. The Chicago, Burlington, and Northern railroad arrived in 1886, which connected local fishing interests to new markets. They sent fish to markets in New York and the South.

Pepin was also home to the Pepin Pickle Company, sawmills, a creamery, a pearl button factory, and a bobsled factory. After the railroad arrived, many businesses moved from First Street to Second Street because the trains scared their horses. The first automobile owned by a local resident hit the local streets in 1908. By 1917, there were 66 in town. There are a few more today, as most residents commute to jobs elsewhere.

STOCKHOLM

In 1849, Erik Peterson and two brothers left Karlskoga, Sweden, to prospect for gold in California. Erik changed his mind in Chicago and went south for a few months, then back north to work in a logging camp along the St. Croix River. Along the way, he passed the location of the future village site in 1851, liked it, and filed a claim. He sent a letter to another brother in Sweden, Jakob, encouraging him to come. When he didn't get a reply, he went back to Sweden only to find that Jakob had already left.

Jakob had a tough voyage to America. His ship's captain died en route, which left his inexperienced son in charge. The ship rammed into an iceberg before turning south to warmer waters. Jakob's group wintered in Moline in 1853, where one of his daughters died. He finally reached Stockholm in the spring of 1854.

While in Sweden, Erik got married and organized a party of 200 to go to America with him. Erik was quite a cad, though. He booked the cheapest passage to Quebec for his fellow Swedes and kept the extra cash as profit. After they reached North America, they traveled to Chicago by train but Erik booked them in cattle cars where a cholera epidemic killed nearly one-third of the group, including his own mother. (He tried to avoid paying for her funeral by claiming that he didn't know her.) When he finally arrived in Stockholm, only 30 of the original group were with him.

With that inauspicious beginning, the proprietors platted the village in 1856 and called it Stockholm on Lake Pepin. Perhaps because of bad karma, the village grew slowly. In the 1870s, Paul Sandquist made a living selling lemon beer, and John Gunderson brewed and bottled spruce beer. By the time the village incorporated in 1903, it had 300 residents but would soon enter a period of steady population loss until reaching bottom in the 1940s when fewer than 100 people called Stockholm home.

On July 18, 1938, Swedish royalty visited the town. Crown Prince Gustaf Adolf, Crown Princess Louise, and Prince Bertil were touring the US to mark the 300th anniversary of the founding of the first Swedish settlement in the US (in Delaware) when they made a 15-minute whistle stop in Stockholm. The town was notified on a Friday that the royals would be stopping on the following Monday, so they spent the weekend prettying-up the town and the rail station. Nearly 700 people turned out. Prince Gustaf later told a Swedish newspaper that the stop in Stockholm was one of the top three highlights of his months-long tour.

The village's fortunes ticked up when artists began moving to town in the 1970s. Most made Stockholm their year-round home and opened shops and galleries that continue to attract visitors from throughout the region.

MAIDEN ROCK

Maiden Rock village and bluff get their names from an old legend about a young, Native American girl called Wenonah, who jumped to her death from the bluff rather than marry to a man she didn't love who was from a rival group…or he could have been a French voyageur, or possibly an English trader. The story has many versions, something noted by Mark Twain (with a healthy dose of sarcasm) in *Life on the Mississippi.*

John Trumbell and brothers Amos and Albert Harris were the first folks to live at the future village site. The village was initially called Harrisburg but after Trumbell bought them out and platted a village in 1857, he changed the name to Maiden Rock.

Maiden Rock did not have a regular steamboat stop because the main channel was on the Minnesota side. This was a major factor in the town's slow start. Early businesses included a sawmill, a shingle mill, a grist mill, a lime kiln, and a shipyard that built boats from 16-foot sailboats to steamboats.

Maiden Rock lacked road connections to nearby communities for many of its early years, prompting someone to call it "a good place to live but a hard place to get out of." The village got a boost in 1886 when railroad connections to Saint Paul and La Crosse were completed, but repeated fire disasters were not helpful. Six fires ravaged the community between March 1911 and August 1912.

This small village knows how to throw a party, though. The town's centennial festival drew a large crowd, especially for the 55-unit parade. The centennial celebration included a beard judging contest with awards for best full beard and best trim.

The major industry today is Fairmount Minerals/Wisconsin Industrial Sand, which mines sand for oil and gas exploration.

BAY CITY

Mr. AC Morton was the first known European to arrive at the future village site. He built a home in 1855. AJ Dexter believed he had purchased the land before Morton's arrival, so he got a bit peeved when Mr. Morton's surveyor, a man named Markle, showed up to plat the village of Saratoga. Dexter killed the surveyor for trespassing.

This didn't create a positive vibe for the village, so Saratoga was abandoned and the buildings moved across the ice to Warrentown. Charles Tyler bought the site in 1856 for

$1,700 in back taxes and rebranded the site as Bay City, naming it for the natural bay that was the site's most distinctive feature. Early 20th century businesses included the predictable saloon, a confectionery, a billiard hall, a grain dealer, and a meat market.

Bay City was once a major commercial fishing center. Around 1910, a school of Scandinavian fishermen relocated from Sevastopol (Minnesota) to Bay City, because it was cheaper to get a fishing license in Wisconsin. Bay City also had a rail station, so the fishermen had access to transportation that could ship their catch across the US.

The fish were typically packed in barrels with ice, but local hero Capp Tyler invented a box (the Tyler Box, of course) that proved to be a more efficient packing method. He opened a box making factory in Bay City and supplied fishermen along the eastern shore of Lake Pepin. Changing tastes in the eating habits of Americans reduced demand for Lake Pepin fish after World War II. The last major commercial fishing company in Bay City closed in 1952. Bay City today has little industry. Most residents commute to jobs in other places.

HAGER CITY AND TRENTON

Hager City had the distinction of getting the first post office in the township but apparently not much else worth writing down. When the railroad came through in 1886, the village was platted as Hager Chatfield, but the following year the Postmaster General suggested that Hager City would be a better name. Wilson Thing (perhaps an ancestor of Thing T. Thing of *Addams Family* fame) was the first Euro-American to move to Trenton. He showed up in 1848. Most of the early residents were Scandinavians. The area had a bustling commercial fishing operation from the 1930 to the 1970s. Nearby Trenton Island was a notorious hangout for gangsters, including Pretty Boy Floyd and John Dillinger, both of whom probably dropped some cash in its brothels and taverns.

Explore Down the West Bank (Minnesota)

PRAIRIE ISLAND INDIAN COMMUNITY

Attractions

The **Treasure Island Resort and Casino** at Prairie Island (5734 Sturgeon Lake Rd.; 800.222.7077) is a huge place with slot machines, blackjack tables, poker tables, and a large bingo room. The resort also hosts nationally known entertainers at the 3,000-seat event center. The Parlay Lounge hosts live music.

Getting On the River

The *Spirit of the Water* at **Treasure Island Casino** (877.849.1640) takes visitors on Mississippi River cruises in a 100-passenger luxury yacht.

Special Events

The annual **Wacipi Celebration** at Prairie Island (800.554.5483; 2nd weekend in July) offers dancing, drumming, and singing that draws Dakota people from around the country. It's also a good chance to meet Native American artists and to buy their work.

RED WING

Attractions

Dr. Alexander P. Anderson, inventor of puffed rice and puffed wheat, built an estate and research center on the northern end of town that is now an artist-in-residence program called the **Anderson Center at Tower View**. Galleries inside the building showcase their work. The adjacent **Anderson Park Sculpture Garden** (163 Tower View Dr., 651.388.2009) features large-scale sculptures and interpretive signs describing ecosystems native to Minnesota.

Hike to the top of **Barn Bluff (He Mni Can** in Dakota**)** for great views of the river and the city (500 E. Fifth St.). The trails go past abandoned quarries, next to limestone cliffs, and across goat prairies.

Memorial Park (542 E. 7th St.; 651.385.3674) sits atop Sorin's Bluff and is another place with great views of the area. A few thousand years ago, Barn Bluff and Sorin's Bluff were islands in a much wider and deeper Mississippi River.

The **Goodhue County History Center** (1166 Oak St.; 651.388.6024) has a wide-ranging collection that traces the history of the region from the earliest inhabitants to today. Long-term exhibits highlight the rich pre-European life in the area, as well as early residents and industries that shaped the city.

Bruce Sexton collected a lot of stuff during a 30-year military career that took him around the world. He turned those items into the **Aliveo Military Museum** (321 Bush St.; 651.327.1569), which houses some remarkable items: rare bayonets, a Philippine Moro Kris sword, a Zulu shield. The broadest collection of items is from WWII-era Germany and Japan.

The **Pottery Museum of Red Wing** (240 Harrison St.; 651.327.2220) showcases the impressive variety of fired clay products made in Red Wing for over a century.

At the **Red Wing Shoe Museum** (315 Main St.; 651.388.6233), you can pose for a selfie next to the World's Largest Boot. It was crafted for the company's 100th anniversary in 2005 and stands 16 feet tall, 20 feet long, and seven feet wide, measuring an impressive size 638 ½ D. It's a perfect fit for the 120-foot tall person in your life.

See what's happening at the renaissance revival **Sheldon Theater** (433 W. 3rd St.; 651.388.8700). The charming building opened in 1904 and hosts movies and live shows.

The **Red Wing Arts Association Art Gallery** (418 Levee St.; 651.388.7569) features the works of local artists in a gallery in the old rail depot.

Red Wing has several riverside parks that are fine spots to picnic and river gaze:

- **Bay Point Park** (1392 Levee Rd.) is next to Boat House Village
- **Levee Park** (432 Levee Rd.) is a small, pleasant riverside park with a memorial to the *Sea Wing* disaster
- Further from downtown, **Colville Park** (510 Nymphara Lane) has plenty of places to spread out along the river

Fair Trade Books (320 Bush St.; 651.800.2030) has a good collection of works from local and regional writers, plus they host live music regularly.

Paved trails abound around Red Wing, such as the popular 21-mile **Cannon Valley Trail** that runs along an old railroad right-of-way from Cannon Falls to Red Wing.

Getting On the River

Captain Brian Klawitter (651.307.8326) takes folks on the river from April 1 through November 1 for two-hour eagle-watching tours.

Drinking and Dining

Falconer Vineyards Winery produces wines from local grapes that can be paired with a homemade pizza (572 Old Tyler Rd.; 651.388.8849).

Get your daily dose of caffeine from **Mandy's Coffee & Café** (419 W. 3rd St.; 651.800.2026), where you can also snack on pastries or have a light lunch.

Sip on local craft beer at the **Red Wing Brewery** (1411 Old West Main St.; 651.327.2200), where you can also nosh on pizza.

Bev's Café (221 Bush St.; 651.388.5227) is a downtown diner that offers heartier, reasonably priced breakfasts. Check out the gritwurst, a house specialty.

Beloved **Stockholm Pie Company** operates the **Pie Plate Café** in Red Wing (2000 Old Main St.; 651.376.8993). Stop in a slice of pie (sweet or savory) or enjoy a wrap or sandwich for lunch.

For casual dining that emphasizes local, seasonal ingredients, head to **Scarlet Kitchen & Bar** at the St. James Hotel (406 Main St.). They offer outside seating with a river view when the weather is nice. For an after dinner cocktail, head downstairs to cozy confines of **The Port**.

Where to Stay

You'll find the most variety of lodging options in Red Wing, which has standard chain motels, a historic inn, and several bed-and-breakfast inns. Most communities around Lake Pepin, though, offer accommodations, including a lot of vacation rentals.

Camping

About six miles from Red Wing, the **Hay Creek Valley Campground** (31655 Highway 58 Blvd.; 651.388.3998) has plenty of overnight sites in a scenic valley adjacent to the Hay Creek Unit of Dorer State Forest. Overnight sites are mostly in an open field with little shade but are large.

Bed and Breakfasts

Don't be fooled by the imposing limestone Italianate house that is the **Moondance Inn** (1105 W. 4th St.; 651.388.8145). The interior is welcoming and artful, decorated with French and Italian antiques. The rooms are in great shape and equipped with private baths including two-person whirlpool tubs.

The **Pratt-Taber Inn** (706 W. 4th St.; 651.388.7392) is in an 1874-era house with four rooms for guests, each with a private bath and decorated with a nod to the past but not handcuffed by it.

Round Barn Farm (28650 Wildwood Lane; 651.385.9250) is lovely. The house is relatively new but looks like a 19th-century farmhouse thanks to generous use of reclaimed materials. Each guest room has a private bath with whirlpool tub and individual climate controls, a fireplace, and a feather bed with a pillow top mattress.

Lodging

The Grande Dame of Red Wing lodging is the historic **St. James Hotel** (406 Main St.; 651.388.2846). No two guest rooms are identical. Each is named for a steamboat and is furnished with a handmade Amish quilt. The range in room types and sizes means rates can vary, but package deals help to reduce the cost.

Special Events

Red Wing's **farmers market** gathers on Saturday mornings on Levee Street near the train depot and again weekday mornings by City Hall (315 W. 4th St.).

River City Days (800.498.3444) takes place in early August and features a Venetian boat parade.

Getting There

Amtrak's *Empire Builder* and *Borealis* trains stop in Red Wing. The *Empire Builder* runs between Chicago and Seattle, with stops along the Mississippi River at La Crosse,

Winona, Red Wing, Saint Paul, and St. Cloud. The *Empire Builder* often runs late. Westbound *Empire Builder* trains (to Seattle) have a scheduled departure time of 9:42pm, while eastbound *Empire Builder* trains (to Chicago) have a scheduled departure time of 9:44am. *Borealis* trains connect Saint Paul and Chicago, with stops along the Mississippi at La Crosse, Winona, Red Wing, and Saint Paul. Northbound trains have a scheduled departure time of 5:40pm, while southbound trains have a scheduled departure time of 12:35pm. Amtrak uses the neoclassical Red Wing Depot (420 Levee St.) but does not maintain a service window. You can buy your tickets on-line, by phone (800.872.7245), or on the train. Fares are based on the number of available seats and therefore vary considerably; in general, the earlier you book, the cheaper the ticket will be.

OLD FRONTENAC AND FRONTENAC STATION

Attractions

Frontenac State Park (29223 County 28 Blvd.; 651.345.3401; vehicle permit required) also has several good hiking trails, including a trail that goes up, down, and around the bluff, and great views of the river below.

Step back in time at **Christ Episcopal Church** (29036 Westervelt Ave. Way; 612.345.3531). Other than the addition of a few electric lights and forced air heat, the church looks much as it appeared when it was built in 1869.

Where to Stay: Camping

The main campground at **Frontenac State Park** (29223 County 28 Blvd.; 651.345.3401; vehicle permit required + camping fee) is in a heavily wooded area; the sites are nicely spaced apart. There are also six cart-in sites that are a short walk from the parking lot.

LAKE CITY

Drinking and Dining

Chickadee Cottage Café (317 N. Lakeshore Dr.; 651.345.5155; open mid-April–October), a café retrofitted into an early 20th century cottage, serves a creative menu of freshly prepared food. Dishes include salads, wraps, sandwiches, and mains like lasagna and quiche. For dinner, they offer a number of pasta dishes, walleye, steaks, and seafood, plus sandwiches and salads.

Where to Stay: Camping

Hok-Si-La Park in Lake City (2500 N. Highway 61; 651.345.3855) is the site of a former Boy Scout camp. The tent-only sites are rather close together but some have lake views; weekdays offer better value.

Where to Stay: Cabins

Just south of Lake City, **Camp Lacupolis** (71000 US Highway 61; 651.565.4318) rents 19 cabins, all with air conditioning and supplied with bed linens. You'll need to bring towels, soap, shampoo, toilet paper, and garbage bags. Most cabins have a small kitchen.

Special Events

Look for the Lake City **farmers market** on Thursday evenings near Ohuta Beach (Chestnut St. at the lake).

Ralph Samuelson invented water skiing in 1922 on Lake Pepin, so naturally the town must celebrate with a festival: **Waterski Days** (last weekend in June). The 18-year-old Samuelson strapped two pine boards to his feet, each board eight feet long by nine inches wide, and got behind a motorboat operated by his brother. When his brother hit the throttle, young Ralph was lifted out of the water. No doubt inspired by Samuelson, in 1973 Lake City resident Dennis Francis, then 27-years old, waterskied the Mississippi from Coon Rapids (Minnesota) to the Gulf of Mexico. Waterski Days includes a parade and a waterskiing demonstration.

READS LANDING

Attractions

The **Wabasha County Historical Society Museum** (70537 206th Ave.; 651.565.4158), housed in an impressive old Italianate schoolhouse, displays a broad collection of artifacts of 19th-century farm life, as well as exhibits on the region's boom times during the logging era.

Drinking and Dining

Housed in a 19th-century riverfront building, the **Reads Landing Brewing Company** (70555 202nd St.; 651.560.4777) serves up dishes with a Southern influence, which you can pair with a locally brewed craft beer.

Where to Stay

Bed and Breakfasts

River Nest Bed & Breakfast (20073 County Road 77; 651.560.4077) rents two suites overlooking the river in Reads Landing, each with a private entrance. Each suite is outfitted with a Jacuzzi tub, cable TV, fridge, walk-in shower, fireplace, and deck; one suite is wheelchair friendly.

Cabins

Located atop a bluff overlooking the lower end of Lake Pepin, **Bending River Cove** (70984 Highway 61; 507.884.0651) rents a full-sized cottage and several small ones, each modern and attractive and offered at reasonable rates. You can rent a tiny house for yourself and your special someone or the whole place for you and your friends.

WABASHA

Attractions

AUTHOR'S PICK: Lake Pepin is a popular hangout for bald eagles, especially around Wabasha, which is also where you'll find the **National Eagle Center** (50 Pembroke Ave.; 651.565.4989), one of the best attractions in the region. The center has exhibits on eagles, naturally, and their symbolic role in many cultures. The center cares for several eagles that were rescued from dire circumstances. Those birds are often out on perches so visitors can get a close look at them.

Driftless Books (159 Main St. W.; 651.380.9035) stocks books about local and regional history, board games, and other fun stuff.

Getting On the River

Take a kayak tour through the thick backwaters of the Mississippi and Chippewa Rivers with **Broken Paddle Guiding Company** (651.955.5222). You don't need to be an experienced paddler to enjoy the trip, and you're likely to see some wildlife.

Where to Stay: Camping

Big River Resort (1110 Hiawatha Dr. E.; 651.565.9932) offers 28 sites with full hookups, including six that are extra large. The resort is just south of town.

Central Red Wing Map

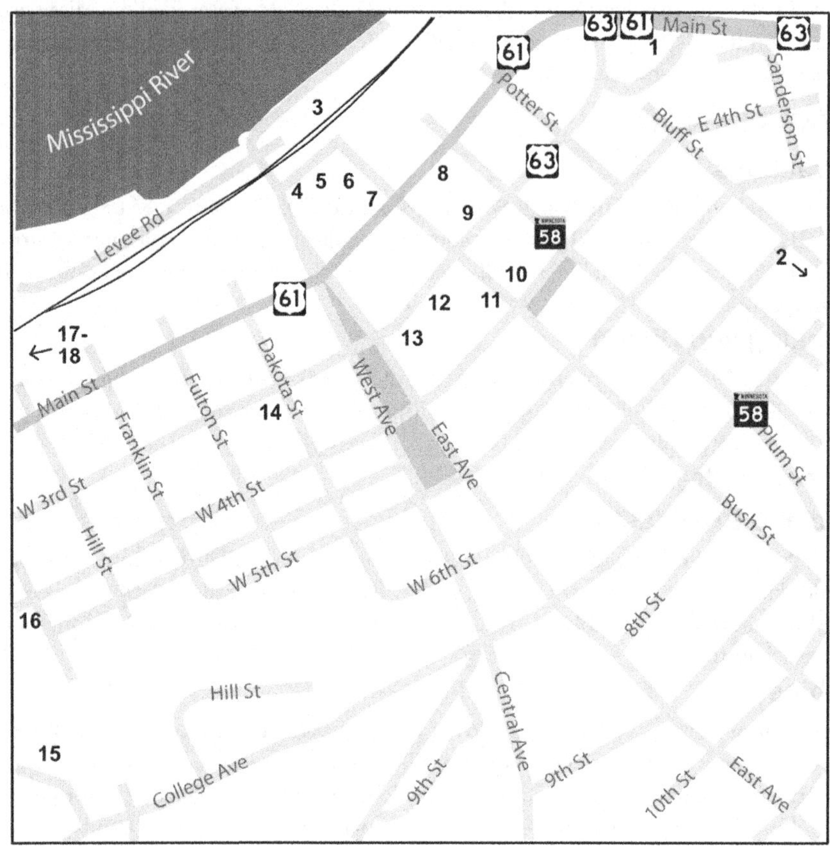

Attractions
10. Aliveo Military Museum
1. Barn Bluff/He Mni Can
11. Fair Trade Books
15. Goodhue County History Center
3. Levee Park
2. Memorial Park
18. Pottery Museum
5. Red Wing Arts Association
8. Red Wing Shoe Museum
13. Sheldon Theater

Where to Eat and Drink
9. Bev's Café
6. Farmers Market
12. Mandy's Coffee and Café
17. Red Wing Brewery
7. Scarlet Kitchen & Bar/The Port

Where to Stay
16. Moondance Inn
14. Pratt-Taber Inn
7. St. James Hotel

Other
4. Amtrak

Bed and Breakfasts

Turning Waters Bed, Breakfast, and Brewery (136 Bridge Ave.; 651.564.1568) offers five lovely rooms in an old Victorian mansion. They can also arrange outdoors experiences from kayaking to bicycling to snowshoeing. A stay includes a full breakfast, plus they have a small brewery on site (**Hoppy Girl Brewing**), so you may never leave!

Lodging

Big River Resort (1110 Hiawatha Dr. E.; 651.565.9932) rents clean, bright budget-friendly rooms. They also rent a cabin with a full kitchen outfitted with grown-up size appliances, a flat screen TV, and a bedroom with a queen bed.

Special Events

Wabasha holds a **farmers market** on Wednesday evenings and Saturday mornings (Main Street West at Allegheny Ave.).

Wabasha throws a tongue-in-cheek celebration of its brush with fame from movies starring Jack Lemmon and Walter Matthau (and penned by Minnesota native Mark Steven Johnson). **Grumpy Old Men Days** (February; 651.565.4158) features events that will make you smile: a hot dish luncheon, minnow races, and the requisite ice fishing contest (which isn't a spectator sport, in case you were wondering).

In March, come back to Wabasha for **SOAR with the Eagles**, which takes place every weekend at the National Eagle Center and features public lectures and tours.

Explore Up the East Bank (Wisconsin)

NELSON

Drinking and Dining

J & J Barbecue in the Nelson General Store (N208 N. Main St.; 715.673.4717) serves up a southern-style barbecue that is tender, moist, and so full of flavor that you can eat it without any sauce and not feel deprived.

The **Nelson Creamery** (S237 State Road 35; 715.673.4725) makes a tasty sandwich that you can follow up with a scoop of ice cream. They also sell Wisconsin cheeses.

Nine miles outside of Nelson, **The Stone Barn** (S685 County Road KK; 715.673.4478; open May-Oct.), housed in the partially reconstructed ruins of a 19th-century stone barn, makes tasty thin crust wood-fired pizzas from local ingredients.

Where to Stay: Cabins

Cedar Ridge Resort (S1376 State Highway 35; 608.685.4998) rents attractive log cabins of various sizes that are nestled into a hillside overlooking the river. Cabins range from an 1860s log home (totally rehabbed, of course) to new large log homes that can sleep twelve. All come with satellite TV, a full kitchen, and modern bathrooms.

PEPIN

Attractions

The **Laura Ingalls Wilder Museum** (306 3rd St.; 715.513.6383) preserves the memory of the author who was born near Pepin. Her first book, *Little House in the Big Woods*, was based on her time in Pepin County; she was 65 years old when she wrote it. She went on to write seven more books about life on the prairie, and her work inspired the 1970s-era TV show *Little House on the Prairie*. The museum features a replica of a log cabin and a store where you can buy her books.

If you're interested in seeing the type of cabin where Wilder was born, check out the **Laura Ingalls Wilder Wayside and Cabin** (N3238 Cty Rd CC; ; 715.513.6383). The replica of the Wilder family cabin is seven miles outside of Pepin.

Smith Brothers Landing (200 E. Marina Dr.; 715.442.2248) offers metal and glass sculptures crafted by Dave Smith, who is descended from an early pioneer family and is well-versed in local history. He makes some cool (and often inexpensive) metal sculptures.

Getting On the River

Enjoy a lazy tour on the water with **Sail Pepin** (300 1st St.; 715.442.2250). They run daily cruises (May-Oct.), including popular sunset experiences.

Drinking and Dining

The **Harbor View Café** (314 First St.; 715.442.3893) is a destination restaurant with a reputation for creating great food without pretension. The menu changes regularly, depending upon what ingredients are available.

Villa Belleza Winery (1420 3rd St.; 715.442.2424) occupies the striking Mediterranean-style building on the north end of town. They have a tasting room where you can sample wines produced from grapes they grow themselves. Check out **Il Forno** if you have an appetite. They serve classic Italian dishes, which you can enjoy on the patio.

Where to Stay: Camping

The **Lake Pepin Campground** (1010 Locust St.; 715.442.2012) rents 200 sites east of the highway, many of them out in the open. They offer full hookups to simple tent sites.

Where to Stay: Bed and Breakfasts

The **Harbor Hill Inn** (310 Second St; 612.599.2757) offers three homey rooms, a two-bedroom guest house above the garage with a full kitchen and room to sleep six, and a fully renovated cottage.

Special Events

Pepin's major event is **Laura Ingalls Wilder Days** (800.442.3011; second weekend in Sept). The weekend includes a fiddle competition, tales from pioneer days, an essay contest, traditional crafts, and a parade.

STOCKHOLM

Attractions

Go for a hike at **Maiden Rock Bluff State Natural Area**. After a 15-minute walk from the parking lot, you'll have one of the best views of Lake Pepin anywhere. (From Stockholm, go north on County J for 0.7 miles to County E and turn left/northwest; after 0.7 miles, turn left on Long Lane and follow it until it ends at a parking lot.)

The **Stockholm Museum** (Spring St.), housed in the former post office, displays an informative timeline of the town's history, old photos, and old records for genealogists.

Where to Stay: Camping

Stockholm Village Park (Spring St.) is a lovely place to camp. The sites are shaded and virtually all have views of Lake Pepin; no showers.

Drinking and Dining

The **Stockholm Pie Company** (N2030 Spring St.; 715.442.5505) makes pie like your grandma made. On any given day they have a dozen or more types of pie, including savory pies. They also offer a range of lunch options.

Special Events

The popular **Stockholm Art Fair** (mid-July) features juried works in a variety of media, including pottery, fiber, photography, painting, and wood carving, plus live music.

MAIDEN ROCK

Drinking and Dining

The **Maiden Rock Winery and Cidery** (W12266 King Lane; 715.448.3502) creates ciders from apples they grow themselves. These are refined, hard ciders that pack a bit of a punch. There is no charge to sample them, but I bet you will have a hard time walking out empty-handed.

The **Smiling Pelican Bake Shop** (W3556 County Highway 35; 715.448.3807) serves fine breads, tortes, pies and other baked goods that inspire otherwise sensible people to drive hours on end to get their fix.

Dine at **Vino in the Valley** (W3826 450th Ave.; 715.639.6677; open from mid-May–late Sept), where you will enjoy fine Italian food al fresco in a scenic rural setting among the grapevines. The menu typically includes dishes like rigatoni rustica, antipasto salad, and pasta caprese; enjoy it with a glass of their wine.

Where to Stay: Camping

Maiden Rock Village Park (W3535 State Highway 35; 715.448.2205) has a few primitive sites next to the river, and a few electric sites next to the woods; no showers.

Where to Stay: Lodging

AUTHOR'S PICK: The **Maiden Rock Inn** (N531 County Road S; 715.448.2608) offers four guestrooms in a 1906-era schoolhouse that has been through a skillful and classy renovation. Each room has an elegant bathroom, wainscoting, and tin ceilings. Common areas include a recreation room with billiards, grotto and courtyard, and a sauna. Follow the circular stairs to a rooftop deck with great views of the area and river.

Pepin Farm Pottery and Guesthouse (3706 110th Ave.; 715.448.3300) is a quaint older cabin adjacent to a working pottery studio that has been through a complete renovation. It has a modern kitchen, screened porch, a large tub, and walking paths on the property where you can enjoy the sounds of nature and views of Lake Pepin.

The Journey Inn (W3671 200th Ave.; 715.448.2424) is a 21st-century country inn built to have a minimal impact on the surrounding environment. The inn is located next to a large state preserve, so there are many adjacent places to hike, snowshoe, or meditate. At press time, they offered overnight rentals for a two-bedroom cottage with a full kitchen, spa tub, and wood-burning stove that can sleep up to six.

BAY CITY

Drinking and Dining

Accomplished chefs Carrie Summer and Lisa Carlson serve fine dining-quality food without pretense at the laid-back **Chef Shack Bay City** (6379 Main St.; 715.594.3060). They are typically open for dinner on Friday and Saturday evenings and Sunday brunch.

Where to Stay: Camping

Bay City Campground (W6490 Lake Pepin Blvd.; 715.594.3229) rents 41 sites with full hookups next to a busy boat ramp, plus eight with water and electric only. The tent sites are on a small peninsula near the water.

HAGER CITY

Drinking and Dining

The **Harbor Bar** (N673 825th St.; 715.792.2417) is a festive place, especially on weekends, with live music, boaters coming and going, and the grill pumping out the best damn Jamaican-inspired entrées this side of Kingston, like jerk chicken and red snapper. You could opt for a salad or sandwich, if you must.

Where to Stay: Camping

Everts Resort (N1705 860th St.; 715.792.2333) rents a few overnight sites with hookups for campers but is not really equipped for tent camping.

Most of the sites at the **Freedom Island Campground & Marina** (N650 825th St.; 715.222.1808) are strung along a single road on an island just across from Red Wing with a good view of Barn Bluff. The sites are shaded, with many right on the main channel of the river.

Where to Stay: Cabins

Everts Resort also rents five basic cabins on the river that are well-suited for groups. It is a laid back place in summer but very busy in spring and fall with anglers. Most of the cabins are equipped with a kitchen, full bath, and bunk beds plus a full or queen bed and can sleep up to eight people. Bring a sleeping bag, pillow, and towel.

For More Information

There are practical limits to how much I can include in a book, but not with a website! Check out the city profiles on my website to see if they include listings that I couldn't fit in this book.

MINNESOTA

Prairie Island: MississippiValleyTraveler.com/Prairie-Island-Indian-Community/
Red Wing: MississippiValleyTraveler.com/Red-Wing
Frontenac Station: MississippiValleyTraveler.com/Frontenac-Station
Old Frontenac: MississippiValleyTraveler.com/Old-Frontenac
Lake City: MississippiValleyTraveler.com/Lake-City
Camp Lacupolis: MississippiValleyTraveler.com/Camp-Lacupolis
Reads Landing: MississippiValleyTraveler.com/Reads-Landing
Wabasha: MississippiValleyTraveler.com/Wabasha

WISCONSIN

Nelson: MississippiValleyTraveler.com/Nelson
Pepin: MississippiValleyTraveler.com/Pepin
Stockholm: MississippiValleyTraveler.com/Stockholm
Maiden Rock: MississippiValleyTraveler.com/Maiden-Rock
Bay City: MississippiValleyTraveler.com/Bay-City
Hager City: MississippiValleyTraveler.com/Hager-City
Trenton: MississippiValleyTraveler.com/Trenton

Upper Mississippi River National Wildlife & Fish Refuge

As cities grew in the Mississippi Valley, they placed tremendous pressure on the Mississippi's ecology. Pristine (or even just reasonably clean) sections of the river were hard to find in 1922 when Will Dilg and 53 like-minded individuals founded the Izaak Walton League of America, one of the earliest conservation organizations in the country.

Earlier efforts to establish a national park along the Mississippi River had failed when the idea attracted few supporters in Congress. Conservationists tried a different tact by capitalizing on plans for a massive drainage project in the Winnesheik Bottoms around Lansing, Iowa, as motivation to act. They argued that the continued draining of wetlands would irreparably harm fish and wildlife habitat and slowly destroy an area that many considered prime hunting and fishing territory. They also questioned the need to create new land for farming at a time when overproduction had depressed crop prices and the value of farm land.

Their arguments found an audience. With remarkable speed and skill, the League organized a successful campaign that resulted in a 1924 bill that designated parts of the Mississippi River as a National Wildlife and Fish Refuge.

The refuge today covers 240,000 acres that span 261 miles from Rock Island, Illinois, to Wabasha, Minnesota. Refuge lands are popular places for public recreation and the expanse of protected lands helps to ensure the survival of habitat for the river's creatures.

The impact is also easy to see. When you drive along the river from Wabasha to the Quad Cities, you pass by rich backwater complexes. Go south of the Quad Cities however—beyond the boundary of the refuge—and most of the wetlands have indeed been drained and are now agricultural fields.

There have been (and continue to be) significant challenges, of course, such as the fact that the refuge must coordinate its activities with four state governments. The biggest challenge (and threat) has undoubtedly been the building of 29 locks and dams along the upper Mississippi to remake the river for bulk shipping. The dams caused serious damage to the river's ecology, and it has taken decades for the Fish and Wildlife Service and US Army Corps of Engineers to develop ways to cooperate to remediate the impact of navigation structures. It remains a work in progress, but they have taken on a few joint projects to rebuild islands and repair damaged ecosystems.

WABASHA TO LA CROSSE

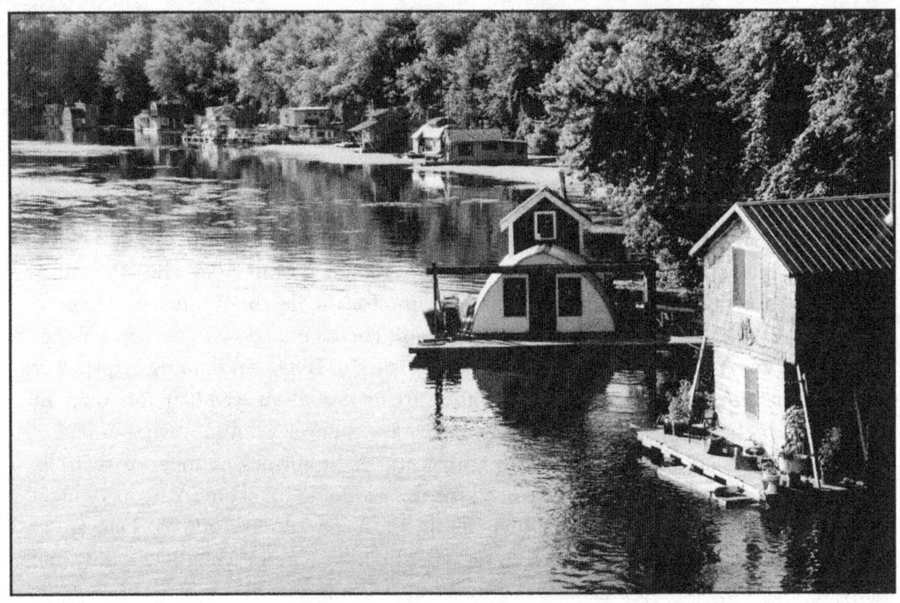

Latsch Island boathouses; Winona, Minnesota

Overview

The Driftless Area, 24,000 square miles of hills and valleys that escaped the crushing force of the last round of glaciers, is one of the most scenic parts of the Mississippi Valley and the United States. This route circles through the heart of the region. You can spend your days getting lost hiking blufftop forests or paddling backwater channels, or tour museums and check out the region's fascinating architecture. In the evening, enjoy a drink and a nice meal and take in a show. Pack your day full of activities or slow down and relax. The biggest cities—La Crosse and Winona—anchor this route. Either city would make a good base for exploring the sites on this route. It's nice to have choices.

History: Minnesota Communities

KELLOGG

In 1854, Isaac Cole settled on section 22 of Greenfield Township on the south bank of the Zumbro River. He established ferry service and built a hotel; a post office opened in 1862 for a place called Pauselim. In 1863, residents built a Methodist church and platted the village. A few other buildings went up but when the railroad built a depot a bit further east, Pauselim faded away and Kellogg sprang to life. The Methodist Church was moved to Kellogg in 1882.

John Huddleson was among the first arrivals in the Kellogg; he built a home around 1870. The village was named by railroad officials to honor a Milwaukee man who supplied signs for the depot. How I long for the days when all you had to do get a town named after you was to donate a couple of signs! Kellogg had 200 residents by 1880, thanks to its role as a shipping point for area farmers' products, and enough economic stability to survive a major fire in 1880. Kellogg has been a small town heavily dependent on agriculture since it was founded.

MINNEISKA

Michael Agnes arrived in 1851 from St. Louis. He and two other early settlers tried to make a living by selling cordwood to steamboats but had a tough go of it. Their community was initially known as Whitewater but was renamed Minneiska when the village was platted in 1854. Minneiska is the Dakota name for the nearby Whitewater River.

In 1884 (and still today), the town the town stretched a mile down one street along the Mississippi. A fire devastated the town on January 6, 1884. Firefighting efforts were hampered by temperatures of -30° F. Another fire in 1900 destroyed half the town, but the 400 residents dutifully rebuilt again. Minneiska was never a boom town, but had a small, stable population, at least until 23 homes and eight businesses, most of them in the oldest section of town, were sacrificed for the widening of Highway 61 in 1959.

The village today is split between two counties and runs along a side road elevated a few feet above the highway. The remaining older buildings are in Wabasha County and many of the newly rebuilt businesses sit in Winona County.

MINNESOTA CITY

When New Yorker William Haddock started the Western Farm and Village Association in 1851, he wanted to help city folks leave the urban environment and resettle in the country. Members paid $5 to join. Most were mechanics from New York City and were foreign born.

Scouts for the company traveled on ice skates upriver from La Crosse on the frozen Mississippi to search for land. They purchased 160 acres from Israel Noracong and founded a village they initially called Rolling Stone Colony. The name was translated from the Dakota word Eyan-omen-man-met-pah (the stream where the stone falls) after a rock in a nearby river that, according to legend, would tremble mystically during periods of high water.

The village was platted in March 1852 and renamed Minnesota City by a unanimous vote of members. The name reflected optimism that their new city was destined to be the new state capital. It attracted residents quickly—500 in the first year alone. Few stuck around, however, once they realized that the land was not ideal for farming and that the village was not directly on the Mississippi River. The initial scouting party had mistakenly believed their site was on the main channel because the water had been unusually high during their scouting trip. Only 20 families stuck out the first winter.

With most of the original colonists gone, other people began moving in. In 1880, the village counted 200 residents. The town developed primarily around feed and flour mills and other agricultural businesses. Cabbage was an important crop for decades. Many farmers came ready to experiment, including some who first attempted to grow apples in the region. Minnesota City also had a strong railroad presence with connections not only north and south along the Mississippi River but also westward to Rochester.

Over time, though, Minnesota City suffered a number of setbacks. The widening of US Highway 61 rerouted traffic from Mill Street and the heart of town to its fringe. Neighboring Goodview annexed portions of town. Winona adsorbed the local school and eventually closed it. Severe flash flooding in 2007 damaged many older buildings. Minnesota City lives on and is today a bedroom community.

WINONA

Around 1800, a band of Mdewakanton Dakota built a summer village they called Keoxah. They were led by a series of chiefs named Wapasha, so the prairie became known as Wapasha's Prairie. The village spread out over a large area, with four long houses elevated next to the river to avoid getting wet during spring floods, a dozen round huts, and a small patch of cultivated land.

Europeans knew at least three Chief Wapashas. The first moved his group to a location along the Upper Iowa River around 1780. His son (who lost an eye as a child during a game of la crosse and styled his hair to resemble an eye patch) moved the group to this prairie around 1807. Wapasha III took over in 1837 and later signed the Treaty of Mendota. Around this same time, other bands in the same Dakota family branch were led by Red Wing and Little Crow. After signing the treaties of Mendota and Traverse des Sioux, the Dakota moved to reservation lands along the Minnesota River.

Steamboat captain Orrin Smith made the first land claims. He arranged transportation for three men to the town site on the steamboat *Nominee*. Just two years later, the new community had grown to 300 residents. By the time Winona incorporated in 1857, it had 3,000 residents and more than a thousand annual steamboat landings. The city is named for Wenonah, who, according to legend, jumped to her death from Maiden Rock Bluff because she was not allowed to marry the man she loved (see page 116).

From 1870 to 1900, Winona prospered because of transportation (steamboats and railroads), lumber (sawmills), and wheat. In 1875, AG Mowbray and LC Porter opened a mill at the foot of Franklin Street that later became Bay State Milling. It's still in business. Winona was also a major supply point for Euro-American settlers continuing west, so it is no surprise that the city's first millionaire, John Latsch, was a wholesale grocer.

Immigration peaked between 1860 and 1900. Germans, 29% of the city in 1880, formed self-sustaining neighborhoods where they spoke German, printed German-language newspapers, and generally kept to themselves. The first Poles arrived in 1855 and grew to 11% of the population by 1880. Most of the Poles came from Kashubia (a region near Gdansk and Bytow). They spoke a language that may be older than standard Polish but has mostly disappeared from Poland today. A handful of Winona residents still speak it. Irish, Norwegians, and Bohemians also moved to Winona in the 1800s. Hmong and Hispanic immigrants began to move into the area in the 1980s.

Winona's economy tanked after the forests were depleted and the lumber mills shut. (The last mill closed in 1909.) Watkins Medical Company thrived, however. JR Watkins founded the company in nearby Plainview but demand for his new product, Dr. Wards Liniment, outstripped his ability to make it in his kitchen, so he moved to Winona in 1885. The Watkins Company grew into one of the nation's largest suppliers of health products, supplements, and flavor additives. You may have used their vanilla. Education has also provided a stable economic base. The State Normal School (now Winona State University) opened in 1858. The College of St. Teresa was founded in 1907 and began admitting men in 1912.

WABASHA TO LA CROSSE ROUTE MAP

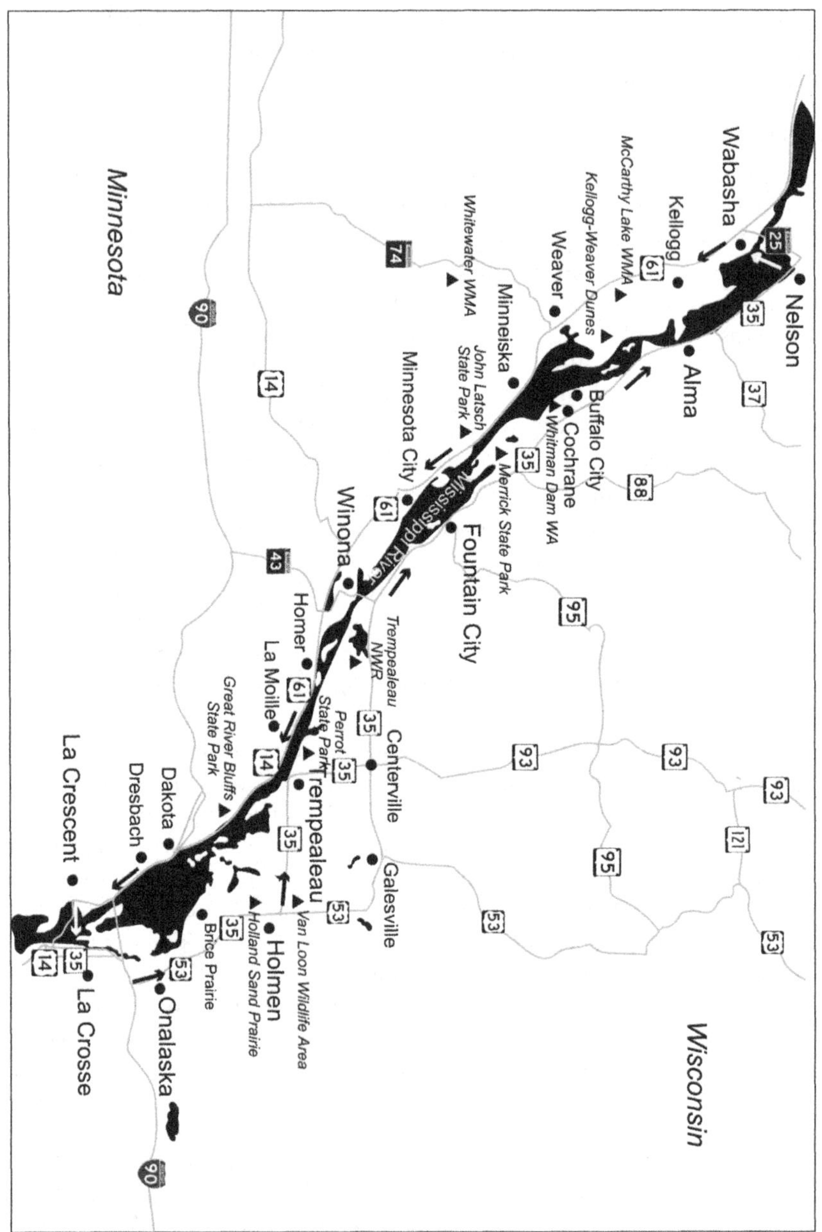

This is another circular route. Follow US Highway 61 on the Minnesota side from Wabasha to La Crescent and State Highway 35 on the Wisconsin side from La Crosse to Nelson. You can cross the river at downtown Winona via State Highway 43 and at La Crosse on either the Interstate 90 bridge or downtown on the Mississippi River Bridge (US Highways 61 and 14). Follow Highway 25 to cross between Nelson and Wabasha. The entire route is about 190 miles.

Like folks in many river towns, Winonians had a live-and-let-live attitude about certain behaviors. The city had an active red-light district for generations that was concentrated along 2nd Street between the depot and downtown. It flourished until a raid in December 1942 shut it down. During Prohibition, local police were not enthusiastic enforcers of the ban on alcohol. The city had at least 200 speakeasies and "blind pigs" (home taverns) and over 500 places to buy liquor. The local liquor trade flourished until federal agents got involved in the late 1920s and regularly raided suspected speakeasies.

Winona, like many communities, faced perplexing problems in its older core as new homes and businesses were built far from the center of town. The city fell victim to some of the same misguided urban renewal plans of the early 1970s, razing entire blocks from the core for parking lots and strip malls. As those projects failed to deliver the promised benefits, preservation efforts gained momentum.

Winona today is a regional commercial and cultural hub, surprising for its range and depth and cultural opportunities.

LA CRESCENT

New York native Peter Cameron, who built a log house in 1851, and Thor Halverson, a native of Norway, who did the same the following year, were two of many people attracted to this small, elevated prairie near the Mississippi. When they arrived, dozens of ancient mounds filled the prairie.

Cameron had been trading along the upper Mississippi since the early 1840s and had business interests in La Crosse. He and his wife Emma were married in 1845, the first couple to be married in La Crosse. Emma was quite familiar with the marriage ritual. She went through it 11 times—Peter was her fourth husband. Peter had big plans for La Crescent that were hampered by poor access to the Mississippi River. The village was separated from the river by a mile of sloughs and marshes. Cameron figured the best solution was to build a canal that would connect the town to the river (and in the process might have diverted the main channel from La Crosse to La Crescent). He died in 1855, though, while building a sawmill in La Crosse, and the canal plan died with him.

In 1855, Harvey and William Gillett platted the village on part of Cameron's old claim and renamed it from Camerons to Manton. They sold all their lots in a year, most of them to the Kentucky Land Company, then left town, probably for a beach in Mexico. The new owners wanted a more appealing name, something with a loftier sound, so they chose La Crescent, which they felt evoked the shape of the bluffs and echoed the name of better-known La Crosse. That's the story that has survived, anyway.

The Kentucky Land Company got busy building a village. A dozen similar two-story houses decorated with elaborate trim went up, then a road across the marsh to the ferry landing. For 20 years, the only way for La Crescent residents to cross the Mississippi River was down the muddy road to the ferry. This did not encourage rapid growth.

John Harris arrived in 1854 determined to grow apples. When he planted his first crop, skeptics were plentiful. They assumed the Minnesota climate was too harsh. They were wrong. His apples eventually grew quite well. Other growers followed suit and orchards became one of the largest industries. Although there are fewer orchards today than in the 1960s, the number of acres dedicated to growing apples is about the same.

Like other small towns in the area, La Crescent experienced a housing boom after World War II as it grew into a suburb of La Crosse. In 1940, the village had 815 residents or about one-fifth the number of people who live there today.

History: Wisconsin Communities

LA CROSSE

When Europeans began exploring the area, they found a prairie where Native Americans played a popular game that the Europeans weren't familiar with. In 1837, the Reverend Alfred Brunson described the sport this way:

> "The game was played with a ball, thrown by a stick some four feet in length, the outer end of which was brought round into a ring, say six inches in diameter, to which is attached a bag of network made of strong thongs of some kind of skin. The parties start at a center post. The ball is thrown into the air as perpendicularly as possible, and when it comes down each party strives to catch it in the bag at the end of their stick and throw it as far as possible against the opposite party. The ball is caught up and thrown so back and forth, and the victors are those who drive it eventually and effectually by the center post on to the side of their opponents. It is a very exciting sport, and many a one gets an unlucky blow, sometimes from friends and sometimes from foes; but as no one is supposed to design it, no offense is given or insult imagined."

Although it is not entirely clear why the French named the sport la crosse (the Ho Chunk called it Caabnaikisik), it may be that the game sticks used by the Native American players bore a strong resemblance to the crook carried by Catholic Bishops that was called la crozier. Regardless, the name stuck and the field where the game was played became known as Prairie la Crosse.

In the autumn of 1841, just six months after leaving a comfortable life in upstate New York, 18-year-old Nathan Myrick headed up the Mississippi from Prairie du Chien on a keelboat, eager to open a trading post at Prairie la Crosse. Loaded with supplies he had purchased on credit at Fort Crawford, he and his partner, Eben Weld, arrived on November 4 after five days of travel. (You can now drive this stretch in about an hour.) Myrick, the city's first postmaster, later shortened the name to La Crosse. In October 1844, his neighborhood grew when a group of Mormons came up from Nauvoo. They spent the winter southeast of his trading post (that area is now called Mormon Coulee).

In 1848, Myrick bought a hundred acres of land but moved away later in the year because of declining business prospects. When Myrick left La Crosse, the village had a handful of houses and a bowling alley where patrons used a ball made from a pine knot.

People began streaming to town around 1850, attracted to its location on a flat, treeless plain high enough to avoid flooding. It also helped that the area was nearly malaria-free. Among the first arrivals was Emfin Emfinson—the area's first known immigrant from Norway. By the end of 1853, La Crosse had a hundred houses and five taverns. (La Crosse may still have a tavern for every 20 households.) A steady stream of covered wagons arrived from the East to cross the river via the ferry at La Crosse. Sixty-one wagons crossed in a single June day in 1856. La Crosse incorporated as a city in 1856 and elected its first mayor, Thomas Stoddard, by a 216-215 vote.

RANDOM FACT: You can still watch a game of lacrosse in La Crosse today; it is a club sport at UW-La Crosse.

La Crosse rapidly grew into a regional commercial center, fueled by logging, banking, grain milling, and large-scale manufacturing. La Crosse was also home to a high concentration of jobbers—wholesale businesses that supplied the retail trade—and had an active ship building and repair industry. The railroads, which connected La Crosse to Milwaukee in 1858, were major employers. La Crosse also had a sizable beer brewing industry, brewing as much product as their counterparts in Milwaukee.

La Crosse also grew through annexation, which was not always welcomed. At one time, North La Crosse was an incorporated city separated from La Crosse by a mile of marsh (it still is). North La Crosse had a number of sawmills, as well as railroads and iron works. Nearly one-third of the residents in North La Crosse were foreign born, many of them Norwegian. The village had incorporated in 1868, but that didn't stop annexation, which La Crosse pulled off through an act of the Wisconsin legislature on March 22, 1871. There was never a public vote. Annexation added 1,494 residents, many of them disgruntled, increasing the city's population to over 9,000.

People coming up the Mississippi found a growing city with a busy steamboat landing. Those early arrivals included African Americans who passed through town in search of economic opportunity. Zacharias Louis Moss, who arrived in 1859, was among the few who made La Crosse home. Descendants of his still live in the area. George Edwin Taylor was another of those early Black residents. Taylor was a strong advocate for labor, politically active, and publisher of *The Wisconsin Labor Advocate*. He left La Crosse frustrated by its racial politics and later became the first Black man to receive a major party nomination for President of the US (the National Liberty Party in 1904).

By the 1890s, the city's economic growth had stalled. The steamboat era had ended in the 1880s, La Crosse's grain milling industry was declining, and the last of the 33 lumber mills would close in 1906. In response, the Board of Trade (a group of private businessmen) subsidized the construction of new factories to transition lumber mill workers into new employment. They didn't take many chances with their money, preferring to fund existing businesses such as the La Crosse Rubber Works.

Anti-German sentiment stirred up by World War I ushered in a number of changes around town: Berlin Street was renamed Liberty Street; sauerkraut became liberty cabbage; and the German Society rebranded as the Pioneer Club. Prohibition nearly killed the local brewing industry. Only the G. Heileman Company survived. During Prohibition, they produced soda water, malt extract, and near-beer products like Coney Island Beer and King of Clubs.

The city generally did well in the 1920s, though. Large employers such as the La Crosse Rubber Works, Trane Company, La Crosse Plow Works, and auto parts manufacturing put enough money in people's pockets to trigger a boom in housing construction. As the Great Depression hit, government-funded programs such as the Works Progress Administration and the lock and dam construction kept many folks afloat.

In the immediate aftermath of World War II, pent-up labor-management conflict led to a series of contentious strikes. A decade later, La Crosse lost a quarter of its manufacturing jobs, a national trend that accelerated in the 1970s and 1980s.

Ethnic Hmong began arriving from Laos in the late 1970s. Many had fought alongside US soldiers in Vietnam but were left to fend for themselves when the US withdrew. Thousands migrated to the US after months or years in refugee camps.

La Crosse continues to adapt. Healthcare is now a leading employer, and education and tourism have grown in importance.

ONALASKA

Thomas Rowe, a native New Yorker, arrived in the area in 1851, apparently with the idea of opening a tavern to serve the lumberjacks working along the Black River, which must have been a good idea, given their numbers. Mr. Rowe was a fan of Thomas Campbell, whose poem *The Pleasures of Hope* references a town in the Alaskan Aleutian Islands that provided the inspiration for the town's name:

"Now fore he sweeps, where scarce a summer smiles,
On Behring's rocks, or Greenland's naked isles;
Cold on his midnight watch the breezes blow;
From wastes that slumber in eternal snow,
And waft across the waves' tumultuous roar,
The wolf's long howl from Oonalaska's shore."

William Carlisle, a lumberman, was so taken with the name that after he left the area, he used it three more times for new communities in Arkansas, Texas, and Washington.

Back to lumber. The first sawmill went up around 1853, and by 1856, there were three sawmills in operation and two more under construction. Most of the workers were immigrants from Germany and Norway. From 1855 to 1899, over six billion board feet of lumber floated down the Black River to Onalaska. That's enough lumber to build two million three-bedroom, 1000-square-foot ranch houses. During the early years, the mills kicked out a lot of sawdust as a byproduct. For a while, the sawdust was dumped on roads to make them more passable, which turned out to be not such a good idea, because sawdust is, of course, flammable and, while flaming streets might be a really cool effect in a video game, they aren't so good for a town trying to convince people to stick around. The lumber business peaked in 1892. Ten years later it was essentially done, as the forests had been depleted. Employment at the Black River mills fell from nearly 2,000 in 1899 to 39 just six years later.

Onalaska grew more slowly than its neighbor to the south because La Crosse had a more favorable river port and got a railroad station 12 years earlier. After the mills closed, Onalaska dipped into a recession. Light manufacturing and agriculture gradually turned the economy around. One of the light manufacturers was the Onalaska Pickle and Canning factory, which occupies 12 pages in the local history book. They packed pickles, cabbage, peas, and corn beginning in 1906. They shipped sauerkraut around the world until they closed in 1958. Onalaska was a favorite ending point for sleighing expeditions. Arriving sleighers would throw a big party with drinking and occasional fights, although this activity probably had less of an economic impact than light manufacturing and agriculture.

Onalaska expanded to the north and east in the 1960s, but this growth was mostly residential. In 1982, the city annexed land in the Town of Medary around Valley View Mall after a lengthy legal dispute and promptly turned loose developers to build the strip mall hell you see today.

HOLMEN

Euro-Americans began filing into the area around 1850, with the Jenks family perhaps being the first to call Holmen home, before it was known as Holmen. The area was initially called Frederickstown in honor of the village blacksmith, Frederick Anderson, then the name Cricken (Norwegian for creek) caught on.

The origin of the town's name is a bit of a mystery, but there are two theories. In 1851, a surveyor passed through whose name was Holmen who went on to win election as a State Senator in Indiana; the postmaster may have suggested naming the town after him. More likely, though, is that the word Holmen is derived from the Norwegian word Holm, which means something like a projection of level, rich land extending into the water. Or it might mean island. The town once had a large pond in the middle of town created by backup from a dammed creek. There was an island in the middle of the pond that was a favorite recreation site. All you Norwegian speakers out there, let me know.

Holmen was never a thriving industrial center, but it had its share of goings-on. The Casberg Mill opened in 1876, grinding corn, wheat, rye, and buckwheat into flour. Holmen also had a factory that made the pins that held log rafts together, a sorghum mill, and an ice harvesting operation.

Most of the early residents were Norwegian and many of the customs they brought with them were practiced by generations of Holmen residents. One of those was a Norwegian Christmas tradition called jule bakking. To participate, one had to dress up in a funny, tacky costume and don a mask, then gather with a big group of friends in similar attire. Once assembled, everyone would head to the neighbors' houses to see if they could guess who's who. Once identities were revealed, everyone celebrated with lefse, lutefisk, rosettes, and grog. This custom has fallen out of practice in recent years.

TREMPEALEAU

The town was named after a distinctive, conical land mass that is completely surrounded by water. Local Native Americans referred it as mountain soaking in the water, which French explorers translated as *la montagne qui trempe a l'eau*.

The village of Trempealeau stirred to life in the 1840s as Reed's Landing (James Reed was an early resident), a small port and fur trading outpost inhabited by a few migrants from Prairie du Chien and French Canada. Platted in 1852 as Montoville then quickly replatted as Trempealeau, the village was formally called Montoville-Trempealeau until 1856, when the confusion ended and the village became just Trempealeau. More people arrived beginning in 1856, many coming upriver by steamboat and others overland in covered wagons. A commercial district developed along the riverfront to serve increasing river commerce and burgeoning agriculture in surrounding areas.

Land speculators trying to make a quick buck, many of them from the East, fueled dramatic inflation in the cost of land. Prices for choice lots that initially sold for $40 were listed for many times that amount just a few months later. Even with cheaper land available in neighboring areas, Trempealeau land owners continued to demand high prices. As a result, many would-be residents moved on to other communities in Red Wing, Winona, and Saint Paul.

Trempealeau's growth also slowed as river transportation waned and wheat production declined after the Civil War. Even after the arrival of a second railroad line in 1887 the village's economic fortunes changed little. The town's economic hopes went up in flames in 1888 when a large fire wiped out most of the riverfront commercial district on Front Street (now First Street). When the town rebuilt its commercial district, new construction was concentrated along the current Main Street, two blocks from the riverfront, reflecting the declining importance of river commerce for the village. This two-block stretch has remained the center of a stable but small population since.

FOUNTAIN CITY

Thomas Holmes showed up in the fall of 1839 with a small party of 13 people and established a trading post. This gave the site its first name: Holmes Landing. He ended up staying until 1846, at which time he felt civilization was getting to close to him, so he moved further west, where he founded about 30 other communities (including Helena, Montana) before retiring in Culman, Alabama.

After Holmes left, Holmes Landing became Fountain City. The new name was inspired by one of the many fountain-like springs that oozed from the bluffs. The city did well between 1847 and 1862, thanks to modest success as a trading and shipping center and a ferry connection to Winona. Early businesses included a cigar factory, lumber yard, foundry, brickyard, rock quarry, planing mills, agricultural implement dealers, commercial fishing operations, and a boatyard.

Most of the early residents were German or Swiss. In 1860, Judge Gale described Fountain City as feeling very much like a German village. The town officers were all German, the primary language used around town was, yes, German, and a number of social clubs organized according to German traditions: Der Turnverein (gymnastic society), Gesangverein (singing society), Schutzenverein (shooting society), and Bierverien (drinking society)—just kidding on that last one.

Fountain City maintains a strong connection to the river to this day. The construction of Lock and Dam 5A in the 1930s provided some much needed work for residents. In addition, the Army Corps of Engineers has had a boatyard at Fountain City since the 19th century. The yard is used for maintenance and to store dredges and other equipment used by the Corps to maintain a shipping channel on the Mississippi River.

ALMA

River pilots named this spot Twelve Mile Bluff because of a rock formation that was visible from the mouth of the Chippewa River 12 miles north of the bluff. Sadly, the rock outcropping that gave the bluff its distinctive shape collapsed in 1881, sending a giant boulder rolling downhill. No one was hurt, but a couple of buildings were damaged and the town lost its most distinctive landmark.

Euro-Americans began arriving in 1848, beginning with Swiss immigrants Victor Probst and John Waecker. They made a living selling cordwood to passing steamboats. And the Swiss just kept coming, supplemented by a smattering of Germans. The village was platted in 1855 with the name Alma.

Alma's growth began with the usual things—hotels, a general store, and a brewery—but the first business in town was supposedly a saloon opened by a guy who came upriver from Keokuk. The town's economy got a boost when Alma won the county seat election in 1860. Zany county seat shenanigans often found on the frontier ensued. Fountain City challenged the election results, but the Wisconsin Supreme Court wouldn't play along. In 1861, Charles Schaettle led a group of Watergate-quality burglars from Buffalo City in an attempt to steal the county papers from Alma and bolster Buffalo City's claim. They failed, and according to one account, the bungling burglars were chased from town while a fiddler played the tune *Wender nit bald heigo, ihr Chaiba*, which means something like "Won't you please decamp, you rascals." (Fighting words!) Alma beat Buffalo City in the 1861 county seat election and never looked back. Many of the disappointed residents from Buffalo City relocated to Alma in the 1860s. Probably not the same ones that tried to steal the county papers, though.

Boathouses

If you're paying attention as you drive around, you may notice some curious structures in places along the shores of the Mississippi. The small floating buildings, usually topped with a tin roof, look big enough for just a room or two. They usually appear in clusters. Are they shacks? Fish houses?

They are boathouses, actually. In most cases, they have just enough space to store a boat and maybe weekend living quarters. Here's some background.

In the early 1900s, folks living off the river (clammers, fishermen, trappers) built floating houses that they could maneuver through the backwaters. During the Depression, more families tried to make a living (or simply get food) from the river. Some had nowhere else to live. When the lock and dam system was built in the 1930s, the water level stabilized and a boathouse became practical full-time living quarters.

Thousands were built. There was essentially no regulation of them until the 1970s. In 1986, the US Congress granted the Corps responsibility for regulating boathouses. The legislation also protected the right of existing boathouses to continue to exist but banned the placement of new ones. States also have regulatory power related boathouses, so you won't see any in Iowa, because their Department of Natural Resources won't permit them.

Boathouses are creative adaptations to building a home in a place where conditions can vary a lot. They float atop plastic barrels, pontoons, or wooden logs and are held in place with spud poles that are connected to shore via a walkway. While boathouses are stationary, they can rise and fall as river levels change. They usually have electricity but aren't allowed to have a bathroom on-board. Each boathouse community instead maintains outhouses on land.

Many no longer have a boat well, as they have evolved into weekend living spaces where groups of friends and families get together to experience the Mississippi River as their backyard. The only place where boathouses serve as a year-round residence is at Winona's Latsch Island. Other places where you can see communities of boathouses are around Fountain City, La Crosse, Brownsville, and Red Wing.

If you want to read more about boathouses and to look at lots of pretty pictures, check out *The Floating Boathouses on the Upper Mississippi River: Their History, Their Stories* by Martha Greene Phillips.

The single most important reason for Alma's early growth was logging. Beef Slough, an area just north of the village, was the site of a major operation where, from 1867 to 1889, logs coming down the Chippewa River were sorted and assembled into log rafts. The Beef Slough Manufacturing, Booming, Log Driving, and Transportation Company was founded in 1867 and grew into one of the largest operations in the US. The company later merged with the Mississippi River Logging Company, which chose Frederick Weyerhaeuser as its leader in 1873.

Alma had a couple of sawmills of its own, plus ice harvesting, lime kilns, boat manufacturing, and a robust cigar manufacturing sector. The Martin Exel Company rolled nearly 60,000 cigars a year in the 1870s, mostly for the local market. By 1897, Alma counted three cigar factories that produced a collective 138,000 cigars every year. The factories had all closed by 1928.

One of the most celebrated local residents was Gerhard Gesell, a photographer and contemporary of Ansell Adams. Gesell ran a studio from 1876 to 1906. He was a gifted photographer who documented daily life in and around Alma. He made a composite photo called *Pioneers of Buffalo Co., Wisconsin* that he created from 156 individual portraits of folks who moved into the area before 1857. You'll find it in the courthouse.

The last of the logging-related businesses shut down in 1905. Alma attracted artists for the summer in the 1920s but only recently have more made Alma their year-round home. Lock and Dam 4 was built in 1932, which ended Alma's days as a port of call for riverboats but provided employment during the Depression.

Explore Down the West Bank (Minnesota)

KELLOGG

Attractions

Independent toy stores are hard to find nowadays but not at Kellogg! **LARK Toys** (171 Lark Lane; 507.767.3387) fits the bill and is a joyous place to pass some time. The store has a wide range of items spread through several rooms: books, silly masks, building blocks, aerobies, plastic spiders and snakes, kits for science experiments, a photo booth, puzzles, games, and wood toys crafted by hand. Don't miss the carousel with beautiful pieces hand-carved by local artist Todd Pasche. They also have a nostalgic display of toys from the past called Memory Lane (free) and an 18-hole mini-golf.

Kellogg-Weaver Dunes Scientific and Natural Area (651.259.5800) is a short detour off the highway and a great place to explore a sand prairie. Dunes, some 30 feet high, roll across the land, most covered in light vegetation. The dunes were created by deposits from the Zumbro, Chippewa, and Mississippi Rivers. The area is home to a number of threatened species of plants (for example, purple sand grass and beach-heather) and rare birds, plus the threatened Blanding's turtle. You may see these turtles crossing the road (drive carefully!), especially in June when they are laying eggs or in late August when the youngsters hatch. Access to the north tract is about four miles from Kellogg. Park on the east side of the road at the sign. The South tract is about six miles from Kellogg at Township Road 141.

McCarthy Lake Wildlife Management Area (507.206.2858), adjacent to the dunes, is an area rich in wetlands created by an old channel of the Zumbro River. If you visit at the right time of year, you are likely to see sandhill cranes, bald eagles, or tundra swans. Access is four miles south of Kellogg.

Getting on the River

If you brought your own canoe or kayak, check out the **Halfmoon Canoe Trail**, five miles of easy paddling through the backwaters. From US 61, take County Highway 18 through Kellogg and turn right on S. Dodge Street, then turn left on County 84; after 4 miles, turn left on 622nd Street and follow it to Halfmoon Landing.

Drinking and Dining

Town and Country Café (Kellogg: 320 E. Belvidere Ave.; 507.767.4593) is a cozy eatery where you can get breakfast all day, but they are especially popular for their pies. When I visited, they had 12 types of pie to choose from.

MINNEISKA

Attractions

Whitewater Wildlife Management Area (507.796.3281) offers 37,000 acres of sublime beauty of Whitewater River marshland along Highway 74 southwest of Weaver. There are many places to pull over and get out of your car to hike or fish (or cross-country ski in winter) or to look for birds.

The primary activity at **John Latsch State Park** (507.932.3007) is a hike to the top of the bluff—450 feet above the parking lot—up a long series of wooden steps. It's not an easy hike, but at the top, you are rewarded with magnificent views of the valley. The park is two miles south of Minneiska. The park is only open during the day.

Drinking and Dining

Minneiska Meats (206 Bennett Ave.; 507.884.8796) offers what you need for a picnic or DIY meal, from meats to grill to summer sausage of many flavors and other dried meats to snack on.

Buck's Bar (206 Bennett Ave.; 507.689.4183) is a good choice for laid-back bar food and your preferred beverage that you can pair with good views of the river.

MINNESOTA CITY

Attractions

The **Minnesota City Historical Association** (140 Mill St.; 507.689.4103) is based in the former First Baptist Church built in the 1870s. It still has the original hand-carved chairs—100 of them—and many other original touches, including the organ, stove, and galvanized tin baptismal bath. While the original church was built for a Baptist congregation, the church had a long history of hosting interdenominational services. The historical society has a small collection of historic photographs, plus a number of records from the village's past.

Getting on the River

If you have a canoe or kayak with you, you may want to paddle the **Verchota Landing Canoe Trail** (507.454.7351), a challenging 11.2 mile route that involves paddling upstream at times. The Verchota landing is just east of the boat club on Prairie Island Road east of Minnesota City.

Where to Stay: Camping

Bass Camp Resort (23651 Rolbiecki Lane.; 507.689.9257), just north of Minnesota City, sits between the highway and the river but is shielded from highway noises. The campsites are nicely shaded and not so close that you feel like you're having dinner with your neighbors every evening. Most have views of the river.

Winona Area Map (#1-#7)

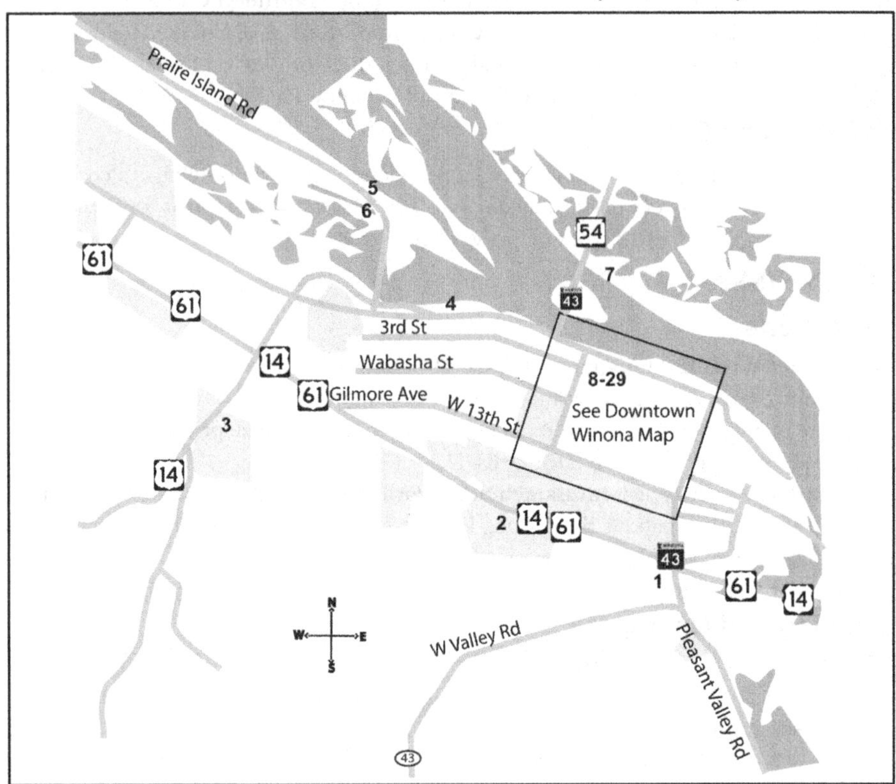

Attractions

7. Aghaming Park
10. Church of St. Stanislaus Kostka
2. Garvin Heights Park
18. Merchant's Bank
4. Minnesota Marine Art Museum
11. Polish Cultural Institute of Winona
6. Prairie Island Park
3. St. Mary's University/Page Theatre
1. Sugar Loaf Bluff
26. Theatre du Mississippi
12. Watkins Administrative Building
12. Watkins Heritage Museum
14. Winona Arts Center
24. Winona County History Center
20. Winona National Bank/African Safari Museum
29. Winona State University

Where to Eat and Drink

17. Acoustic Café
9. Bloedow Bakery
23. Blue Heron Coffee House
22. Boat House Restaurant
19. Bub's Brewing Company
25. Café Sapori di Sicilia
15. Ed's (no name) Bar
21. Farmers Market
8. Lakeview Drive Inn
16. Nosh Scratch Kitchen

Where to Stay

13. Alexander Mansion B&B
27. Carriage House B&B
5. Prairie Island Campground

Other

28. Amtrak

Downtown Winona Map (#8-#29)

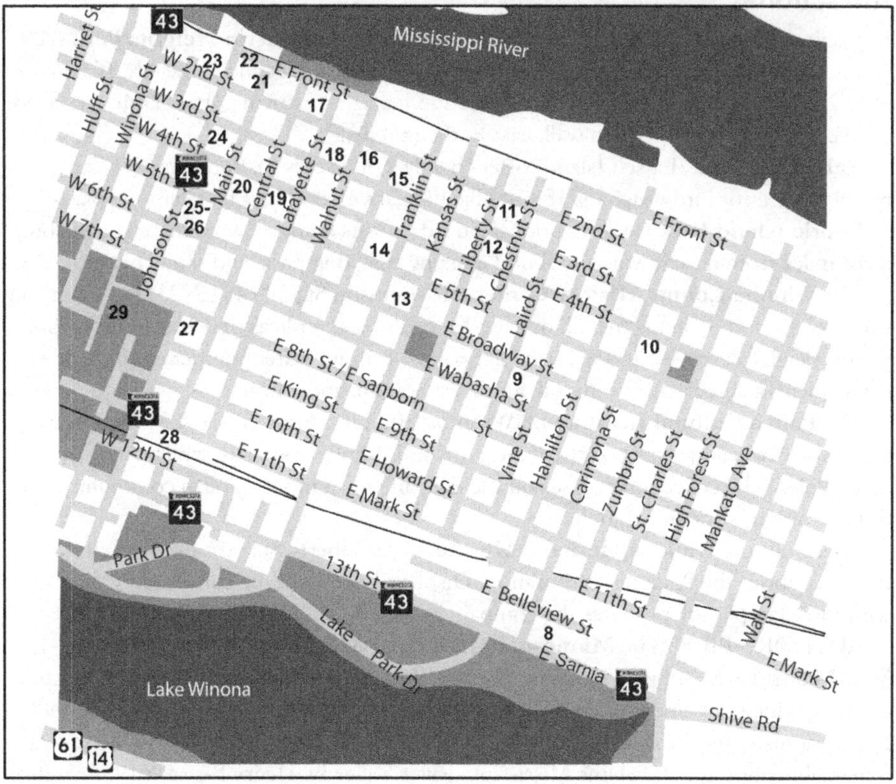

A NOTE ABOUT GETTING AROUND WINONA

Winona's street planners went out of their way to confuse visitors. Some numbered streets also have names, so 8th Street is also Sanborn, 6th Street is also Broadway, etc. If that doesn't confuse you, then the way buildings are numbered just might. Rather than increasing by 100 for each block (so the buildings between 7th and 8th Street would all be numbered in the 700s, for example), building numbers only advance by half that for each block, so the buildings between 7th and 8th Streets are actually numbered 350-399. This numbering system applies to all streets, so if you are looking for an address in the 400-449 range and you see an address for 220, you have four blocks to go, not two. That's probably way more than you need to know, but hey, that's why I'm here.

WINONA

Attractions

For a bit of perspective on the city of Winona, head up to **Garvin Heights Park** (200 Garvin Heights Rd.) and take in the panoramic views 530 feet above the city. If you'd like to stretch your legs, you can hike to the top instead of driving. (Park at the gravel lot on West Lake Boulevard, then walk east to the trail head.)

Aghaming Park (Latsch Island) offers nearly 2,000 acres of floodplain forest; it is a popular place for bird watching. If you hike here, it's a good idea to wear long pants.

Prairie Island Park (1120 Prairie Island Rd. N) sits along a backwater channel about three miles from downtown. You'll find a hiking trail, dog park, and sandy beach.

The **Winona County History Center** (160 Johnson St.; 507.454.2723) has a fun and varied collection of items that illuminate Winona's past: replicas of 19th-century storefronts, sleighs, carriages, and big stuff like a 19th-century water pumper from the fire department, a sulky reaper with sail, a delivery wagon, and a hearse.

The **Polish Cultural Institute of Winona** (102 Liberty St.; 507.454.3431) is housed in the former headquarters of the Laird Norton Lumber Company, which employed many Poles. The collection focuses on the daily life of Winona's Polish community, with displays about work and church.

Check out the **Watkins Heritage Museum** (150 Liberty St.; 507.457.6095) to learn the story about the Watkins Corporation. Displays document the corporation's history, with fun examples of products the company has made and sold over the years.

AUTHOR'S PICK: The **Minnesota Marine Art Museum** (800 Riverview Dr.; 507.474.6626) is a gem in Winona's rich cultural scene. The nautically themed collection of fine art includes a permanent gallery with paintings from the Hudson River School, Impressionists, and Vincent van Gogh's *The Beach of Scheveningen.* You'll also see several remarkable photographs of the Mississippi River Valley by Henry Bosse, a 19th-century mapmaker and photographer who worked for the US Army Corps of Engineers.

The **Winona Arts Center** (228 E. Fifth St.; 507.453.9959) features rotating exhibits from local artists and occasionally screens independent films.

The **Theatre du Mississippi** (Masonic Temple, 255 Main St.; 507.459.9080) is a performing arts center that stages shows throughout the year.

The **Page Theatre at St. Mary's University** (700 Terrace Heights; 507.457.1715) hosts performing arts including dance, theater, and music during the school year.

Architecture

Winona National Bank (204 Main St.; 507.454.4320) is two parts fine architecture and one part silliness. The bank, designed by George Maher and completed in 1916, has an Egyptian Revival exterior but a Prairie School feel inside. The interior features impressive bronze work and an art glass window made by the Tiffany Studio. For the silliness, check out the **African Safari Museum** on the second floor.

Merchant's Bank (102 E. 3rd St.; 507.457.1100) opened in 1912. Mostly Prairie School in design, the architects, William Purcell and George Elmslie, were once associates of Louis Sullivan. The bank has an outstanding collection of art glass windows.

HEY, WHAT'S THAT? The stub of rock at the south end of Winona is known as Sugar Loaf Bluff (Wapasha's Cap to the Dakota). Most of the bluff was quarried in the 19th century, leaving just the portion you see today.

The dome of the **Church of St. Stanislaus Kostka** (625 E. 4th St.; 507.452.5430) rises stately above the floodplain, visible for miles up and down river. This Baroque/Romanesque gem was completed in 1894. The vast, ornate interior uses a Greek cross design and can seat 1,800. Enter through the door on Carimona Street.

The **Watkins Administrative Building** (150 Liberty St.) is another local landmark designed by Chicago architect George Maher. Built for a staggering $1.2 million from 1911–1913, the exterior is blue Bedford stone, and the entrance vestibules are covered with Italian marble. The interior is adorned with rich mahogany and mosaics. Look up and around to check out the ornate dome and art glass windows depicting Winona.

Winona is an epicenter of **stained glass craftsmanship**. Home to several nationally known studios, the city also has an impressive collection of windows in buildings around town. While you can only tour the shops as part of a large group, there's nothing stopping you from checking out the windows. Pick up a brochure to Winona's stained glass treasures at the **visitors center** (924 Huff St.) and take a self-guided tour of the windows in the Watkins Administrative Building, Merchant's Bank, Winona National Bank, the County Courthouse, and the Winona County History Center.

Drinking and Dining

Ed's (no name) Bar (252 E. 3rd St.) is a good choice for live music, good beer, and friendly folks.

If you prefer something baked for breakfast (or a snack), head to **Bloedow Bakery** (451 E. 6th/Broadway; 507.452.3682) where you can get a big cinnamon roll or a handful of donuts.

This being a college town, there are plenty of options for coffee. The **Acoustic Café** (77 Lafayette St.; 507.453.0394) has an eclectic, creative clientele and you can sate your hunger with a pita, sandwich, or a bowl of freshly made soup.

The **Blue Heron Coffee House** (162 W. 2nd St.; 507.452.7020) prepares sandwiches, fresh salads, and soups with an emphasis on local, organic ingredients.

The food at the **Boat House Restaurant** (2 Johnson St.; 507.474.6550) is as good as the views from the riverside windows and deck. The menu emphasizes seasonal ingredients, and includes a good mix of lighter fare including salads and snacks and hearty steak and fish entrées.

The **Lakeview Drive Inn** (610 E. Sarnia; 507.454.3723), the oldest restaurant in Winona, has been pleasing Winonians' palates since 1938. It has a standard menu of diner foods that are freshly prepared and can be rolled out to your vehicle by a carhop. Don't miss their delicious, house-made root beer. Wednesday is classic car night, so you are encouraged to roll up in your '57 Chevy.

Housed in an attractive historic building, **Bub's Brewing Company** (65 E. 4th St.; 507.457.3121) offers more sandwich options that you can shake a pickle at. It is also a popular place to enjoy an adult beverage.

Café Sapori di Sicilia (211 Main St.; 507.474.6155) tempts with tasty snacks, fresh breads, savory entrees, and delightful sweets. Give in. Enjoy the flavors of Sicily near the banks of the Mississippi.

Freshness is the guidepost at **Nosh Scratch Kitchen** (102 Walnut St.; 507.474.7040), a fine dining restaurant that works with ingredients from local farmers and makes everything from scratch. Bread is baked fresh daily; sausages are made in-house. The menu changes with the availability of ingredients. A meal at Nosh is a delightful experience.

La Crosse Regional Map (#1-#13)

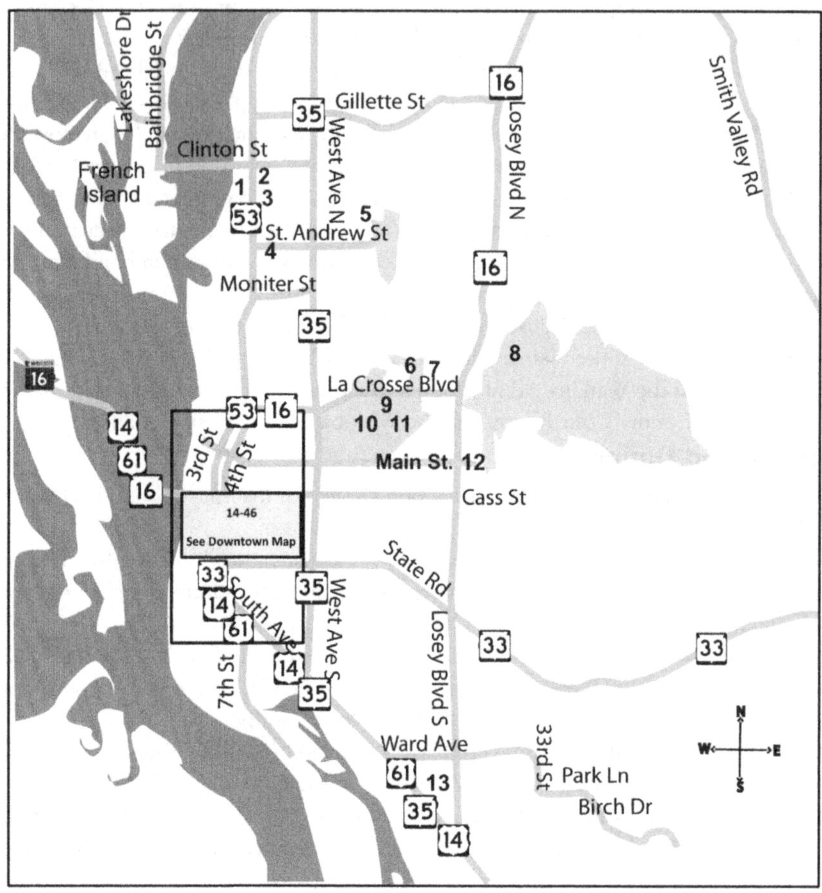

Attractions

26. Children's Museum of La Crosse
22. Christ Episcopal Church
1. Copeland Park
12. Grandad Park
8. Hixon Forest
24. Hixon House Museum
14. King Gambrinus
25. La Crosse Area Heritage Center
29. La Crosse Community Theater
44. La Crosse Queen
17. Maria Angelorum Chapel
11. Mississippi Valley Archaeology Center
6. Myrick Park
45. Pettibone Park
28. Pump House Regional Arts Center
43. Riverside Park
10. University of Wisconsin – La Crosse
15. World's Largest Six Pack
16. Viterbo University

Where to Eat and Drink

34. Bodega Brew Pub
40. Charmant Hotel
2. The Damn Tasty
27. Farmers Market
42. Freight House
35. Grounded Patio Café
23. Hmong's Golden Eggrolls
41. La Crosse Distilling Company

Downtown La Crosse Map (#14-#46)

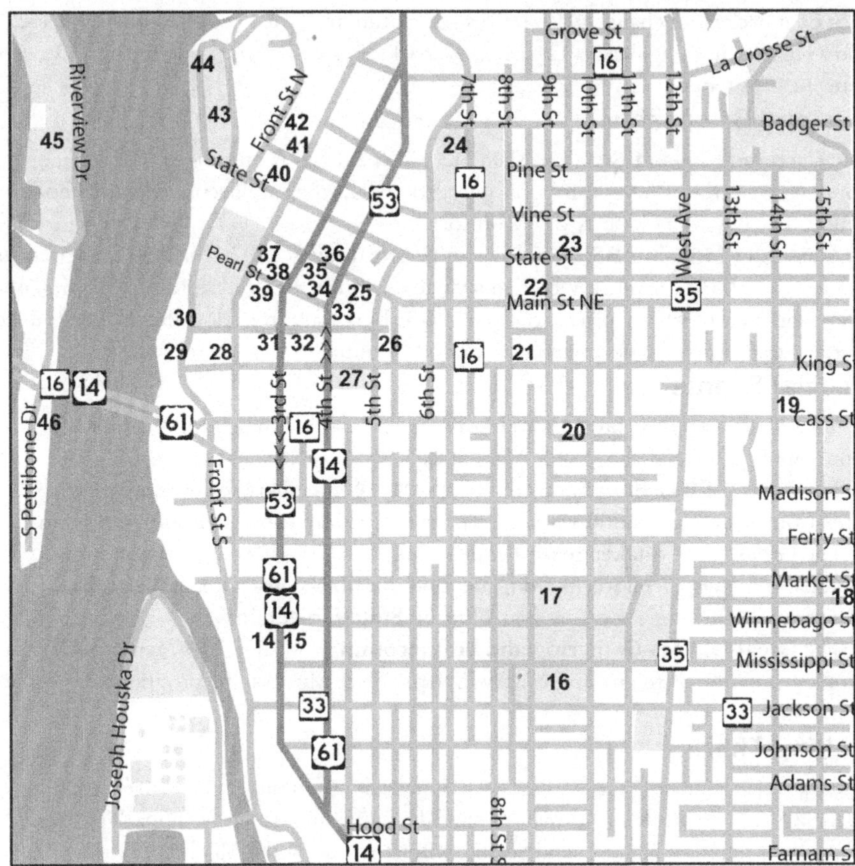

31. Lovechild
36. Meringue Bakery & Café
38. Pearl Ice Cream Parlor
5. Pearl Street Brewery
18. Ranison Ice Cream
39. Starlite Lounge
3. Sweet Shop
33. Taqueria Pato Azul
37. Turtle Stack Brewery downtown
30. Waterfront Restaurant and Tavern

Where to Stay

20. Bentley-Wheeler Bed and Breakfast
7. Bluff View House
21. Cargill-Pettibone House
19. Castle La Crosse Bed and Breakfast
40. Charmant Hotel
46. Pettibone Resort
13. Welch Motel

Other

4. Amtrak
32. Jefferson Lines/Downtown
9. Jefferson Lines/UW-L Student Union

Where to Stay: Camping

Prairie Island Campground (1120 Prairie Island Rd.; 507.452.4501) occupies a quiet spot on a backwater channel with large sites, mature trees that provide copious shade, and a small swimming beach. The offer over 100 sites with water and electric and a separate area for tents.

Bed and Breakfasts

The **Carriage House B&B** (420 Main St.; 507.452.8256) is literally an old carriage house converted to four comfortable guest rooms. Rooms are decorated with a nod to period style but are not stuffy or uncomfortable.

Alexander Mansion B&B (274 East 6th/Broadway St.; 507.474.4224) is a spectacular example of 19th-century Victorian style updated for the 21st century, with gorgeous woodwork and plenty of places to relax. It is a short walk from downtown. The four restored guest rooms are decorated with period furniture.

Special Events

Winona hosts a popular **farmers markets** on Saturday mornings and Wednesdays (2pm–5pm) at Levee Park (2nd & Main Sts.).

The **Frozen River Film Festival** (507.459.8090) in January features provocative films from around the world with an emphasis on cultural and environmental themes.

The **Great River Shakespeare Festival** (507.474.7900) livens up summers in Winona, running several weeks from late June to early August with shows at the DuFresne Performing Arts Center at **Winona State University**.

The **Great Dakota Gathering and Homecoming** (507.452.2278) reunites Dakota people from around the region, usually in September. Most of the programming is open to the public.

Getting There

The train station is near the Winona State University Campus (65 E. 11th/Mark St.; 507.452.8612). **Amtrak's** *Empire Builder* and *Borealis* trains stop in Winona. The *Empire Builder* runs between Chicago and Seattle, with stops along the Mississippi River at La Crosse, Winona, Red Wing, Saint Paul, and St. Cloud. The *Empire Builder* often runs late. Westbound *Empire Builder* trains (to Seattle) have a scheduled departure time of 8:40pm, while eastbound *Empire Builder* trains (to Chicago) have a scheduled departure time of 11:01am. *Borealis* trains connect Saint Paul and Chicago, with stops along the Mississippi at La Crosse, Winona, Red Wing, and Saint Paul. Northbound trains have a scheduled departure time of 4:36pm, while southbound trains have a scheduled departure time of 1:40pm. Fares are based on the number of available seats and therefore vary considerably; in general, the earlier you book, the cheaper the ticket will be.

Jefferson Lines (800.451.5333) operates regional bus service to Winona. Schedules and fares are so damn confusing and change so often, you are better off just calling them directly for the most current info. The cheapest rates are for 21-day advance purchase, especially for travel Su–Th. In Winona, the bus stops on the Winona State University campus at the transit shelter on Huff Street between 9th and 10th Streets. If you are buying tickets at the last minute, check fares for Amtrak, too.

HOMER

Built in the 1850s for Willard and Matilda Bunnell, the three-story "Steamboat" Gothic **Bunnell House** in Homer (36106 Old Homer Rd.; 507.454.2723) is the oldest home in

Winona County. The house has many period furnishings plus a few items owned by the Bunnell's, including the piano in the parlor.

Where to Stay: Camping

Pla-Mor Campground (22718 Little Smokies Ln.; 507.454.2851) has two groups of shaded campsites flanking the highway. The sites east of the highway are near the river with nice views of Trempealeau Mountain. They offer full hookups to basic sites for tents.

LA MOILLE

Wilson and Timothy Davis and George Grant opened the **Pickwick Mill** (26421 County Highway 7; 507.457.0499) in 1858 and did their job so well that it was a working mill until 1978. The mill is an impressive six stories tall and was built from limestone quarried nearby. The 20-foot overshot waterwheel produced the power that turned the millstones that could produce over a hundred barrels of flour every day at its peak.

DAKOTA

Great River Bluffs State Park (County Road 3; 507.643.6849) has seven miles of hiking trail in its 3,000 acres, many of which end at dramatic overlooks of the river valley. In winter, enjoy nine miles of trails for cross-country skiing or snowshoeing.

Where to Stay: Camping

Great River Bluffs State Park (507.643.6849) has 31 sites atop a bluff not far from La Crescent. Sites are nicely shaded, and the campground is usually quiet. The sites don't come with water or electric, but there's a shower house at the campground.

LA CRESCENT

Attractions

The **Apple Blossom Scenic Drive** (507.895.2800) is a lovely ten-mile route from La Cresent to Dakota that weaves across ridges and through coulees. Along the way, you pass by orchards, nice views, and retail stores selling produce in season. The most rewarding times of year to take this drive are in spring when the apple trees are blooming and late summer when apples are on sale. From La Crescent, follow Elm Street north to begin the route.

Eagles Bluff Park (McIntosh Rd. E.; 507.895.2595) is a protected natural area in the middle of La Crescent with nice views of the river valley. There's a hiking trail to the top that follows a gentle uphill slope for two-thirds of the hike, then gets steeper for the last leg. When you reach the top, go left and follow the ridge trail to get to a small goat prairie with a view. Allow at least an hour for the round trip. To reach the park, take Elm Street to McIntosh Road and turn east. After the stop sign you will see a sign for the West Bank Addition. Park on the street and walk up the hill.

La Crescent's history is on display at **History Center and Apple Museum** (328 S. 3rd St.; 507.895.1857; by appt.), which has fun items that include 19th century ice skates, photos from the city's history, and a shed full of items that tell the history of the local apple industry.

Explore Up the East Bank (Wisconsin)

LA CROSSE

Attractions

Grandad Park (3020 Grandad Bluff Rd.) has been a beloved local landmark nearly as long as the city has existed. In 1912, the city acquired 533 acres atop the bluff for a park. The views from the top reach into Minnesota and Iowa on a clear day. Follow Main Street east. It will become Bliss Road as it starts to switchback its way to the top where you'll find spectacular views of the river valley. Five miles of multi-use trails criss-cross through the park (the **Gateway Trail System**) offering sometimes challenging elevation changes and great views from the top. There are access points at the top and also at the base of the bluff along 29th Street and along Ebner Coulee Road.

Hixon Forest (2600 Quarry Rd.) offers 800 acres of hilly beauty with 13 miles of trails that wind up and through the forest and to several overlooks. In winter, some trails are groomed for cross-country skiing or snowshoeing. To reach the parking lot for the trails of lower Hixon, take Highway 16 north from the city. After La Crosse Street, go 0.3 miles to Bluff Pass and turn right, then turn right onto Milson Court and follow it to the lot.

In winter, take your skis or snowboard and fly down the hills at **Mount La Crosse** (N5549 Old Town Rd.; 608.788.0044).

Riverside Park (100 State St.) is a great public space, popular for hanging out and watching the sun set. It's also where you'll find many of the city's big festivals. Follow State Street until it ends at the Mississippi.

Directly across the Mississippi from Riverside Park, **Pettibone Park** (700 N. Pettibone Dr.) takes up part of Barron Island. The island was part of Minnesota when Alzono Barron sketched plans for Island City, a development that never happened. Lumber baron (and former mayor) AW Pettibone purchased the entire 200-acre island in 1901 and donated it to the city. In 1918, the US Congress approved a swap in which Minnesota gave Barron Island to Wisconsin in exchange for an island in Pierce County. Like its neighbor across the river, the park is a popular place to picnic and hang out.

Copeland Park (1130 Copeland Park Dr.) runs along the Black River. Check out the restored steam engine *Alice the Goon* at the northern end of the park.

It's not on the Mississippi, but **Myrick Park** (2000 La Crosse St.) is a peaceful city park that borders the La Crosse River marsh and has a few Native American burial mounds, including a rare turtle effigy.

The **La Crosse River State Trail** (608.269.4123) runs 22 miles from La Crosse to Sparta. To ride the trail, everyone over 16 years of age must purchase a pass, which you can buy at one of the kiosks at trail parking lots.

On the northwest part of French Island, quiet **Nelson Park** (608.789.7533) is a great place to picnic next to Lake Onalaska. Follow Lakeshore Drive north until it ends.

For a good overview of the history of the region, start at the **La Crosse Area Heritage Center** downtown (506 Main St.; 608.782.1980). Exhibits highlight the continuing influence of the Ho Chunk (Winnebago) people in the area, the city's brewing history, and fun exhibits about steamboats and the community's relationship with the Mississippi, plus a few artifacts recovered from the wreck of the steamer *War Eagle*.

Lumber baron Gideon Hixon built a palace for his family in 1859, which is now preserved as the **Hixon House Museum** (429 N. 7th St.; 608.782.1980). It is one of the oldest residences in the area. The Italianate mansion has been beautifully restored. The house is loaded with exquisite woodwork and decorated with a quirky Turkish sitting room. Remarkably, the house has retained most of its original furnishings.

The **Mississippi Valley Archaeology Center** (1725 State St.; 608.785.8463), housed in a small brick building near the Cartwright Center on the campus of the University of Wisconsin-La Crosse, features exhibits that showcase the cultural history of native populations, including musical instruments and art.

The **Children's Museum of La Crosse** (207 5th Ave. South; 608.784.2652) offers a playful and educational experience for children up to age 12. Let your kids simulate controlling the flow of the Mississippi River or build a bridge. Hands-on exhibits include a model of a fire truck for the future firefighter in the family.

The **Pump House Regional Arts Center** (119 King St.; 608.785.1434) hosts rotating exhibits highlighting regional art with an occasional national show. They also host some live shows in a second-floor theater.

For live theater, check out the schedule at the **La Crosse Community Theater** (428 Front St.; 608.784.9292). They perform each year from September to June. And, don't forget to check the schedules for **college productions** at Viterbo University (Fine Arts Center; 608.796.3100) and UW-La Crosse (Toland Theater; 608.785.8522).

Architecture

Christ Episcopal Church (831 Main St.; 608.784.0697) is one of the oldest faith communities in the area, with a history dating back to the 1850s. The current Richardsonian Romanesque building was completed in 1898 when the congregation hoped it would become the cathedral for the region's Episcopal population. It didn't, but locals still got a wonderful church. The spacious interior is notable for two particular art glass windows. On the south side, the luminous window called *Transfiguration of Christ* was created by the Louis Tiffany Company. On the opposite side of the transept, *The Beatitudes* was created by the Charles Connick Studio of Boston and installed in 1933. It is one of the few church windows known to commemorate those famous verses from the Bible.

Maria Angelorum Chapel at St. Rose Convent is a beauty (912 Market St.; 608.784.2288). The rich Romanesque chapel, completed in 1906, has an Italian marble altar, pillars of onyx, dozens of Bavarian art glass windows, and mosaics that incorporate mother-of-pearl and Venetian glass. The complex is the motherhouse for the Sisters of Perpetual Adoration. Call ahead to reserve a spot on a tour.

The **Shrine of Our Lady of Guadalupe** (5250 Justin Rd.; 608.782.5440) has attracted a large following since the first building opened in 2002. The 100-acre site has a visitor center, votive candle chapel, outdoor Stations of the Cross, and a striking Romanesque church that looks like it was transplanted from the European countryside.

In a city that loves to drink that is located in a state known for its beer, it's only fitting that one would find the **World's Largest Six Pack** (1111 S. 3rd St.). These giant storage containers hold 688,200 gallons of beer—enough beer for one person to have a six-pack a day for 3,351 years. Walk across Third Street to check out the statue of the legendary (and possibly mythical) Flemish **King Gambrinus**, the patron saint and purported inventor of hopped malt beer.

Getting on the River

The **La Crosse Queen** (608.784.8523) is a replica of a 19th-century paddlewheeler that cruises from Riverside Park. It offers a variety of cruising options: a 90-minute sightseeing cruise (from Memorial Day–Oct.), weekend dinner cruises, and Sunday brunch.

Drinking and Dining

Get your coffee drink of choice at **Grounded Patio Café** downtown (308 Main St.; 608.784.5282) and enjoy it on the lovely patio.

On the north side, indulge at **The Damn Tasty** (1217 Caledonia St.; 608.519.1882) for inspired breakfast and lunch dishes, elegant pastries, or a coffee drink to go. They have options regardless of your dietary needs.

Stop at **Meringue Bakery & Café** (313 Main St.; 608.519.2683) where you can get a delicious eclair or a slice of raspberry chocolate mousse cake from chef Jen Barney—a two-time winner of baking competitions on the Food Network—and pair it with café au lait or caramel hot chocolate.

The **Starlite Lounge** (222 Pearl St.; 608.796.0905) features a 1950s futuristic vibe and is the hip place for martini lovers. Look for live jazz a couple of times a week.

The **Bodega Brew Pub** (122 S. 4th St.; 608.782.0677), located in a storefront that has had a café since 1875, is a must stop if you love good beer. They offer over a dozen on tap and 400+ in bottles.

Pearl Street Brewery (1401 St. Andrew St.; 608.784.4832) is based in the former La Crosse Footwear building. Visit the tasting room and enjoy beer right from the source.

For another take on local craft beer, check out the cozy **Turtle Stack Brewery** downtown (125 2nd St.; 608.519.2284), which can have as many as nine beers on tap.

Housed in a modern space with an industrial feel, the **La Crosse Distilling Company** (129 Vine St.; 608.881.8800) prepares delicious cocktails using their own spirits and also serves tasty, seasonal foods that range from snacks to filling entrées.

Hmong's Golden Eggrolls (901 State St.; 608.782.0096) offers a taste of southeast Asia, with steaming bowls of pho, curries, and the delicious namesake eggrolls.

Taqueria Pato Azul (127 4th St. S; 608.519.3036) showcases a creative take on Mexican cuisine, tacos, especially. This isn't the standard Mexican-American fare. The food, fresh and rich, goes in new directions, like duck carnitas. Expect a wait on weekends.

AUTHOR'S PICK: **Lovechild** (300 3rd St. S; 608.433.2234) is a breath of fresh air in the fine dining scene. The interior blends a retro-modern sensibility between exposed brick walls in an old storefront, while the menu features creative dishes built from seasonal ingredients. It's a great place to relax and feel spoiled.

The **Freight House** (107 Vine St.; 608.784.6211) is a popular choice for top-quality steaks and seafood in a historic 1880-era railroad warehouse that can get a bit loud.

The **Waterfront Restaurant and Tavern** (328 Front St. South; 608.782.5400) offers a tasty menu of sophisticated entrées that change with the seasons, all without pretension. Nab a seat on the patio when it's open.

The **Charmant Hotel** downtown (101 State St.; 608.519.8800) offers several options to please your palate. The rooftop lounge serves cocktails and snacks. The restaurant serves dishes inspired by rustic French cuisine. The Parlour is a great place to enjoy a cappuccino and croissant in the morning or a glass of wine in the evening.

La Crosse also has three good options to satisfy your craving for sweet frozen treats. **Pearl Ice Cream Parlor** (207 Pearl St.; 608.782.6655) is an old-fashioned soda fountain. They make their own ice cream, which you can enjoy as a double scoop in a house-made waffle cone, a root beer float, or a banana split. The line often extends onto the sidewalk in summer. They also run a chocolate shop next door.

For a shorter wait, check out **Ranison Ice Cream** (706 16th St. S.; 608.782.1987), a charming neighborhood shop with deep roots in the area that makes it own ice cream.

On the north side of the city, the **Sweet Shop** (1113 Caledonia St.; 608.784.7724) is another old-fashioned ice cream parlor. They have been producing their own ice cream for over a century (since 1921), and they also make tasty chocolates from scratch and old-fashioned sodas with fizzy water.

Where to Stay

La Crosse has a full range of lodging options, but rooms can fill up quickly if there's a special event. If you're planning on visiting for Octoberfest, you should book a room months in advance. The places below stand out.

Camping

Goose Island County Park (W6488 County Road GI; 608.788.7018) packs campers in tightly at its 400 sites. Don't expect spacious, private sites, but the area is beautiful and many sites are next to the river.

Pettibone Resort (333 Park Plaza Dr.; 608.782.5858) is another large campground, this one in the floodplain along the backwaters. Sites (water and electric to basic tent sites) have plenty of shade but not much space.

Bed and Breakfasts

The **Wilson Schoolhouse Inn** (W5718 Highway 14-61; 608.787.1982) is gorgeous and comfortable, with a spacious living room bathed in generous amounts of natural light. The inn has two bedrooms, two baths, a modern kitchen, and room for eight guests.

The restored and updated **Cargill-Pettibone House** (145 8th St. S; 608.519.3101) rents four beautiful suites in a historic Italianate mansion near downtown. They offer four rooms, all with bathrooms en suite, and there's plenty of space to spread out.

A beauty of a Victorian mansion, **Bentley-Wheeler Bed and Breakfast** (950 Cass; 608.784.9360) rents three suites and an old guest house. Each unit is equipped with luxury details, such as high thread count sheets and LCD televisions. The rate includes a continental breakfast.

For a taste of life like royalty, spend a night or two at **Castle La Crosse Bed and Breakfast** (1419 Cass St.; 844.726.5808), a monumental mansion that dates to 1891. The four guest rooms are loaded with luxury touches, including fine linens, marble countertops, en suite bathrooms, and a full breakfast.

Lodging

The **Welch Motel** (3643 Mormon Coulee Rd.; 608.788.1300) is a good budget option. The place has a 1950s vibe, especially on the exterior, with 16 small, tidy rooms.

You won't find a more unique place to stay than the **Bluff View House** (751 22nd St. N.; 608.317.4311). Built in 1949, this is one of only 2,499 Lustron pre-fab all-metal houses built in the US and one of about 1,600 left. The two-bedroom house has a full bath, full kitchen, washer and dryer, and garage.

For a taste of the high life, spend a night or two at the **Charmant Hotel** (101 State St.; 608.519.8800). Once a candy factory, the building has been transformed into an impressive luxury hotel that doesn't skimp on the details.

Special Events

La Crosse hosts a popular **farmers market** on Friday evenings and Saturday mornings at Cameron Park (400 King St.).

La Crosse's major summer festival is **Riverfest** (608.782.6000), which happens the week of July 4th at Riverside Park. Join the crowds for food, music, and fireworks.

The granddaddy of regional festivals is **Oktoberfest** (608.784.3378), and it is one helluva party, spanning two weekends and attracting tens of thousands of visitors. Expect to find a lot of happy people, and occasionally a few that are too happy, but don't let that stop you from enjoying the pomp, parades, and bratwurst. If you are planning to visit La Crosse either weekend, book your room well in advance, or you'll be driving an hour from town to find a place to stay.

In October, head to Veteran's Park (Highway 16 near West Salem) for the **Hmong New Year's Celebration** (608.781.5744). You can sample food that is hard to find in the region and take part in events that celebrate Hmong culture (entry fee per car).

Getting There

The train station is on the north side under the Rose Street viaduct (601 Caledonia; 800.872.7245). **Amtrak's** *Empire Builder* and *Borealis* trains stop in La Crosse. The Empire Builder runs between Chicago and Seattle, with stops along the Mississippi River at La Crosse, Winona, Red Wing, Saint Paul, and St. Cloud. The *Empire Builder* often runs late. Westbound *Empire Builder* trains (to Seattle) have a scheduled departure time of 8:04pm, while eastbound *Empire Builder* trains (to Chicago) have a scheduled departure time of 11:37am. *Borealis* trains connect Saint Paul and Chicago, with stops along the Mississippi at La Crosse, Winona, Red Wing, and Saint Paul. Northbound trains have a scheduled departure time of 3:58pm, while southbound trains have a scheduled departure time of 2:16pm. Fares are based on the number of available seats and therefore vary considerably; in general, the earlier you book, the cheaper the ticket will be.

La Crosse Regional Airport is north of downtown on French Island (2850 Airport Rd.; 608.789.7464) and is served by American Airlines.

Jefferson Lines (800.451.5333) operates regional bus service to La Crosse. Schedules and fares are so damn confusing and change so often, you are better off just calling them directly for the most current info. What I can tell you is that the cheapest rates are for 21-day advance purchase, especially for travel Su–Th. In La Crosse, the bus stops downtown (314 Jay St.) and at UW-La Crosse (Student Union, 521 East Ave. N.).

ONALASKA/BRICE PRAIRIE

Attractions

The **Great River State Trail** runs 24 miles from Onalaska to Trempealeau, mostly on a hard surface, and is great for bicycling and walking. The trailhead is at **Great River Landing** on the west side of Highway 35 at Main Street. The Great River Trail connects to the **La Crosse River State Trail**, which runs 22 miles from La Crosse to Sparta. For both trails, you must purchase a trail pass if you are over 16 years old; buy one at a kiosk at one of the parking lots.

The **Onalaska Area Historical Museum** (741 Oak Ave. S.; 608.781.9568) occupies a room at the Onalaska Public Library. Exhibits display Native American artifacts, stories about the lumber history, local schools, plus an occasional rotating exhibit.

Stop by the **Upper Mississippi River National Fish & Wildlife Refuge Visitor Center** in Brice Prairie (N5727 County Rd Z; 608.779.2399), where you can stroll through several acres of restored prairies that are brilliant in spring and summer with blooming plants.

Drinking and Dining

Nutbush City Limits Bar & Grill (3264 George St.; 608.783.0228) is about as local as it gets. Breakfast is their best meal, with plenty of affordable, hearty options.

The **Red Pines Bar & Grill** (W7305 County Road Z; 608.779.2800) sits along the backwaters of the river in Brice Prairie, just west of Onalaska. Dine on the patio and enjoy walleye cheeks (chunks of deep-fried walleye), stringer of sunfish or catfish, or pizza. On the lighter side, get a sandwich and pair it with chips made on-site.

Where to Stay: Bed and Breakfasts

Rainbow Ridge Farms (N5732 Hauser Rd.; 608.783.8181), a small farm near Onalaska, does double duty as a B&B. Guests are welcome to help with chores such as feeding goats, sheep, llamas, ducks, and chickens, or not. Each of the four guest rooms has its own bathroom and overlooks a pond. Located in a quiet setting deep in a coulee, you are just a 20-minute drive to restaurants and entertainment in La Crosse. Guests are served a full breakfast on weekends, expanded continental during the week.

HOLMEN

Attractions

Holland Sand Prairie (McHugh Rd.; 608.784.3606) preserves 61 acres of native sand prairie and natural dunes west of Holmen, which are home to some rare plants.

Van Loon Wildlife Area (608.266.2621) occupies a serene and mystical 4,000 acres along the marshy Black River floodplain. The area is known for six rare bowstring arch truss bridges built between 1905 and 1908, but the peaceful preserve also offers good birding and easy hiking. It's a beautiful place to hike in the fall. From Highway 35, head north on Amsterdam Prairie Road for 1.6 miles to the parking lot on the left.

Drinking and Dining

The **Holmen Locker and Meat Market** (412 N. Main St.; 608.526.3112) is a traditional butcher shop fused with a boutique grocer: fresh and smoked meats, plus local artisan food items including jams, flour, and Wisconsin cheese. They also have a good selection of regional beer and wine, and enticing scents of smoked foods.

TREMPEALEAU

Attractions

Perrot State Park (W26247 Sullivan Rd.; 608.534.6409) is another jewel along the Mississippi River. The park has good hiking, scenic vistas, camping, and a canoe route through the backwaters. The dramatic vistas are best enjoyed from Brady's Bluff. The East Brady's Bluff trail is a relatively easy hike with switchbacks and a gradual ascent until you reach the top, while the West Brady's Bluff trail is more vertical and harder work.

The **Centerville Curling Club** (W24854 Highway-54; 608.539.3651) has been active since 1947. Visitors are welcome to drop by and watch the action, especially on winter weekends when bonspiels (tournaments) fill the ice. Most events are free.

Trempealeau National Wildlife Refuge (W28488 Refuge Rd.; 608.539.2311) offers 6,220 acres of splendid isolation north of Trempealeau. The refuge has a varied topography from sand prairies to bottomland forest with wildlife to match. Wildlife is more active around dawn or dusk. The refuge has a visitor center (open M–F), an observation deck overlooking the backwaters, a 4 1/2 mile auto route, and flat hiking trails.

Drinking and Dining

Get your coffee fix at **Driftless Bike 'N Bean** (11369 Main St.; 608.534.5500) and a snack or sandwich to fuel the rest of your day. You can also rent a bike or get some work done on the one you brought along.

Sample wines at **Elmaro Vineyard** (N14756 Delaney Rd.; 608.534.6456) or enjoy a glass outside on nights they host live music.

Stop for a meal at the historic **Trempealeau Hotel** (11332 Main St.; 608.534.6898), which opened in 1871 and managed to survive the big fire in 1888. Good thing, otherwise you might never have had the chance to try a Walnut Burger. If that's not your thing, it has plenty of other options like catfish and bluegill fillet sandwiches for lunch or dinner entrées of grilled meats, pasta, and fish.

At **Sullivan's Supper Club** (W25709 Sullivan Rd.; 608.534.7775) you can enjoy an Irish Handshake (tenderloin tips and scallops), the Dublin Delight (shrimp and barbecue pork ribs), or a number of other Irish-named combo entrées. Or you can just select a standard steak or seafood entrée and enjoy good food with a great view, especially from the riverside patio.

Just northwest of Trempealeau, fresh produce abounds. Five generations have tended **Ecker's Apple Farm** (W27062 Highway 35; 608.539.2652; open Aug–Dec.). They grow about a dozen varieties of apples, and sell homemade apple pie, to boot. Stick around for a beverage in their beer garden. **The Berry Patch** (N16414 Kriesel Lane) is a great place for fresh, seasonal fruits and vegetables, including some that you can pick yourself: strawberries, blueberries, snozberries, tomatoes. **Sacia's Orchards** (N16545 Kriesel Lane; 608.582.2511) sells strawberries and asparagus in spring, plus apples in the fall.

Where to Stay: Camping

Perrot State Park (W26247 Sullivan Rd.; 608.534.6409) has 102 sites (38 with electric) near Trempealeau. If you want some privacy when you camp, sites 87–95 (electricity available only at sites 94 and 95) are more remote than the rest and heavily shaded. There are a handful of sites on the water (there's an extra charge for the water view).

Where to Stay: Lodging

The **Trempealeau Hotel** (11332 Main St.; 608.534.6898) rents eight simple rooms above the bar in the space that was the original hotel. The rooms share a bath and a common sitting area. The hotel also rents four motel-style units in a building near the lock and dam (the Kingfishers) that have good river views, especially from the decks. They also rent three beautiful suites around town.

The **Little Bluff Inn** (11451 Main St.; 608.534.6615) rents 16 rooms in many configurations, including six kitchenettes and a large suite.

Special Events

Trempealeau Catfish Days (608.534.6780) is a weekend party that includes bicycle tours, a motorcycle run, and a fishing tournament. Yes, it also includes catfish cooked in many forms—just not on a stick. Try a burger made from locally caught catfish and stick around on Sunday for the parade and fireworks.

COCHRANE AND BUFFALO CITY

Attractions

Prairie Moon Museum & Sculpture Garden (S2921 County Road G; 608.685.6290) lands on many lists for quirky attractions, and it's on mine, too. When farmer Herman Rusche retired in 1952, he needed something to do, so the self-taught artist began creating sculptures out of stone and concrete. In 1979, at age 94, he retired again and auctioned his pieces so he could spend more time fishing. He died in 1985, just a few days after his 100th birthday. Interest in his work grew, and in 1992, the Kohler Foundation bought and restored the site. They brought back most of the original pieces and created a sculpture garden, then donated it all to Milton township. Since that time, the collection has grown with the addition of pieces from John Mehringer's Fountain City Rock Garden that he created in the 1930s. The grounds are open all year.

Whitman Dam Wildlife Area (608.685.6222) is a diverse backwaters area popular with birders, especially the easy two-mile walk along the dike. Follow the signs to Buffalo City. When County OO makes a sharp turn at the south end of town, continue on South River Road for 1.2 miles to the parking lot for the Upper Spring Lake Landing. Park and walk toward the river, where you'll see a path along the dike.

Drinking and Dining

If you'd detour for locally sourced and produced food, or if you just love a good pizza, head to **Suncrest Gardens** (S2257 Yaeger Valley Rd.; 608.626.2122). This small farm transforms into a boutique pizza joint on weekends from May to October (F 4-8, Sa 3-8), putting together pizzas made with ingredients grown on their farm. All pizzas are 16 inches and cooked quickly at high temperatures in a wood-fired oven. They supply the pizza, some sides and drinks, but it's a good idea to bring utensils, drinks, and something to sit on, then relax and savor your pizza in a scenic coulee. To get there from Cochrane, take County Highway O east to State Highway 88, go left, and follow it to Yaeger Valley Road. Go left and then left again at the Y, and you're there.

FOUNTAIN CITY

Attractions

The **Fountain City Historical Museum** (7 Main St.; 608.687.8730) maintains an interesting collection of displays on steamboats and Fountain Brewery memorabilia, but the most impressive section is the wall-sized display of 1,700 Native American arrowheads, ax heads, spear points, and other artifacts collected by Roscoe Stoll, who kept this display at his hardware store until he retired.

For some peace and quiet, head up the bluffs above Fountain City to **Kinstone** (S3439 Cole Bluff Lane; 608.687.3332), a unique collection of stone sculptures reminiscent of Stonehenge in some spots and a meditation center in others. The 30-acre site sits on restored prairie with good views of the Mississippi. Visitors are encouraged to enjoy the scenery and serenity and to respect the sanctity of the land.

Drinking and Dining

Seven Hawks Vineyards (17 North St.; 866.946.3741) makes a variety of wines of good quality at reasonable prices. You can sample before you buy.

If you like Irish pubs (if you don't, don't talk to me), you'll love the **Monarch Public House** (19 N. Main St.; 608.687.4231). Housed in an 1894 building that has been a tavern in Fountain City from the start, the pub still has many original furnishings, including the impressive bar. They also serve beers from the once-defunct Fountain City Brewing Company that were brought back from the archives in 1997. The menu includes Irish stew, Galway pot pie, and many other dishes inspired by the Emerald Isle.

Where to Stay: Camping

Merrick State Park (S2965 State Highway 35; 608.687.4936) offers three different camping areas north of Fountain City. The sites at the north campground are shaded and close to the shower house but packed in tightly. The island sites are primitive walk-in sites that are more private and on the water. The south campground sites are all primitive and a bit of a hike from the shower house but not as crowded and many are close to the water (sites 51 and 52 are walk-in sites on the water and have no neighbors).

Where to Stay: Lodging

The **Fountain City Motel** (810 S. Main St.; 608. 687.3111) is a bargain, with 13 moderately-sized rooms in good shape. All rooms have cable TV, fridge, microwave, and coffee. Some rooms are decorated with a theme, like the Harley room.

Great River Road Inns (340 S. Main St.; 608.468.1021) offers a relaxing and affordable stay in a small rivertown. The historic home has been updated and the three suites are modern and comfortable. Each room has a private bath but they are not all en suite.

The folks at **Seven Hawks** (320 Hill St.; 651.293.0803) have an eye for dramatic locations and a gift for designing comfort. They rent two one-bedroom suites (Hawks View Suites), five cottages that remind me of treehouses without the ladders (Hawks View Lodges), and two large lodges (Osprey and Blackhawk), in case you're traveling with a brigade. Expect great views, well-tended rooms, and a call to sprawl and relax.

ALMA

Attractions

Buena Vista Park (Buena Vista Rd.; 608.685.3330) offers one of the most dramatic overlooks along upper Mississippi. From a vantage point some 540 feet above the river, you can see Lock and Dam 4 and the Whitman Bottoms. You can drive to the top via County Highway E and Buena Vista Road, or, alternatively, you can hike to the top. Start at the trailhead at 2nd and Elm.

The **Alma Area Museum** (505 S. 2nd St.; 608.685.6290) is housed in a former schoolhouse, and they use the space well. The second floor has fun, historic photos (including some by local son Gerhard Gesell), an informative display about logging tools and logging camps, and a touching display about the tragic 1940 Armistice Day blizzard.

The **Castlerock Museum** (402 S. 2nd St.; 608.685.4231) is a unique, if somewhat out-of-place, wonder. The museum is the brainchild of Gary Schlosstein, who began his life as a collector at age 10 when he bought a Civil War-era musket and has not stopped since. He and his partners do a phenomenal job of describing the evolution of arms and armor from the Roman Empire to the cusp of the gun powder era. The museum has a number of impressive pieces, like the 16th century German Maximillian-era armor—rare for being a complete set. I especially like the way the museum uses art to illustrate how the pieces were worn.

The **overlook** at Lock & Dam #4 is a fun place to watch boats coming and going.

Wings Over Alma (110 N. Main St.; 608.685.3303) displays the work of local and regional artists.

Check the schedule at the **Big River Theatre** (121 S. Main St.; 608.685.4002) and catch a live show in the historic venue.

Normally, I wouldn't include a church that is only 50 years old, but one of the windows at **St. Lawrence Catholic Church** (206 S. 2nd St.; 608.685.3898) is worth checking out: Christ of the Mississippi. Designed by the priest at that time, Father Thomas Ash, an avid fisherman, the window depicts Jesus with a fishing pole standing in a boat on the Mississippi with Lock and Dam 4 in the background.

Drinking and Dining

Get your caffeine (or ice cream) fix in Alma at **Fire and Ice** (305 N. Main St.; 612.423.3653), then take it out back to enjoy it in the beautiful garden.

At **Danzinger Vineyards & Winery** (S2106 Grapeview Rd.; 608.685.6000) you can sample locally produces wines at a scenic blufftop location.

Where to Stay: Camping

Riecks Lake Park (608.685.3330), two miles north of Alma, has 20 sites with electricity, shared water, and coin-op showers on a narrow strip of shaded land between Highway 35 and a backwaters lake.

Where to Stay: Bed and Breakfasts

Tritsch House Bed and Breakfast (601 S. 2nd St.; 507.450.6573) is a 1902 Queen Anne mansion beautifully redone. The five guest rooms have private baths, four with Jacuzzi tubs, and flat screen TVs that are hooked up with cable TV. You can pass the time sitting on the deck or screened porch or playing pool in the billiard room.

Where to Stay: Lodging

Hotel de Ville (305 N. Main St.; 612.423.3653) offers a variety of lodging options in tastefully rehabbed historic buildings. All units have pillow-top mattresses and French-inspired décor. The suites and cottage all have a private bath and full kitchen or kitchenette. The two-bedroom Garden Suite is above the art shop, while the two-bedroom Falcon Cottage is next door. The Swan and Eagle suites are across the street and along the riverfront. Take time to enjoy the lush gardens around the hotel.

For More Information

There are practical limits to how much I can include in a book, but not with a website! Check out the city profiles on my website for information I couldn't fit in this book.

MINNESOTA RIVER TOWNS

Kellogg: MississippiValleyTraveler.com/Kellogg
Minneiska: MississippiValleyTraveler.com/Minneiska
Minnesota City: MississippiValleyTraveler.com/Minnesota-City
Winona: MississippiValleyTraveler.com/Winona
Homer: MississippiValleyTraveler.com/Homer
La Moille: MississippiValleyTraveler.com/La-Moille
Dakota: MississippiValleyTraveler.com/Dakota
La Crescent: MississippiValleyTraveler.com/La-Crescent

WISCONSIN RIVER TOWNS

La Crosse: MississippiValleyTraveler.com/La-Crosse
Onalaska: MississippiValleyTraveler.com/Onalaska
Holmen: MississippiValleyTraveler.com/Holmen
Trempealeau: MississippiValleyTraveler.com/Trempealeau
Fountain City: MississippiValleyTraveler.com/Fountain-City
Cochrane: MississippiValleyTraveler.com/Cochrane
Buffalo City: MississippiValleyTraveler.com/Buffalo-City
Alma: MississippiValleyTraveler.com/Alma

LANSING TO GUTTENBERG

McGregor, Iowa

Overview

This route passes through some old river communities, places with ancient roots and deep ties to the Mississippi River. Prairie du Chien is the second oldest community in Wisconsin. Euro-Americans lived in the area long before there was a United States of America, and Native Americans long before that. The river gives life and meaning to the towns on this route. Spend a weekend getting to know the people and their communities and you too may feel the Mississippi River flowing in your veins.

History: Wisconsin Communities

PRAIRIE DU CHIEN

A wide prairie stretches north from the confluence of the Wisconsin and Mississippi Rivers. The prairie was an important trading area before Europeans arrived and that tradition continued when it anchored the western end of the Fox-Wisconsin waterway, a key transportation route for fur traders, voyageurs, and missionaries that connected Montreal and the Great Lakes to the Mississippi River. Each spring and fall, Native Americans and traders assembled (rendezvoused) to conduct business.

A community grew in the prairie called La Prairies les Chiens. When Jonathan Carver passed through in 1766, he found a thriving village of:

"...about three hundred families; the houses are well built after the Indian manner, and pleasantly situated on a very rich soil, from which they raise every necessary of life in great abundance."

The town's name apparently dates to the 1730s when fur traders encountered a Meskwaki (Fox) Indian camp on the prairie. The Chief's name was Alim, which meant dog, so the French traders translated the word into its French counterpart: *chien.*

After France ceded its North American lands in 1763, Britain gained considerable influence, which persisted even after the British lost the Revolutionary War. Prairie du Chien was far from the minds of the new American government. Zebulon Pike passed through the area in 1805, but no other American military forces reached the village until the War of 1812. British traders continued to dominate commerce along the upper Mississippi. When George Washington was sworn in as the first President of the United States in 1789, not a single American trader conducted business at Prairie du Chien.

British control of the fur trade finally ended when the Americans won the War of 1812, although some British traders remained active for years. John Jacob Astor moved in and took control of the fur trade through his company, the American Fur Company. He built a monopoly that lasted until his retirement in 1834, and the fur trade remained lucrative until nearly 1850.

General Thomas Smith supervised construction of the first Fort Crawford in 1816. Two years later, Crawford County was established as part of Michigan Territory with Prairie du Chien as the county seat.

In August 1825, the US government convened a large council of Native Americans at Prairie du Chien to demarcate land boundaries for each nation, although the US would later move to negotiate (or just take) land within these newly defined boundaries. Among the leaders who attended were Wabasha, Red Wing, and Little Crow (all Dakota), Keokuk (Sauk), and Decorah (Ho-Chunk). Black Hawk, an influential Sauk leader, did not attend, though.

Lieutenant Colonel Zachary Taylor (a future US President) arrived in 1829 to command Fort Crawford. He supervised early construction of a new stone fort that was located on the mainland safely out of the Mississippi River's reach. Taylor left Fort Crawford in 1830 but returned in 1832 (the same year a cholera epidemic killed a hundred soldiers) to command troops during the Black Hawk War. The fort declined in importance after that, and the last US soldiers left on June 9, 1856.

As the fur trade waned, Prairie du Chien became an important port for shipping wheat and lumber and attracted new residents. The Milwaukee and Mississippi Railroad arrived in 1857 (the first rail line across Wisconsin). Irish immigrants moved to town with the railroad, followed by waves of Bohemians (Czechs) and Germans. The old French families turned to farming, mostly in the northern part of town. River shipping declined after the Civil War, but the local economy chugged ahead thanks to railroads and pearl button manufacturing, cigar factories, and woolen mills.

A fire in 1873 shifted the business district to its current location along Blackhawk Avenue. After the big flood of 1965 and several smaller ones in subsequent years, the Army Corps of Engineers used Prairie du Chien as a test case for its first flood protection program that did not involve building taller levees. The Corps purchased property in flood-prone areas and moved residents to higher ground. Between 1978 and 1984, 121 properties were purchased and residents relocated. Some people took their homes with them. In one case, an entire block of six houses was moved.

LYNXVILLE

Brothers John and James Haney set up shop here in 1848, building a trading post and a log cabin, thus giving the future town of Lynxville its first name: Haney's Landing. When the village was laid out in 1857, the surveyors chose the name Lynxville, because they had just arrived on a steamboat that was called the *Lynx*.

For most of its existence, Lynxville's economy was heavily dependent upon the Mississippi River. The town had a good harbor at a spot in the river called Devil's Elbow, so big boats traveling between St. Louis and Saint Paul made regular stops. Commercial fishing was the main industry for many years, with huge yields of fish shipped to places as far as New York City. In December 1873, the Johnson brothers harvested 80,000 pounds of fish in a single day by drawing a seine under the frozen Mississippi River.

One of the largest log rafts ever assembled on the Mississippi took shape at Lynxville in 1896. The raft was 270 feet wide and 1550 feet long. It contained more than two million board feet of lumber—enough to build nearly 700 three-bedroom ranch houses. In the winter, Lynxville residents harvested ice from the river. It was stored in sawdust and sold in summer. When Lynxville was incorporated in 1889, it counted 313 residents. The railroad reached town in 1895 and folks did a nice business shipping wheat, livestock, and apples to regional and national markets.

FERRYVILLE

Ferryville began when Misters Sanborn and Stillwell arrived and built a race track to train their horses. The village was first known as Humble Bush, a name with real character, if you ask me. The town became known as Ferryville when ferry service was established to Lansing, Iowa. Ferryville became an important shipping point for wheat when Charles Huffschmidt built a large warehouse. A tornado in 1873 destroyed the warehouse and much of the town. It took nearly a decade for Ferryville to recover. The arrival of the railroad in 1886 provided the usual economic boost, with Ferryville becoming a popular spot for railroad workers to pass the time.

Many early Euro-American settlers were from Pennsylvania and New England, but a large number of Norwegians put down roots in the area, too. In 1939, Prince Olaf, the future King of Norway, made an appearance at the depot as his train passed through town, making the resident Norwegians very happy.

It snowed on June 2, 1929. Just thought you might like to know that. Here's a fun news item from November 29, 1932:

> "Last Sunday, John Nicholson and his fiancée, Ms. Mildred Seymour and C.C. Howard went hunting rabbits, just around the bend out of town. Howard sighted a rabbit near a brush pile, and both men got out to shoot. Nicholson bidding the young lady to stay by the car. Howard shot at the rabbit first and Nicholson on the other side of the brush pile also shot, neither one hitting the rabbit, but to Nicholson's surprise he heard a cry from Miss Seymour who had followed along and was standing opposite him on the other side of the brush pile. The charge from his gun hit the frozen ground and rebounding, two shots hit her in the ankle. She was taken at once to the local doctor, who inoculated her for tetanus and the shot still remains in her limb without troubling her."

DE SOTO

Two French traders named Godfrey were among the first Europeans in the area. They worked for the Astor Fur Trading Company and farmed and trapped before moving to Prairie du Chien. The village was initially known as Winneshiek's Landing in honor of the Ho Chunk chief who made regular visits to trade with the French. Chief Winneshiek died in 1848 at Lansing and was reportedly buried atop the bluff just north of town that is named after him.

Moses Strong laid out the village in 1854 and renamed for Hernando de Soto, the man who led the Spanish invasion of the American Southeast and who, in 1541, was among the first Europeans to see the Mississippi River. The town's proprietors included several doctors who originally sought to create a village that would be composed only of people who shared their New England roots. The bustling sawmills in the mid-1850s, however, needed laborers more quickly than you can say chowdah, so they had to settle for a more varied group. Most of the new arrivals were Norwegians and Germans.

Unlike some of its neighbors to the south, De Soto lacked a good spot for a steamboat landing. Using that famous frontier ingenuity, in 1867, a few dozen men from town used the cover of night to construct a wing dam, which was technically in violation of federal law. The dam, off Woodbury's Island, was meant to divert the flow of the river so it would dig a deeper channel near the village. It worked. Four grain elevators were soon built and De Soto became an important shipping point for grain, at least until the railroad reached nearby Viroqua and grain shipping shifted there. Shoemaking propelled the town into the national limelight when, in 1884, local cobbler Patrick De Lap was proclaimed the oldest shoemaker in America.

The De Soto Evangelical Lutheran Church was organized in 1896 by 13 residents, five of whom were named Ole. Four years later, they built a small Gothic Revival frame church atop Powers Hill on land donated by Ole Nasseth. When the basement was added in 1933, the church became a hot spot for lutefisk suppers. Services, conducted only in Norwegian until 1918, were held once a month on a Monday because of the difficulty of securing a pastor. When the Mississippi River bridge washed out in 1946, the pastor, who was serving congregations in Lansing, Ferryville, and De Soto had to cross the river in a boat—a rowboat, to be precise—which he did for a while before the constant back-and-forth wore him out. The church was wired with electricity in 1948 but never got running water. The congregation built a new church in 1966 and sold the old church to a local farmer.

History: Iowa Communities

LANSING

Euro-American settlers moved into the area in 1848, just as the Ho Chunk were forced out. Among the first residents was William Garrison, who hailed from Lansing, Michigan. He did not stick around, but his name for the town did. The following year, Galena transplants John Haney and his son, James, arrived, followed in short order by HH Houghton. They built a few mills in Lansing and prospered. Houghton used part of his fortune to build a stone mansion on the side of Mt. Hosmer in 1863 (it is still there).

Lansing was a remote outpost in those early years. Boats passed town just a few times a month and rarely stopped. Communication with the outside world was sporadic in the winter, with mail arriving only once a week. Residents had to travel across the frozen

Mississippi to Prairie du Chien, which had the nearest railroad. When the ice was not thick enough to walk across, Lansing residents were on their own.

The town had a good spot for steamboats to land and eventually became a key supply point for the region. Lansing grew five-fold in 20 years—from 440 residents in 1854 to 2,280 in 1875.

Just south of nascent Lansing, the town of Columbus also had a bustling boat landing. Columbus was chosen as the first county seat in 1851. When the town was platted in 1852, two acres were set aside for county buildings. This was the beginning of an intense battle for the seat of county government. It would take ten elections over 25 years to settle the issue, and most of the elections were decided by a handful of votes.

The fighting began when an area called The Stake was chosen as the first county seat in 1849. No one really liked the decision and in 1851 Columbus won an election to host the county seat. They didn't keep it for long, however. Another election was held in 1853 and this time Waukon won. Feeling confident of their hold on the county seat, Waukon residents built a courthouse in 1859. Alas, another election in 1861 took the county seat from them and gave it to The Point (in south Lansing). Residents of The Point quickly tried to cement their hold on the county seat by building another courthouse. In 1866, several Waukon residents, including the sheriff, raided the courthouse at The Point and stole county records. A posse from Lansing pursued and caught them, returning the records to The Point. But, in 1867, the Iowa Supreme Court declared that Waukon was the rightful winner of the last election and was again awarded the county seat. In 1875, one more election was held and Waukon won again. No county seat elections have been held since. Both courthouses are still standing, which is more than can be said for Columbus (now mostly farmland) or The Point (now part of Lansing).

Lansing's residents have been resilient in the face of changing economic fortunes. The town's initial growth was fueled by a booming trade in shipping grain. The Kerndt brothers (Gustav, Moritz, William, and Julius) were part of the reason. They built a warehouse in 1859 and an elevator in 1861. Both riverfront structures are still standing. Fortunes slumped for a while as the wheat harvest declined, but farmers eventually switched to dairy, livestock, and other crops. Local industry received a boost when the Chicago, Milwaukee and St. Paul railroad arrived in 1872. Townsfolk threw an exuberant party on May 8 to celebrate the arrival of the first train.

Lansing also profited from the lumber business in the late 1800s. During the peak years of the lumber trade, log rafts floated regularly downriver. As the great northern forests were depleted around the turn of the 20th century, Lansing developed an industry producing pearl buttons from Mississippi River mussels. As the pearl button industry declined in the 1920s, commercial fishing took up the slack. Lansing's economy today is closely tied to farming, with a boost from the tourist trade.

HARPERS FERRY

It took a while for folks here to decide what to call their town. In the early years, it was called Paint Rock Prairie, then Vailsville (after early resident Horace Vail). The village was platted in 1852 as Winfield by William Hall and Dresden Howard. The Iowa Legislature changed the name to Harpers Ferry in 1860, in honor of David Harper. Harper recognized the potential for this area as a steamboat landing, with its wide, flat plain extending a mile to the bluffs and three miles along the slough, a potential that never materialized. The town counted 300 residents in 1913, about what it claims today.

Among the early residents of the town were a number of Norwegians, including Ole Larson and Ole Knutson who arrived in 1850. Another early resident, Asle Knutson—another great name!—was adept at improvising shelter. After he arrived, he cut down a hollow basswood tree, then cut off a 16-foot section. In one end, he stuffed hay, his belongings, and then himself. He closed the other end with more hay. A knot hole provided ventilation and, with the log oriented to the east, also served as an alarm clock. Asle was single, in case you were wondering.

MARQUETTE

Around 1785, when the area was under Spanish rule, Basil Giard built three cabins and began farming to establish a land claim. The American government refused to recognize it, so in 1808, he moved back to Prairie du Chien. After his death, his claims were ultimately upheld and awarded to his heirs, who sold off the land. Some of the land became the town of McGregor, and some became North McGregor.

When the railroad reached Prairie du Chien in 1857, Iowa got a serious case of railroad envy. Speculation that a rail line would be built up Bloody Run Valley led to the development of a supply point in 1857 at the mouth of Bloody Run Creek. A small community grew up around it that was called North McGregor. Just a year later, North McGregor had 300 residents and was booming.

Construction of the proposed line from North McGregor to Monona, Iowa, was finally completed in 1864. North McGregor was eventually tied into the first all-rail route between Chicago and the Twin Cities that was completed in 1867. The only missing rail link was across the Mississippi River at North McGregor.

All of this excitement doubled the town's population in ten years. The presence of the railroad spurred other business growth, such as a foundry and Flemming Lumber—once one of town's largest employers. In 1870, construction began on another railroad line, one that paralleled the Mississippi River from Dubuque. In late 1871, the tracks reached North McGregor, making it a two-railroad town. In 1874, an innovative pontoon bridge opened across the Mississippi River, completing a reliable rail connection between Iowa and Wisconsin.

In 1920, residents of North McGregor voted to change their town's name to Marquette in honor of the 17th-century Jesuit priest, Father Jacques Marquette. The village has suffered through high water from the Mississippi River many times, but flash floods have been more damaging. On May 24, 1896, five inches of rain fell in an hour. A wall of water 20 feet high raced down Bloody Run valley. The flood washed out bridges and railroad tracks and tossed box cars around like rubber duckies, killing more than 20 people. A similar rain event triggered a flash flood on June 1, 1916, causing severe damage to the rail yards and roundhouse, but without the fatalities. After the 1916 flood, the railroad built new yards west of town on a higher grade and re-routed Bloody Run Creek. Marquette still has the railroad lines, but it is no longer a rail terminal.

MCGREGOR

The future town of McGregor began in 1837 when Alexander MacGregor, son of Scottish immigrants, initiated ferry service to Prairie du Chien. For the next 20 years, few people lived here, even after Alexander's brother, James, bought land nearby. Steamboat commerce ignited a population boom in the mid-1850s. The town's population exploded from 280 in 1856 to 5,500 just ten years later. McGregor incorporated in 1857 without the "a" found in the town's namesake (but with his permission). Many early

Lansing to Guttenberg Route Map

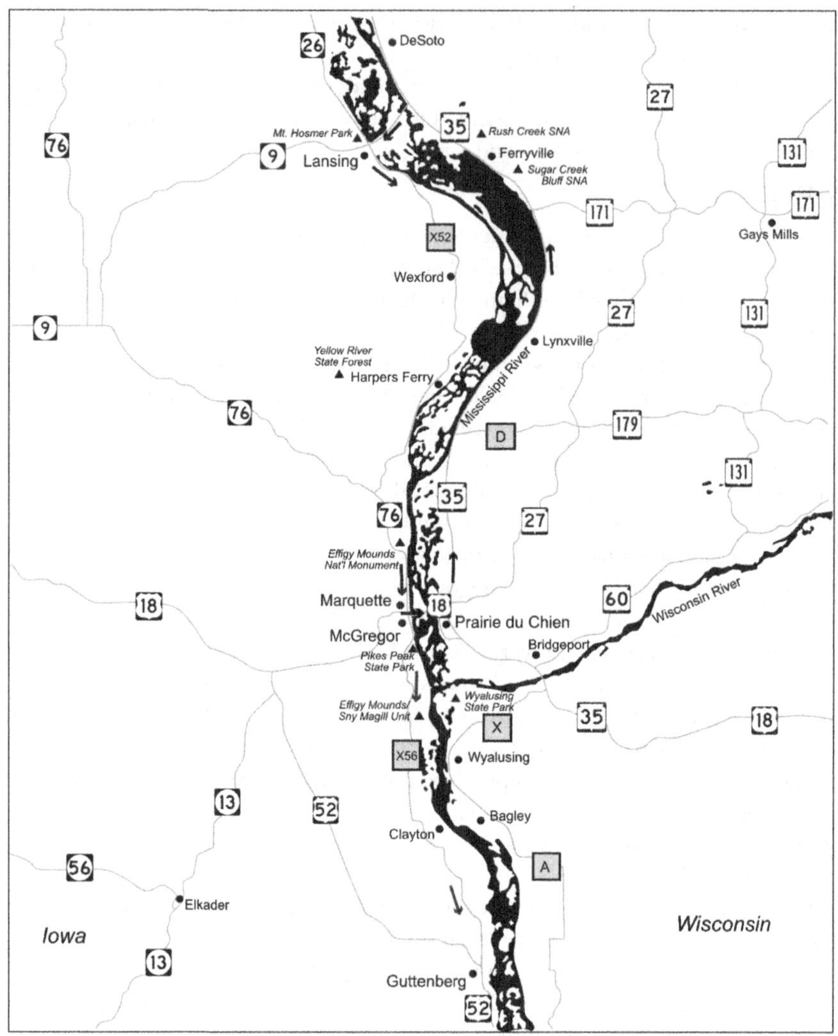

This is a circular route, mostly. It starts on the east side at Prairie du Chien and goes north on Highway 35 to the next river crossing (just south of De Soto). It crosses to the west side at Lansing on the narrow Blackhawk Bridge, then heads south on County Highway X52, then State Highway 76 to Marquette and US Business 18 into McGregor. You can end the route there, and cross back into Prairie du Chien on US Highway 18 and the modern Marquette-Joliet Bridge. This is a 65-mile route.

I suggest, however, continuing south on County Highway X56 for 20 miles to the lovely town of Guttenberg. Once in Guttenberg, follow the signs for the Great River Road to reach River Park Drive downtown. From Guttenberg, the next river bridge to the south is at Dubuque, but from May to October you can cross to Wisconsin on the Cassville Ferry (see page 182).

Central Prairie du Chien Map

Attractions

15. Brisbois House
13. Dousman Hotel
2. Fort Crawford Cemetery
1. Fort Crawford Museum
4. Holy Trinity Episcopal Church
18. Mississippi River Sculpture Park
1. Prairie du Chien Museum
14. Rolette House
16. St. Feriole Island Memorial Gardens
20. St. Gabriel Archangel Catholic Church
17. St. Germain dit Gauthier-Coorough House
6. The Planted Tree
19. Villa Louis/Fur Trade Museum

Where to Eat and Drink

12. Farmers market
9. Fort Mulligans
7. Pete's Hamburger Stand
8. Simply Café
5. The Local Oven
3. Valley Fish and Cheese

Where to Stay

10. River District Hotel
21. Sports Unlimited Campground
11. Waterfront Hotel

businesses grew in response to the abundant supply of wood coming downriver—a sawmill, steam planing mill, a door and sash factory—as well as many businesses catering to the transient worker population: seven hotels, six restaurants, seven taverns.

Further development in McGregor was hampered by an unfortunate feud between the MacGregor brothers. For 20 years, beginning in 1853, the MacGregor brothers and their heirs sued each other over who rightfully owned which parcels of land. The dispute obscured titles for many properties in town for years. At one point, Alexander's corpse had to be removed from his grave when the property where he was buried was awarded to James. Alexander now rests in Prairie du Chien.

McGregor has been home to more than its share of people who attained fame. The Ringling family lived in McGregor for a few years in the 1860s. The brothers who went on to found one of the world's best-known circuses apparently saw their first circus while living in McGregor. (Their former house still stands, but it is a private residence.) Diamond Jo Reynolds, one of the most successful river men of the 19th century, lived in McGregor in the building across from Triangle Park.

One of the more colorful residents in contemporary times was Mildred Quimby, who created *Quimby's Harbor Guide* (now *Quimby's Cruising Guide*), the bible for thousands of pleasure boaters in the Midwest. A journalist by training, Ms. Quimby lived in a trailer near the Mississippi River just north of town from 1962 until her death in 1983. She personally researched every navigable inch of the Mississippi River to produce her guide. I can respect that.

GUTTENBERG

Early French visitors called this area Prairie la Porte, which means something like door to the prairie, because the interior prairies were easily reached though the valleys (the doors). For the Sauk and Meskwaki people, this plain was a favorite summer hangout.

Euro-American settlers trickled into the area in the late 1830s. By 1838, Clayton County had been established and a sheriff had been hired who was based at Prairie La Porte. The Graybill Tavern served as the temporary courthouse. In those early years, Clayton County was the administrative center for an area that now includes most of the Dakotas, all of Minnesota, and about a quarter of Iowa. The territory had far fewer residents then, of course, but that's still a lot of territory! Alas, fate is a fickle mistress, and the county seat was moved out of town in 1843.

The loss of the county seat did not kill Prairie la Porte entirely, though. Naham Dudley identified abundant deposits of lead, and the mining industry took off. In 1843, the Western Settlement Society of Cincinnati, a group founded to assist Germans arriving in the US, purchased land in Clayton County. They planned on building a town called Gutenberg. The first German families arrived on March 8, 1845, and found little more than the abandoned Graybill Tavern (Herman Graybill had died in 1843).

Germans continued to pour into town in the 1840s and in January 1847, the Iowa legislature approved a name change: Prairie la Porte became Gutenberg. The town's founders honored the famed 14th-century German inventor of movable type, Johannes Gutenberg. The first appearances of the town's name in print were spelled the same as the inventor's surname, but an 1848 plat by GA Mengel Lithographing Company of Cincinnati spelled the name with a double "t" and the misspelling stuck. (In 1949, Guttenberg residents voted down a measure to restore the original spelling by dropping the extra 't' in the name.)

The Germans who arrived were generally well-educated folks. They chose street names that honored both their native German culture, as well as that of their new American homeland. To the south, streets were named after German cultural figures Christoph Wieland, Johann Herder, and Johann Goethe. To the north, streets bore the names of musicians Haydn and Mozart, plus early American heroes George Washington, Thomas Jefferson, and two of the foreign officers who fought with the Americans in the Revolutionary War: the Marquis de LaFayette and Tadeusz Kosciusko.

Guttenberg grew to a thousand residents by 1851. In the next decade, the town experienced steady growth that triggered a building boom. Many of those structures were built of native limestone from the nearby bluffs and are still around.

Ferry service to Glen Haven (Wisconsin) started in 1855, and several hotels and breweries opened. In 1856, Guttenberg won an election and again became the county seat, but that success would prove fleeting, too. Elkader won the 1859 election and has had the county seat since. (In 30 years, citizens of Clayton County voted for a county seat 11 times as the county seat moved from Garnavillo to Guttenberg to Elkader.)

After the Civil War, fewer immigrants arrived. Guttenberg became a railroad town in 1871, just as the farm economy assumed a central role in the town's fortunes and as a pearl button factory grew into the town's single largest employer. In 1905, the US Army Corps of Engineers shifted the main channel from the Glen Haven side to the Guttenberg side, much to the dismay of Glen Havenians.

Guttenberg's residents were not fond of attempts to ban sales and consumption of alcohol. When Iowa voted on an alcohol ban in 1880, Guttenberg's residents were strongly opposed (78% voted no in Clayton County vs. 55% yes statewide). The town had five breweries and two distilleries at that time. Local breweries cut back production but didn't close. In spite of Prohibition, Guttenberg had seven licensed saloons in 1891, and six more opened the next year. Guttenberg even managed to keep its three wholesale beer distributors operating by giving them peddler's licenses. In the fine tradition of many rivertowns, Guttenberg's municipal government relied on saloon taxes for much of its revenue, and the city wasn't about to let a little thing like state law get in its way.

Alas, Guttenberg couldn't fight Big Brother forever. A new law in 1910 restricted the number of taverns to one per thousand residents. Five of Guttenberg's six taverns had to close. In 1917, Iowans voted on a constitutional amendment to ban the manufacture and sale of intoxicating beverages. The measure lost statewide in a close call, but residents around Guttenberg rejected the amendment 510 to 26!

By the time the US officially adopted prohibition in 1918, Guttenberg residents had gained valuable experience in the art of home brewing, giving them a head start as bootleggers. Congress repealed Prohibition in February 1933, but true to Guttenberg's roots, the city issued its first post-Prohibition liquor licenses in April, nearly eight months before Prohibition was officially over.

In 1937, Guttenberg threw itself a big party to celebrate the centennial of its founding and the completion of Lock and Dam 10. One ceremony was called Mingling of the Waters and involved mixing water from the Gulf of Mexico with water from the Mississippi River headwaters. The mayors of New Orleans and Bena, Minnesota, were asked to contribute samples from their respective ends of the river. New Orleans sent its water in a glass decanter that had been owned for 100 years by an old-time New Orleans family. They spent $7.69 to ship the package by airmail. Bena sent its water in a beer can. They spent .08 cents on postage.

Explore Up The East Bank (Wisconsin)

PRAIRIE DU CHIEN

Attractions

Old Prairie du Chien was located on **St. Feriole Island**, most of which is a park today (Lawler Park). There are several attractions worth visiting.

Villa Louis (521 N. Villa Louis Rd.; 608.326.2721) is the impressive Victorian home built by the Dousman family. The home was built on top of an Indian mound. The interior is dark but elegant. Most of the furnishings are original to the house. The Villa Louis tour includes several other buildings on the property and the nearby **Fur Trade Museum**, built in the 1850s for the last fur trader in Prairie du Chien, BW Brisbois.

The **Mississippi River Sculpture Park** (N. Villa Louis Rd.; 608.326.8555) is the brainchild of sculptor Florence Bird, who has ambitious plans to chronicle in bronze several thousand years of human history in the region. Several sculptures currently are in place, including Black Hawk, Dr. William Beaumont, The Touring Lady, Emma Big Bear, and The Voyageur. Bird hopes to complete a total of 24 sculptures.

As you go around the island, you'll notice several attractions:

- The imposing **Dousman Hotel** (Water St.) was built in 1864 for railroad passengers. It is now an events center.
- The **Rolette House** (Water St.) is the white frame building next to the Dousman Hotel. It was built in the early 1840s for fur trader Joseph Rolette, who, like many frontier entrepreneurs, made and lost a lot money, living in luxury and dying in poverty.
- Joseph Rolette built the **Brisbois House** (Water St.) for his ex-wife, Jane Fisher, when they separated. The house was completed around 1836 from limestone left over from the construction of Fort Crawford. It is currently owned by the Wisconsin Historical Society and is typically open only for special events.
- **St. Feriole Island Memorial Gardens** (200 N. 4th) includes a walking trail through rows of flowers and native plants.
- The restored **St. Germain dit Gauthier-Coorough House** (419 5th St.), a log cabin that was built in the early 1800s in the traditional French-Canadian *pièce du pièce* style: squared logs were laid horizontally with ends notched to fit together; gaps were filled with moss, then the exterior was plastered.

Back on the mainland, the **Planted Tree** (109 W. Blackhawk Ave.; 608.326.8733) showcases the works of local and regional artists, as well as handcrafted items to decorate your home or RV.

St. Gabriel Archangel Catholic Church (506 N. Beaumont; 608.326.2404) dates to the late 1830s when it was built under the guidance of Father Samuel Mazzuchelli (see page 183). The church has undergone several alterations during its lifetime. The original bell tower is gone. An expansion in 1908 added a vestibule and towers on the west side of the church and an addition on the east side that increased the depth of the sanctuary. Just outside the church is the grave of Father Lucien Galtier, the person who is at least partially responsible for the fact that the town across the Mississippi River from Minneapolis is now known as Saint Paul instead of Pig's Eye.

Fort Crawford Museum at Prairie du Chien (717 S. Beaumont Rd.; 608.326.6960) consists of two museums. The **Fort Crawford Museum** is housed in the reconstructed

Andrew Clemens, Sand Artist

Andrew Clemens was a remarkable man. He created, seemingly with ease, timeless works of art using a fragile medium.

Clemens was born in Dubuque on January 29, 1857. His father was a successful wagon builder who moved the family to McGregor in 1858 to take advantage of the town's booming economy. At age five, Clemens contracted encephalitis. He survived, but the disease wiped out his hearing. He was home-schooled until age 13, at which time his parents sent him to a private school in Council Bluffs, Iowa, where he learned some carpentry but not much else. On his summer vacations, he collected colored sand and used it to create simple geometric designs in glass bottles.

Clemens returned to McGregor permanently in 1877 (after the school burned down) and concentrated fully on the art of creating designs from colored sand. Clemens' work was meticulous.

He collected sand from the base of a bluff where iron oxide created more than forty shades of color. He painstakingly separated each color, then selected grains of uniform size. Most designs were created upside down using hickory tools he made himself: a curved wand to place the sand and a straight one to achieve perspective. The sand was tamped into place, then the bottle corked and sealed with wax.

A simple design could be completed in a couple of days, but a complex one could take weeks. Completed pieces sold for as little as $1 but not more than $8. Some of his pieces were commissioned, like the pontoon bridge he did for John Lawler, the bridge's owner. Clemens died in May 1894. He was just 37 years old.

He almost certainly made hundreds of pieces, but only a few survive. The most extensive collections are at the Iowa Historical Society in Des Moines (which also has some of his tools) and the McGregor Historical Museum.

hospital building of the Second Fort Crawford and has exhibits about the fort and on the history of medicine, including a 19th-century pharmacy and an exhibit on Dr. William Beaumont, who performed experiments on Alexis St. Martin, "the man with a hole in his stomach." The **Prairie du Chien Museum** has the usual memorabilia and displays: fossils, arrowheads, Mississippi mussels, river bridges, an iron lung, plus two transparent female mannequins with organs that light up during the 13-minute anatomy lesson, so it even has something for the kids.

Fort Crawford Cemetery (413 S. Beaumont Rd.; 414.382.5300) is just down the road from the fort. It is the smallest national cemetery in the US. Sixty-four people are interred in its half-acre.

Holy Trinity Episcopal Church (220 S. Michigan; 608.326.6085) was organized in 1837 to serve officers at Fort Crawford. The current Gothic Revival church was built in 1856 and still looks much as it did when it was built. The bell tower and bell were added in 1870. The church pews are original. They were installed in 1856.

La Riviere Park (62036 Vineyard Coulee Rd.; 608.326.7207) is a sprawling city park on the east side of town with a nature center, hiking trails, mountain biking, and an archery range, plus the standard picnicking and playground options.

Drinking and Dining

AUTHOR'S PICK: **Valley Fish and Cheese** (304 S. Prairie St.; 608.326.4719) is a great choice for local food products, including fresh and smoked fish (carp, catfish, sturgeon), pickled fish, cheese, specialty meats like summer sausage, turtle, and fresh morel mushrooms (in season). Buy a gift box to take home to all your friends!

If you're in the mood for fresh-baked pastry or bread, **The Local Oven** (213 E. Blackhawk Ave.; 608.326.0960) has what you need, including deep-fried fruit pies.

Simply Café (204 W. Blackhawk Ave.; 608.326.7467) serves a variety of coffee drinks, breakfast sandwiches, and fresh soups, salads, and sandwiches.

Pete's Hamburger Stand (118 W. Blackhawk Rd.; 608.326.6653) a local institution. They have been serving burgers grilled in a hint of water and topped with grilled onions, since Pete Gokey grilled the first one in 1909. The Gokey family still runs it. It's a popular place, so don't be surprised if you have to wait in line for a while. You won't get anything fancy here, just a darn good burger.

Fort Mulligans (214 Blackhawk Ave.; 608.326.0639), housed in an 1850s-era building long known as the French Store, serves a couple dozen sandwiches and burgers, plus a range of fried foods, pasta, and above-average entrées.

Four miles north of Prairie du Chien, the **Spring Lake Inn** (State Highway 35 at County Highway N; 608.326.6907), a popular and highly regarded country inn, serves several varieties of hearty half-pound sirloin burgers and chicken sandwiches.

Where to Stay: Camping

Sports Unlimited Campground (32800 County Road K; 608.326.2141) is a big place on the north side of town with full hookup sites, mini-golf, and a marina.

Lodging

The **Prairie Motel** (1616 S. Marquette Rd.; 608.326.6461) has 32 clean, spacious rooms equipped with microwave, refrigerator, and coffee pot.

The **River District Hotel** (130 S. Main St.; 608.326.7878) is a former chain hotel near downtown and the riverfront that is now independently owned. Rooms come standard with a small fridge, microwave, and coffee pot.

Windsor Place Inn (1936 S. Marquette Rd.; 608.326.7799) has 35 modern rooms hidden behind a row of chain motels. Each room is non-smoking and is equipped with a coffee pot, refrigerator, microwave, and cable TV.

The **Waterfront Hotel** (113 S. Main St.; 608.380.1021) offers 55 tidy deluxe rooms between St. Feriole Island and downtown Prairie du Chien. Some rooms have river views. A stay includes a continental breakfast.

Special Events

The **farmers market** assembles on downtown on Saturday mornings (406 E. Blackhawk Ave.)

The **Prairie Villa Rendezvous** (608.822.6916) kicks off the summer festival season in mid-June with a big crowd of men and women in leather tights reliving the glory of 18th-century trapper life.

The **Prairie Dog Blues Festival** (608.326.0085) started as a private party but is now two full days of live blues next to the Mississippi in late July.

In September, the **Village Louis Carriage Classic** (608.326.4436) stages an antique carriage riding competition for two days on the grounds of Villa Louis, and it is way cool. The competition is sanctioned by the American Driving Society (no relation to AAA) and has grown to become an important national event, if you're into Artesian stocks or carriages. Several categories of competitions and exhibitions occur over the course of two days, including things like the Junior Reinsmanship, Antique Turnout, Large Pony Open Cross Country, and Picnic Class. The carriages, antiques all, are beautiful examples of art meets function, and the horses are the picture of grace and elegance, even when occasionally feisty and impatient.

LYNXVILLE

Getting on the River

Hubbard's Fishing Float (608.732.1084) is just below Lock and Dam #9. To get there, head to the boat ramp across from the Falling Rock Inn and raise the flag; a boat will come get you. Don't forget your fishing license.

Where to Stay: Camping

Mississippi Bend Campground & RV Park (Lynxville: 251 Hillside Dr.; 608.412.0483) is located in a shady valley on the south end of town. They typically have a few sites available for RVs and overnight campers.

FERRYVILLE

Attractions

Sugar Creek Bluff State Natural Area (Lagoon Rd.; 608.784.3606) has great views of the river valley from the top of the bluff. The hiking is moderately difficult, partly because of the incline and partly because the trail is only roughly cut through the forest. Wear long pants or your legs may get cut up. Give yourself at least 60–90 minutes for the round-trip hike, longer if you want to linger at the top. The natural area is at the south end of Ferryville. Turn on Lagoon Street (across from Sugar Creek Park). Go a quarter-mile across the Sugar Creek Bridge and park along the road. The sign for the trail is about 100 feet down the gravel driveway.

Riverview Park (Across from the Sportsmen's Bar & Grill) is a good spot for river or train watching (dozens of trains a day pass through here). The observation deck has a viewing scope for a closer look at birds and other critters on the river.

Rush Creek State Natural Area (Rush Creek Rd.; 608.785.9000) just might have the best overlooks along the Mississippi River. Two goat prairies atop the bluffs provide a wide panoramic view of the Mississippi Valley, from which you can see the river make a sweeping bend to the west. The hike is moderately strenuous, as you have a steady uphill climb via an old service road, sometimes through waist-high brush. The hike from the parking lot on Rush Creek Road (cross the road and walk east to the old service road) to the top will take 30–45 minutes. Give yourself at least two hours to explore and enjoy. I would suggest you find somewhere else to hike during deer hunting season, though. You should also be aware that rattlesnakes nest in the area, although you aren't likely to encounter them. Rush Creek Road is just north of Ferryville.

Drinking and Dining

Swede's Swing Inn (106 Main St.; 608.734.9916) was a popular watering hole for railroad workers in the late 1800s, maybe because it counted prostitutes among its customers. One of them, Blue Moon, was murdered at the tavern and many believe her ghost still haunts the place. The food is about what you'd expect: burgers and sandwiches, and steaks and fried stuff. Offer a toast to Blue Moon while you're here.

Where to Stay: Camping

Sugar Creek Park (State Highway 35; 608.734.9406) has several primitive sites with firepits. All share a common water source and there are no showers.

Where to Stay: Lodging

The **Grandview Motel** (14812 State Highway 35; 608.734.3235) is an exceptional place with nine well-kept, wood-paneled rooms, four of which have kitchenettes. Room 1 is a kitchenette with two queen beds, a wood-burning stove, and large picture windows to take in the expansive views of the Mississippi River.

For something completely different, why not stay in a retrofitted railroad caboose? The **Coulee Junction Caboose** (10414 Coulee Creek Rd.; 708.341.3255) is set on railroad tracks on five acres deep in a coulee 10 minutes from Ferryville and outfitted with nice features like a big deck, a barbecue grill (bring charcoal), a fire pit, and hot tub. The interior has wood floors, a fireplace, a kitchen with a microwave, and enough room to sleep four adults, but probably best for two.

Special Events

Ferryville hosts a **farmers market** on Saturday mornings at Sugar Creek Park off Highway 35.

DE SOTO

Drinking and Dining

The **Great River Roadhouse** (9660 Highway 35; 608.648.2045), just north of De Soto, is a popular stop for food and drinks, pizza especially. Broasted chicken is another popular choice. I thought that implied some kind of oven roasting. Wrong. It's just deep-fried in a pressure cooker using a "broaster" probably made in Wisconsin, so I guess that makes it local food. If you prefer something different, they also have sandwiches and entrées that run the gamut from seafood to ribs to pasta dishes. Expect to wait for a table on a weekend evening.

Where to Stay: Camping

Blackhawk Park (E590 County Road BI ; 608.648.3314) campground, three miles north of De Soto, stretches out along a backwater channel with several separate camping areas. The sites nearest the shower house are cramped and have little shade, but there are a few primitive sites at the boathouse camping area that are separated from the rest of the campground and are right next to the river with great views. The sites around Peck Lake are generally more private, especially around the east side of the lake. Some sites have electric, but none have a full hookup.

Where to Stay: Lodging

J&J Riverview Cabins (121 Crawford St.; 319.826.4967) offers five cabins and two apartments with a full kitchen, cable TV, and linens. One cabin is wheelchair accessible.

Scenic View Cabins (S7602B State Highway 35; 608.648.3329) rents six roomy, well-maintained cabins in a secluded location above the highway, a large stand-alone cabin, and a mobile home that is available for overnight rentals. Each unit has a refrigerator and an oven or microwave.

Explore Down the West Bank (Iowa)

LANSING

Attractions

The **Driftless Area Education and Visitor Center** (1944 Columbus Rd.; 563.538.0400) sits at the south end of town with panoramic views of the river. Inside, you'll find displays on the area's unique river ecology and human history.

The **Museum of River History** (60 S. Front St.; 563.538.4641) is one of my favorite local history museums along the Mississippi. Housed in the Kerndt & Brothers Elevator, the collection is focused on—get out!—river history. Displays illustrate the fishing business with tools of the trade for clamming, fish processing, and ice harvesting. Heck, they even have a collection of outboard motors. Visit the museum whenever Coffee on the River is open.

If you enjoy panoramic views of the Mississippi River, look no further than **Mount Hosmer Park** (N. 6th St.; 563.538.4757), a 75-acre bluff-top park that rises 440 feet above the water. It was named after one Harriet Hosmer, a rather well-known sculptor from the East Coast in her day, who was reported to have raced up the hill in record time during a steamboat stop in June 1851.

Horsfalls Lansing Variety (300 & 360 Main St.; 563.538.4966) is an old-fashioned variety store—two variety stores, to be precise—where "variety" is taken seriously. Wander through tightly packed aisles stacked high with toys, kitchen supplies, greeting cards, and just about anything else you can imagine. You may want to leave a trail of bread crumbs to find your way back out.

Check out the landscape paintings at **Easker Art Studio Gallery** (271 Main St.; 319.393.1423), many of which feature the Mississippi River and nearby areas. Artist Fred Easker is usually in the studio the first two Fridays and Saturdays of the month. but call ahead to confirm if you want to visit the studio.

Check out Erik Burke's building-sized **mural** called *Reverse Effigy* at 3rd and Main.

Drinking and Dining

Coffee on the River (60 S. Front St.; 563.538.2899) serves the usual coffee and tea drinks in a beautiful historic stone building along the river. They also offer sandwiches and salads that you can enjoy from the back deck overlooking the river.

The Buck Stops Here (367 Main St.; 563.538.9284) cooks up hearty and creative dishes for breakfast and lunch. Check out the daily specials for something new.

Shep's Riverside Bar and Restaurant (10 S. Front St.; 563.538.2009) serves burgers and sandwiches with great views of the river.

Where to Stay: Lodging

The **Scenic Valley Motel** (1608 Main St.; 563.538.4245) rents 12 rooms, some with small refrigerators, and a cabin with microwave, refrigerator, and stove. Rooms are well maintained and clean, but not big.

The **River View Inn** (563.537.0072) rents four affordable rooms in an old stone warehouse that come with good river views.

McGarrity's Inn on Main (203 Main St.; 563.538.2080) offers four impressively rehabbed, luxury suites. Each unit is spacious, beautiful and loaded with amenities like exposed brick walls, wood floors, cable TV, full bath, and kitchenette.

If you're traveling with a family or small group, you might want to book the **Blue Heron Inn** (20 N. Front St.; 563.419.0550). The circa 1850 stone building on the riverfront has been lovingly renovated and includes two bedrooms, full kitchen, and deck.

WEXFORD

In 1850, the Reverend Thomas Hore led a group of 450 people out of Ireland to escape the famine. After reaching the US, they traveled from New Orleans up the Mississippi River to Arkansas, where many immigrants stopped and joined small Irish enclaves nearby. A few continued north to St. Louis with Father Hore. In spring 1851, he bought 2,000 acres in Allamakee County, then returned to St. Louis and accompanied 18 families to the Wexford Creek valley.

In short order, they built a log church they called St. George. Father Hore returned to Ireland in 1858—he would die there a few years later—and nearby Trappists picked up his ministry. The log church burned down and was replaced by a frame church around 1858. It proved to be too small, so the parish built a stone church that was dedicated in 1867 as St. George but renamed Immaculate Conception Catholic Church in 1870. A small community developed around the church and creek.

Immaculate Conception Catholic (1416 Great River Rd.; 563.586.2150) is a simple country church built of limestone quarried from nearby hills and surrounded by a cemetery on three sides and a hill on the fourth. The church has been through many alterations over time, but it retains a timeless beauty. The building is usually open during the day if you'd like to look around the inside.

HARPERS FERRY

Attractions

Yellow River State Forest (729 State Forest Rd.; 563.586.2254) is a jewel in the crown of Iowa public lands. Just west of Harpers Ferry, the state forest consists of many separate units, but most of the recreational opportunities (hiking, mountain biking, fishing, hunting, canoeing, horseback riding) are centered in the Paint Creek Unit, which is about five miles from Harpers Ferry. If you want to canoe on the Yellow River, rentals are available through **Big Foot Canoe Rental** (319.238.2064).

Drinking and Dining

Mohn Fish Market (1144 Great River Rd. 563.586.2269), just north of Harpers Ferry, is the place to get fresh, local fish, whether ready-to-cook, smoked, or pickled.

Where to Stay: Camping

Scenic View Campground (420 Old 16 Rd.; 563.535.7347) is a full-service campground southwest of Harpers Ferry and next to the Yellow River. They rent about two dozen sites for overnight campers that range from primitive to full hookups.

The Paint Creek Unit at **Yellow River State Forest** has two campgrounds with primitive sites, a horse campground, and sites for back-country backpackers. (Who knew it was possible to go back-country backpacking in Iowa?)

Where to Stay: Bed and Breakfasts

Friendliness is a priority at the **Point of View Bed and Breakfast** (416 Luster Heights Rd.; 563.586.2061), which sits atop a ridge just south of Harpers Ferry with four rooms and a cottage for rent. The house has views of the Mississippi Valley and backwaters (especially from the widow's nest), plus extensive grounds with hiking trails.

Where to Stay: Cabins

Andy Mountain Cabins (2335 Andy Mountain Lane; 563.586.2123) rents five beautiful log cabins for overnight rental just south of Harpers Ferry, plus overnight camp sites for RVs. Cabins have full kitchens and rentals include linens. They are open all year.

MARQUETTE

Attractions

Effigy Mounds National Monument (151 State Highway 76; 563.873.3491) preserves a series of remarkable burial and ceremonial mounds on the bluffs overlooking the Mississippi River north of Marquette. Dozens of animal-shaped mounds were built by Native Americans between 850 and 1,400 years ago. The most common design is a bear, but you will also see birds, turtles, bison, and lizards. Start at the Visitor's Center for an overview of the history of the mounds and their construction. The mounds in the Marching Bear Group in the South Unit are especially impressive; getting to them requires a moderately strenuous four-mile round-trip hike. In the North Unit, the longest hiking route is seven miles and includes several good overlooks of the Mississippi River. You can easily spend half a day at Effigy Mounds. You won't find any drinking fountains along the trails, so bring water for anything other than a short hike.

Effigy Mounds National Monument has a third unit that I'm a big fan of, but it is a bit of a drive from the North and South Units. The **Sny Magill Unit** has over a hundred mounds that are mostly conical and linear in design, but the quiet location along a backwater slough radiates a palpable spirituality. The road floods frequently, which closes the site at times. The Sny Magill Unit is eleven miles south of the park office along County Highway X52 and four miles south of Pikes Peak State Park. The road to the site does not seem to have a name, but it is the gravel road on the north side of the bridge over Sny Magill Creek and just north of Keystone Road.

The **Marquette Depot Museum** (216 Edgar St.; 563.873.1200) packs a lot of information into a small space. Most of the displays highlight the city's railroad history. Take time to flip through the clippings and photos housed in the display cases, which document the pontoon bridge and the many floods that the town's residents have endured.

The **Casino Queen** (100 Anti Monopoly; 563.873.3531) is one of the last riverboat casinos still floating on the Mississippi. The pink elephant in front is a local legend. Built for a Republican political convention in Sparta, Wisconsin (and painted gray), the owners of the Pink Elephant Supper purchased the elephant after Iowa passed liquor by the drink in 1964. In 1978, local Democrats took the elephant waterskiing (it sat on a pontoon boat) on the Mississippi in advance of a visit by President Jimmy Carter.

Learn about the unique ecosystems of the upper Mississippi River at the **Driftless Area Wetlands Centre** (509 US Highway 18; 563.873.3537). Walk around the prairies just west of Marquette and check out the interactive exhibits inside.

Getting On the River

Maiden Voyage Tours offers relaxed cruises on the river from Marquette, including a Friday night music cruse. Call for information on tour times (563.880.8970).

Where to Stay: Lodging

The **Natural Gait Resort** (1878 Old Mission Dr.; 563.419.0837), a few miles outside of Marquette, is a soothing place for a getaway, especially if you bring your horse to explore the 20 miles of trails that connect to Yellow River State Forest. Six fully equipped cabins are cozy and have great views of the area; they can sleep from four to fourteen people. They also rent six lodge rooms. If that's not enough, they also have several campsites in two separate camping areas geared toward horse owners but open to anyone. Several sites have good views looking down to the Yellow River.

The **Frontier Motel** (101 S. First; 563.873.3497) offers 20 simple, clean rooms along the riverfront and next to the casino.

Special Events

The **farmers market** takes place on Friday evenings at Driftless Area Wetlands Centre (509 US Highway 18).

MCGREGOR

Attractions

The **McGregor Historical Museum** (254 Main St.; 563.873.2221) has an informative collection of exhibits, mostly focused on characters who lived in the area. The most impressive pieces are the sand art bottles created by Andrew Clemens, which is reason enough to visit the museum.

Paper Moon (206 A St.; 563.873.3357) is a shop that defines eclectic and eccentric. Part book store, part novelty store, part local history purveyors, everything they do, they do well and with a healthy sense of humor.

The Left Bank Shop and Gallery (158 Main St.; 563.329.2010) occupies a beautiful space in a historic building in McGregor, which it uses to showcase the works of local and regional artists, as well as to host art classes.

Pikes Peak State Park is at the top of the hill after you leave McGregor on County Highway X56 (563.873.2341). Named for Zebulon Pike, the park has the standard amenities (hiking trails, picnic tables, campgrounds, mountain biking) but the real treat is the spectacular overlook and its expansive views 500 feet above the confluence of the Mississippi and Wisconsin Rivers. Most visitors stop only for the overlook, so if you explore the trails, you are likely to escape the crowds.

Detour: South of Prairie du Chien

If you've got some extra time, there are several places south of Prairie du Chien that are worth a side trip, including an outstanding state park and a museum that'll take you on a trip back in time.

Wyalusing State Park (County Highway X; 608.996.2261) is simply spectacular. Located at the confluence of the Mississippi and Wisconsin Rivers just ten minutes south of Prairie du Chien, the park overlooks the spot where Louis Jolliet and Father Jacques Marquette first caught sight of the Mississippi River on June 17, 1673. The park has a full range of outdoor activities, including hiking, mountain biking, swimming, and camping, plus a number of spectacular overlooks and a few mounds. There is a signed canoe route on the Mississippi River backwaters.

It's a bit further from Prairie du Chien, about 40 minutes by car, but **Nelson Dewey State Park** (Cassville: 12190 County Road VV; 608.725.5374) is worth the trip, especially if you're thinking of camping. One of several outstanding Wisconsin state parks along the Mississippi River, it offers good hiking and great views. The short hike along the Prairie Trail through Dewey Heights offers a glimpse of the blufftop prairies that were once common in the area.

If you've got a couple of hours to explore, cross the road to **Stonefield & the State Agricultural Museum** (Cassville: 12195 County Road VV; 608.725.5210). It occupies part of the original estate of Nelson Dewey, the first Governor of Wisconsin. The site includes a replica of a 19th-century village, original buildings from the Dewey farm, and a collection of antique farm implements. There are three buildings you can only visit as part of a guided tour.

Where to Eat

The **Cassville Farmers Market** convenes on Saturdays (8a-noon) on the riverfront.

Lucky's Bar & Grill (Bagley: 150 S Bagley Ave.; 608.996.2204) is a spacious bar and restaurant and a popular place to boot. The bar menu is fairly standard tavern fare, but they also have a supper club that serves steaks and seafood.

Where to Stay

Wyalusing State Park maintains two campgrounds. The Wisconsin Ridge Campground has 54 shaded sites (24 with electric) and a concession stand. The twenty sites on the north side sit on the edge of the ridge with spectacular views. The Homestead Campground has 55 sites (nine with electric) that are bigger and offer more privacy.

Nelson Dewey State Park (12190 County Road VV; 608.725.5374) has 46 shaded and spacious campsites. If you don't mind a short hike, the park also has four walk-in sites that are along the edge of a bluff and have spectacular views.

Upper Miss River Adventures (105 W. Amelia St.; 608.732.6184) rents two highly recommended units in Cassville. Contemporary (think flat-screen TVs) with historic accents (clawfoot tub), the units are spacious, comfortable, and beautiful.

First Lutheran Evangelical Church sits atop Swede Ridge on County Highway X56 just south of Pikes Peak State Park. The building is a simple frame "preaching box" with a tower. Built as the Norwegian Evangelical Lutheran Church in 1861, this may be the oldest frame church west of the Mississippi. The interior has simple accents: wood carving on the chancel, a carved pump organ, oil lamps (the building has no electricity), white and gold trimmed altar, and tiny wooden collections baskets. If you are interested in a tour, contact the McGregor-Marquette Chamber of Commerce (563.873.2186).

Drinking and Dining

Old Man River Restaurant & Brewery (123 A St.; 563.873.2002) serves pub food such as burgers and pizza plus daily specials that you can pair with a pint of craft beer.

Detour off the highway and down a coulee to enjoy a tasty meal with great river views at the **Clayton Lighthouse** (100 N. Front St.; 563.964.1100). The menu includes standard bar food options but with a supper club touch, and those river views will keep you smiling through your meal. The restaurant is 11 miles south of McGregor in the hamlet of Clayton.

Where to Stay: Camping

Clayton Hills Campground (Garnavillo: 31846 Clayton Rd.; 563.964.2236) offers full hook-ups and large sites in a peaceful wooded setting between McGregor and Guttenberg.

Bed and Breakfasts

Hickory Ridge Bed, Breakfast, & Bridle (17156 Great River Rd.; 563.873.1758) is a fine country retreat located atop a ridge south of Pike's Peak State Park, with good views of the Mississippi River. The four rooms have a comfortable, rustic feel.

Cabins

Grumpsters Log Cabin Getaway (535 Ash St.; 563.873.3767) rents three beautiful log cabins, a large one that can sleep ten and two smaller ones that can each sleep five. All come equipped with a kitchen and full bath.

Lodging

Little Switzerland Inn (126 Main St.; 563.873.2057) rents four units, including a log cabin built in 1848 (but fully updated, of course), that are as spacious, well appointed, and include a full breakfast.

American House Inn (116 Main St.; 563.873.3364) rents two spacious, fully-equipped suites reminiscent of 19th century. The second-floor suite has three bedrooms (Mark Twain slept in one of them) and good views of the Mississippi.

Special Events

The **Hole in the Sock Gang** stages Old West shootouts in Triangle Park in McGregor several times during the summer, usually on the last Saturday of the month from June through October.

GUTTENBERG

Attractions

Generations of rural primary school students attended the **Pleasant Ridge School** (563.252.3776) from 1893 to 1954, with never more than 19 students in any year. The interior remains as it was when the school closed in 1954, complete with desks, chalk-board, and the original school bell. The school is a few miles north of Guttenberg on

County Highway X56. In summer, it is typically open the 1st Saturday of the month from 1-3. At other times, call to inquire about a tour.

For a **spectacular view** of Guttenberg and the Mississippi River, pull over at the overlook on US Highway 52 just north of town.

The **Upper Mississippi River Fish Hatchery** (331 S. River Park Dr.; 319.252.1156) has a few small aquariums displaying fish species native to the Mississippi River and Iowa streams. Stop in for a few minutes while you are walking along the riverfront.

In most places, a copy of an original is not a major attraction, but the **Facsimile Gutenberg Bible** in Guttenberg is not your typical copy (Guttenberg Public Library, 603 S. 2nd St.; 563.252.3108). This copy is one of about 300 printed in 1913 in Leipzig. It was on display in Mainz, Germany, in 1942 when the city was bombed. Charles Millham, the former publisher/editor of the *Guttenberg Press*, purchased the book after WWII and loaned it to the library to display. The book is protected in a glass case with one set of pages open to view the exceptional craftsmanship.

Just south of Guttenberg, **Turkey River Mounds State Preserve** (Estes Point Rd.; 563.873.2341) is a gem of a preserve hidden at the end of a dirt road. The site is home to 38 mounds that date to the Woodland Period (1,100 to 2,500 years ago). Most are conical, but there is a panther effigy, too. There are no maintained trails, but if you want a challenging hike with good views, this is the place. You can hike through any part of the preserve but the quickest route to the mounds (in the northwest corner) is as follows: Park at the triangle formed where a private road goes north and Estes Point Road narrows. Walk east along the road and, after you pass the sign for the preserve, hike uphill. You can hike along the ridge from the mounds at the northwest end for about a mile to the spot where the flag pole sits (about 250 feet above the valley), with only a few anxious moments where the path narrows next to steep cliffs. You should be in good shape for this hike and wear hiking shoes that can handle slippery terrain.

Getting On the River

If want to get on the river from Guttenberg but don't have a boat, The Landing (703 S. River Park Dr.; 563.252.1717) operates a **fishing barge** and will run you out there and back (for a fee, of course).

Drinking and Dining

Enjoy a pint of locally brewed beer at the **Guttenberg Brewing Company** (530 S. 1st St.; 563.252.2739) or relax with a drink and your friends in the limestone-walled cellar tavern at **The Rathskeller** (218 S. River Park Dr.; 608.632.4806; open weekends).

Joe's Pizza (608 S. River Park Dr.; 563.252.2376) serves a good pizza pie in a friendly and laid-back restaurant.

Elkader, Iowa is 25 minutes from Guttenberg, a small town named for Abd el-Kader, an Algerian who led a 19th-century resistance movement against the occupying French forces. Fittingly enough, Elkader has an Algerian restaurant: **Schera's Restaurant and Bar** (107 S. Main; 563.245.1992) where the food is delicious, affordable, and they even have burgers, in case you are traveling with someone less adventurous than yourself.

Where to Stay: Camping

Great River Road RV Campground (601 Koskiusko St.; 563.920.1725) offers full hook-ups for overnight camping in an open area near the Guttenberg marina, but most of the sites are occupied by seasonal campers.

Where to Stay: Lodging

The modest **Guttenberg Motel** (927 S. Highway 52; 563.252.1433) rents a dozen budget rooms that have been nicely freshened up.

Atop a bluff at the north end of town, the **Eagle View Motel** (115 Acre St.; 563.252.1653;) offers bargain rooms with a million-dollar view. The ten rooms are clean and well-maintained and many have spectacular river views.

Rosemary's Bed and Bath (518 S. River Park Dr.; 563.880.5469) offers four updated, affordable rooms along the main drag. They only accept cash or checks.

The Landing (703 S. River Park Dr.; 563.252.1615) offers 19 updated rooms, including nine suites, in an 1858-era limestone building on the riverfront.

Special Events

Find the **farmers market** on Saturday mornings next to the river downtown (400 S. River Park Dr.)

German Fest (563.252.2323; September: last Saturday) is the biggest party in town, when residents celebrate their German heritage with food, music, and more food.

Getting Around

From May-October, you can cross the Mississippi River on the Cassville Ferry (cassville.org/ferry) that connects rural Clayton County, Iowa, with Cassville, Wisconsin. There is a fee to ride it. Follow US 52 south of Guttenberg to the Turkey River, then go east on County Highway C9Y until you see the sign for the ferry at 360th Street.

For More Information

There are practical limits to how much I can include in a book, but not with a website! Check out the city profiles on my website to see if they include listings that I couldn't fit in this book.

WISCONSIN COMMUNITIES

Prairie du Chien: MississippiValleyTraveler.com/Prairie-du-Chien
Lynxville: MississippiValleyTraveler.com/Lynxville
Ferryville: MississippiValleyTraveler.com/Ferryville
De Soto: MississippiValleyTraveler.com/De-Soto

IOWA COMMUNITIES

Lansing: MississippiValleyTraveler.com/Lansing
Wexford: MississippiValleyTraveler.com/Wexford
Harpers Ferry: MississippiValleyTraveler.com/Harpers-Ferry
Effigy Mounds: MississippiValleyTraveler.com/Effigy-Mounds-National-Monument
Marquette: MississippiValleyTraveler.com/Marquette
McGregor: MississippiValleyTraveler.com/Mcgregor
Guttenberg: MississippiValleyTraveler.com/Guttenberg

There's no shortage of stories about the Great River, which is why I started the **Mississippi Valley Traveler podcast**. In each episode, I go deep into a topic about the river's culture, history, and natural world. It helps the miles fly by as you drive the Great River Road. Find it everywhere podcasts are available, including Spotify, Apple podcasts, and YouTube.

The Architect Priest

Carlo Gaetano Samuele Mazzuchelli was born November 4, 1806, in Milan, Italy, to a wealthy merchant family. The Mazzuchellis lived on the stately Piazza Fontana in the shadows of one of the world's great houses of worship, the Milan Duomo, They were also within walking distance of the abandoned Dominican priory of Santa Maria delle Grazie, which is the home of Leonardo da Vinci's masterpiece *The Last Supper.*

A political career seemed inevitable, but at the age of 17, he shocked his family when he announced that he felt called to a religious vocation. A short time later, he joined the Dominican Order and gave up a familiar and privileged life for the alien world and privation of the American frontier.

At 22, he endured a grueling, seven-month journey to America. He arrived in Cincinnati in 1828 with only a crude understanding of English. After his ordination in 1830, he was assigned to serve Native Americans and fur traders in the outposts of the Northwest Territory: Mackinac Island, Green Bay, and Sault Ste. Marie. In 1835, his mission shifted to the growing communities in the lead mining region around Galena, Illinois, and Dubuque, Iowa. For eight years, he served Catholics in booming communities along the upper Mississippi River from Prairie du Chien to Fort Madison, Iowa.

While his ultimate purpose was to save souls, he devoted considerable energy to the construction of buildings to serve that aim. For someone with no apparent training in architecture, his buildings are stout and show a diversity of design influences—Romanesque, Gothic, Greek Revival and Italian Renaissance—and materials— wood, stone and brick. He also knew how to get the most church for the money. Using a combination of salesmanship, donated materials and labor, and his own frugality, he stretched available resources to build churches that were often a little grander than a community could afford.

Another part of his legacy is the Dominican monastery at Sinsinawa Mound in southern Wisconsin (585 County Road Z). The monastery downsized in 2023 but still maintains their motherhouse on the campus. An exhibit about Father Mazzuchelli is located in the Stone building and is well worth a visit. As this book went to press, the exhibit was scheduled to reopen in 2025. Call ahead to find out when it is open (608.748.4411). The monastery is a 15-minute drive from Galena or Dubuque.

Want to Know More? I posted a description of the extant buildings he designed at: MississippiValleyTraveler.com/Father-Mazzuchellis-Churches.

LEAD COUNTRY: DUBUQUE, GALENA & POTOSI

Dubuque, Iowa from the Julien Dubuque monument

Overview

Dubuque and Galena share a common history. Both communities owe their beginnings to lead mining and both have maintained much of their historic character. They are hardly twin cities, however. Galena is a small town with a booming tourism business, while Dubuque is a medium-sized city in the midst of a generational transition away from a manufacturing-based economy. In both cities, though, visitors will find a wealth of small businesses, unique lodging, and enough good food to stay busy and keep them dreaming of coming back.

History

DUBUQUE

In the early 1700s, Pierre-Charles Le Sueur noted the locations of lead mines in the area, but it was nearly a century later when Julien Dubuque rode into town and negotiated with the Meskwaki people for exclusive rights to mine lands west of the Mississippi River.

After Dubuque died in 1810, the Meskwaki, who still had sovereignty over their territory, were concerned about losing the mines to the Americans, so they dug out the ore and smelted lead themselves. At the same time, lead mining on the east side of the river was growing rapidly and thousands of Euro-Americans were crossing the river illegally. Many of the squatters were driven out by federal troops, but by 1832 the Meskwaki were forced to abandon the mines in the face of hostilities with nearby Dakota people.

Who Was Julien Dubuque?

Julien Dubuque's life has taken on a nearly mythical status. He didn't leave much of a paper trail, and many of the stories about his life appeared decades after he had died. Many were totally fabricated. What do we really know about him?

Dubuque was born in St. Pierre les Becquets, Quebec, in 1762. In the next 48 years, he lived in territory ruled by France, England, Spain, and America. He traveled to Prairie du Chien with his brother around 1781. In 1788, Meskwaki (Fox) leaders granted him exclusive mining rights, which he later registered with the Spanish Governor. Dubuque made good money from mining, but his efforts were superficial and left large underground deposits unexplored.

Dubuque lived more like a middle-class businessman than the backwoods trader of legend. He built a large house and staffed it with servants and farm hands. He had an extensive personal library. Dubuque was probably married, but it is not clear to whom. No written records of a wife or children exist, yet letters addressed to him while he was alive reference a "Madame Dubuque." Any reference to a wife named Potosa is pure speculation. There is no known portrait of Dubuque. The only existing painting was completed many years after he died and has an uncanny resemblance to the artist who painted it.

In 1804, Dubuque sold half of his mining claim to Auguste Chouteau (of St. Louis) to settle debts. Chouteau envied Dubuque's landholdings and was anxious to get a piece of them. When Dubuque died on March 24, 1810, rumors circulated that he was broke, but in reality, he had probably just hidden his assets. Chouteau served as Dubuque's executor and plundered the estate. Chouteau bought items at low prices, then resold them on the open market (all while taking a 10% commission on each transaction). Chouteau made no effort to find Dubuque's family in Canada or to ascertain if the Meskwaki had any legitimate claims.

Dubuque's death triggered a decades-long dispute over ownership of his land that wasn't resolved until 1854 when the US Supreme Court ruled that Dubuque's original agreement with the Meskwaki was limited to mineral rights only. The Court also rejected claims by Dubuque's family and speculators who had purchased lots. The court decision cleared titles to the land for the thousands of people who had moved into the area.

The Meskwaki buried Dubuque in a dirt mound atop a bluff. Dubuque's friend, Chief Peosta, was buried next to him about five years later. Thieves raided the graves in the 19th century. When Dubuque's remains were reassembled, examiners determined that Dubuque was about 5'7" and Chief Peosta about 6'2". Dubuque's remains were re-interred on October 31, 1897, and the limestone turret dedicated. Peosta's bones, however, were fastened together and put on display in local museums. His remains were not re-buried until 1973.

A short time later, the Meskwaki lost ownership of the mines permanently as part of the settlement of the Black Hawk War.

After the land cession, mining camps quickly sprung up along the west side of the Mississippi River. The area that became known as Dubuque's Mines evolved into the town of Dubuque by 1834. While lead mining was good business, it was never as prosperous as in neighboring areas. Good agricultural prospects lured many miners into farming, and some miners left in the California Gold Rush. High water levels also plagued some mines, which prevented extracting ore. Lead mining's mercurial history was essentially finished in Dubuque by the 1850s.

The first Euro-Americans who moved into the area found a territory with no official government and lived on land for which legal ownership was still being litigated. One person described Dubuque as a lawless territory of "dram shops where armed men congregated to drink and fight." In the 1840s, Dubuque transformed from a rough-and-tumble mining camp into a civilized town, more or less. Stone and brick buildings replaced log cabins, and streets were laid out. Local industries expanded beyond mining.

In the 1840s, locals nicknamed Dubuque "Key City" because of its role in spreading development across Iowa and points west. In the 1850s, Dubuque's population grew from 3,000 to 14,000, fueled by the arrival of immigrants from Ireland and Germany. Wealthier residents built houses on the bluff. Downtown was populated with hotels that catered primarily to single men and transient families. Steamboats propelled further growth, which helped Dubuque remain Iowa's largest city until 1875.

During the Civil War, a substantial number of Dubuquers had pro-Southern leanings, even though only a small percentage of its population had ties to the South. Its Democratic politics were largely anti-Catholic and anti-foreigner, influenced by the Know Nothing movement of the day. In the 1860 presidential election, Dubuque city went for Stephen A. Douglas over Lincoln. Nevertheless, Dubuque contributed a substantial number of volunteers to the Union Army.

Although railroad construction was booming on the east side of the Mississippi River (the railroads reached Dunleith, now known as East Dubuque, in 1855), attempts to build railroads from Dubuque to the west wouldn't succeed until after the Civil War when Dubuque's first railroad bridge across the Mississippi River opened.

Even as railroads replaced steamboats, river traffic didn't fade away. Diamond Jo Reynolds moved his headquarters to Dubuque in 1874 and built a shipyard at Eagle Point that stayed active until the early 1900s. Another boatyard opened at Ice Harbor, the Dubuque Boat and Boiler Works, built iron-hulled boats until 1972.

Dubuque's population doubled between 1870 and 1900, growth due mostly to manufacturing, particularly lumber and woodworking, brewing, and meat packing. One of the best-known manufacturers was the Cooper Wagon Works, which began in the 1860s and earned a national reputation for its exceptionally solid wagons. Even as Dubuque's population grew, the city didn't see the waves of immigrants in the early 1900s that other American cities saw. By 1915, only one of eight Dubuquers was foreign born.

The city's culture was heavily influenced by Germans and therefore stung deeply by the rise in anti-German sentiment when World War I broke out. In May 1918, Iowa Governor Harding issued the infamous "Babel Proclamation" that prohibited the speaking of foreign languages in public—including on the telephone, at church, and at school. Even after World War I, anti-foreigner sentiment continued to increase in Dubuque and the Ku Klux Klan gained a foothold. Dubuquers may have been crankier than the rest of the nation in the 1920s, because the economic boom that the United States experienced had largely bypassed them. They also suffered greater hardship during the Great Depression than the country as a whole.

The economy received a boost from Roosevelt's public works projects. Two in particular had a lasting impact: the building of Lock and Dam #11 and the reshaping of Eagle Point Park. With the end of World War II, Dubuque finally caught a break. The Dubuque Packing Company found a new owner and began a robust expansion, while the John Deere Company built a massive factory at Peru Bottoms north of the city.

Dubuque fell victim to the misguided urban renewal philosophies of the 1970s and 1980s and leveled large sections of old neighborhoods as new development (and housing) pushed west. As in many other places, the anticipated new development never delivered as promised. Gradually, historic preservation took root in the 1980s and beyond.

Like many old industrial towns, the 1980s were tough in Dubuque. The recession resulted in big-time job losses, strikes, and a steep decline in union jobs. The city never regained those manufacturing jobs. Dubuque today is on the rise, though, and has attracted new jobs in the tech sector. Still, the city remains something of an enigma. What can you say about a town that has elected as mayors an avid Harley rider known as "Poor Boy" and a nun?

EAST DUBUQUE

Native Americans built numerous mounds on the hills above East Dubuque 1,500 to 2,200 years ago. One of the first Euro-Americans to move into the area was Eleazor Frentress, who arrived in 1827. Thomas Jordan showed up five years later and got a license to operate a ferry across the Mississippi River, so the community was therefore known as Jordan's Ferry for a while.

A town was platted nearby in 1853 and named Dunleith, perhaps in honor of a Scottish city that may or may not have ever existed. (There is no town named Dunleith in Scotland today.) Dunleith got a big boost in 1855 with the arrival of the Illinois Central Railroad. It triggered an economic boom that lasted for the next decade. When Dunleith incorporated in 1856, its industry included breweries, a nail factory, farm machinery, and a barbed-wire manufacturer.

In March 1866, one hundred East Dubuque Catholics walked across the frozen Mississippi River to attend mass (their priest was ill). On the way home, the ice broke free and they were carried down river. Four bone-chilling hours later, the ice rammed into a sandbar, allowing all of them to escape unharmed.

Dunleith developed something of an unsavory reputation, so the town decided a name change was just the fix it needed. In 1879, Dunleith became East Dubuque. Old habits die hard, however, and the town couldn't shed its rough-and-tumble image. A riot erupted on June 30, 1919, the day before Prohibition took effect, as anxious drinkers took out their frustrations on civic landmarks. Rioters damaged city hall and the fire station and set prisoners free from the jail.

During Prohibition, stills operated in the hills and islands. Al Capone was reputed to be involved in the local liquor trade. Folks began to call East Dubuque Sin City because of its speakeasies, roadhouses, and gambling halls. When Prohibition ended in 1933, Illinois enacted liquor by the drink and Iowa did not, which was good for businesses on the city's Sinsinawa Avenue.

Local doctor US Lewis got his 15 minutes of fame in 1949 when he was featured in a *Ripley's Believe it or Not* cartoon for delivering three babies in three states (Illinois, Wisconsin, Iowa) within 24 hours (seven hours, actually). The local economy received a boost in 1964 with the construction of a fertilizer plant (still around) and again in 1967 with the arrival of go-go girls (long gone-gone).

GALENA

John and Tyler Armstrong arrived from Green Bay in 1818 and built the first home in what would become Galena. They only stayed a few months, but Francisco Bouthillier, an interpreter for the British at Prairie du Chien, moved into their cabin. He also set up the first ferry service across the Fever River. A steady flow of people looking for a fresh start soon followed, including many Irish, French, and relocated Americans from south-central states like Missouri and Kentucky, followed later by immigrants from Wales.

In 1822, the US government granted Colonel James Johnson a lease to mine lead around Galena. After negotiating with local Ho Chunk (Winnebago) leaders, he got to work, and his mine flourished. In 1823, 425,000 pounds of ore were shipped down the Fever River. Just six years later, Galena exported 13 million pounds. Galena grew in nearly equal proportion, even if folks had a hard time deciding on a name. Are we La Pointe, Fever River Diggings, or Bean River Settlement? Stores and taverns opened, including a trading post owned by Frederick Dent, the father-in-law of Ulysses S. Grant.

When the *Virginia* completed the first steamboat trip up the upper Mississippi River in 1823, it became the first of many steamboats to navigate the Fever River (now called the Galena River). You wouldn't guess it by what you see today, but the Galena River used to be wider and deep enough to handle steamboats from the Mississippi (300 feet wide and 15 feet deep—several feet deeper than the Mississippi at that time).

By 1826, the town had become a bustling trading post populated with miners, gamblers, traders, rivermen, trappers, and other reputable characters. In that year, a certain Doctor Newhall observed that "neither law nor Gospel can pass the rapids of the Mississippi." By the end of the year, residents met to formally name their community. After rejecting the names Frederickstown, Jo Daviess, Harrison, and others, they settled on Galena—the Latin word for lead sulphide.

In 1828, the number of buildings in town doubled, and the population reached 800. That same year, the burgeoning town experienced its first serious flood, which had an upside when one resident caught a 106-pound catfish.

Galena suffered a brief decline from 1829–1832 when miners cut lead production to increase prices but uncertainty created by the Black Hawk War also was a factor. Once hostilities ended, however, the economy kicked into high gear again. Excitement about the area started to attract a wider range of residents, many of whom were more interested in farming, and Galena also became a regional hub for grain shipping. By 1840, there were more farmers than miners.

The 1840s were prosperous years for Galenians, with productive mines, good farming, and a growing city. For the next two decades, Galena was the richest town in Illinois and arguably its most prominent community, producing several future governors and a future US Secretary of State. By 1850, Galena counted 6,000 residents.

Lead production peaked in 1845 at 54 million pounds. In just a few years, the US had gone from importing lead from England to dominating the world lead market. Eighty percent of that lead came from the mines around Galena. By 1854, residents were increasingly concerned that the name of their river—the Fever River—might scare people away, so they petitioned the state legislature to rename it the Galena River.

The glory days were about over, however. Years of clear-cutting hillsides for mines and farms had sped up soil erosion, which sent tons of silt into the Galena River. Navigating the river became increasingly difficult. Mining was also in decline, as the remaining deposits were deeper and more expensive to extract. Further complicating matters, the railroads bypassed Galena in the 1850s. In 1858, Galena's population peaked at 14,000. Four years later, it had fallen to 10,000.

Galena was deeply affected by the Civil War. Nine men with ties to Galena served as generals in the Union Army. One of the generals, Ulysses S. Grant, was a recent transplant. Grant was a West Point graduate and 15-year Army veteran. After he retired, he failed at several private sector jobs. He and his family arrived in Galena in 1860, where he got a job as a clerk in his father's tannery business. He had lived in town for just one year when Fort Sumter was attacked and the Civil War began. Grant quickly became involved with organizing and training local recruits and would eventually answer President Lincoln's call to lead Union forces.

As men abandoned their normal trades to enlist in the Army, Galena transformed from a regional commercial hub into a center for recruiting and equipping volunteers. Several Galenians became high-ranking military officers, including Major General John Rawlins (Grant's Chief of Staff). Grant returned to Galena in August 1865 to a cheering crowd of 10,000. Galenians presented him a new, fully furnished home as a token of thanks. He was elected President of the US just three years later. The Grants returned to Galena in 1879 after a world tour—to an enthusiastic crowd again—and lived in Galena until 1881. Grant died in New York City on July 25, 1885.

By 1870, the value of farm products in the area had surpassed lead production, but the overall economic trend was down. The decline sent property values plummeting: the city's total assessment went from $1,500,000 in 1857 to $450,000 just ten years later.

Galena's economic decline is perhaps the main reason that the downtown core has remained intact. The city didn't have the money to tear down buildings and experiment with the latest urban renewal trends. That nearly changed in 1970 when city leaders, based upon the recommendations of outside consultants, proposed a plan to demolish 22 buildings and replace them with parking lots and strip malls. The plan triggered a revolt: Galenians voted down the plan 80% to 20%.

In short order, the process of renovating downtown buildings began. The key event may have been the collapse of one wall of the Coatsworth Building (the building that once housed the leather goods store where Grant had worked). Mayor Enisweiler turned back efforts to demolish the building. Instead, he saw it as the anchor that could kick-start rehab efforts for the whole district. It worked. In 1978, the DeSoto House Hotel got an overhaul, and momentum picked up. You can see the results as you walk down Main Street today.

POTOSI

Potosi began as a typical lead mining community. Eager miners arrived in the 1820s, before the Black Hawk War, and scoured the hollows for signs of lead. While folks knew as early as 1829 that lead sulfide deposits were abundant, little mining occurred because conditions were not stable and Americans had no legal title to the land until after the Black Hawk War. In 1832, Willis St. John and Isaac Whitaker moved in. St. John founded a mine and got rich quickly. He found a cave rife with lead and also with snakes, which is why the area around his cave became known as Snake Hollow. St. John died a pauper in 1853, however, after losing all his money in a bank crisis.

Mining took off full bore around 1835, and Snake Hollow boomed. Separate communities grew up in different sections of the hollow. Lafayette was south of Snake Hollow on the banks of the Grant River; that town was laid out in 1837. Van Buren was located in the lower portion of the hollow (near the Potosi Brewery), and the town was laid out in 1839. Van Buren had the first post office but Lafayette had the steamboat landing (the "Port of Potosi") and ferry service to Iowa.

In 1839, these disparate communities consolidated into a single town called Potosi. Businesses quickly moved toward the new center and out of Lafayette and Van Buren. By the time Potosi incorporated in 1841, the town claimed 1,300 residents and within a few years, it had an economy nearly as large as Galena's. The bulk of the town was concentrated along a three-mile hollow pierced with a single road. Rain often turned the road into a dangerous creek (it can still happen after torrential rain).

Like Galena, the decline of lead mining had a dramatic impact on the town's economy. Between 1849 and 1852, scores of miners abandoned Potosi for the California gold rush. They left in two waves. Potosi weathered the first wave, but the second one, fueled in part by a cholera epidemic in 1852, devastated the town. At the peak of the exodus, ferries were so busy that emigrating miners had to wait up to five days to cross the Mississippi. Another factor in Potosi's decline was the fact that Grant Slough, the area that had the steamboat port, filled with silt because of deforestation, so steamboat landings became impossible. Unable to dock at Potosi, river commerce shifted south to Dunleith (East Dubuque) and north to Cassville.

The town emptied out so quickly that incorporation was repealed in 1854. Even the town clerk's books vanished. The Chicago, Burlington, and Northern railroad reached Potosi in 1884, injecting new life back in the village. Potosi reincorporated in 1887, but by 1895 the town's population had fallen to 454 or roughly one-quarter of what it had been at its peak.

Potosi has never again experienced the economic prosperity it knew during the lead mining years, but it did settle into the life of a small town with a farm-centered economy. Today, many of its residents commute to jobs in other towns, although tourism is becoming a more important part of the local economy.

Explore on the West Bank (Iowa)

DUBUQUE

Attractions in North Dubuque

Mathias Ham was an early lead miner in the region—too early, in fact. His first attempt to make money involved organizing a group of 50 miners and taking them across the Mississippi illegally into Meskwaki lands. They were eventually forced out by federal troops. After the Black Hawk War, mining opened up and Mathias Ham moved in, legally, got rich, then lost most of his fortune. When he died, his mansion was his last remaining asset. That house is now the **Mathias Ham House Historic Site** (2241 Lincoln Ave.; 563.557.9545). Constructed of native limestone, the house looks imposing from the outside, but the interior has an understated elegance.

Eagle Point Park (2601 Shiras Ave.; 563.589.4238) was created in 1909 and underwent considerable renovation during the Depression thanks to a grant from the Works Progress Administration. If the buildings remind you of Frank Lloyd Wright, it's because the superintendent who designed them, Alfred Caldwell, was a big fan of Wright's

Prairie School architecture. Besides the impressive buildings, the park has great views of the river and no shortage of places to picnic. The park is open to auto traffic from May through October ($1/car; free for pedestrians and bicyclists). The rest of the year, take Shiras Avenue up the hill to Eagle Point Drive and follow it around the top of the bluff to a parking lot, then walk into the park.

Just downriver of **Lock & Dam #11, AY McDonald Park** (Hawthorn St. and Volunteer Dr.; 563.589.4238) has a paved walking path next to the river and picnic tables. It is also an excellent spot to watch bald eagles in the winter.

Miller-Riverview Park (2 Admiral Sheehy Dr.; 563.589.4238) is next to the Mississippi River on Schmitt Island. You'll find a Vietnam War Memorial, good views of the river, and a few spots for a picnic near the campground.

Attractions at the Port of Dubuque

AUTHOR'S PICK: The **National Mississippi River Museum & Aquarium** (350 E. 3rd St.; 563.557.9545) offers fun, enlightening exhibits about life in and around the Mississippi River. Indoor exhibits include displays of aquatic life native to Mississippi River ecosystems. Check out the fish in the Main Channel display—sturgeon, blue catfish, paddlefish, and don't even get me started on the alligator gar. There are also exhibits on the history of river navigation, two theaters, a collection of river-related art, a coastal aquarium, and exhibits on river delta ecosystems. You can virtually pilot a tow (using a computer simulation), visit the National Rivers Hall of Fame, tour the *William Black*, an old dredge, and walk through a wetland ecosystem. If that's not enough, the museum also hosts special events throughout the year.

The **Diamond Jo Casino** (301 Bell St.; 563.690.4800) offers 36,000 square feet of gaming space, with a concert venue, the Mississippi Moon Bar (563.690.2100), a 30-lane bowling alley, and several places to eat.

The **Old Shot Tower** (on the riverfront) was built in 1856 to manufacture lead shot. Molten lead was hauled to the top and poured through a series of screens that shaped it into pellets. A water bath at the bottom cooled and hardened the pieces. You'll find it towering over the riverfront across the railroad tracks from the winery.

Attractions Downtown

Lower Main Street was the heart of the original (1833) commercial district. The **Town Clock**, a Main Street landmark, originally sat atop the John Bell and Company store was once famous for it accurate timekeeping. In 1971, the 13-ton clock was placed on a pedestal and surrounded by a plaza, which is now a popular place for summer events.

The standout **Dubuque County Courthouse** (720 Central Ave.) is a masterful, if over-the-top, Beaux Arts building designed by Fridolin Heer and completed in 1891. Built with gray Indiana limestone, red brick, and terra cotta, the exterior is marked by intricate brick work, steeples, Grecian pediments, statues, and a 190-foot-tall tower with a 14-foot bronze statue of Justice atop it. The gilt dome was added in the 1980s.

Check the schedule at the **Five Flags Center** (405 Main St.; 563.589.4254) for concerts and performing arts.

The **Dubuque Museum of Art** (701 Locust St.; 563.557.1851) has a few Grant Wood paintings on permanent display but otherwise hosts rotating exhibits.

The **Fenelon Place Elevator** (4th St. at the bluff; 563.582.6496) was originally built for the personal use of JK Graves in 1882, who wanted an easier way to get to his home on top of the hill. In the past 120 years, the only major overhaul was in 1977 when the cars were replaced. It's a fun ride with expansive views of Dubuque from the top.

NORTHEAST DUBUQUE MAP (#1-#8)

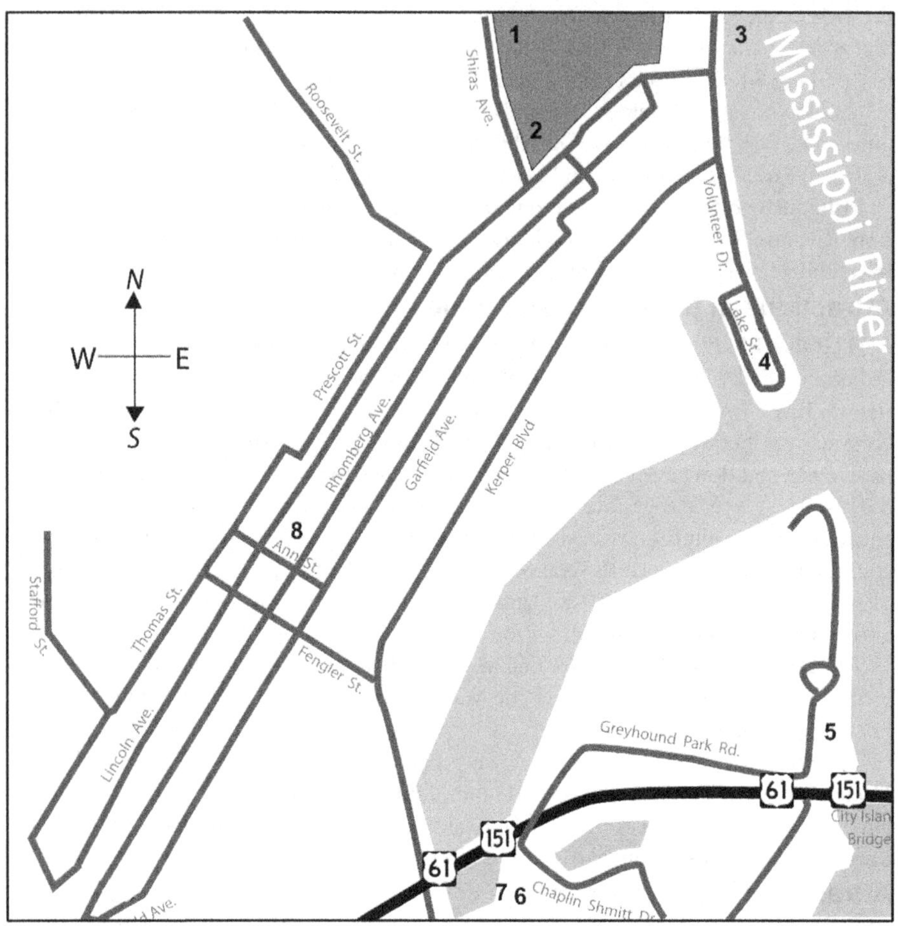

Attractions

6. American Lady Yacht Cruises
4. AY McDonald Park
41. Cathedral of St. Raphael
31. Diamond Jo Casino
23. Dubuque County Courthouse
26. Dubuque Museum of Art
1. Eagle Point Park
36. Fenelon Place Elevator
21. First Congregational UCC
33. Five Flags Center
3. Lock and Dam #11
2. Mathias Ham House Historic Site
5. Miller-Riverview Park
32. National Mississippi River Museum
28. Old Shot Tower
18. River Lights Bookstore 2nd Edition
11. Saint John's Episcopal Church
24. Smokestack
20. St. Luke's United Methodist Church
10. Steeple Square/St. Mary's Church
25. Town Clock

Where to Eat and Drink

15. Brazen Open Kitchen
7. Catfish Charlie's River Club
9. Convivium Urban Farm
39. Dimensional Brewing Company

Central Dubuque Map (#9-#41)

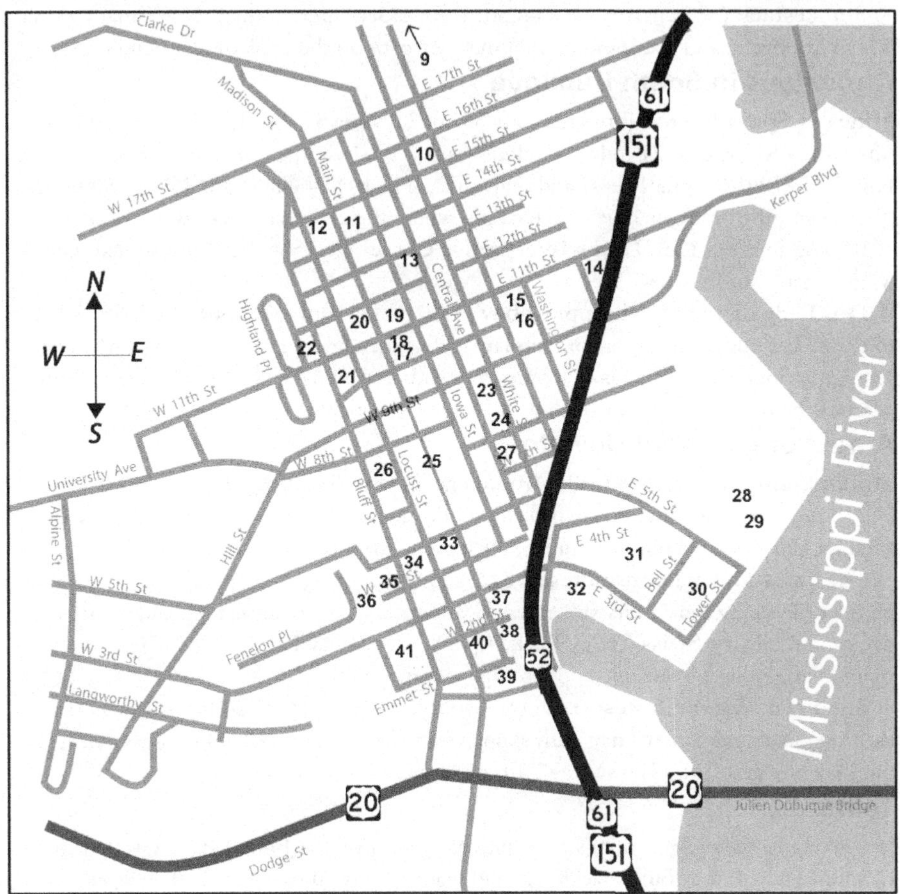

27.Dottie's Café
8. Europa Haus & Bier Stube
13. Farmers Market
19. Jubeck New World Brewing
17. L May Eatery.
35. Monk's Kaffee Pub
40. Paul's Tavern
29. Stone Cliff Winery
38. The Lift
16. Wayfarer Coffee

Where to Stay
30. Grand Harbor Resort
22. Hancock House
37. Hotel Julien Dubuque
5. Miller-Riverview RV Park
34. Redstone Inn
12. Richards House B&B

Other
14. Burlington Trailways Bus Stop

River Lights Bookstore (1098 Main St.; 563.556.4391) is an independent bookstore with a good selection of books, including many by local authors, and excellent service.

Smokestack (62 E. 7th St.) is a unique three-story entertainment venue that specializes in live music and art. Bands sometimes perform on the roof of the building.

Attractions in South Dubuque

Mines of Spain Recreation Area (563.556.0620) spreads over 1,400 acres along the Mississippi River, with 21 miles of hiking trails. The three-quarter-mile hike around Horseshoe Bluff is a fairly easy and quick hike. The park includes the Julien Dubuque Monument, the dramatic bluff-top location where the city's namesake was buried in 1810. The adjacent **E.B. Lyons Interpretive Center** (563.556.0620) houses exhibits on wildlife native to the area.

Our Lady of the Mississippi Abbey (8400 Abbey Hill Lane; 563.582.2595) is home to Cistercian nuns who live a contemplative life. They host prayer services at noon and vespers at 5pm. The public is welcome to attend. The nuns have a small organic farm and pay their expenses by producing and selling Trappistine Creamy Caramels.

Attractions West of Downtown

The **Dubuque Arboretum** (3800 Arboretum Dr.; 563.556.2100), located in Marshall Park on the city's northwest side is divided into several theme beds such as Japanese, English, sun-loving perennials, and a 900-species hosta bed.

The **Swiss Valley Nature Preserve** (13606 Swiss Valley Rd.; 563.556.6745) offers a number of hiking trails in its 500 acres of wilderness, plus trout fishing and an interpretive center. Nearby **Swiss Valley Park** (13069 Swiss Valley Rd.; 563.556.6745) offers more hiking trails, picnicking, and a campground.

Sundown Mountain Resort (16991 Asbury Rd.; 563.556.6676) will help you pass the time on a cold winter's day, with skiing from late November until mid-March. It features six lifts and 20 trails down a 475-foot slope.

Tours

If you're into seeing how things get built, take a tour of the **John Deere Factory** in Dubuque, where they build backhoes, skid loaders, and other big stuff. The 90-minute tour takes you through the manufacturing process. The tour is free, but you must submit a tour request through an online form (https://johndeeretours.deere.com).

Getting On the River

American Lady Yacht Cruises (1630 E. 16th St.; 563.557.9700) sails the Mississippi on a modern yacht. They offer daily sightseeing cruises (with an option to add lunch), plus happy hour and dinner cruises.

Drinking and Dining

The Lift (180 Main St.; 563.584.9712) is a spacious basement pub with an Irish theme in a historic downtown building.

Paul's Tavern (176 Locust St.; 563.556.9944) is a neighborhood bar with cheap beer and a lively crowd, where you can stare at animal heads behind glass while you drink.

AUTHOR'S PICK: **Jubeck New World Brewing** (115 W. 11th St.; 775.375.5692) started as a home brewing hobby and evolved into a popular microbrewery. From their home in a historic 19th century storefront, they offer a dozen or more beers on tap (and a cider or two) at any given time. It's a place tailor made for relaxing and chatting with the people around you. They also serve pizza and sandwiches.

Dubuque's Historic Churches

Downtown Dubuque's impressive architecture includes some beautiful historic churches. It's best to call in advance if you want to tour inside.

If you only have time to visit one church, head to **St. Luke's United Methodist Church** (1199 Main St.; 563.582.4543). Founded in 1833, it is home to the oldest congregation in Iowa. The current Romanesque church was completed in 1897 and is an exquisite, beautiful, sublime, stunning temple to God that is home to dozens of Tiffany art glass windows, including five large and resplendent ones. You can borrow a guidebook from the office. The church is open to visitors Monday through Thursday (9a-4p).

The Gothic Revival **Cathedral of St. Raphael and St. Patrick Church** (231 Bluff St.; 563.582.7646) was built between 1852 and 1859. The interior has frescoes created by Luigi Gregori and art glass windows imported from London in 1889. The basement has a solemn Italian marble-lined mortuary chapel (built in 1903) that was off-limits to the public until 1997.

St. Mary Catholic Church (1584 White St.; 563.582.5469) was completed in 1867 for a predominantly German parish. Designed by John Mullany, an architect with a specialty in Gothic revival design who also designed the Cathedral of St. Raphael, the structure is distinguished by a 252-foot steeple that was modeled after Salisbury Cathedral in England. Many of the art glass windows were created by Bavarian artist FX Zetteler. They were shipped from Munich in 1912, just ahead of the violence that triggered World War I. The windows depict key events in the life of Mary, beginning with her birth (west side window at the front) and ending with her death (east side window at the front). The mural of the Assumption behind the altar was painted by Matilda Brielmaier in 1912. The mural, 35 feet tall, was painted on three pieces of canvas in the artist's studio, installed in the church, and finished. The church closed in 2010 and is now an events center called **Steeple Square**. Call ahead to arrange a visit (563.235.3584).

Saint John's Episcopal Church (1410 Main St.; 563.556.0252) was founded in 1836. The current English Gothic building was finished in 1882. The limestone exterior is set off by doors painted a deep red—symbols of the blood of early Christian martyrs and Christ. The striking interior is rich in detail: a vaulted ceiling built to resemble the hull of a ship, five Tiffany windows, and a Baptismal font from 1851.

Another old congregation, the **First Congregational United Church of Christ** (255 W. 10th St.; 563.582.3648) dates to 1839; the current building was dedicated in 1860. When news of Lee's surrender reached Dubuque in 1865, the church bell was rung so vigorously that it cracked. The bell was not replaced until 1886. The sanctuary is spacious and adorned with elaborate woodwork, a Tiffany window, and an impressive organ behind the altar. The organ was installed in 1869 after a difficult trip from the manufacturer in Massachusetts. For the last leg, the organ had to be moved across the iced-over Mississippi River. The organ is still being used. The building was closed for renovations in 2024, so call ahead to find out when it can be toured again.

Dimensional Brewing Company (67 Main St.; 563.265.2693) is also a good choice for a craft beer, and one that can be bustling, especially when they host live music.

Settle in and sample some wine or locally brewed beer at the **Stone Cliff Winery** (600 Star Brewery Dr.; 563.583.6100), which is housed in the historic Dubuque Star Brewery building. Enjoy either with live music on weekend nights.

Monk's Kaffee Pub (373 Bluff St.; 563.585.0919) is about as laid-back as a coffee shop can be. The coffee is good, as one would hope, and adult beverages and live music are good reasons to go when you don't need that caffeine fix.

Dottie's Café (504 Central Ave.; 563.556.9617) has a devoted group of locals who love the burgers, but they also serve a good breakfast.

Wayfarer Coffee (955 Washington St.; 563.583.8338) is a good choice for a cup of coffee or tea in the Millwork District. They also sell pastries, soups, and sandwiches.

In a town with a strong German lineage, one would hope that it is still possible to get traditional German food. It is, thanks to **Europa Haus & Bier Stube** (1301 Rhomberg Ave.; 563.588.0361; kitchen open W-Sa). Step into the friendly Bavarian-style pub and dine on German staples like sauerbraten, Wiener schnitzel, and rouladen.

AUTHOR'S PICK: **Convivium Urban Farm** (2811 Jackson; 563.557.2900) is bringing a new vision to the food scene in Dubuque. Greenhouses on site supply some of the raw materials for breakfast and lunch, and a focus on community means that this will be a place where you can do more than eat and run. Stick around and enjoy a leisurely meal (or coffee) in the airy main seating area or the outdoor patio.

Catfish Charlie's River Club (1630 E. 16th St.; 563.582.8600) serves well-prepared steaks and seafood (including locally caught fish) in a casual atmosphere next to the marina. If the weather is nice, try to snag a table on the deck.

L May Eatery (1072 Main St.; 563.556.0505) serves fresh, handcrafted food using seasonal ingredients. Options generally include gourmet pizza, steaks, pasta, and fish dishes. The menu changes regularly.

Fine foods made with care from locally sourced ingredients fill up the menu at **Brazen Open Kitchen** (955 Washington St.; 563.587.8899). Head there for dinner or Sunday brunch. The restaurant is located in a historic brick building in the city's reinvigorated Historic Millwork District.

Step back into a more traditional dining experience at the **Morocco Supper Club** (1413 Rockdale Rd.; 563.582.2947), which has been pleasing folks for over 50 years. Sometimes it's the little touches that grab your attention, like the spreads (such as braunschweiger) that come with the bread, but they also know how to cook a good steak.

Get a taste of the traditional supper club life at **Chop's Kall Inn** (Hazel Green: 4089 Sandy Hook Rd.; 608.748.4393), located at the base of a bluff near the river. The emphasis is steak and seafood, but they do most everything well. The restaurant is ten minutes north of Dubuque in Wisconsin.

It's about a half-hour drive from downtown Dubuque, but **Breitbach's Country Dining** (Balltown: 563 Balltown Rd.; 563.552.2220) is worth the drive. It has been a local favorite for generations. Jacob Breitbach bought the town's restaurant in 1891 (it originally opened in 1852) and it has been in the Breitbach family for six generations now. The restaurant survived two devastating fires in less than a year, but the intrepid Breitbach's gave it one more shot. They are popular for their hearty country fare—deservedly so—but save room for pie.

Where to Stay

Camping

Miller-Riverview RV Park (2 Admiral Sheehy Dr.; 563.599.2852) on Schmitt Island is a popular site to camp and can feel cramped when full, which is most summer weekends. Flooding occasionally closes the park.

Massey Marina Park (9526 Massey Station Rd.; 563.556.6745) is in a shady, secluded area south of Dubuque next to the Mississippi River backwaters. Most of the sites have electricity.

Swiss Valley Park (Swiss Valley Rd.; 563.556.6745), west of Dubuque, has a compact campground with 97 sites. Most have electric hookups.

Bed and Breakfasts

Dubuque has a good selection of bed-and-breakfasts. All of these places provide a full, hot breakfast unless otherwise noted.

Richards House B&B (1492 Locust St.; 563.557.1492) rents six guest rooms, four with a private bath, in an elegant 7,000-square-foot Queen Anne mansion. While the scaffolding outside looks discouraging, the inside is a wonder, where Victorian furnishings abound. The house has stunning woodwork and unique features, like fireplaces that are lined with fairy-tale-themed tiles.

The **Redstone Inn** (504 Bluff St.; 563.582.1894) is a massive Richardsonian Romanesque mansion built by Augustin Cooper (the wagon manufacturer) in 1894 as a wedding present for his daughter (ten years after the fact; better late than never). Each of the 14 guest rooms has a private bath. The inn is within walking distance of downtown attractions.

Hancock House (1105 Grove Terr.; 563.235.0000) occupies a lovely 1891 bluff-top Queen Anne home with great views of Dubuque and the river and within walking distance of downtown. The nine rooms are in pristine condition and most have a Jacuzzi tub; all have private baths. A full breakfast is served on weekends only.

Lodging

AUTHOR'S PICK: The historic **Hotel Julien Dubuque** (200 Main St.; 563.556.4200) is a gem, right down to the Italian marble floor in the lobby that greets you when you arrive. Rooms range from spacious suites to cozy singles. All have luxury amenities like walk-in showers, granite countertops, and sinfully soothing bedding. The hotel also has a swimming pool, restaurant, lounge, and spa and a location convenient to many downtown attractions.

The **Grand Harbor Resort** (350 Bell St.; 563.690.4000) rents 193 rooms next to the river that come in a variety of configurations. All are comfy and equipped with a coffee pot, microwave, and refrigerator. Odd numbered rooms face the river.

AUTHOR'S PICK: For a quiet place with great views, you can't beat **Four Mounds Inn** (4900 Peru Rd.; 563.556.1908), a Craftsman-style house located on 60 bluff-top acres. The six guest rooms have period furnishings. Only the suite has a private bath. Four Mounds also rents a two-room cottage with kitchenette.

Special Events

The **farmers market** is next to City Hall (50 W 13th St.; Sa 7a-noon). In winter, the market moves indoors to the Colts Center (11th and Central Streets; Sa 9-noon). In summer, there is another farmers market on the west side of town at the county fairgrounds (Tu,Th 3p-6p).

Galena Map

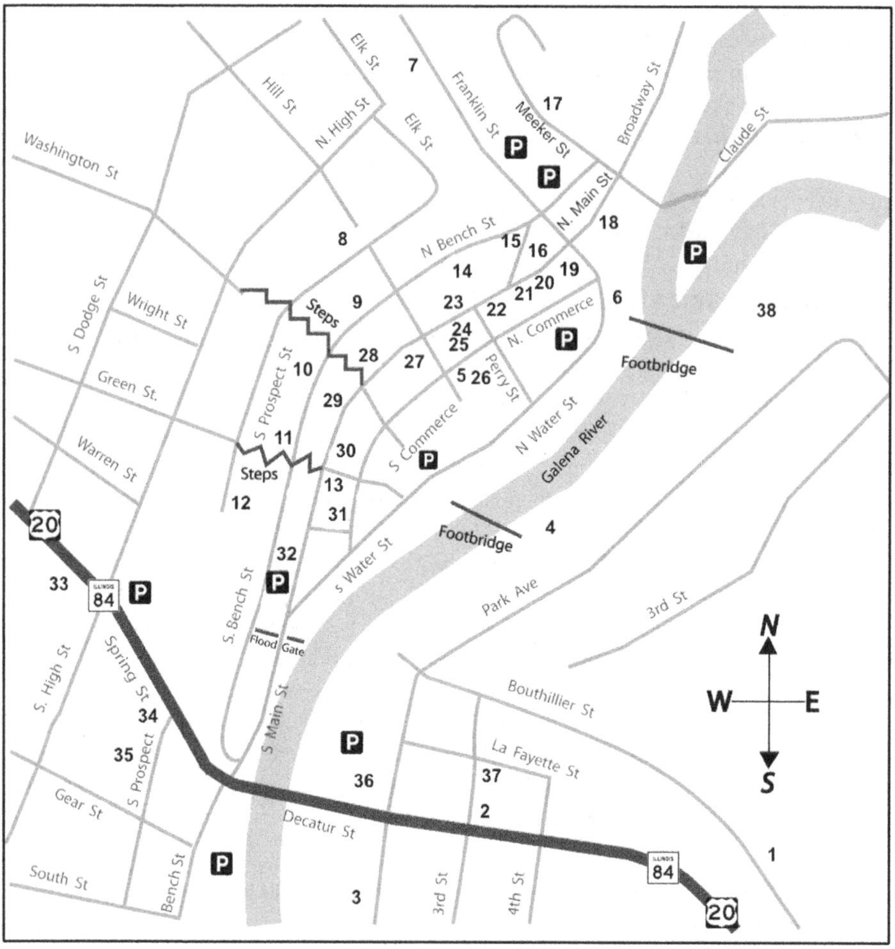

PARKING TIPS FOR GALENA

Galena can get crazy busy, especially on weekends, so parking can be a challenge. Most spots along Main Street and adjacent streets have a three-hour maximum, and the city reliably polices those spots. If you go longer than three hours, don't complain if you get a ticket. Most of the lots in those areas also charge a fee. On the other hand, the parking lots around the depot on the east side of the Galena River and around US Highway 20 are free all day. If you're planning on sticking around for a while, check there first. Otherwise, patience, persistence, and the willingness to walk are indispensable.

Galena Walking Tour

1. US Grant Home State Historic Site
2. Washburne House
3. Belvedere Mansion
4. Grant Park
5. Hello Galena
6. Old Blacksmith Shop
7. Church of St. Mary
8. Grace Episcopal Church
9. First Methodist Church
10. Galena & US Grant Museum
11. St. Michael Catholic Church
12. Linmar Gardens
13. River Bend Gallery
14. Old Stockade
15. Dowling House

Other Sites in Galena

28. Amelia's Galena Ghost Tours
38. Buehler Preserve
36. Galena River Bike Trail Access
31. Galena Trolley Depot
25. Mark Twain and the Laughing River

Where to Eat and Drink

29. Bread & Vine Bakery
26. Farmers Market
21. Fried Green Tomatoes
18. Fritz and Frites
32. Galena Bakehouse
19. Galena Brewing Company
24. Galena Cellars Vineyard & Winery
23. Galena Roasters Coffee Shop
20. Gobbie's Sports Pub & Eatery
27. La Michoacana Irmanaju
22. Log Cabin Steakhouse
16. Miss Kitty's Grape Escape

Where to Stay

33. Abe's Spring Street Guest House
37. Aldrich House
30. DeSoto House Hotel
34. Riverboat Suites
17. Jail Hill Inn
35. Steamboat House

DRIVING DIRECTIONS TO GALENA AND POTOSI

US Highway 20 connects Dubuque and Galena. It's a 20-minute drive between the two cities.

Potosi is a 25-minute drive from Dubuque. From Dubuque, follow US Highway 61 into Wisconsin, then Highway 133 into town.

Ice Fest (January; 800.226.3369) at the National Mississippi River Museum is all things frozen, including ice carving, ice harvesting demonstrations, snow sculpture, and assorted winter games.

Dubuque hosts a traditional **County Fair** (14569 Old Highway Rd.; 563.588.1999) in July, complete with rides on the midway, funnel cakes, beauty contests for cows, and cotton candy.

Stick around into August for **Dubuquefest** in Washington Park,and pick up a piece of art from a local artist.

Getting There

Dubuque Regional Airport (11000 Airport Rd.; 563.589.4127) sits nine miles southwest of downtown on US Highway 61 and is served by Avelo and Sun Country Airlines.

Burlington Trailways provides long-distance bus service to Dubuque (950 Elm St.; 319.583.3397).

Explore on the East Bank (Illinois/Wisconsin)

EAST DUBUQUE (ILLINOIS)

Attractions

Gramercy Park (Beecher St.; 815.747.3100) preserves 26 mounds from the Hopewell Period, most of which are reached by a paved walking path. Interpretive signs describe the mounds' construction and history. Being atop a bluff, the park also has some nice views of the river.

Where to Stay: Camping

Frentess Lake Campground (830 Gill Rd.; 815.747.3155) offers spacious RV sites with full hook-ups in a treeless area just outside of East Dubuque. Guests have access to the adjacent marina, a restaurant, and other amenities.

GALENA (ILLINOIS)

There's plenty to do in Galena, especially if like touring historic sites, browsing in shops and wandering without an agenda. Galena has an abundance of small, locally owned shops, and many feature the work of local artists. If you have the time, check out as many as you have the stamina for. If you're in more of a hurry, the recommendations below will help you maximize your time. In between the shopping and touring and eating, you'll also find many ways to enjoy the outdoors. A couple of days is just about the right amount of time to do Galena justice.

Central Galena Walking Tour

The best way to explore central Galena is by walking. For tips on parking see page 198. Give yourself at least half a day, longer if you tour the houses. If you want to visit one of the churches, call ahead to make sure it is open for visitor.

I suggest beginning at the former residence of President Grant, which is now the **Ulysses S. Grant Home State Historic Site** (500 Bouthillier St.; 815.777.0248). The interior has been maintained in the style in which the Grants lived in 1881 and has some impressive period pieces, although they are not original to the house.

The **Washburne House** (908 Third St.; 815.777.9406) was completed in 1845 as a single-story Greek Revival home then enlarged 16 years later. The home's namesake, Elihu Washburne, was a lawyer, politician, and friend of Grant. The future president was sitting in the library of this house in 1868 when he learned that he had won.

Nothing is subtle about the **Belvedere Mansion** (1008 Park Ave.; 815.777.0747). Built in 1857 by Russell Jones, a future ambassador to Belgium, this Italianate house was his home for barely four years. When he moved away from Galena, he took his possessions and stripped the house to the rafters. Recent owners showered love on the house and open it for public daily tours from Memorial Day to Halloween. The house is furnished with an exquisite collection of antiques, including chairs from the movie *Marie Antoinette*, furniture once owned by Liberace, and green curtains from the movie *Gone with the Wind* (no, not those curtains).

Grant Park (Park Ave.) is across the Galena River from downtown and offers good views and plenty of shade for a picnic. It was created in 1891 to honor the former President. The park has several antique cannons, including one that was part of the Confederate battery that started the Civil War by firing on Fort Sumter in 1861.

From Grant Park, take the pedestrian bridge across the Galena River to the main business district. This section includes four churches; if you want to go inside them, you should call each in advance as they are usually locked.

Stop at **Hello Galena** (121 N. Commerce St.; 815.777.1448) and browse the work of local artists, you just may take home a little something to brighten your day.

You can watch demonstrations of a craft that once seemed on the verge of disappearing (but can now be found at just about any historical park) at the **Old Blacksmith Shop** (245 Commerce St.; 815.777.9131). Kidding aside, the blacksmiths are skilled and worth watching, and you can purchase their hand-made iron products in the gift store.

Frontier priest Father Samuel Mazzuchelli (see page 183) designed the brick **Church of St. Mary** (406 Franklin St.; 815.777.2053) for a growing congregation of German parishioners. He also delivered a sermon at the first mass in December 1860. The high altar and the painting of the Assumption (just above it) were completed in 1878. The entire church has been through a series of renovations in the past 25 years and is in excellent condition.

Gothic **Grace Episcopal Church** (107 S. Prospect St.; 815.777.2590) was completed in 1849 from limestone quarried on-site. Belgian art glass windows illuminate the interior, and the oldest pipe organ in the Upper Midwest—donated to the church in 1838 by the widow of Alexander Hamilton (the first US Secretary of the Treasury)—fills it with joy. Hamilton's son, Colonel William S. Hamilton, worked the mines around Galena from the early 1820s to 1849. The impressive choir stalls and altar are walnut.

The Romanesque Revival **First Methodist Church** (125 S. Bench; 815.777.0192) was dedicated in 1857 and was once the home church for the Grant family. Their pew is still marked. The church has a dozen art glass windows that date to the church's construction (and were restored in 1980s) and a Moline Pipe Organ from 1880.

The **Galena & US Grant Museum** (211 S. Bench St.; 815.777.9129) hosts two floors of exhibits about Galena's history. The exhibits about lead mining and Galena's Civil War history are especially interesting.

The first **St. Michael Catholic Church** (227 S. Bench St.; 815.777.2053) was completed in 1842 for the astronomical sum of $14,000 but was destroyed by fire just 14 years later. Father Mazzuchelli designed the replacement. Construction started in 1856, but troubles with financing delayed completion until 1863. At 135 feet long and 60 feet wide, this is the largest church designed by Father Mazzuchelli and is arguably his finest building. In order to eliminate the need for columns inside the spacious nave, Father Mazzuchelli designed a special truss to support the roof, an innovation well ahead of its time. The interior has been through several renovations, most recently in the late 1980s. Call ahead if you want to visit the interior.

If you feel up to a good climb, take the Green Street stairs uphill (just south of St. Michael), then go left and walk to **Linmar Gardens** (504 S. Prospect St., 815.777.1177) where you can tour the three acres of waterfalls, church ruins, and architectural salvage cleverly hidden in a densely landscaped hillside above town.

Photographer Geoffrey Mikol has a gift for capturing special images of the places in and around Galena. Stop in to **River Bend Gallery** (112 N. Main St.; 815.281.9199) to see for yourself.

The last stretch takes you along Main Street. Don't rush. Take time to explore the shops, grab a bite to eat or snack on a pastry, and check out the following places.

Preserving the history of the **Old Stockade** (208 Perry St.) has been a labor of love. The building was constructed as a warehouse around 1828 in the French post-on-sill style in which logs were placed vertically on the foundation instead of horizontally. Inside the building, you will see cutaways showing the interior construction and displays of local history.

Dowling House (220 Diagonal St.; 815.777.1250) is the oldest extant house in Galena, dating to 1826. After sitting empty for 50 years, an architect from Chicago purchased the property in the 1950s and used it as a country retreat. It has since been restored to resemble a country trading post on the first floor (with some fun antique tools) and a 19th-century residence on the second floor. Guided tours only. You can buy a combo ticket with Belvedere Mansion and save a few bucks.

The **Galena River Bike Trail** runs eight miles (one-way) across a flat, crushed-rock trail, mostly shaded, that is great for biking in summer and cross-country skiing in winter. The trail begins at Depot Park (91 Bouthillier St.).

Attractions Away from Central Galena

West Street Sculpture Park (620 S. West St.; 815.777.9591) is the creation of a single artist who works on a large scale. His playful creations have titles such as *Eyeful Tower* and *Leaning Tower of Farming*. A map and description of the pieces is available from a kiosk on-site.

Galena Center for the Arts (971 Gear St.; 815.402.3111) showcases artists who work in a variety of media with special exhibitions and a retail store.

Buehler Preserve (102 Jefferson St.; 815.858.9100) is an 18-acre preserve along the south bank of the Galena River and just east of the Meeker Street footbridge. This is a good spot for an easy hike with good bird-spotting.

Just four miles from Galena, the 85 acres of **Caspar Bluff** (870 Pilot Knob Rd.; 815.858.9100) rise above the Mississippi River floodplain. The site has 51 Native American mounds, and even though many aren't visible, the most dramatic—a bird effigy—is a short walk from the parking lot at the southern end of the preserve.

On the other side of the river, **Galena Gateway Park** (9300 Powder House Hill Rd.; 815.858.9011) offers 180 acres of prairie with great views of Galena.

Horseshoe Mound Preserve (1679 N Blackjack Rd.; 815.858.9011) offers pleasant walks through prairies with dramatic views of Driftless Area topography.

Located atop a bluff about nine miles southeast of Galena, **Chestnut Mountain Resort** (8700 W. Chestnut Rd.; 815.777.1230) is a year-round resort destination. In winter, ski and snowboard on your choice of 19 trails that descend 475 feet. In summer, check out the 2,500-foot alpine slide, mini-golf, and the views of the Mississippi.

Tours

Galena Trolley Tours (314 S. Main St.; 815.777.1248) will take you around town on either a one-hour tour of historic sites or a two-hour tour of historic homes.

Gregg Painter offers guided birding tours along the Mississippi River and other habitats in the region via **Galena Birding** (815.777.0621). Call for tour times and locations.

A town as old as Galena is bound to have its share of characters who refuse to go away. **Steve Repp's All About a Ghost Tour** (DeSoto House Hotel, 230 S. Main St.; 815.777.9252) will introduce you to some of those characters and other mysteries in Galena's past while walking around town.

Amelia's Galena Ghost Tours (129 Main St.; 815.994.2868) also offers several tours into Galena's mysterious past and present, including a pub crawl and a bus tour.

Getting On the River

Ninety-minute **eco-cruises** on the Mississippi River depart from the base of the bluff below Chestnut Mountain Resort (8700 W. Chestnut Rd.; 815.777.1230).

Drinking and Dining

Enjoy a taste of locally made liquors at the **Blaum Brothers Distilling Company** (9380 W. US Highway 20; 815.777.1000). You can sample beverages on site–like their gin, bourbon, or vodka–before deciding what to take home with you.

Sample locally produced wine at **Galena Cellars Vineyard & Winery** (111 N. Main St.; 815.777.3330), then enjoy a glass or two of your favorites in the spacious building.

Miss Kitty's Grape Escape (242 N. Main St.; 815.214.0003) is a wine and martini bar, so there's something for everyone.

The **Galena Brewing Company** (227 N. Main St.; 815.776.9917) is a popular hangout for tourists and residents alike, with several taps of locally made beer at the ready, plus filling and tasty sandwiches and salads.

Galena Roasters Coffee Shop (118 N. Main St.; 815.776.0504) is obsessed with perfecting the roasting process and turning those beans into a great cup of coffee. They do a fine job with both.

In Galena, you can sample sweet treats from around the world. The **Galena Bakehouse** (421 S. Main St.; 815.402.3308) features sumptuous made-from-scratch cinnamon rolls, cookies, and macarons, as well as savory treats like quiche, empanadas, and Argentine cheesy biscuits known as chipas.

Bread & Vine Bakery (217 S. Main St.; 815.402.2100) dazzles with tartlettes, eclairs, and more macarons, plus they offer sandwiches with an international flair and flat breads that you can pair with a glass of wine or cocktail.

If that's not enough, **La Michoacana Irmanaju** (110 S. Main St.; 815.402.2284) specializes in ice cream and Mexican-style sweets.

Gobbie's Sports Pub & Eatery (219 N. Main St.; 815.777.0243) serves up gigantic sandwiches and awesome pizza with crusts from thin to pan-thick in a sports-bar atmosphere.

Frank O'Dowd's Pub (Irish Cottage Boutique Hotel, 9853 US Highway 20 West; 815.776.0707) serves food with a decided Irish influence, albeit a modern one. It is also a fun place to relax with a drink and take in live music.

Fried Green Tomatoes (213 N. Main St.; 815.777.3938) serves classic Italian dishes, steak, and seafood in an atmospheric restaurant housed in a restored commercial building.

Fritz and Frites (317 N. Main St.; 815.777.2004) serves an unlikely mix of German fare and classic French dishes, but the food is top-notch and the bistro setting comfortable. The menu changes with the seasons.

The **Log Cabin Steakhouse** (201 N. Main St.; 815.777.0393) is a long-time favorite of Galenians. Steak reigns supreme, but they have a host of seafood entrées, as well as some entrées with a Greek touch.

Where to Stay

Galena may be the boutique accommodations capital of the Mississippi Valley, with a healthy number of bed-and-breakfasts and small inns, although budget accommodations are rare. Rooms fill up quickly for summer weekends, so book in advance.

Camping

The **Palace Campground** (11357 US Highway 20 West; 815.777.2466) is the only full-service campground in the immediate area. It has 200 campsites on a sprawling site.

Budget Lodging

The **Grant Hills Motel** (9853 US Highway 20; 877.421.0924) has 33 updated rooms on the outskirts of Galena. All rooms have a refrigerator and some also have a microwave. All guests have use of a common kitchen and dining area, picnic area with grills, and laundry room.

The **View Motel** (US Highway 20 & State Highway 84; 815.858.2205) is 15 minutes east of Galena. It is a great bargain. Its 11 rooms are immaculate and each has a 25" flat screen TV, which may be why most summer weekends fill up well in advance.

Cabins

Galena Log Cabin Getaway (9401 W. Hart John Rd.; 815.777.4200) is only a few miles outside of Galena but feels hours removed from civilization. The eleven cabins were constructed with 19th-century techniques but furnished for the 21st century, with amenities such as a microwave, satellite TV, and small refrigerator. The property includes two miles of hiking trails and a herd of alpacas.

Bed-and-Breakfasts: In Town

Abe's Spring Street Guest House (414 Spring St.; 773.573.3453) rents two suites in a former ice house decorated with the handiwork of local sculptor and potter Charles Fach, one of the owners. One suite has a bathroom with Jacuzzi tub in a cool former root cellar. Guests have use of a private sauna and hot tub.

Riverboat Suites (328 Spring St.; 815.657.9442) rents ten rooms that won't break your budget, including six suites in a pair of 1830s buildings. All rooms have a private bath and some have a small refrigerator and microwave.

The **Steamboat House** (605 S. Prospect St.; 815.777.2317) offers five antique-rich guest rooms in the house built for another steamboat pilot/lead miner, Daniel Harris, brother of Robert Harris. Check out the period furnishings.

Aldrich House (900 3rd St.; 815.777.3323) occupies one of the first houses converted to a bed-and-breakfast in Galena. In its storied history, the solid brick home has hosted Abraham Lincoln and Ulysses Grant, and you could be next! Rooms are immaculate and tasteful, and emphasize comfort over everything else.

For a special night or two, book a stay at the **Jail Hill Inn** (319 Meeker St.; 815.534.1906). First-rate service and first-class touches make this property a popular place to stay for a luxury get away. Expect amenities such as soft bedding, a gourmet breakfast, a Bluetooth friendly sound system, and an afternoon wine and cheese plate. It is within walking distance of Main Street.

Country Escapes

AUTHOR'S PICK: The **Inn at Irish Hollow** (2800 S. Irish Hollow Rd.; 815.777.6000) is a luxurious retreat in a bucolic location. The Inn rents three spacious rooms accented with seasonal decorations. They also rent five cottages that range from simply elegant to spectacular. Some cottages have showers with four showerheads! All units have a private bath and are tastefully elegant. The setting is peaceful and isolated, all the better to savor the gourmet meals. If you are looking for a special splurge, stop looking!

Alpine-themed **Chestnut Mountain Resort** (8700 W. Chestnut Rd.; 800.397.1320) is nine miles from Galena atop a ridge with great views of the Mississippi River. The rooms are spacious, comfortable, and many have river views.

The first thing you will notice about the **Le Fevre Inn & Resort** (9917 W. Deininger Lane; 815.777.3929) is the great panoramic views, which are especially impressive at sunset. Rooms are elegant but comfortable and often a good deal for the area. The property includes five miles of hiking trails and outdoor heated pools and hot tub.

Hotels

The **DeSoto House Hotel** (230 S. Main St.; 815.777.0090) was built as a five-story hotel in 1855 in anticipation of the arrival of the railroad, but demand never lived up to expectations and the top two floors were shaved off in 1880. The building was completely renovated in the 1980s after years of neglect. The 55 rooms evoke 19th-century style without sacrificing comfort and put you in the middle of Main Street.

The **Irish Cottage Inn & Suites** (9853 US Highway 20; 815.776.0707) has 75 spacious rooms decorated with Irish County themes in a hotel/entertainment complex.

Special Events

The **Galena Farmers Market** is held on Saturday mornings at the Old Market House Square from May to October (123 N. Commerce St.; 815.777.1838).

Mark Twain and the Laughing River (111 N. Main St.; 815.777.8030) is actor Jim Post's well-regarded musical interpretation of the life of one Samuel Clemens (you might know him as Mark Twain).

The **Great Galena Balloon Race** (800.690.1287; mid-June) features 20 or more hot air balloons that lift off from Eagle Ridge Resort in Galena Territory.

The **Country Fair** (Grant Park; 815.777.0817; Columbus Day weekend) draws about 20,000 people every year for its well-regarded art and craft vendors. Plan far in advance if you want to stay around Galena for this weekend.

POTOSI (WISCONSIN)

Attractions

The **Passage Through Time Museum** (104 Main St.; 608.763.2745) hosts a modest but informative collection of local history memorabilia (such as displays about barn design, barbed wire, and the Potosi Brewery), as well as Native American artifacts from a local collector.

Hike the **Badger Hut Trail** and search for relics of the lead mining days, like the ruins of the badger huts and the Old Irish Cemetery. Look for the trail just south of St. Thomas Catholic Church.

The hottest attraction in town is one of the oldest: the **Potosi Brewery** (209 S. Main St.; 608.763.4002). The brewery was founded in 1852 by Germans Gabriel Hail and John Alrecht. Albrecht later sold his share, and Gabriel ran it until his death in 1878. John Hail, Gabriel's brother, ran the brewery until he killed himself in 1881. The brewery struggled for a few years. It even closed at one point. Adam Schumacher purchased it in 1886 and three generations of Schumachers then operated the brewery until it closed in 1972.

The building sat empty for three decades. After a massive restoration effort spearheaded by several members of the local community, the brewery reopened in 2008. The group formed a non-profit corporation (profits are funneled back to support the business or donated for other local projects). The building now houses a brewpub and two museums. **The National Brewery Museum** fills several rooms with beer industry memorabilia like neon signs, advertising posters, glasses, and mugs. Also on site is the **Potosi Brewing Company Transportation Museum**, which highlights ways that the old brewery distributed its product around the area.

Next door to the winery, visit **David Woodworks** (100 Brewery Hollow Rd.; 608.763.2047), the showroom for woodworker extraordinaire Gary David where you can buy his artfully crafted furniture. David was also one of the people responsible for bringing the Potosi Brewery back to life.

The **Potosi Recreation Area** (608.822.3501), also known as **Potosi Point**, is a narrow strip of land that juts far into the Mississippi River. The views are magnificent, especially in spring and fall when migrating birds pass by. In summer, water lilies carpet the shallow areas near shore. The Point, a popular spot to fish, is south of town, near the spot where State Highway 133 turns sharply to the west. Go forward instead of turning north, then under the railroad trestle. Follow the bumpy road for a half-mile until it ends.

Drinking and Dining

The **Potosi Brewery** (209 S. Main St.; 608.763.4002) is a top-notch and popular brewpub. The lunch menu is mostly sandwiches, wraps and salads. Try the sweet potato fries. Dinner entrées include a killer mac-and-cheese, steaks, and fish. And don't forget to sample the beer brewed on-site.

If wine is more to your liking than beer, step across the street from the brewery to **Whispering Bluffs Winery** (196 S. Main St.; 608.763.2468), where you can choose from an impressive selection of red and white wines. Many pair quite nicely with the gourmet chocolates they carry.

Where to Stay: Camping

Grant River Recreation Area (River Lane Rd.; 309.794.4527) is a compact site wedged between railroad tracks and the river. The full-service campground has 73 sites, most of which have electric. The views of the river are great, but some folks have a hard time getting used to the frequent, loud trains that pass by.

Cabins

Pine Point Lodge (219 S. Main St.; 608.763.2767) has four lovely cabins in a quiet setting on the edge of town. Small cabins sleep four, while the large cabin can sleep 12. Each includes a fully furnished kitchen, central air/heat, TV, and bedding.

Special Events

The big event of the season is **Potosi Area Fireman's Catfish Festival** (608.763.2300), which is usually held the second week of August.

The **Potosi-Tennyson farmers market** gathers every other Saturday morning from June to mid-September at the intersection of US Highway 61 and State Highway 133.

For More Information

There are practical limits to how much I can include in a book, but not with a website! Check out the city profiles on my website to see if they include listings that I couldn't fit in this book.

Dubuque: MississippiValleyTraveler.com/Dubuque
East Dubuque: MississippiValleyTraveler.com/East-Dubuque
Galena: MississippiValleyTraveler.com/Galena
Potosi: MississippiValleyTraveler.com/Potosi

More Places to Visit in Lead Country

Remnants of the lead mining era can be found in a few places outside of Galena and Dubuque:

- **St. Augustine Church** in New Diggings, Wisconsin (County Highway W; 608.965.4517) dates to 1844 and is the only existing building that stands as Father Mazzuchelli designed it. When the church was built, New Diggings was a lead mining boom town and a wild place. Father Mazzuchelli built the church to draw the miners out of the bars and brothels. The building is predominantly Greek Revival in style with a bit of Gothic flair (e.g., the pointed arches on the windows). St. Augustine closed in 1925 and sat neglected until 1959 when the Mazzuchelli Assembly 4th Degree Knights of Columbus adopted the building and began to restore it. It is usually open on summer Sunday afternoons.
- **Swindler's Ridge Museum** in Benton, Wisconsin (25 W. Main St.) displays artifacts and exhibits about the town's history during the lead mining era. It is open weekends between Memorial Day and Labor Day.
- **The Mining and Rollo Jamison Museums** in Platteville, Wisconsin (405 E. Main St.; 608.348.3301) includes the usual mining artifacts but also an underground tour of a former lead and zinc mine that was first excavated in 1845. The museum is open Wednesday through Sunday from May through October; mine tours run at specific times and should probably be booked in advance.

DUBUQUE TO CLINTON

De Immigrant Windmill; Fulton, Illinois

Overview

South of Dubuque and Galena, the rough edges of the Driftless Area smooth out and farm fields creep closer to the Mississippi River. Towns stretch out between the bluffs and the river, home to the descendants of Meskwaki and Sauk people, plus Irish, Dutch, German, and Luxembourgian immigrants. Narrow roads wind across the land through wild areas and wetlands. It's a great drive for rolling down the windows and letting the world of the Mississippi wash over you. It's an easy route to drive in a day, but you'll find yourself tempted to stop so often, why not make a weekend of it?

History: Iowa Communities

ST. DONATUS

When Flemish missionary Father Louis Hennepin came through this area around 1680, the ground was littered with bones and skulls from a major battle. He called the area Tetes des Morts or heads of the dead, which survives to this day as the name of the township in which St. Donatus is located.

Most of the people who founded the town of St. Donatus were natives of Luxembourg who left Europe in the 1840s to escape growing poverty and famine. John Noel came first, in 1838, and his brothers, Franz and Johann, joined him a short time later. In 1846, Peter Gehlen arrived and founded the village. He chose to name the village after Donatus of Arezzo, a fourth century martyr who some say killed a dragon. Early residents built log cabins until they had cut up enough limestone to build more permanent structures. Gehlen built a large limestone house and barn in the late 1840s that served as his private residence, as well as the village post office, store, hotel and saloon.

St. Donatus has remained a small village closely tied to the farm economy. Things aren't much different today. Its impressive collection of 19th century Luxembourg architecture earned the entire village a spot on the National Register of Historic Places.

BELLEVUE

The future city of Bellevue was part of the six million-acre Black Hawk Purchase that opened to Euro-American settlers after the end of the Black Hawk War. John Bell was one of the first people who arrived. He platted the town in 1835 and named it Bell View, which later became Belle Vue before taking its current form.

Bellevue was one of a handful of towns in the country that received its charter directly from the US Congress. In 1835, the 24th Congress authorized the Surveyor General of Public Lands to plat Bellevue and directed the townsfolk to elect trustees within six months. Residents were apparently not in much of hurry, however, as the first Trustees were not elected until six years later.

Part of the delay may have been due to the fact that town was mired in a struggle against a group of resident outlaws. William Brown, who arrived around 1836, served as Justice of the Peace for a couple of years and built a hotel and grocery. Early on, he was suspected of masterminding a local gang of thieves and outlaws. His main rival (and one-time friend), William Warren, became Jackson County Sheriff in 1838.

Warren and 24 other men signed a secret pledge in January 1840 to drive out Brown and his gang. A couple of months later, a rash of petty crimes provided legal cover for the group to move on their plan. Warren issued a warrant for the arrest of Brown and his associates. Brown, however, found out about the warrant and the assembling posse. He and his allies retreated to his hotel and holed up. On April 1, the posse/mob of 40 armed men surrounded the hotel. Negotiations to force a peaceful surrender failed, and the town emptied out. When the posse moved in, Brown's gang fired at them, then retreated to the upper floors of the hotel. To entice them out, the mob set the building on fire. The tactic worked, and Brown's group surrendered.

Four men in the posse died in the gun battle, as did Brown and two of his men. Thirteen men associated with Brown were arrested; a few others escaped. After their capture, the mob wanted to hang the prisoners, but officials convinced them to wait a day to decide their fate. That next day, a majority of the assembly (mostly men who were in the posse) voted to whip the prisoners rather than hang them.

After the whipping, the prisoners were put on skiffs on the Mississippi River with three days of supplies. The skiffs were pointed downriver, and the men were told to never return. One prisoner—William Fox—was later implicated in the murder of Col. George Davenport in Rock Island. Fox was arrested in Indiana for the crime but escaped and was never found again.

With calm restored, Bellevue residents returned to the business of building a town, which got a boost in 1872 when the railroad arrived. Bellevue became a regional hub for grain shipping. A few warehouses from that era still stand. By the end of the 19th century, Bellevue had 1,800 residents, about two-thirds of whom were German immigrants.

In the 20th century, Bellevue's economy remained connected to the river through ice harvesting, clamming, and pearl button manufacturing, but also included light industrial and manufacturing. Early 20th-century businesses manufactured clay pots, iron implements, flour, beer, lime, and cigars. Perhaps the best-known local business was Iowa Marine Engine & Launch, which built racing boats in first half of the 20th century (the Red Tops brand). One of their boats, *Red Top III*, set a record in the 1920s when it completed a course at an average speed of 35.56 MPH. Bellevue today has maintained a base of light manufacturing but also relies on tourist dollars to stay afloat.

SABULA

Early French in this area called it Prairie la Pierre or Pierre's Prairie. I don't know why, but I'm guessing a French guy named Pierre once lived there. When the town was platted in 1837, it was called Carrollport, which few folks liked, because an unpopular fellow named Carrol lived in town, and residents didn't want anyone to think the town was named for him. They renamed the town Charleston, which seemed like a good idea because there was a Savanna nearby, thus bringing a little Carolina to the Midwest. The new name proved problematic, however, because there was already a Charleston in Iowa, and mail often ended up in the wrong town. In 1846, William Hubbel—mindful of the fact that no one liked the names Prairie la Pierre, Carrollport, or Charleston—took notice of the area's exceptionally sandy soil and suggested basing the town's name on the Latin word for sand: Sabulum. According to local legend, a woman at a party liked the word but thought that "Sabula" was more elegant and easier to pronounce. Sabula incorporated in 1864.

In 1868, town leaders realized that the original town plat had disappeared, which meant that no one had legal title to their property. This being a significant inconvenience, Sabula's leaders asked the Iowa legislature for help, which granted permission for a new survey. Sabula had a solid industrial base in the late 1800s, with a meat packing plant, a sawmill, a planing mill, and a jewelry company that created sleeve buttons, combs, brooches, and other wonders from local clam shells. In the late 19th century, the backwaters around Sabula were home to a productive celery industry, but it went under when causeways and levees were built and the fields were permanently flooded.

Sabula was also an important railroad community from the time the first engine steamed into town in 1872. Trains were ferried across the river in summer. In winter, temporary tracks were laid across the ice. A railroad bridge was completed in 1880, then replaced with the current steel truss swing bridge in 1906. For a small town, Sabula had a busy depot in the early 1900s. Up to 17 passenger trains stopped in town every day. The last passenger train left the Sabula depot on April 28, 1958.

In the early 20th century, tent shows were a popular form of entertainment and Sabula was home base for two well-known companies: the Brooks Stock Company and the Marshall Players. The tent shows were part vaudeville, part circus, and part stage dramas. Some of the companies began performing in opera houses in the early 1900s. As movies took over those venues, the shows hit the road and performed under big tents.

After severe flooding in the 1950s, new levees were built that completely surrounded the village to protect it from major flooding. Still, seepage tends to fill some basements during high water. Sabula can therefore claim to be Iowa's only island city, and maybe it can also say it is the only city in Iowa that is completely surrounded by a levee.

CLINTON

Early in the 19th century, a string of small river towns lined the river where Clinton is today. Elijah Buell, a former river pilot, founded the first community when he arrived in 1835 and built a log house. This stretch of the Mississippi River was known as "the narrows" for the reason you'd think—because the river is narrower here. Buell struck a deal with his neighbor across the river, John Baker, to start ferry service between the two locations. Buell's spot would grow into a town called Lyons. Baker's town became Fulton, Illinois. The town of Lyons was platted in 1837 and incorporated in 1855.

A bit south of Lyons, Joseph Bartlett built a log cabin in the early 1830s and ran a store. The town that grew around him was called New York. It was platted in 1836 but, unlike its more famous namesake, his village fell into a deep sleep until the Iowa Land Company was organized in 1855. At that time, speculators were buying land in anticipation of the construction of a new railroad bridge. The folks around New York eventually won and got the bridge. The town's name was changed to Clinton in honor of the respected former Governor of New York, DeWitt Clinton. You probably wouldn't be surprised to learn that many of the early residents migrated from the eastern US.

The railroad's arrival spurred growth. By 1860, the town counted a thousand residents. In those early, heady days, Clinton's growth was driven almost entirely by the railroads because the city lacked a wharf big enough for steamboats. Lyons (to the north) and Camanche (to the south) remained the primary docking points for steamboats.

Clinton grew rapidly after the end of the Civil War. As the vast forests of Minnesota and Wisconsin were cleared, logs were assembled into giant rafts and floated down the Mississippi River to sawmills. Log rafts often arrived at odd hours, which would wake up the whole town. Even in the pre-dawn hours, stores and saloons opened their doors to serve the arriving raftsmen.

The first mills were built in 1855 and eventually spread over five miles of riverfront from Clinton to Lyons. Employees of the mills, many of whom were immigrants from England, Ireland, and Northern Europe (especially Denmark, Sweden, and Germany), worked 12-hour shifts, six days a week for the six months or so the mills operated. They earned less than $1.50/day on average. Work conditions were often hazardous, and many men were killed on the job. The mill owners were not obligated to care for injured employees but some did occasionally cover doctor bills for their injured workers. Fires were a constant problem. Lamb & Sons alone suffered four fires. The mills closed in the winter because logs don't float well down a frozen river. Some workers supplemented their incomes by harvesting ice from the Mississippi River.

In 1894, the citizens of Lyons approved a merger with Clinton, but Lyons maintained a separate school system until 1954. To this day, residents of the north part of Clinton are more likely to identify their hometown as Lyons than Clinton.

Lumber processing reached its peak in Clinton between 1880 and 1894 and was essentially finished by 1900. The last mill closed in 1910. In the late 1890s, as the mills closed, several thousand workers left Clinton in search of work elsewhere. Stores shuttered. Banks failed. Home were abandoned. In 1897, Clinton had 28,150 residents but only 3,100 were employed, including 700 in the last two mills that would soon close. Today there is little left of Clinton's lumber mills. The last remaining structure from any lumber-related business was razed in 1977 to make room for the levee.

The booming lumber business created a disproportionate number of millionaires in Clinton. Families such as the Youngs, Lambs, Joyces, and Curtises got very rich and built grand mansions, many along 5th Avenue South. Sadly, most of the mansions, as well as the stately elms that formed a canopy over the street, are long gone.

In the 20th century, the Curtis Company was arguably the most important employer in town. As the giant sawmills closed down, the Curtis Company continued to expand

Dubuque to Clinton Route Map

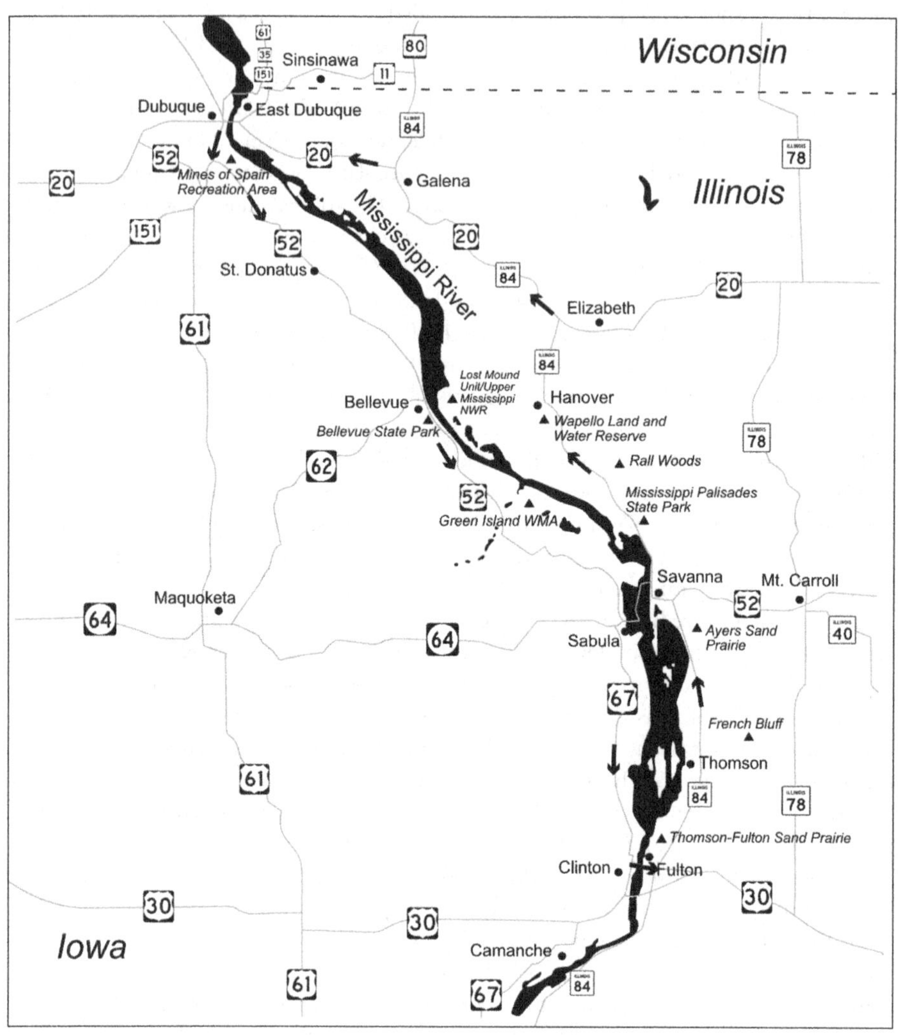

Starting on the west side from Dubuque, go south on US Highway 52. Just before Sabula, go south on US Highway 67 to Clinton. Take the US Highway 30 bridge across the Mississippi River to Fulton and the east side of the river. On the Illinois side, follow Highway 84 past Hanover. When you reach US Highway 20, you can stop in Galena or continue back to Dubuque. The entire route (starting at and returning to Dubuque) is about 130 miles.

Clinton Maps

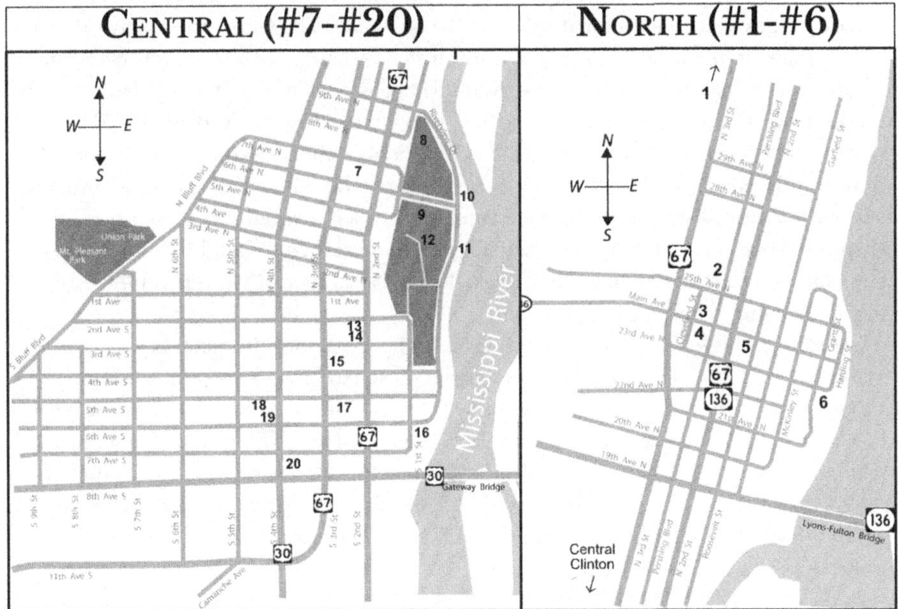

Attractions

2. Catholic Historical Center
11. Clinton Area Showboat Theater
7. Clinton County Courthouse
16. Clinton County Historical Society Museum
12. Clinton Riverview Park
18. Curtis Mansion
1. Eagle Point Park
20. Felix Adler Discovery Center
9. NelsonCorp Field/LumberKings
17. River Arts Center
6. Sawmill Museum

Where to Eat and Drink

14. 392° Caffé
10. Candlelight Inn
5. Farmer Market
15. Great Revivalist Brewery
13. Nora's Café
3. Rastrelli's Restaurant
4. Sweetheart Bakery

Where to Stay

19. Fisher House B&B
8. Riverview RV Park

A NOTE ABOUT GETTING AROUND CLINTON

Clinton has numbered streets and avenues; generally speaking, streets go north-south and avenues east-west. In order to find your way around town, please note that the avenues are numbered and divided into north and south. Thus, there are two 3rd Avenues: 3rd Avenue North and 3rd Avenue South. Clinton is also bisected by US Highway 30, also known as the Lincoln Highway, which was the first cross-country highway in the United States.

its business manufacturing window sashes, doors, and interior and exterior woodwork. Their business also grew because of an important innovation they developed: glazing window sashes at the factory instead of at the build site. The Curtis Company provided some stability in the local economy as Clinton slowly developed a more diverse manufacturing base. In 1907, Clinton Sugar Refining began operations. It would later become Clinton Corn Processing, then get absorbed into Archer-Daniels-Midland (ADM).

Much of Clinton's economy was (and still is) dependent upon the farm economy, so Clinton suffered earlier than the rest of the country when the farm economy slumped before the Great Depression. Clinton's economy got a boost during the Depression when the Works Project Administration employed local men to build Riverview Stadium and also to remake Eagle Point Park. The building of Lock and Dam #13 also provided a number of needed jobs.

Clinton was hit hard by the flood of 1965. In Lyons alone, 50 square blocks of real estate became Mississippi river bottoms, as did 25 square blocks in south Clinton. The disaster of 1965 resulted in a new, $23 million levee. Coincidentally, the following year the Curtis Corporation was no longer able to stay afloat and shut down after a century of doing business. The closure signaled hard times for the rest of town, as a number of other Clinton-area businesses also closed and the city lost nearly one-third of its population. It looks like the worst is over though. The ADM plant is growing and adding new jobs, and a casino provided a boost, too.

CAMANCHE

Dr. George Peck arrived in 1835 and founded a community called Camanche. He reportedly named the town either after the Comanche Indians—none of whom ever lived in this area—or after his race horse. I'd bet on the latter. The town seemed destined for greatness, at least within Clinton County. Camanche was the first county seat and a leading commercial center in the mid-19th century, home to mills and farm implement dealers and commercial fishing. The town also served as a major transport hub. Ferry service to Albany, Illinois, dated back to the town's founding.

Alas, the town's fate was changed forever on June 3, 1860, when an apocalyptic tornado wiped out most of the town. Dozens of people were killed and momentum for new development shifted from Camanche to Clinton. Camanche became a quiet river town, albeit one with a large country club for Clinton's wealthy families. The Camanche Club was a grand resort known throughout the area for its opulence. It even had its own power plant. The economic downturn leading up the Great Depression caused its demise, and the building was razed in the 1930s.

History: Illinois Communities

FULTON

Long before Euro-Americans arrived in this area, Native Americans (Meskwaki, Ho Chunk, and Potawatomi) were drawn here for its plentiful game and easy Mississippi River crossing. Remnants of a large Native American village were visible well into the 19th century.

John Baker set down roots in 1835, which explains why the town was first called Baker's Ferry. He built a three-room log cabin near Cattail Creek, and by 1837, he had been joined by his nephew, John W. Baker, and 27 other people. The new community was named in honor of Robert Fulton, the man who transformed steamboat travel from a rough idea to a successful business. A post office was established in 1838, and John Baker was appointed the first postmaster. It was a cush job in the early years—mail arrived only three times a month.

In 1840, Caleb Clark received the first license to operate a ferry, which kicked off a business that would last for nearly a century. Other new arrivals during this period included Michael and Catherine Reagan, immigrants from Tipperary County, Ireland, whose great-grandson, Ronald, would become President of the US in 1980.

Like much of the country, Fulton experienced a wave of industrial growth and an influx of immigrants around 1900. New industries included the Hellerstedt Carriage Company and the Ohio Stove Company (later the Mississippi Valley Stove Factory). Fulton attracted a lot of Dutch immigrants, many of whom settled south of the city center in a neighborhood known as Holland Town and worked for one of the railroads.

Fulton's industrial base was similar to its neighbors—a few sawmills, lime kilns, and a railroad roundhouse—but Fulton also was a center for clay pipe manufacturing because of the exceptional quality of the local clay. Nick Gerten opened the first factory in 1869 and three other factories opened soon after that. At their peak, the four factories produced 72,000 clay pipes every month that were used in shooting galleries and as souvenirs. The last factory closed in the 1930s.

Fulton was also home to the Patent Novelty Company. The company started manufacturing the So-E-Z Dustpan in 1906—gather up that dust without bending over!—and eventually made over a million of them a year, in spite of the occasional explosion that resulted from the combustible production process. The company expanded its production line to include mailboxes, kitchen racks, curling iron racks, and other modern conveniences. It is now called the Fulton Corporation and is still churning out mailboxes and dustpans.

THOMSON

Thomson is one of those communities that exist because of a decision made by a railroad executive. In 1864, the Western Union Railroad selected this location for their tracks, which bypassed the older and more populous community of Bluffville that was located two miles to the northeast. The first post office carried the name Sandville, but the town was eventually named after GA Thomson, one of the officers in the same railroad company that created the town. In its early years, Thomson grew as the railroads attracted stockyards, warehouses, and most of the businesses from Bluffville. The sandy soil around Thomson has sustained a melon industry for generations.

SAVANNA

Savanna sprang to life in 1828, several years earlier than most other river towns in this area. Aaron and Harriet Pierce and their four children came south from Galena, guided through the wilderness by Vance Davidson. They were soon joined by the families of William Blundell and George Davidson who reached the same spot only hours after the Pierces by traveling via the Fever River and down the Mississippi.

Luther Bowen bought the claims of the original residents and platted the town of Savanna in 1836. The town was named for the marshy plain it inhabits. Savanna had about 200 residents by 1840 and was a regular stop for steamboats. The usual businesses sprang up: hotels, a sawmill, a ferry, a brickyard. By the late 1840s, Savanna was growing steadily enough to withstand the defection of many early residents for the California Gold Rush, including Vance Davidson.

Savanna's steady economy was initially based fueled by its status as an important Mississippi River port, but railroads later filled that role. The Western Union Railroad arrived in 1865 and by 1880, a railroad bridge across the Mississippi had been completed. In 1886, the Chicago, Burlington, and Quincy Railroad also reached Savanna. At their peak, the railroad companies switched 4,500 freight cars every day.

In 1918, the federal government purchased land just north of town and established the Savanna Proving Grounds to test artillery. It would grow into a large military base called the Savanna Army Depot. Between the success of the railroads and the opening of the Proving Grounds, Savanna's population grew steadily, reaching 5,237 in 1920.

Flush with cash and facing the demands of a growing city, town leaders began a series of improvements after 1900: sewers were built, telephones installed, a power plant built, cement sidewalks laid, a library opened, parks created (including Marquette Park along the Mississippi River), and the Sabula-Savanna Bridge opened for passenger cars.

Savanna's dependence on the two major employers, however, led to dramatic fluctuations in employment and population. During the Depression, both industries struggled and had to cut jobs, but both recovered with World War II. The good times didn't last, however, and the railroad and Depot, which accounted for over half of the jobs in Savanna, scaled back their operations. Savanna lost nearly one-quarter of its population between 1970 and 1990. By the time the Savanna Army Depot officially closed on March 18, 2000, most of the damage to the local economy had already been done. Savanna today is working to revive its economy by emphasizing light industry and the tourist trade.

HANOVER

In 1827, George Charles Eams and Daniel Fowler moseyed down from Galena, found a Meskwaki and Sauk settlement along the Apple River led by Chief Wapello and immediately made a land claim. They came back in the spring of 1828 to farm and were soon joined by James Craig who built a sawmill, grist mill, and the first of many dams on the Apple River. The nascent town, known as Craigsville, lost one of its founders, Charles Eams, during the Black Hawk War.

Following the end of hostilities, the town, like many in the region, welcomed an influx of new residents. In 1836, the village was platted under the name Wapello, in honor of the Native American chief. In 1849, the resident postmaster, James White, suggested that the town's name should be changed because they were getting confused with Wapello, Iowa. Perhaps feeling a little sentimental, he recommended the name of his hometown—Hanover, New Hampshire.

Hanover held its first Fourth of July celebration in 1852. The man in charge of firing the cannon, Jesse Conant, shot it off prematurely and blew off his hand. Four years later, 60 local women followed the example of Delinda Craig, Daniel Boone's granddaughter, and took the fight for temperance literally. They attacked the town's saloon and gambling hall with ropes and crowbars and reduced the building to rubble, presumably while it was unoccupied.

One of the town's leading businesses, the Hanover Woolen Mill, opened in 1864. At its peak, the company processed 2.5 million pounds of wool each year. Raw wool came directly to the plant, where it was washed, carded, spun, woven, and finished. The company shipped finished cloth to manufacturers around the Midwest. Although the company weathered the early years of the Depression, it went out of business in 1931. The building next housed Invensys, which manufactured automotive thermostats, thermal elements, and similar heating control parts. They closed the Hanover plant in 2015.

In 1935, a representative from the Research Institute of Civic Development in Hanover, Germany, visited Hanover, Illinois. The institute was shooting a film called *Hanover, A City Wanders Over the Face of the Earth* about towns named Hanover around the world—all 77 of them. It didn't win an Oscar. (If you've seen this movie, let me know if Hanover, Illinois, got any screen time.)

Explore Down the West Bank (Iowa)

ST. DONATUS

Attractions

St. Donatus Catholic Church (97 1st St. E.; 563.583.0092) was dedicated in 1860. Interior highlights include the German Baroque altars and the Statue of Our Lady of Luxembourg on the right side of the nave. (This statue is usually on the left, but the family that paid for it sat on the right side.) Next door to the church is the rectory, which was built from the same native limestone in 1857.

The **Outdoor Way of the Cross**, behind St. Donatus Catholic Church, was completed in 1862 under the leadership of Father Michael Flammang, the same priest who directed construction of the church and school building. The path is not paved—unless you count sheep dung as paving—and it does get a bit steep—and slick—at times, but it is worth the effort to go all the way to the Pieta Chapel (built in 1885) at the top. The cemetery behind the church has some remarkable headstones from the 19th-century.

Drinking and Dining/Where to Stay

Kalmes Restaurant (100 N. Main St.; 563.773.2480) offers a fairly standard supper club-type menu with steaks and seafood, sandwiches for those with smaller appetites. They also make a handful of Luxembourgian dishes, such as homemade pork sausage.

The **Gehlen Barn & Inn** (101 Main St.; 563.213.8014), one of the oldest barns in Iowa, hosts live music that you can listen to while drinking a handcrafted beer. If you'd like to stay a while, they also rent six antique-themed rooms in a historic building next to the barn.

Special Events

In St. Donatus, **National Luxembourg Day** is celebrated in traditional Midwestern style: with a buffet dinner (Kalmes Restaurant, 100 N. Main St.; 563.773.2480; June 23 unless it falls on a weekend night). Luxembourg has been celebrating the sovereign's birthday since the 18th century. Grand Duchess Charlotte had a long reign in the early 20th century, but her birthday—January 23—was a tough time of year to throw a good party. In 1961, the official celebration was set to June 23. Dig in and enjoy the homemade noodles, cabbage, triepen (blood sausage without casing), or Wiener schnitzel.

BELLEVUE

Attractions

Bellevue State Park (563.872.4019) consists of two units south of Bellevue. The Nelson Unit (24668 US Highway 52; has hiking trails, an overlook with good views of Bellevue, and a butterfly garden. The Dyas Unit (US Highway 52 at 429th Ave.) has three short hiking trails and another overlook with a view of the Mississippi River.

Water Street Landing (307 S. Riverview St.) features the works of local and regional artists in an old riverfront warehouse that has been beautifully restored. Go down the steep driveway to reach the entrance.

Drinking and Dining

Stop in for a locally brewed pint of beer at **River Ridge Brewing** (303 S. Riverview). The family-run operation brews in small batches and regularly rotates through different styles, so you have plenty of reason to keep coming back and to enjoy your drink on the patio (in an igloo in winter!) with great views of the Mississippi.

Stop into **Moore Local** (100 N. Riverview) where you can stock up on locally produced food items, plus you can get your favorite coffee drink and sip it while enjoying good views of the Mississippi.

Check out **Field of Chocolate Dreams** (106 S. Riverview; 563.872.8090) for a wide selection of sweet delights, savory pastries, local wine, and assorted gifts, all of it housed in a delightful old storefront.

Richman's Café (602 S. Riverview St.; 563.872.3749) is a popular diner whose food will remind you of good home cooking, with hearty breakfasts, sandwiches and burgers, and daily specials like meatloaf. Save room for a slice of pie.

From late summer through fall, pick up fresh, local apples at **Gravert's Apple Basket Orchard** (54757 Highway 52; 563.687.2298), about 15 miles south of Bellevue.

Where to Stay: Camping

Just north of Bellevue, **Spruce Creek Park** (396th Ave.; 563.652.3783) rents 85 sites, all with electric and some next to the river.

Bellevue State Park's Dyas Unit (US Highway 52 at 429th Ave.; 563.872.4019) offers 47 campsites, 23 with electricity, in a secluded area that could use some shade.

Bed and Breakfasts

Mont Rest Inn (300 Spring St.; 563.872.4220) occupies the house built by Seth Baker in 1893, the founder of Glen Ellyn (Illinois) and Bakersfield (California) and a real-life rags-to-riches-to-rags story. A native of Bellevue, he got rich in the California Gold Rush, came home and built this eccentric home, then lost it—and most of his fortune—by gambling it away. The house has been through three major fires (1895, 1916, and 1997) and rebuilt each time. The inn has 12 guest rooms, each with a private bath, and guests have access to a spectacular rooftop deck and hot tub. The tower room might not be the most spacious room, but it is the coolest one.

Cabins

At **Moon River Cabins** (905 S. Riverview; 563.872.5443), you can choose from four fully rehabbed cottages next to the Mississippi River. They were originally erected in the 1930s to house Works Progress Administration workers who were building the lock and dam. Each cabin has a private bath and kitchenette.

Special Events

Look for the Bellevue **farmers market** on Thursdays from 4-6:30 (303 Riverview).

The **Jackson County Pro Rodeo** (563.872.3799) draws a large crowd to the grounds of the Bellevue Horsemen's Club (25125 297th Ave) on the third weekend in June.

SABULA

Attractions

The backwaters at **Green Island Wildlife Management Area** (515.281.5918), just north of Sabula, draw few visitors, in spite of the fantastic birding–over 250 species have been documented. The network of dirt roads and levees allows easy access deep into the protected wetlands. Follow Green Island Road from US 52 as it loops through the WMA.

Where to Stay: Bed and Breakfasts

The **Castle B&B** (616 River St.; 563.357.5467) is located on the river side of Sabula and has good views. There are three rooms for rent, or if you're a big group, you can rent the whole house. The rooms share a bath.

Floating Cottages

Island City Harbor Marina (305 South Ave.; 563.687.2825) offers a unique lodging opportunity—floating cottages (houseboats, basically). The cottages include a small kitchen and range in size from cozy for two up to large enough for a family.

CLINTON

Attractions

Eagle Point Park (3923 N. 3rd St.; 563.243.1260) is one of the most scenic parks along the upper Mississippi. There has been a park on this site since the late 1800s, no doubt because of those dramatic vistas overlooking what is now—because of the lock and dam system—one of the widest parts of the river. In the 1930s, the Works Progress Administration built several stone structures in the park, including the watchtower at the south end. You'll have no trouble finding a spot for a picnic, even on a summer evening.

The **Sawmill Museum** (2231 Grant St.; 563.242.0343) honors Clinton's lumber mill past with exhibits about log rafts, lumber barons, and milling equipment. Take time to watch the movie on the history of the industry.

Stroll through 14 acres of gardens at the **Bickelhaupt Arboretum** (340 S. 14th St.; 563.242.4771) west of downtown.

The **Catholic Historical Center at St. Boniface** (2520 Pershing Blvd.; 563.206.1314) houses artifacts from Clinton's old Catholic churches in the former St. Boniface Church, a towering Gothic revival structure built in 1908. They are usually open Tuesday mornings and Saturday afternoons, but you can call to arrange a visit, too.

The **Clinton County Courthouse** (612 N. 2nd St.) is an imposing Romanesque structure in the middle of town. Designed by G.S. Mansfield, it was completed in 1897 at a cost of $168,000. The exterior was built with red sandstone and granite, with a central tower made of copper. There's not much to see inside, except government offices.

The **Clinton County Historical Society Museum** (601 S. First St.; 563.242.1201) fills two floors and four rooms with objects and displays tied to Clinton's past. You'll find exhibits on the lumber industry and military uniforms from every US war, plus a tattered Japanese flag from WWII. There's a display of dioramas that offers a peek into past lifestyles and an exhibit on Clinton native Lillian Russell who rocketed to fame as an actress. There's also a spacious room filled with large agriculture machinery.

In the late 1800s, Clinton counted 13 millionaires among its 2,000 residents, a proportion that would make many cities envious. Most of their mansions are long gone, but you can still tour one—the **Curtis Mansion** (420 5th Ave. S; 563.242.8556). George

M. Curtis built this Queen Anne-style house between 1883 and 1885. He made his fortune manufacturing windows, doors, moldings, and other wood products. The house itself is a marvel, especially on the first floor, with elegantly carved molding of richly grained woods like cherry and oak. The upstairs rooms were rented for 60 years by the Clinton Women's Club to generate revenue for house maintenance, so they lack the elegance of the first floor.

Clinton Riverview Park (563.243.1260) parallels the river just east of downtown. It is a popular spot to walk or bike, stop for a picnic lunch, swim at the public pool, or take in a Clinton Lumber Kings baseball game.

The **Clinton Lumber Kings** (563.242.0727) are a professional baseball team in the Prospect League. Games are played in Riverview Park's NelsonCorp Field, a stadium built in 1937 by the Depression-era Works Project Administration.

The **River Arts Center** (229 5th Ave. S; 563.243.3300) features a small gallery that highlights the work of local artists.

In summer, the **Clinton Area Showboat Theater** (311 Riverview Dr.; 563.242.6760) stages live shows, mostly musicals, at the Lillian Russell Theater on a restored paddlewheeler.

The **Felix Adler Discovery Center** (332 8th Ave. S; 563.243.3600) offers a science-oriented hands-on experience for kids under 12. It was named after the Clinton native who was known as the "King of Clowns" for his 50-year clowning career, much of it with the Ringling Brothers and Barnum & Bailey Circus.

Drinking and Dining

Just north of Clinton and 1.2 miles down a couple of gravel roads you'll find **Wide River Winery** (1776 Deer Creek Rd.; 563.340.5678), home to organic wines of good quality, snacks, and a beautiful blufftop setting.

For food light on your wallet but high in carbs, head to **Sweetheart Bakery** (245 Main Ave.; 563.242.4105), where you can get bismarks and long johns, turnovers, and a treat called a Blarney—a piece of sweet cake covered with frosting and rolled in crushed peanuts that is sweet but not as sweet as you might think.

Get your coffee fix at **392° Caffé** (216 S. 2nd St.; 563.484.0392), which offers the usual range of specialty coffee drinks, cute and delicious pastries, and a decent lunch.

Nora's Café (212 S. 2nd St.; 563.243.1009) serves hearty food at cheap prices with small town diner ambiance.

Rastrelli's Restaurant (238 Main Ave.; 563.242.7441) has been pleasing palates in Clinton and beyond since 1939 with sandwiches, pasta, Italian entrées, and pizza.

You can't beat the views from the **Candlelight Inn** at the Clinton Marina (511 Riverview Dr.; 563.243.3200). You can sample lighter fare like salads and sandwiches or fill on prime rib.

Can I get a hallelujah? The folks behind **Great Revivalist Brewery** (238 4th Ave. S; 563.521.2337) turned a deconsecrated Episcopal church into a temple of gustatory delight. The restaurant has been seamlessly molded into the existing historic features of the building; the mosaic art over the old altar area will quickly grab your attention. On top of that, they serve good food from breakfast through dinner that you can enjoy with their tasty craft beers.

Where to Stay: Camping

Bulger's Hollow Recreation Area (170th St.; 815.259.3628) offers primitive camping sites next to the river north of Clinton in a shaded area.

Riverview RV Park (9th Ave. North & Riverview Dr.; 563.242.3600) is open year-round, although there is no water service from October to April. The 24 sites are rather close together, but all sites have water and electric hookups. There isn't much shade, and they can't accommodate tents.

Where to Stay: Bed and Breakfast

Fisher House Bed & Breakfast (407 5th Ave. S; 563.249.8948) rents four rooms in a stunning 19th century Queen Anne masterpiece. Guests are served a full breakfast.

Special Events

The Clinton **farmers market** takes place at Lyons Square Park (Main Ave. at Roosevelt St.) on Saturday mornings (8-noon) and Wednesday evenings (4-6).

CAMANCHE

Attractions

The **Camanche Historical Society** (1307 S. Washington Blvd.; 563.259.1285; Su 1-4) hosts a collection of historic photos, antiques, and a genealogy library. They also manage the old **Camanche Depot**, which is next to the library (102 12th Ave.).

Just south of Camanche, the **Mississippi River Eco Tourism Center** at **Rock Creek Marina** (3942 291st St.; 563.259.1876) houses an aquarium and river history displays that the kids can crawl through and around. In winter, they rent snowshoes and cross-country skis.

Getting on the River

Blue Heron Eco-Cruise offers two-hour excursions on the river from Rock Creek Marina (3942 291st St.; 563.259.1876) from June through October. Sunset cruises depart on Thursday evenings (7pm in summer/earlier in fall), but they also run occasional tours on weekend mornings. Also check the schedule for special cruises that may feature music or highlight wildlife such as mussels or eagles.

The same marina rents canoes, kayaks, and paddleboats.

Where to Stay: Camping

Located about six miles southwest of Camanche, **Rock Creek Marina and Campground** (3942 291st St.; 563.259.1876) offers a range of camping options in a shady, spacious setting. Some sites have electric hookups, but primitive sites are also available.

Where to Stay: Cabins

Rock Creek Marina and Campground (3942 291st St.; 563.259.1876) offers year-round rentals for two modern cabins, as well as six basic cabins with a microwave and small fridge but no bathroom, and a large cabin with bathroom and kitchenette. Bring your own sheets, pillows, and towels.

Explore Up the East Bank (Illinois)

FULTON

Attractions

The 62-mile **Great River Trail** runs from Rock Island to Savanna and passes through Fulton and Thomson.

There are many places in the Mississippi Valley to see ancient mounds, but few are as informative as **Albany Indian Mounds State Historic Site** (Cherry St.; 309.887.4335). The site south of Fulton protects Hopewell era-conical mounds built 1,700 to 2,200 years ago. The mound builders had extensive trade networks that stretched across much of North America. This site once had nearly 100 mounds; about half remain. Many are still visible and follow a well-groomed trail with frequent interpretive signs.

Fultonians work hard to preserve their Dutch heritage. One way they did so is by building an authentic, functional Dutch windmill next to the river in 2000 called **De Immigrant** (1st St. & 10th Ave.; 815.589.4545). Take a free tour, then stop at the gift shop and buy flour that was milled on-site.

The **Windmill Cultural Center** (10th Ave. & 1st St.; 815.589.4033) exhibits a fascinating collection of 21 windmill models built by enthusiastic hobbyists Hank and June Hielema. Some of the models are up to six feet tall and decorated with rich details, including dormered windows and brick and stone textures.

The **Fulton (Martin House) Museum** (707 10th Ave.; 563.321.0318), a two-story brick home whose pedigree stretches back to 1855, has a collection of exhibits about the town's Dutch history, the Reagan connection, and samples of products made in Fulton, including a cool coal-burning stove.

Fulton's **Heritage Canyon** (515 N. 4th St.; 815.589.4545) is also worth a look. Enjoy a pleasant walk through a replica of a historic village tucked into a narrow hallow near the Mississippi. Actors in period costumes wander the grounds during special events such as Dutch Days, the Fall Festival, and the Christmas Walk.

When the glaciers retreated at the end of the last ice age (about 13,000 years ago), an ice dam formed 40 miles downstream of Fulton that diverted the Mississippi River and created a lake that extended up to Savanna. As the flow slowed, sand and sediment settled to the bottom. After the ice dam broke and the lake drained, the river left behind sand prairies. Many of them have been lost to development, but there are still a few remnants, including the **Thomson-Fulton Sand Prairie Nature Preserve** (Railroad Lane; 815.244.3655). To get there, go north from Fulton on Illinois Highway 84, turn west on Lock Road, then take the first right. The preserve is one mile on the west side of the road. There is a gate another 0.2 miles further on Railroad Lane where you can park.

Drinking and Dining

The **Fulton Meat Market** (211 11th Ave.; 815.589.3213) has the usual supplies, plus treats like smoked herring and other Dutch food products. They also sell a variety of prepared foods, in case you want to get supplies for a picnic lunch next to the river.

Schafer Fisheries (21985 Waller Rd.; 800.291.3474), one of a dying breed of commercial fisheries along the Mississippi River, is another place to stock up for a picnic lunch. Stop in to buy live or smoked catfish, buffalo fish, carp, or frozen seafood from around the country (clams, alligator, shrimp) for that Mississippi bankside clambake.

Special Events

Fulton celebrates its Dutch heritage with **Dutch Days** (815.589.2616; 1st weekend in May), which includes a parade and traditional Dutch crafts and dancing.

THOMSON

Attractions

The **Thomson Depot Museum** (907 Main St.; 815.259.2361) has the usual relics of local history, plus railroad memorabilia, an old telephone switchboard, a cool antique post office service window, and post office boxes.

Thomson Causeway Recreation Area (1600 Lewis Ave.; 815.259.2353) is located at one of the widest spots along the Mississippi River. The area has plenty of space to picnic, fish, or just hang out next to the river. This is a popular spot on summer weekends. To get there, follow Main Street in Thomson to Lewis Avenue.

Just east of Thomson, **French Bluff State Natural Area** (2911 Scenic Bluff Rd.; 815.273.2731) was once the site of the village of Bluffville. It withered away when the railroad chose Thomson. You can hike uphill through the natural area on old service roads to a blufftop ridge, but the views of the valley are blocked by trees in the summer. Go west on Argo Fay Route, then north on Scenic Bluff Road.

Where to Stay: Camping

Thomson Causeway Recreation Area (815.259.2353) is one of the better Corps-operated recreation areas. The campground has plenty of shade and is not too cramped. Most of the 120 sites have electricity and access to drinking water.

SAVANNA

Attractions

Ingersoll Wetlands Learning Center (7071 Riverview Rd.; 815.273.2723), south of Savanna, is information central for the Upper Mississippi River National Wildlife Refuge and houses some fun exhibits. The parking lot across the road is a terrific spot for bird watching.

Ayers Sand Prairie Nature Preserve (815.244.3655) is another remnant of the sand prairie that once spread across the immediate area. It is located north of Thomson near the Savanna Airport. Head east on Airport Road for a half mile from Highway 84.

Take time to tour the **Savanna Museum and Cultural Center** downtown (406 Main St.; 815.275.1958). The centerpiece is the exhibit of Civil War soldiers created as a labor of love by a teacher, Gene Wright. He outfitted 150 mannequins in historically accurate clothing and wrote a short profile of each person depicted, which brings their stories to life.

The **Savanna Train Car Museum** (25 Main St.; 815.273.3292) showcases railroad trinkets in an old passenger rail car.

Savanna seems an unlikely place for a castle, yet somehow **Havencrest Castle** (140 N. 5th St.; 815.273.3900) is here. Francis and Margaret Greenleaf built a Queen Anne-style home atop a hill above town and the Mississippi River in 1901. After ownership changed hands multiple times Alan and Adrianne St. George transformed the house into a gilded-age mansion. It is a sight to behold. They tripled the number of rooms and filled it with fine art and exquisite furnishings. The castle is open for public tours on weekends in May and October.

The **Iron Horse Social Club** (314 Main St.; 815.273.2600) is a popular tavern in a restored 19th century building with an impressive tin ceiling and gorgeous back bar. It's a popular stop on the Harley circuit and not just for the motorcycle museum in the back.

Mississippi Palisades State Park (16327A State Highway 84; 815.273.2731) is another spectacular park along the Mississippi River. The park features a few Indian mounds, several overlooks, and an extensive trail network. A short hike on the Indian Head trail leads to a spectacular view of the Mississippi Valley. Please be careful. It's a long fall. If you are the adventure sport type, this is one of the few public parks along the Upper Miss where rappelling is allowed. Call the office to find out where it is OK.

Part of the former Savanna Army Depot is now part of the Upper Mississippi River National Wildlife and Fish Refuge, an area known as the **Lost Mound Unit** (3159 Crim Dr.; 815.273.3184), . The refuge features an overlook and a short hiking trail, with plans to develop more trails as money permits. Please stick to the areas along the road. It will take a little while to get to the overlook, because you will probably be distracted by deer and the abandoned buildings of the old depot, including the old bunkers that bear more than a passing resemblance to Indian mounds. Other parts of the unit are accessible by boat only but, if you can get to them, are fine spots for swimming and camping. Be aware that some areas along the shore are off-limits. Don't camp or park your boat in spots that are marked with "No trespassing" or "Danger" signs—but I really don't need to tell you that, do I?

Rall Woods State Natural Area (11039 S. Airhart Rd.; 815.745.3302), north of Savanna, is a good stop for a quick, moderately steep hike that leads to a nice view of the Mississippi Valley. The easiest hike is via a partially groomed trail that begins on the right-hand side of the parking lot. Some of the terrain is rocky, so wear good hiking shoes. Hiking is not recommended during hunting season, which is usually in April or May and again in late October and late November.

Drinking and Dining

Seidemann Fisheries (7634 State Highway 84; 815.677.3669), just south of Savanna, sells live, dressed, and smoked Mississippi River fish (carp, catfish, and sturgeon) for reasonable prices.

Poopy's Pub N Grub (1030 Viaduct Rd.; 815.273.4516) offers a shitload of food options night and day. Breakfast includes generous-sized pancakes and omelets. Lunch and dinner entrées are primarily grilled or fried meats served in ridiculously large portions. Poopy's also hosts live music on weekends.

Where to Stay: Camping

Seven Eagles Campground & Resort (9734 State Highway 84; 815.273.7301) is tucked between Frog Pond and Spring Lake along the River Road. They have sites with full hookups.

The sprawling campground at **Mississippi Palisades State Park** (815.273.2731) offers 241 campsites (110 with electric), many well-shaded, including several primitive sites that are accessed by a 1½ mile hike. The sites are close together in some areas.

Cabins

Tucked into a wooded hill on the north end of Savanna, **Rustic River Cabins** (www.rusticrivercabinssavanna.com) rents modern log cabins that come with spacious porches, a microwave, refrigerator, and coffee pot. Some cabins have river views.

River Rail Retreats at Palisades (563.570.0132) rents three comfortable, private cabins in a quiet setting just a short walk from Mississippi Palisades State Park. Each cabin has a spa tub, microwave, fridge, and coffee pot. Book through Airbnb.

Lodging

South of Savanna, **Seven Eagles Campground & Resort** (9734 State Highway 84; 815.273.7301) rents five immaculate motel rooms equipped with a microwave, coffee pot, and a small fridge.

Savanna Inn & Suites (101 Valley View Dr.; 815.273.2288) offers standard motel rooms at affordable prices. Rooms come with a microwave, small refrigerator, and a large parking lot.

The biker friendly **Two Wheel Inn** (330 Main St.; 815.273.2661) offers two spacious, affordable rooms above the Iron Horse Social Club in central Savanna, a popular tavern for folks on the motorcycle circuit.

Special Events

Look for the Savanna **farmers market** on Thursday afternoons (3p-6p; 708 Main St.).

HANOVER

Attractions

Just south of Hanover, the 170 acres of **Wapello Land and Water Reserve** (8642 Illinois Highway 84; 815.858.9100) mark the site of 11,000 years of Native American settlements. The site is now a nationally recognized prairie restoration area.

The **Hanover Historical Museum** (500 Fillmore St.; 815.591.3623) is a little tricky to find but worth a short diversion with several fun old photos and displays on the woolen mill. The museum is located at the back of the Hanover Township Park District building (the old elementary school). From Highway 84 turn south on Garfield, then left on Fremont to the parking lot at the end of the road.

Drinking and Dining

Rocky Waters Vineyard (2003 W. Hanover Rd.; 815.591.9706) is two short miles east of Hanover atop a ridge with great views.

Fergedaboudit Vineyard & Winery (4595 W. Speer Rd.; 815.591.2126) occupies fertile ground two miles west of Hanover. Stick around for a while to sample their wines and enjoy the views (sometimes with live music).

Special Events

Hanover hosts a **farmers market** on Saturday mornings from 9-11 (204 Jefferson St.)

Hanover's **Mallard Fest** (815.591.3512; 3rd Saturday in September) invites folks and their families to celebrate the colorful waterfowl with activities that include duck calling.

For More Information

There are practical limits to how much I can include in a book, but not with a website! Check out the city profiles below for listings that didn't fit in this book.

IOWA COMMUNITIES

St. Donatus: MississippiValleyTraveler.com/St-Donatus
Bellevue: MississippiValleyTraveler.com/Bellevue
Sabula: MississippiValleyTraveler.com/Sabula
Clinton: MississippiValleyTraveler.com/Clinton
Camanche: MississippiValleyTraveler.com/Camanche

ILLINOIS COMMUNITIES

Fulton: MississippiValleyTraveler.com/Fulton
Thomson: MississippiValleyTraveler.com/Thomson
Savanna: MississippiValleyTraveler.com/Savanna
Hanover: MississippiValleyTraveler.com/Hanover

QUAD CITIES

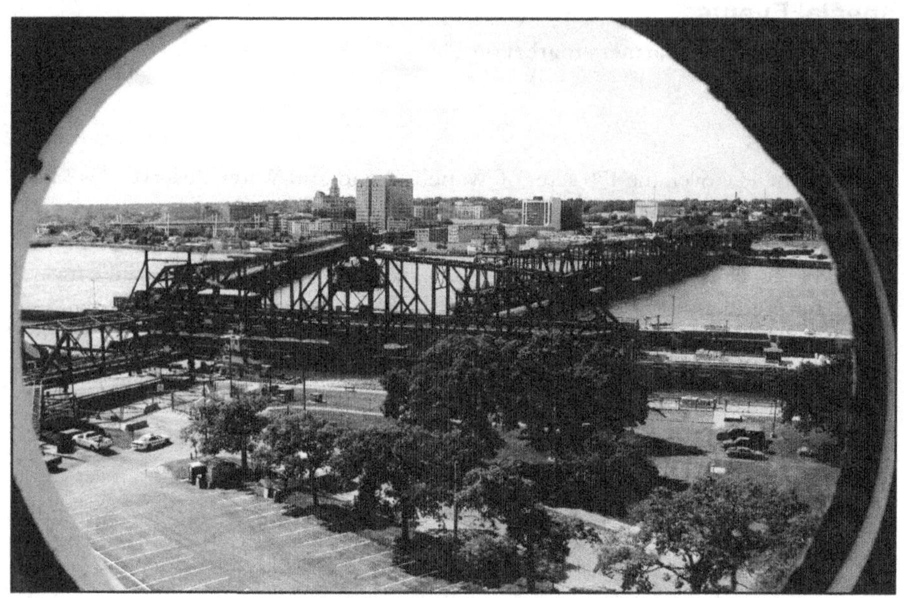

Davenport, Iowa from the Rock Island Clock Tower

Overview

Welcome to the Quad Cities, where the Mississippi River flows from east to west—to get from Iowa to Illinois you have to go south! The Quad Cities consist of the Iowa cities of Davenport and Bettendorf and the Illinois cities of Rock Island, Moline, and East Moline. Yes, around here "Quad" actually means five. The Quad Cities metro area also encompasses several smaller river towns, including the villages of Pleasant Valley, Riverdale, and LeClaire in Iowa and Hampton, Rapids City, and Port Byron Illinois.

The Mississippi River cuts through the heart of the region—*is* the heart of the region. The cities stretch from the river's banks up and over the bluffs excavated by the Mississippi River. In the Quad Cities, downtown is literally the part of town that is down the hill. The Mississippi River is the reason that people put down stakes here for centuries, and people still flock to its banks to fish, walk, gamble, or just to sit and enjoy the view. The Mississippi River unites these disparate cities into a cohesive region.

There are plenty of quality ways to pass the time and the people are among the friendliest you will meet anywhere. I know every guide makes that claim, but I genuinely mean it. So come on down. Explore the cities. Check out a festival or two. Learn about the region's fascinating history and related stories of American expansion, industrialization, and the shifting economies that continually make and remake cities.

Early History

The earliest inhabitants migrated into this region about 12,000 years ago, on the tail of one of their food sources—mastodon and mammoth. Anthropologists labeled this group Big Game Hunters. When mastodon and mammoth became extinct about 10,000 years ago, the Big Game Hunters settled into small communities of hunters and gatherers, so anthropologists called them Small Communities of Hunters and Gatherers. (Just kidding.)

The area was blessed with an abundance of natural resources and these communities flourished between 1,000 and 2,500 years ago (the Woodland Period). They had extensive trade routes with cultures as far west as the Rocky Mountains and probably deep into South America, with the Mississippi River serving as a key transit route.

In the 17th century, Sauk and Meskwaki (Fox) people moved into the areas. The two groups were closely related. They spoke a similar dialect of Algonquin and had roots in northeast Canada. The Sauk and Meskwaki were forced to migrate west for many reasons, including a need to find new hunting grounds, land pressure from advancing Europeans, and a retreat from the Haudenosaunee (Iroquois), against whom they had lost a series of battles. The Sauk had a relatively peaceful migration. They eventually settled along the Rock River, where they built a village called Saukenuk (in present day Rock Island, Illinois). In contrast, the Meskwaki were nearly wiped out en route. Those who survived sought shelter with the Sauk along the Rock River.

In the late 1820s, frustrated by increasing encroachments on Indian lands, the Sauk leader Ma-ka-tai-me-she-kia-kiak (Black Hawk Sparrow or simply Black Hawk as he came to be known) took an aggressive stand to fight back. A group led by Kiyo'kaga (Keokuk) had acceded to US demands to leave Saukenuk and had settled west of the Mississippi in 1829. Black Hawk, however, continued to return to the east side of the river from their winter homes for the next two years. When he returned to Saukenuk in 1831, he found squatters living in the lodges at Saukenuk. Any thoughts Black Hawk might have had of retaliating against the incursions were dissuaded by the presence of large numbers of federal troops that had recently moved into the area. Black Hawk instead signed a new treaty promising to stay on the western side of the Mississippi River and recognizing Keokuk as the legitimate leader of the Sauk.

Tensions between Sauk and Meskwaki people and squatters never abated, however. Euro-American settlers regularly ambushed Native communities and desecrated their graves. Meanwhile, the federal government failed to supply the corn it had promised under the terms of a treaty. Faced with starvation, some Native people returned to their ancestral lands in Illinois to harvest the remaining corn, but that only exacerbated tensions with Euro-Americans.

In the middle of this conflict, Black Hawk accepted an offer from White Cloud to relocate to a Ho-Chunk (Winnebago) village along the Rock River in north-central Illinois, which broke his agreement with the US government. Encouraged by rumors that the British would offer support, Black Hawk crossed the Mississippi in April 1832 with 800 Sauk and Meskwaki and 200 Ho-Chunk, intent on re-establishing the Sauk in ancestral lands and proving the injustice of American claims. Black Hawk's actions did not go unnoticed. Illinois rapidly organized several hundred volunteers to pursue him.

The conflict escalated into more of a lengthy game of hide-and-seek than an organized military campaign, with Black Hawk and his followers on the run most of the time trying to stay ahead of a motley group of undisciplined volunteers. Black Hawk tried to surrender at least three times, each of which was misinterpreted by the militias and led to more battles and continued retreat. The Sauk moved through northwestern Illinois and into southern Wisconsin before making a break for the Mississippi River along the Bad Axe River (north of Prairie du Chien).

On August 2, the pursuing troops finally caught up with the majority of the Sauk force. The soldiers killed many Native people along the river valley and many more as they tried to escape across the Mississippi River. The ones who managed to reach the Iowa shore were quickly attacked by a group of Dakota (Sioux) working with the American forces. Of the 1,000 people who had followed Black Hawk at the beginning of the campaign, fewer than 200 survived.

Black Hawk escaped the worst of the battle but later surrendered to the Indian agent at Fort Crawford in Prairie du Chien. In the aftermath of the war, the American government forced many Native people—even those who had cooperated with the United States—to make additional land concessions. Black Hawk and White Cloud were escorted by Jefferson Davis, the future President of the Confederate States of America, to a prison camp at Jefferson Barracks in St. Louis and spent several months in prison.

With the war over and Native Americans removed to the West, development took off and the area around the confluence of the Rock and Mississippi Rivers would grow quickly into an important transportation and manufacturing center.

THE CITIES EMERGE

Among the early Euro-Americans who moved to the area, few left bigger footprints in the Quad Cities, both literally and figuratively, than Antoine LeClaire. Born on the Michigan frontier to a French-Canadian father and a Neshnabé (Potawatomi) mother, LeClaire was a gifted polyglot. He spoke French, Spanish, English, and at least a dozen Native languages, and he put those skills to good use as a professional translator. The most valuable compensation he received was land—gifts from the Native Americans he befriended. He came to own enormous expanses of real estate in the area where the cities of Davenport, Moline, and LeClaire would later emerge. His girth grew with his wealth—he was reputed to weigh upwards of 350 pounds in his later years.

The series of rapids along this stretch of the Mississippi River made it an ideal location for building cities. For 14 miles (Davenport to LeClaire), rock outcroppings stretched across the channel. Most of the time, passing boats stopped at either end of the rapids to unload their goods and passengers, then passed through the rapids under the careful guidance of a specialized pilot. Emerging industries tapped that fast-flowing water to generate power for emerging industries.

More than 20 towns sprang up along the Mississippi River in the first seven years after Black Hawk's surrender. Many of them disappeared as quickly as they were planned. In spite of those failures, the core cities—Davenport, Rock Island, and Moline—took root and grew into important population centers. Steamboat traffic fueled trade and the presence of the rapids ensured that the Tri-Cities would serve a vital role in the transportation network. Railroads built routes to the Tri-Cities, adding to the economic momentum. Immigrants arrived from the south and the east—Germans, then Swedes, Belgians, Irish, and Greeks—pumping additional life into the region.

After the Civil War, sawmills boomed. Huge log rafts, some nearly a half-mile long, floated down the Mississippi from the pine forests of Minnesota and Wisconsin. Rock Island-based Mead, Smith, and Mersh opened a sawmill in nearby Coal Valley and hired young Frederick Weyerhaeuser as manager. When the mill in Rock Island went under, Weyerhaeuser and his brother-in-law, Frederick Denkmann, bought it. The sawmill succeeded and Weyerhaeuser and Denkmann became a dominant force in the industry.

The Weyerhaeuser mill in Rock Island closed in 1905, but the Tri-Cities remained a vibrant manufacturing center. The John Deere Company employed thousands of workers, as did other farm implement manufacturers. The downtown areas became retail centers. Universities such as Augustana College began offering classes. By 1900, the Tri-Cities region was a bustling regional hub with a total population near 100,000.

After rapid growth through the 19th century, the older Tri-Cities were joined by a couple of upstarts. The Bettendorf brothers built a huge manufacturing plant in the town of Gilbert, which promptly voted to rename itself in honor of the industrialists. Across the river, EH Guyer's dream of turning a swamp into a thriving city began to take shape when his city incorporated in 1902 as East Moline. Both cities attracted new industries and immigrants, including a substantial number of workers recruited from Mexico to fill labor shortages during World War I.

During the Great Depression, public works programs kept a lot of folks busy. One of the biggest projects was construction of a lock and dam at Davenport and Rock Island. Earlier, the Corps of Engineers had tried blasting a path through the rocks and even built a canal around them. Neither was especially effective. When Lock and Dam #15 was completed as part of a system of two dozen locks and dams on the Mississippi River, the rapids were submerged under more than ten feet of water.

World War II sent the Quad Cities' manufacturing industry into overtime. The federal government purchased the old Bettendorf factory and built tanks. Employment at the Rock Island Arsenal grew from 3,000 in 1939 to 19,000. Many of the new employees were African Americans from the South who had been recruited by the Arsenal. The flood of new workers faced a housing shortage, in part because Blacks were excluded from most neighborhoods, so the federal government built 300 apartments in Rock Island's west end.

The years immediately after World War II were often chaotic. Incomes dropped as overtime work dried up. Returning soldiers displaced women and minorities who had been hired to work during the war. Labor and management conflict that had been held in check during the war exploded into the open; labor unions fought each other for the right to represent workers. In spite of these troubles, the Quad Cities, like much of the United States, enjoyed robust economic growth. Each city annexed land and new housing subdivisions popped up seemingly overnight.

Everything changed in the 1980s, though. The area suffered a series of devastating job losses as major employers shuttered factories or went out of business: the Rock Island Railroad went under in 1980, eliminating 7,000 jobs; the IH/Case Farmall plant in Rock Island closed in 1986 and the IH/Case plant in Bettendorf followed in 1987; Caterpillar closed its Bettendorf plant in 1986 and its Davenport facility in 1987; even stalwart John Deere made deep cuts in its workforce.

The Quad Cities region today has rebounded, though. After hemorrhaging thousands of jobs in the 1980s, the region's economy diversified into the health care and service sectors. The community refocused back on the river. Riverboat gambling arrived in the early 1990s and has now expanded into land-based casinos. New parks and trails were built along the river. The arts scene is growing. People are returning to the downtown areas, some to live, some to work, and many to play along the river. The Quad Cities today have many of the amenities of bigger cities but with fewer of their problems.

Below are brief descriptions of how the major cities sprang to life.

History: Iowa Communities

LECLAIRE

The area at the upriver end of the Rock Island Rapids has long been an attractive site to build a community. In the late 1700s, French soldiers built Marin's Post just north of LeClaire at the mouth of the Wapsipinicon River to facilitate trade with local Native Americans. A hundred years later, the American Fur Company built a trading post on Smith Island (south of LeClaire).

Antoine LeClaire, the founder of Davenport and a major landowner in the area, platted a village in 1836. Eleazor Parkhurst had arrived in 1834 and was soon joined by two brothers. The three of them established a village that became known as Parkhurst (surprise!) but was renamed Berlin in 1842. In the 1830s and 1840s, riverboats landed at a small harbor near the beginning of the rapids. Both Berlin and LeClaire grew slowly through the 1840s, though. In 1848, each town counted just fifteen buildings.

By the early 1850s, the economy was picking up steam. People opened mills and lime kilns. Factories churned out plows and bricks. A busy quarry supplied limestone for the first buildings at Rock Island Arsenal and for Old Main at Augustana College. German immigrants streamed into the area, undeterred by an unusually wet trio of years that triggered deadly outbreaks of malaria and cholera.

Antoine LeClaire sold the land between the two villages to a firm headed by Adrian Davenport (no relation to Colonel George Davenport). For a short time, this section was known as Middletown. In 1855, the town of LeClaire incorporated by merging the two older villages with the upstart Middletown. Adrian Davenport served as the first sheriff of Scott County and later became the first mayor of LeClaire.

LeClaire's position at the head of the rapids ensured it would have a prominent role in river commerce. The rapids created a need for a special type of pilot to guide boats through the treacherous stretch. Philip Suiter was the first licensed rapids pilot. Many more followed, including three of his sons and a grandson.

LeClaire also had a booming business from its boat yard, the LeClaire Marine Railway. The yards built several steamboats and repaired thousands of others. LeClaire, like many thriving ports, had dozens of saloons. The southernmost one was called The First Chance, and the northernmost was called The Last Chance (or so the story goes!).

After the Civil War, logging and sawmills boosted the economies of towns all along the Mississippi, and LeClaire was no exception. One LeClaire resident, Sam Van Sant, perfected a method for steamboats to guide the massive log rafts that floated down the Mississippi.

Competition from the railroads triggered the demise of river commerce in the early 20th century and led to a significant decline for LeClaire. The town lost population through the 1930s as car ownership increased and people could drive to Davenport to do their shopping.

LeClaire's population decline finally ended when the Quad Cities landed several new factories and thousands of new jobs. This time, expanding car ownership helped LeClaire, as many people moved out of central cities and into new housing developments. LeClaire, just a 15-minute drive to Davenport, developed into a residential suburb of the Quad Cities. Today, tourism is a major industry.

BETTENDORF

The villages of Lillienthal and Gilbert might have stayed sleepy rural villages if not for the arrival of two brothers and their industrial ambitions. Brothers William and Joseph Bettendorf moved to the area and soon after revolutionized an industry. In the process, they changed the landscape of the Quad Cities.

William left home at age 13 and found a niche designing farm machinery. One of his inventions was an all-metal plow wheel. In 1886, he built in a factory in Davenport and his younger brother Joseph joined him to help run the business. For nearly 25 years, the Bettendorf brothers worked together in remarkable harmony—William as the inventor genius and Joseph as the business manager.

The Bettendorfs suffered a major setback in 1902 when a fire destroyed their Davenport factory. Community leaders in Gilbert jumped on the opportunity. They collected $15,000 to purchase a large tract of land along the river and offered the land—free—to the Bettendorfs. They accepted. In April 1903, grateful residents voted to incorporate their home town under the name Bettendorf.

Initially, the Bettendorf Company built steel wagon gears and metal parts for farm machinery. Business exploded after William designed a railroad car that was cast in a single mold. Before William's invention, railroad cars were constructed of several different parts that were bolted together and therefore had limited durability. William's invention was more stable and proved popular with the railroads. It also made the Bettendorf brothers very wealthy.

The number of Bettendorf employees grew from 300 in 1903 to 3,000 by 1920. Many of the early workers were Armenian and Greek immigrants. During World War I, however, the Bettendorfs faced serious labor shortages, so they recruited hundreds of workers from Mexico.

Most of the Mexicans who arrived in Bettendorf lived in housing that was built by the company near the river. Their neighborhood eventually became known as Holy City, perhaps because many of the workers were reportedly renamed "Jesus" by company employees who did not speak Spanish well enough to understand their real names. The neighborhood was devastated by a flood in 1926, but descendants of many of those workers still live in the region.

The Bettendorf Company peaked between 1903 and 1933. Their success gave them the capital to purchase other businesses, like the Micro Company that successfully developed and marketed a bread-slicing machine that was sold to commercial bakeries around the world. Early machines for slicing bread had been developed by a few bakeries in Davenport, but the Micro Company gets credit for spreading the technology around the world. Yes, you could say sliced bread was invented in the Quad Cities.

Even with its manufacturing prowess and diversified interests, the Bettendorf Company was hit hard by the Depression. The factory closed in 1932, and Joseph died the following year. The factory manufactured tanks during World War II, then it was sold to the Case Company before being demolished in the 1950s for the construction of a new bridge. William Bettendorf, Joseph' son, sold the last of the Bettendorf business interests in 1953 and retired the Bettendorf name from local industry.

Bettendorf has since evolved from a gritty industrial town into a bedroom community, with a standard of living substantially higher than its neighbors.

DAVENPORT

After winning the county seat battle with Rockingham, Davenport became a key port-of-call for steamboats. By 1857, it counted nearly 1,600 annual steamboat landings. Goods coming up the Mississippi River supplied not only the immediate residents of the area but also farmers living in the fertile plains to the west.

The arrival of thousands of Germans in the 1840s also gave Davenport a big boost. Most of the immigrants were political refugees from Schleswig-Holstein. When they arrived in America, they created private schools that were purely secular—a radical idea at the time—and they danced and drank on Sundays—another radical practice!

Davenport also attracted a large number of immigrants from Ireland. Around 13% of Davenport's residents claim Irish ancestry. The greatest number arrived during the famine years (*An Ghorta Mhóir*, or the Great Hunger). Many of the new citizens emigrated from County Clare, ordinary folks who were looking for a shot at a better life.

Some descendants of those early Irish immigrants achieved considerable success. Patrick Walsh, who was born in Davenport in 1855 on St. Patrick's Day, landed several contracts to build railroads in the region. He went on to found a construction company whose name is still attached to many projects around the world.

A unified community emerged after the Civil War, albeit one with a rebellious side. As Iowa tried to enact alcohol prohibition in the late 19th century, Davenport officials fought enforcement of the law within their boundaries, ensuring that its residents lived in one of the few places in Iowa where alcohol could be purchased legally. Most of the taverns were confined to a four-square-block district called Bucktown where the fun continued until sunrise at its 150 bars, 42 brothels, gambling halls, and boxing rings. Bucktown inspired Davenport's Bishop Henry Cosgrove to call his hometown "the wickedest in the nation." Nothing like showing a little hometown pride.

After remarkable growth in the 19th century, Davenport's 35,000 residents had reason to feel good. The 20th century, however, would be marked by continuing boom and bust periods. The city has persisted through the changes and is today seeing a rebirth in older parts of the city, especially downtown.

History: Illinois Communities

ROCK ISLAND

In 1831, the Illinois legislature created Rock Island County and set in motion a contentious battle for the county seat between Hampton and Farnhamsburg. An election was set for July 1833 to settle the issue, but the men of Farnhamsburg had already decided that their town would get the courthouse. They just needed to ensure that the vote confirmed their decision.

They enlisted the help of George Davenport, who was asked to summon additional voters if it appeared Farnhamsburg was lagging behind. The moment arrived and Davenport gave the signal by waving his handkerchief. The men of Hampton, though, were were ready. They saw the handkerchief and were afraid that it was intended to draw soldiers from Arsenal Island to vote, so the Hampton contingent seized the poll book and raced away. That would ordinarily have prevented any further votes from being cast.

The men of Hampton had been outwitted, though. The election clerks were alerted to the impending raid by men from Hampton, so they replaced the real poll book with a blank one. The Hampton contingent stole the blank poll book. When the Hamptoners were safely out of sight, the clerks retrieved the real book and voting continued. Farnhamsburg won.

Just two years later, the county designated a new 62-acre site as the future county seat and called it Stephenson. In 1841, the name was changed to Rock Island, and the new town expanded by annexing territory that included old Farnhamsburg.

Following consolidation in 1841, Rock Island grew into a transportation and manufacturing center. The first railroad reached town in 1854, just as steamboat traffic peaked. Charles Buford founded the Buford Plow Company in the mid-1800s, which kicked off farm implement manufacturing in the region, arguably the most important industry in the Quad Cities. By the 1870s, Rock Island three major railroads connected the city to markets from New York to San Francisco, while the Mississippi River ensured access to markets from Minneapolis to New Orleans. Construction of a railroad bridge in 1856 gave a big boost to the railroad business in Rock Island.

In the early 20th century, Rock Island was more or less ruled by a mobster named John Looney, who cultivated a culture of fear and corruption that dominated the city. The city's reputation was so foul that when future President Woodrow Wilson visited the region in April 1912, he moved the location of his speech from raucous Rock Island to mild-mannered Moline.

Like the other cities in the region, Rock Island had a tough time at the end of the 20th century, but stalwart Augustana College is a solid anchor for the east side of the city and creative efforts continue to breathe life back into the older parts of town.

ARSENAL ISLAND

The United States acquired title to Arsenal Island in 1804 through a disputed treaty with the Sauk and Meskwaki people, who challenged the validity of the treaty for many years. The first military outpost, Fort Armstrong, was built on the western end of the island in 1816. George Davenport ran the fort's commissary and lived a short distance away. The fort served as military headquarters during the Black Hawk War but closed just four years after the war ended. The last remnants of the fort were razed in 1864.

The US government lost interest in the island until the Civil War. After Confederate troops destroyed the Harper's Ferry Armory in 1861, the US needed a safe location to store armaments. Congress created the Rock Island Arsenal in 1862. It was quickly called to serve an unintended purpose: as a prison camp for captured Confederate soldiers. At its peak, nearly 8,600 Confederate soldiers were housed on the island. Rotating groups of Union soldiers served as prison guards, including a turn by the 108th Regiment, US Colored Infantry. Between 1863 and 1865, about 2,000 Confederate POWs died at the Arsenal Island camp, mostly from diseases such as smallpox and pneumonia.

Major Charles Kingsbury, the Arsenal's first commander, began construction of the first building (the Clock Tower) in 1863, but logistic and financial challenges delayed completion until 1867. The Arsenal's second commander, Brevet Brigadier General Thomas Rodman, laid out the grand plans that gave the installation its current shape: a group of ten large workshops, quarters for the commanding officer, and a bridge to connect the island to Iowa. Rodman died unexpectedly in 1871, but his plans were completed by his successor, Lieutenant Colonel Daniel Flagler.

The ten shops, each covering a full acre, were built with imposing limestone facades. They are still in use today. Quarters One, home for the commanding officer, was completed just after Rodman died. The ornate Italianate building has 19,000 square feet of living space, making it the second-largest single-family home in the government's real-

Quad Cities Route Map

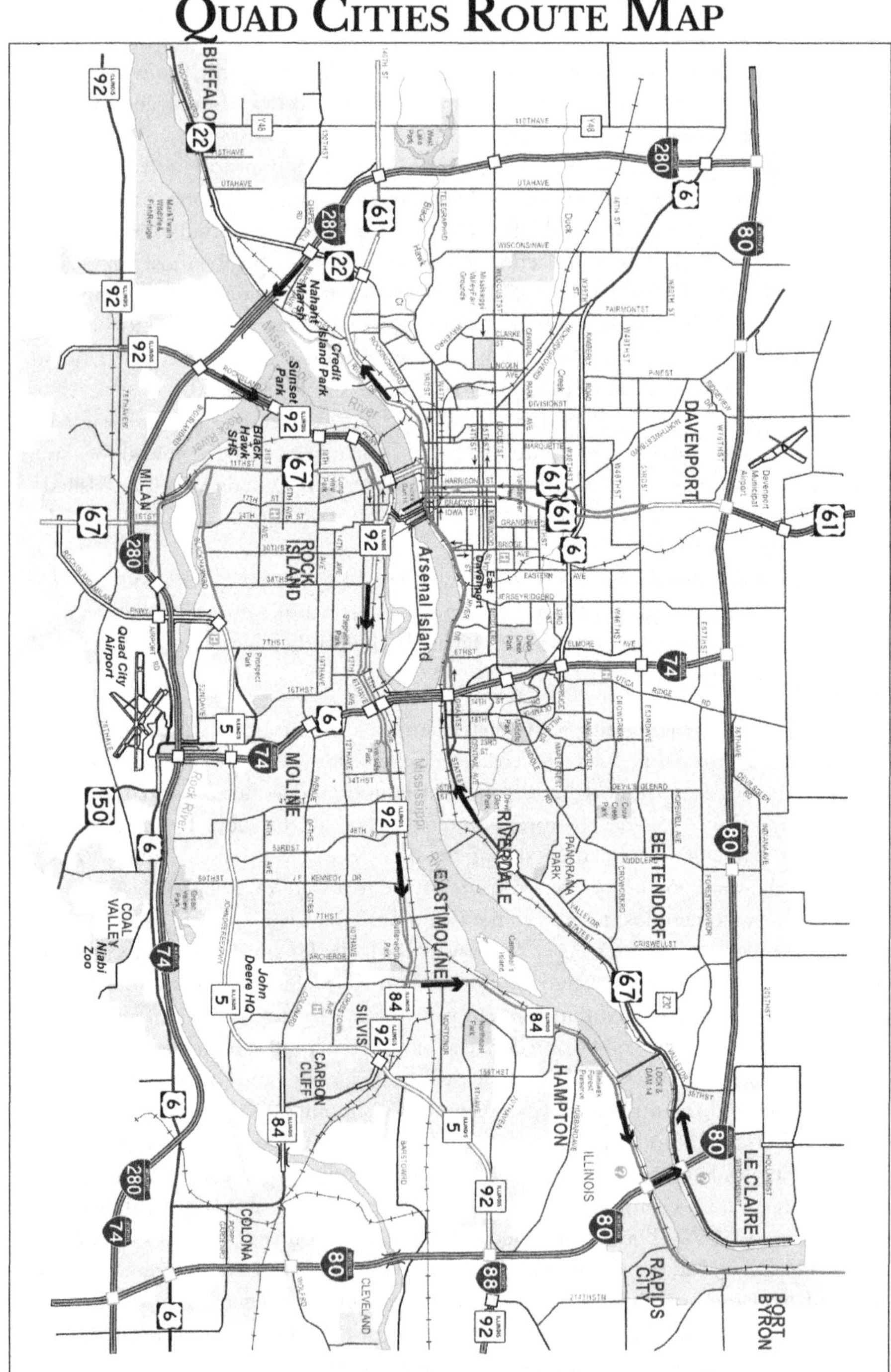

Great River Road Driving Directions/Quad Cities

This is a 43-mile circle route that runs, more or less, from the Interstate 80 bridge at the upriver end of the Quad Cities to the Interstate 280 bridge at the downriver end. On the west (Iowa) side from Interstate 80, the Great River Road follows:

- US Highway 67 to US Highway 61, then Iowa Highway 22

On the east (Illinois) side, heading back upriver from Interstate 280, the Great River Road follows:

- Illinois Highway 92 to River Drive in Moline, then Illinois Highway 84.

MISSISSIPPI RIVER BRIDGES

There are five river crossings in the Quad Cities:

- The Fred Schwengel Memorial Bridge is a functional, uninspired bridge that was completed in 1966 for Interstate 80 between LeClaire and Rapids City, Illinois.
- The Iowa-Illinois Memorial Bridge (two bridges, actually) that connects Bettendorf and Moline via Interstate 74. These visually striking bridges were built with cables that connect to form a "basket handle" arch to support the roadway. The bridge opened in 2021 and will be a Quad Cities landmark for years. The bridge also has a separate pedestrian and bicycle path.
- The historic Government Bridge (aka the Arsenal Bridge) that connects LeClaire Street in Davenport to 1st Avenue and 24th Street in Rock Island. The Government Bridge was completed in 1896 on the piers of the 1872 bridge. It is a steel truss design with a unique swing span that can rotate 360° to allow river traffic to pass.
- The Rock Island Centennial Bridge for US Highway 67 connects Gaines Street in Davenport to 15th Street in Rock Island. Completed in 1940 and paid for entirely by the city of Rock Island, the Centennial Bridge is a graceful steel arch design. It was the first four-lane bridge across the Mississippi River.
- The Interstate 280 Bridge, completed in 1970, is a sharp contrast to the area's other interstate bridge, with a graceful steel arch supporting the road deck. I bet Fred Schwengel wished this bridge carried his name. It connects Davenport and Rock Island.

estate portfolio. Only the White House is larger. The bridge Rodman envisioned was completed in 1872, then completely overhauled in 1896.

For the first dozen years of its existence, the Arsenal was only authorized to serve as a depot. In 1875, the Arsenal began manufacturing its first products for the Army and continues to do so to this day. For the most part, the Arsenal has produced small arms such as howitzers, rifles, rocket launchers, and machine guns, plus supplies like mess kits, harnesses, and canteen carriers. The main products manufactured at the Arsenal now are gun mounts, recoil mechanisms, artillery cartridges, and tools for field repairs.

The Arsenal has been a major employer for the region since its inception but especially during wartime. During World War II, employment peaked at nearly 19,000 but has more typically hovered around 2,000 employees in peacetime.

MOLINE

Moline is another municipality that was founded on land originally owned by Antoine LeClaire. He sold several parcels to early Euro-American settlers, many of whom were migrants from New England. One of them was David Sears, who built a dam between the mainland and Rock Island to power a mill. It opened in 1838 and worked out so well that he built two more. These early mills may have provided the inspiration for the town's name, which the early leaders chose because they believed it was derived from a French word for "Milltown."

John Deere moved his primary factory to Moline in 1848 because of the location's proximity to coal, transportation, and a good supply of workers. The company grew quickly and its plows—and the John Deere name—spread throughout the Midwest. Early on Deere partnered was John Gould. Deere bought him out within a few years, but Gould went on to establish a furniture factory, then a sawmill, before becoming a bank president, so he did OK for himself, anyway.

The railroads reached Moline in 1854. The following year, Moline re-incorporated, then passed strict liquor laws and new powers to maintain the city's thoroughfares. The city required able-bodied men between 21 and 50 years old to work on road projects up to three days per year. Moline's early leaders, proud of their Puritan heritage, reportedly encouraged people with inferior values to settle elsewhere, like in Rock Island.

People from many European nationalities—Swedes, Germans, Irish, and Belgians—worked the factories that lined Moline's riverfront. The Belgian community grew into the second largest in the United States. For many years Moline was home to a Belgian consulate. With the exception of the Belgians, most factory workers actually lived in Davenport or Rock Island, not Moline.

In 1900, Moline counted 22,000 residents, about one-quarter of whom worked in factories. John Deere alone accounted for one-third of the factory workers, with another 1,200 at Moline Plow. No wonder Moline was nicknamed "Plow City" and "John Deere Town." Many of those factories have since closed, but John Deere is still going.

EAST MOLINE

Before there was East Moline, there was the coal-mining town of Happy Hollow and a waystation called Watertown. By the time East Moline was platted in 1895, those early villages had vanished, and the land was mostly uninhabited swamp. The only signs of "civilization" were a railroad shack and one house.

Rock Islander EH Guyer had previously purchased options on the property and was ready to begin a massive public relations campaign to sell land to fulfill his dream of creating an industrial powerhouse of a city. The initial attempt to auction off plots of land, however, was a miserable failure and would have killed the whole venture except for the generosity of two men—Jeremiah Keator and Charles Deere—who stepped forward with enough cash to keep the effort alive.

Revitalized, Guyer moved on with his plans and slowly attracted business and residents. In the early years, East Moline succeeded in attracting industry, but housing construction lagged. The opening of the Rock Island Railroad yard in neighboring Silvis only exacerbated the housing shortage. It would take several years for East Moline to build enough housing to satisfy demand. East Moline today is a diverse community that is the home of one of the remaining John Deere factories.

HAMPTON

Henry McNeal left his native Canada at a young man and went west. He worked on the Great Lakes and in the lead mines around Galena for a while. In 1828, at the ripe old age of 17, he moved further south and built a log cabin next to the Mississippi River. A small community grew up around him that became known, appropriately enough, as McNeal's Landing.

The villages of Milan (not the current one but the one that was first called Well's Ferry) and Hampton, which included the older settlement of McNeal's Landing, were platted in 1837 and 1838 and both villages grew quickly. Hampton had a steamboat stop and two hotels by the late 1830s, plus a horse-powered Mississippi River ferry.

The town seemed destined for prosperity, perhaps even greatness. Alas, 19th-century political chicanery put a halt to its rapid growth. In 1833, Hampton and rival Farnhamsburg (now Rock Island) competed for the coveted county seat (see the story above under Rock Island). Farnhamsburg won the spirited contest, and Hampton was consigned to the life of a quiet river town.

Explore Down the West Bank (Iowa)

LECLAIRE

Attractions

The **Buffalo Bill Museum** (199 N. Front St.; 563.289.5580) is packed with memorabilia, photos, and antique tools. The museum's namesake was born near LeClaire, so naturally there are exhibits about his life. Other highlights of the museum include a Red Cross quilt made in 1919 and embroidered with the names of 834 donors, creepy horsehair coats, and a dog-powered butter churn. Also on-site is the *Lone Star*, a steam-powered paddlewheel towboat that was built in 1869 and operated on the Mississippi River for a remarkable 100 years (and piloted for many years by Orrin Smith, the last of the famous rapids pilots).

If you've seen the TV show *American Pickers*, check out **Antique Archaeology** (115 1/2 Davenport St.; 563.265.3939), the store run by the show's stars Mike Wolfe, Frank Fritz, and Danielle Cushman, where you may be able to find some fun antiques among all the Antiques Archaeology merch.

Getting On the River

The **Riverboat Twilight** (800.331.1467) offers 90-minute sightseeing cruises on Saturdays, as well as two-day cruises from LeClaire to Dubuque and back that leave LeClaire on Tuesdays and Thursday (Memorial Day to mid-October).

Drinking and Dining

Kick off the day with a tasty coffee or tea drink from **Cody Road Coffee** (114 N. Cody Rd.; 563.289.2436), then enjoy it at a sidewalk table and watch the world hurry by.

For a low-key way to pass the time, consider spending an afternoon or evening sipping locally made spirits like gin and vodka at the **Mississippi River Distilling Company** (303 N. Cody Rd.; 563.484.4342). They buy their raw materials from local farmers and create their beverages on site in LeClaire. Free tours are offered regularly, and you get to finish your tour with a sample. You can also relax with a cocktail at their Cody Road Cocktail House.

If spirits aren't your thing, perhaps wine is. You can sample and buy locally crafted wines at the **Wide River Winery Tasting Room** (106 N. Cody Rd.; 563.289.2509).

And if you don't care for spirits or wine, you still have options! How about sipping local craft beer at the **Green Tree Brewery** (309 N. Cody Rd.; 563.729.1164)? They have several different beers on tap and a spacious outdoor patio to enjoy your beer while watching the river flow.

Just five miles north of LeClaire, **Three 33** (Princeton: 333 River Dr.; 563.635.5014) serves tasty bar food with expansive views of the Mississippi. Grab a patio seat if the weather is good.

Where to Stay

The Old Mill Guest House (419 N. Cody Rd.; 309.314.7702) rents two units in a historic riverfront house. The downstairs unit comes with two bedrooms and small kitchen. Upstairs, you'll find a cozy apartment with a king bed and small kitchen. Each unit has a deck facing the river.

Special Events

When it comes to river festivals, you just can't beat (563.289.3946). Thousands of people descend upon the small towns of LeClaire, Iowa, and Port Byron, Illinois, the second weekend of August for a spectacle that is part county fair and part athletic competition. For three hours, the Mississippi River is closed to all commercial traffic. Organizers lay out a 2,400-foot rope and stretch it from bank to bank so teams of 20 from Iowa and Illinois can compete. While the individual tugs are taken seriously, you can't help but notice that the whole event feels like one big gag, and everyone is in on it. Carnies line the LeClaire riverfront offering old-school games of chance with large stuffed animals as prizes. You can dine on a hand-dipped corn dog, then choose either a deep-fried Twinkie or fried Snickers bar for dessert (or both, I suppose, if you dare). Bring a chair and get there early to stake a claim to a good spot to watch the action. If you're in Port Byron, check out the 30-foot tall sculpture of a Victorian man on a penny-farthing bicycle. **Will B. Rolling**, as it is known, was donated by Lawrence and Carol Bay. (Lawrence Bay served as mayor for a while.)

BETTENDORF

Attractions

Rivermont Collegiate (1821 Sunset Dr.; 563.359.1366) is housed in the mansion built for Joseph Bettendorf. The English Manor-inspired house was completed in 1915 on a 17-acre estate high on a bluff overlooking the river and the Bettendorf factory. In 1973, Rivermont Collegiate purchased the house. Rivermont is a non-sectarian private school educating children from preschool through high school. The mansion serves as both administrative office and classroom. They are happy to provide guided tours if you call in advance. Summers are best for tours as no classes are in session.

The first floor is still mostly original. Highlights include the beautiful wood inlays, marble floors, an intricately carved staircase, and ceilings decorated with canvas paintings that were shipped to the mansion in finished form and installed. One curiosity about the mansion is that none of the fireplaces are functional. According to one story, Joseph suffered an eye injury during a blaze at his factory, which left him with a healthy fear of fire. When he built the mansion, he had fireplaces installed, but he insisted that they be decorative only.

The **Family Museum** (2900 Learning Campus Dr.; 563.344.4106) features a collection of interactive exhibits about science and nature for children, such as *Lil 'Ssippi Valley*, a scale model of a portion of the Great River where guests can get a taste of river life. Pre-teens won't be bored.

While most of the Bettendorf Company complex is long gone, the original Art déco **headquarters building** is still standing and worth a drive by (2117 State St.).

The **Isle Casino** (1777 Isle Parkway; 800.843.4753) offers 35,000 square feet of casino action with nearly a thousand slot machines and 20 gaming tables. The complex, completely land-based as of 2016, includes a 500-room hotel, restaurants, and a marina.

Getting On the River

It is easier to get near the Mississippi than on the Mississippi in the Quad Cities. The best way to get up close and personal with the river is by riding the **Channel Cat Water Taxis**. Catch a ride at one of the following stops: 1) Moline Landing (Celebration Belle pier), 2) Isle of Capri in Bettendorf, 3) Village of East Davenport, and 4) John Deere Commons in Moline. For $8 you can ride all day. They even have room for a few bicycles. If you do a complete circuit, the ride will take about an hour.

Another way to get near the water is by walking or biking across the Interstate 74 bridge, where you can enjoy spectacular views of the river.

Drinking and Dining

For a sample of locally crafted beer, check out the spacious **Crawford Brew Works** (3659 Devil's Glen Rd.; 563.332.0243), which brews a very tasty porter.

Ross' Restaurant (2297 Falcon St.; 563.355.7573) is a forward-looking old-school family diner. The namesake Ross was the type of quick-witted character you hope to chat with over morning coffee. One of his favorite gimmicks was serving bologna sandwiches on Election Day. If you are craving waffles or a fried banana split, this is your place. If you are really hungry, try to scale the Magic Mountain, a tower of ground beef and fries atop Texas toast and dripping with cheese sauce.

Enjoy lunch or dinner at local favorite **Harris Pizza** (2520 18th St.; 563.344.8727). They make a style of pizza that is ubiquitous in the Quad Cities—cheesy, medium-thick crispy crust, slightly sweet and herby tomato sauce, and sometimes outlandish ingredients. Sure, you can get pepperoni and mushroom, but why would you when you could have the Three Alarm Pizza (BBQ sauce, jalapeños, onions, and pepper jack cheese)?

Enjoy a cool treat from **Whitey's Ice Cream** (3515 Middle Rd.; 563.332.4189), another local institution.

Where to Stay: Lodging

The 500+ rooms at Bettendorf's **Isle of Capri** (1777 Isle Parkway; 800.843.4753) aren't inexpensive but put you in the middle of the casino action and next to the river.

DAVENPORT

Attractions

Founded in 1851 around the logging industry, the **Village of East Davenport** (known locally as the East Village) was annexed by Davenport in 1856. The historic district has a collection of 19th-century buildings that now house shops, restaurants, and bars. The neighborhood also hosts several festivals during the summer.

Lindsay Park (2200 E. 11th St.) is where Black Hawk camped before signing the Treaty of 1836 that ceded most of Iowa to the US government and where artist George Catlin painted his portrait. Cross East River Drive at Mound Street to Lower Lindsay Park, and you'll find one of the area's more unusual attractions: the life-size wooden **sculptures** created by artist Thom Gleich that were inspired by the characters from Seurat's painting, *A Sunday on La Grande Jette.*

The **Davenport Skybridge** is hard to miss—it's that angular glass structure that stretches 600 feet from downtown to the riverfront. The views from the bridge are memorable, especially on the south end. At night, the bridge is lit up in a variety of rotating colors. It's pretty cool. Enter from the 100 block of West 2nd Street.

The **Bix Beiderbecke Museum & Archive** (129 N. Main St.; 563.326.1333, x114) showcases the life and legacy of the city's musical prodigy and jazz pioneer. In his tragically short life, Beiderbecke stood out as one of the best cornetists of his day. He impressed his contemporary, the legendary Louis Armstrong, and played with the top bands of the 1920s. The museum brings Beiderbecke's story to life.

The **Figge Art Museum** (225 W. 2nd St.; 563.326.7804), the large glass structure that looks something like a fragile towboat, features great art from around the world. Most of the exhibits turn over frequently, so you'll want to make regular visits to see what's new. Some of the highlights among the permanent exhibits include a colorful collection of Haitian art, paintings by native Midwesterner artists Thomas Hart Benton and John Steuart Curry, and the Grant Wood Gallery.

Many of the early immigrants to this area were Germans who were escaping political upheaval and economic collapse at home. The **German American Heritage Center and Museum** (712 W. 2nd St.; 563.322.8844) tells their stories with exhibits about the challenges they faced to start over in a new country and their lasting influence on the Quad Cities (and much of the US).

If you're interested in the history of the Irish in the area, there's a **memorial to Irish immigrants** downtown (2nd and Harrison Sts.). There's also a Celtic cross on the campus of St. Ambrose University just north of the athletic fields. And don't forget to check out the only bi-state St. Patrick's Day Parade in the country (see below).

St. Anthony Catholic Church (417 Main St.; 563.322.3303) is one of Iowa's oldest churches. The original church was built in 1838 by Father Samuel Mazzuchelli (see page 183), with support from Antoine LeClaire. That building is currently the religious education center. When Davenport grew, the parish needed a bigger church. The new building was completed in 1853 and is still in use. The sanctuary is only open to the public about 30 minutes before mass. Otherwise, call ahead to schedule a tour of the interior.

In 1895, Daniel David Palmer popped the back of one Harvey Lillard at his office in downtown Davenport, thus performing the first known chiropractic adjustment. In 1906, Palmer was jailed for 23 days for practicing medicine without a license, an event that recurred across the country and launched a movement to legitimize the chiropractic profession. You can learn about this (and more!) at the **Palmer Family & Chiropractic History Museum** in Vickie Ann Palmer Hall (115 W. 7th St.; 563.884.5714). Museum displays are scattered about the building, but you will find most of them in the basement and first floor lobby. Exhibits include a display case with a variety of animal skeletons, a giant clam shell, and a replica of the office used by Palmer. Call 24 hours in advance to schedule a visit.

One block north, the **Palmer Mansion** (808 Brady St.; 563.884.5714) presents a fine example of what happens when eccentricity is mixed with wealth. The porch has a number of curiosities, including a built-in pipe organ that still works, stunning samples of forbidden stitch embroidery, a room built to resemble a circus big tent, and a chair whose legs are made from genuine elephant feet. Tours are generally offered on Friday mornings at 11 when classes are in session, but you must call at least a day in advance to make a reservation.

Make time to relax and enjoy the riverfront, as long as it's not underwater. **LeClaire Park** has a bandshell and hosts many summer festivals. **Modern Woodmen Park** stands out as one of America's great baseball stadiums. Completed in 1931, it is the home field for the **Quad Cities River Bandits** (209 S. Gaines St.; 563.322.6348), a minor league baseball team affiliated with the Kansas City Royals. The stadium is in one of the most scenic spots for a baseball game—anywhere. A tall **Ferris wheel** operates next to the stadium, which offers great views of the riverfront as you rotate around.

Just downriver of the bridge, **Centennial Park** features a skate park, a water spray area, and plenty of places to picnic or sit and watch the river. The paved walking/bicycling path extends westward to Credit Island Park and eastward to the Isle of Capri Casino in Bettendorf.

The **Putnam Museum** (1717 W. 12th St.; 563.324.1933) hosts several excellent exhibits on the region's natural and cultural history. *River, Prairie, and People* covers the region's history, from pre-colonial times to the present. *Black Earth/Big River* is an interactive exhibit about the ecology of the Mississippi River valley. The museum also has an IMAX theater with rotating shows.

Credit Island Park (2500 W. River Dr.; 563.326.7812), the site of an early French trading post, is a good spot to rest your feet, hike through the woods, ride a bicycle, and for people watching, too.

Nahant Marsh Education Center (4220 S. Wapello Ave.; 563.336.7766) occupies 305-acres on the site of a former shooting range. A cooperative effort between public and private agencies helped to remove hazardous amounts of lead and restore the marsh. The preserve has a couple of short walking trails and viewing platforms good for bird-watching, especially during migration season.

Davenport's **Rhythm City Casino** (7077 Elmore Ave.; 563.328.8000) built a land-based home in 2016 at the intersection of Interstates 74 and 80. The 285,000 square-foot complex includes about 800 slot machines and 35 gaming tables.

Davenport has several venues to take in **live shows**. The **Redstone Room** at Common Chord (129 Main St.; 563.326.1333) and the **Raccoon Motel** (315 E. 2nd St.; 563.424.0819) offer intimate venues to enjoy live music. The **Adler Theatre** (136 E. 3rd St.) specializes in performing arts, including touring shows. The restored **Capitol Theatre** (330 W. 3rd St.) is another good venue for national touring acts and shows.

Central Davenport Map

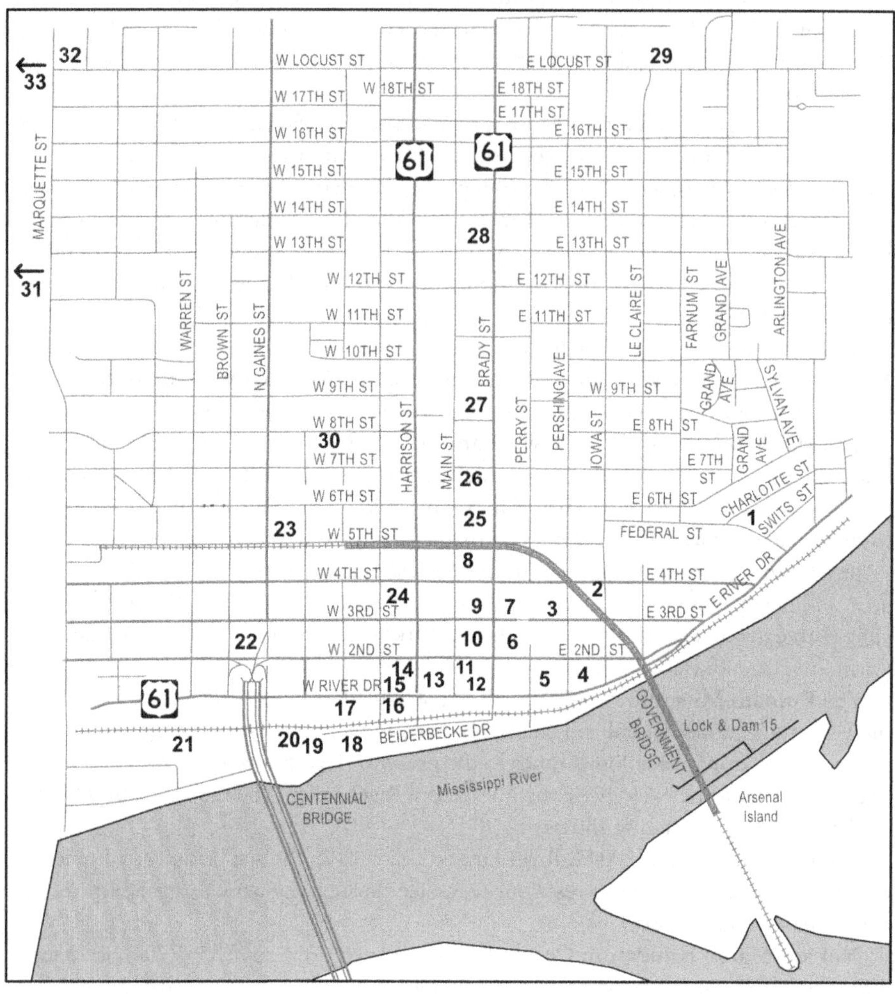

Want to **Know More** about Bix Beiderbecke? Read about his life at MississippiValleyTraveler.com/Bix-Beiderbecke

Attractions

7. Adler Theatre
11. Bix Beiderbecke Museum & Archive
24. Capitol Theatre
21. Centennial Park
12. Davenport Skybridge
19. Ferris Wheel
13. Figge Art Museum
22. German American Heritage Center
1. Isabel Bloom Production Studio
18. LeClaire Park
14. Memorial to Irish Immigrants
33. Mississippi Valley Fairgrounds
20. Modern Woodmen Park
27. Palmer Mansion
26. Palmer Museum
31. Putnam Museum
11. Redstone Room
8. St. Anthony Catholic Church
16. Union Station

Where to Eat and Drink

3. Bix Bistro
9. Boozies Bar & Grill
23. Café D'Marie
6. Chocolate Manor
17. Farmers Market
5. Front Street Brewery
29. Harris Pizza/Locust
2. Redband Coffee Company/E. 4th
28. Redband Coffee Company/W. 13th St.
25. The Miss Phay Café
10. UP at the Current Hotel
32. Whitey's Ice Cream

Where to Stay

30. Beiderbecke Mansion
3. Hotel Blackhawk

Other

15. Ground Transportation Center

A NOTE ABOUT GETTING AROUND THE QUAD CITIES

Most every city in the region uses numbered streets *and* avenues, which means if you follow 15th Street when you really want 15th Avenue, you may end up in the Mississippi River instead of that brewpub you want to check out. It also means that when you are asking about an address, you need to know which city it is in. Asking for 14th Street isn't good enough. You need to know that the 14th Street you want is the one in Davenport, not the one in Moline.

If that's not confusing enough, you may notice that streets go perpendicular to the river, except in Davenport, where they parallel the river. In most cases, perpendicular to the river means north-south, except for Hampton, where perpendicular to the river is nearly east-west, which is the direction streets in Davenport go, even though they parallel the river. I'm sure that clears up the confusion.

Maybe this will simplify things. If you are like me and you use the river as a landmark to help navigate around town, remember that the Mississippi flows from east to west through the Quad Cities, so when you are driving parallel to the river, you are therefore going east or west. It takes some getting used to. I've gotten turned around many times.

Getting On the River

It is easier to get near the Mississippi than on the Mississippi in the Quad Cities. The best way to get up close and personal with the river is by riding the **Channel Cat Water Taxis**. Catch a ride at one of the following stops: 1) Moline Landing (Celebration Belle pier), 2) Isle of Capri in Bettendorf, 3) Village of East Davenport, and 4) John Deere Commons in Moline. For $8 you can ride all day. They even have room for a few bicycles. If you do a complete circuit, the ride will take about an hour.

Tours

Isabel Bloom (736 Federal St.; 800.273.5436) makes popular sculptures out of cast concrete. Each figure is handcrafted and goes through rigorous quality control. Guided tours of the production facility take about an hour. Call in advance for tour times.

If you're into seeing how things get built, take a tour of the **John Deere Factory** in Davenport where they build graders, loaders, and other big stuff. The 90-minute tour takes you through the manufacturing process. The tour is free, but you must submit a tour request through an online form (https://johndeeretours.deere.com).

Drinking and Dining

Get your java fix at **Redband Coffee Company** (329 E. 4th St. and 110 W. 13th St.; 563.823.1107), which has re-purposed a couple of cool old buildings to serve its house-roasted coffees, pastries, and breakfast sandwiches.

Chocolate Manor (110 E. 2nd St.; 563.355.6600) is a family-run boutique chocolatier. Their hand made products include gorgeous truffles, sinful dark chocolates, and luscious chocolate-covered fruits. Stop in, sample, and stock up.

11th Street Precinct Bar and Grill (2108 E. 11th St.; 563.324.9545) serves sandwiches and pizza. Check out the pork tenderloin sandwich, which violates all kinds of Midwestern cooking rules by not being breaded and fried.

Lagomarcinos (2132 E. 11th St.; 563.324.6137) has a more celebrated location in Moline, but this one serves up the same delicious homemade ice cream, hot fudge sundaes, and old-school sodas.

Boozies Bar & Grill (114 ½ W. 3rd St.; 563.328.2929) consistently gets props for its burgers, especially the namesake Boozie Burger topped with bacon, a trio of cheeses, and just about anything else you could want. If you are not in the mood for a burger, they have an assortment of other pub-inspired sandwiches and entrées.

It probably doesn't make sense to assert that a place that has been pleasing people for over a decade has, in fact, largely flown under the radar, but that's the case for **Café D'Marie** (614 W. 5th St.; 563.323.3293). The restaurant occupies a historic Victorian house in Davenport's Gold Coast neighborhood. The dining areas are cozy and bright and the food prepared fresh every day. Expect a tasty selection of quiches, soups, sandwiches, and salads, plus tasty tea and coffee drinks. They are only open for lunch.

Harris Pizza has two locations in Davenport: on the west side at 1601 W. 3rd St. (563.326.3551) and on the east side at 524 E. Locust St. (563. 322.2411).

Front Street Brewery (208 E. River Dr.; 563.322.1569) serves up a range of salads, sandwiches, and above average pub-grub entrées. If you just want to sip some beer, head to their Taproom at the Freighthouse (421 W. River Dr.)

For an inspired take on the cuisines of southeast Asia, settle in to **The Miss Phay Café** (512 Brady St.; 563.888.1053) where you can enjoy a steaming bowl of pho, steaming noodle dishes, and curries.

Relish snacks and drinks with a view at the **Current Hotel** (215 N. Main St.), where the rooftop bar **UP** (563.231.9557) is waiting for you with tapas and cocktails.

For a more upscale experience, dine at the classy **Bix Bistro** at the Hotel Blackhawk (200 E. 3rd St.; 888.525.4455). The menus change with the availability of fresh, locally sourced ingredients, but lean into steaks and fish.

Satisfy your sweet tooth at local favorite **Whitey's Ice Cream** (1230 W. Locust St.; 563.322.0828).

Where to Stay: Camping

Interstate RV Park (8448 Fairmount St.; 563.386.7292), just north of I-80 at Northwest Boulevard, has 98 sites including many with full hookups.

Bed and Breakfasts

The **Beiderbecke Mansion B&B** (532 W. 7th St.; 563.323.0047) offers a comfortable bed-and-breakfast experience in the handsome house built by the grandparents of Bix Beiderbecke. All four rooms have a private bath. The Mississippi Rose Room has a balcony and a nice view.

Lodging

A thorough renovation in 2010 brought back to life the storied but once neglected century-old **Hotel Blackhawk** (200 E. 3rd St.; 888.525.4455), where presidents and celebrities have stayed. The 130 spacious rooms offer upscale lodging in the heart of Davenport.

Special Events

The **Freight House Farmers Market** (421 W. River Dr.; 563.322.6009) is a bustling place on Saturday mornings, with dozens of food and craft vendors and plenty of shoppers. Vendors set up all year, and on Sunday mornings, too.

The **St. Patrick's Day Grand Parade** begins in Rock Island and crosses into Davenport via the Centennial Bridge, thus giving the Quad Cities bragging rights as the host of the only St. Patrick's Day Parade that marches in two states, and, I imagine, that crosses a big river in the process (309.324.5000; March, generally the Saturday before St. Patrick's Day).

The most well-known event is the **Bix Beiderbecke Jazz Festival** (August), named after the renowned cornet player and jazz composer, whose legend has continued beyond his untimely death at age twenty-eight. The event began in 1971 when musicians from the Bix Beiderbecke Memorial Jazz Band of New Jersey came to Davenport to play on the 40th anniversary of his death. When word leaked out that the group was going to jam at the Holiday Inn, 2,000 people showed up. Thinking that this was a sign of continuing interest in the legacy of Bix, an annual festival was created. Good thinking. The festival is now based at Davenport's Rhythm City Casino.

Alternating Currents celebrates live music, film screenings, visual art, and comedy at multiple venues around downtown Davenport (late August).

Join one of the largest paddling parties on the Mississippi in mid-August. **Floatzilla** (563.322.2969) brings together hundreds of people to celebrate the Mississippi River, paddling, and community. You can paddle anywhere from a half-mile to 11 miles on the Mississippi (it is closed to commercial traffic during the event), then enjoy food, live music, and hanging out afterwards. Register in advance (floatzillaqc.org).

The Palmers

Three generations of Palmers are largely responsible for giving birth to and raising to adulthood the chiropractic profession. Daniel David (DD) Palmer was born near Toronto in 1845 but migrated to the United States with his brother, Thomas, after the American Civil War ended. DD initially settled in New Boston, Illinois, where he raised bees.

In 1885, he moved to Davenport to open a practice in "natural magnetic healing." Through self-study and observation, he developed a theory of disease that was far outside the mainstream medical box. He came to believe that virtually all disease was the result of the misalignment of spinal vertebra or "sub-luxation" as he called it. He believed that nerves transmitted not just basic impulses but an intelligent, healing energy. Disease happened when sub-luxations blocked these impulses from reaching internal organs.

His theory was put to the test in 1895 when he popped the neck of Harvey Lillard, a janitor in DD's office building. Mr. Lillard had been deaf for 17 years and traced his hearing loss back to a day on which he heard a loud pop in his back while stooped over. DD found a bump in Lillard's vertebra and asked him to lie on a table face down. DD then gave a vigorous thrust into the back of Lillard's neck. Lillard reported that he could hear again immediately after the adjustment. DD and his friend, Reverend Samuel Weed, coined the term "chiropractic" for the new profession, a term derived from Greek that means "done by hand."

DD founded the Palmer School in 1897 and his son, BJ, joined him shortly thereafter. The two had trouble collaborating, though, and BJ bought out his father in 1904. In the nearly 60 years that BJ ran the Palmer School, he fought for the legitimization of chiropractic, built a professional school, and tried to prevent philosophical schisms in the emerging profession. Nevertheless, he guided the Palmer School's development into a full-fledged professional school with active clinical and research programs. BJ's wife, Mabel, also was active in the Palmer School. She was the resident anatomy expert and a popular teacher.

BJ was a true eccentric. He slept irregularly and often woke in the middle of the night with an idea that he would immediately start working on. He had lived around the circus as a child and remained fond of it throughout his life. He even built a room in his house that resembled the big top and retired around Sarasota, Florida, near the winter home of the Barnum & Bailey circus.

The third Palmer, David D, took the reins at the Palmer School after BJ's death in 1961 and renamed it the Palmer College of Chiropractic. He modernized the campus, established the college as a non-profit entity, and founded an alumni association. Shortly after his death in 1978, the Palmer College received full accreditation.

Explore Up the East Bank (Illinois)

ROCK ISLAND

Attractions

Black Hawk State Historic Site (1510 46th Ave.; 309.788.0177) mixes preservation with outdoor recreation. Visit the **Hauberg Indian Museum** (309.788.9536) for the history part. It is located inside the impressive lodge built by the Civilian Conservation Corps in the 1930s and features dioramas displaying Sauk and Meskwaki life in the 18th century and a dugout canoe. To explore the park, just walk around. A wide range of wildflowers add a dramatic touch to the landscape between mid-April and mid-May. Black Hawk Prairie is west of the lodge, a small area set aside to replicate the type of tallgrass prairie that once dominated the landscape here.

When it comes to the architecture for the dead, few places have impressed me more than **Chippiannock Cemetery** (2901 12th St.; 309.788.6622). You are welcome to stop at the office and pick up a guide but wandering aimlessly can also be rewarding. Most of the older sections will be on your left as you enter the cemetery and then to the right and up the hill. The markers are a testament to the incredible carving skills of stone masons: a cloth draped delicately on a marker, a perfectly chiseled anvil, a chalice support by tree limbs. Colonel Davenport and his family are buried here. Their graves are marked by a simple obelisk near the top of the hill. Also interred here is lumber baron Frederick Weyerhaeuser.

Perhaps the most remarkable memorial, though, is dedicated to siblings Eddie and Josie Dimich, who were five and nine years old, respectively, when they died from diphtheria on the same evening in 1878. The children had a devoted pet dog, a Newfoundland, who used to follow the children everywhere. After the children died, the dog would make the short walk from home to the cemetery every day until he himself died, or so the story goes. Regardless, when the dog died, the children's father commissioned a stone carver to create an image of their beloved family pet and had it placed next to his children's graves.

Sunset Park (Between 18th Ave. & 31st Ave.; 309.732.2000) is a good place to stop for a picnic and to take in some river views. In winter, look for bald eagles here.

Quad Cities Arts (1715 2nd Ave.; 309.793.1213) is housed in the 1920s-era London Building. It is part gallery space and part retail space that shines the light on the work of local and regional artists. The quality is consistently high, and you can find something in virtually any price range.

Schweibert Riverfront Park (17th to 20th Streets next to the river) is a fun public space, with water jets, public art, occasional outdoor shows, and great views of the Mississippi River.

Circa '21 Dinner Playhouse (1828 3rd Ave.; 309.786.7733) is a dinner theater with a busy performance schedule throughout the year.

Quad City Botanical Center (2525 4th Ave.; 309.794.0991) offers quiet spaces to enjoy in its tropical house and multiple outdoor gardens.

Augustana College has a few sites to visit. The **Augustana College Art Museum** (Centennial Hall, 3703 7th Ave.; 309.794.7231) houses an impressive collection of art in temporary exhibits in the upper and lower lobbies, as well as pieces from their permanent collection in a lower level gallery. The **Fryxell Geology Museum** (309.794.7318) may be modest in size, but it makes a big impression with its collection of fossils and

Central Rock Island Map

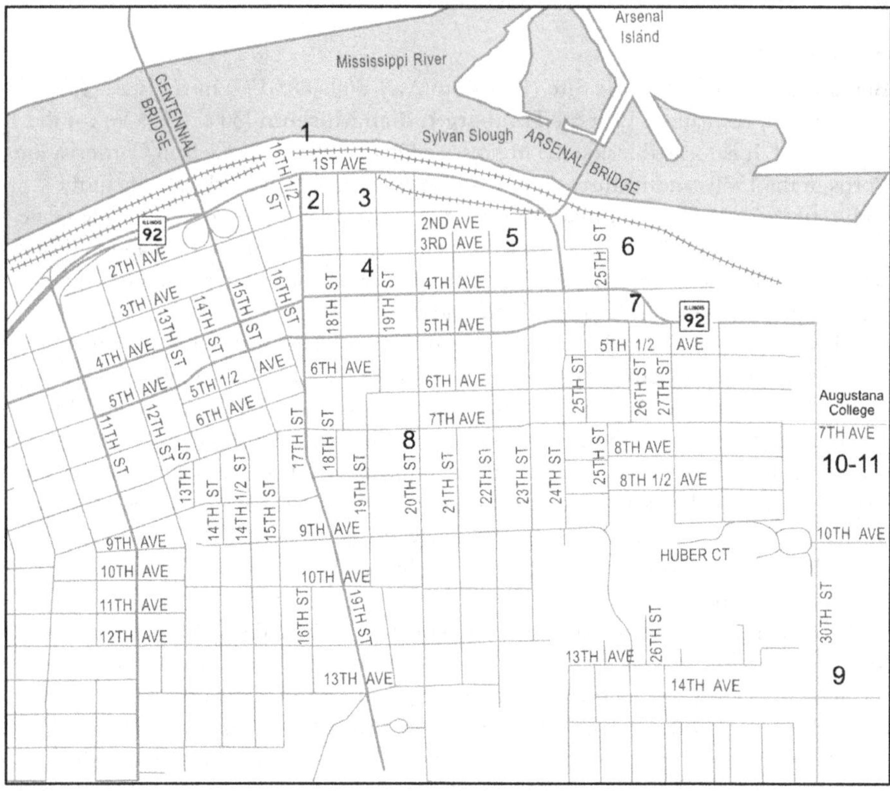

Attractions

10. Augustana College Art Museum
4. Circa '21
11. Fryxell Geology Museum
5. Navarro Canoe Company
2. Quad Cities Arts
6. Quad City Botanical Center
1. Schweibert Riverfront Park

Where to Eat and Drink

9. Radicle Effect Brewerks
3. Soi 2 Thai Street Food
7. Wake Brewing

Where to Stay

8. Victorian Inn

Central Moline Map

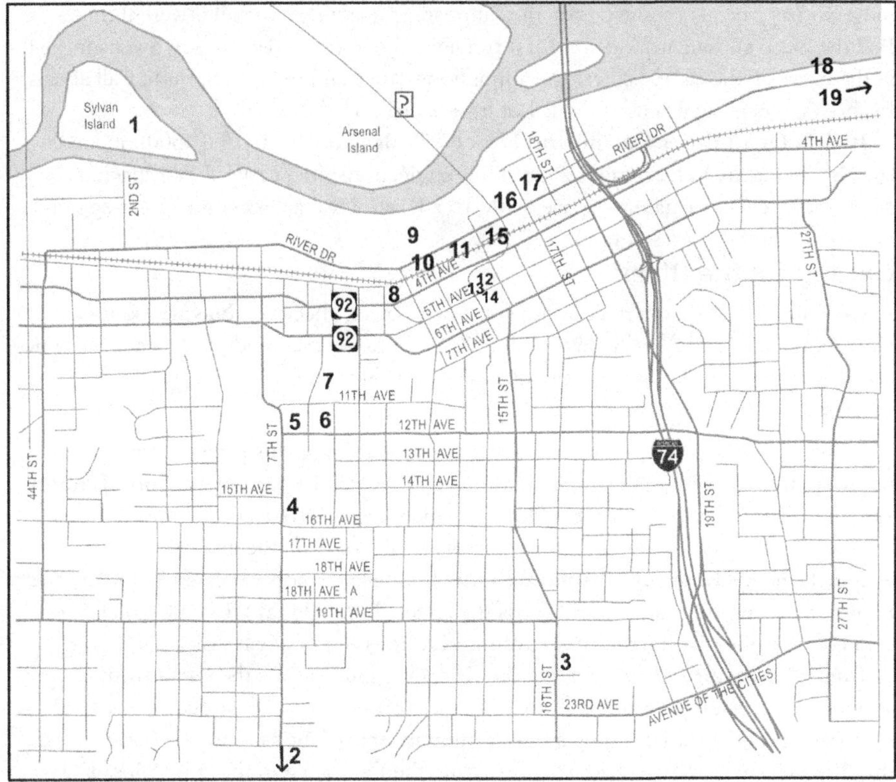

Attractions

16. Bass Street Landing
5. Butterworth Center
18. Celebration Belle
4. Center for Belgian Culture
7. Deere-Wiman House
11. John Deere Pavilion
6. Rock Island County Historical Society
1. Sylvan Island
9. Vibrant Arena at The MARK

Where to Eat and Drink

13. Bent River Brewing Company
15. Dead Poet's Espresso
2. Katy's Imports
14. Lagomarcinos
12. Lemongrass
19. Milltown Coffee
3. Restaurante Sabor Catracho

Where to Stay

8. Element Moline
17. Stoney Creek Inn

Other

10. Centre Station

rocks. The fossil of a Tylosaurus Proriger, a 16-foot-long eel-like reptile, will either impress or scare the heck out of you. Look for it on the rear wall. The back corner of the museum has a display showing off the fluorescent quality of several different minerals. Pull the black curtain around you for a fun light show. The museum is in Swenson Hall in the heart of the campus, near the admissions office and the planetarium. Call ahead for hours, especially when school is not in session.

Bally's Quad Cities Casino and Hotel (777 Bally Blvd.; 309.756.4600) opened a land-based facility in December 2008. The Art déco-inspired casino has a spacious 42,000 square feet of gaming space, with over 1,100 slot machines and 24 gaming tables, plus a hotel and restaurants.

Getting On the River

If you'd like to get on the river under your own power, check out **Navarro Canoe Company** (2219 3rd Ave.; 563.265.1492). They make several models of beautiful, functional canoes you can purchase for your next river journey.

Tours

The City of Rock Island published a driving tour that highlights places around town that were tied to its infamous mobster. You can download a copy of the **John Looney Legend Tour** (www.rigov.org/825/John-Looney-Legend-Tour), or you pick up a free copy at the Rock Island Public Library or City Hall. Some of the more notorious sites include Looney's Roost (2012 16th Ave.), the Looney mansion (1635 20th St.), and the house of his lawyer, Frank Kelly, across the street (1703 20th St.). Even if you opt to skip the tour, the brochure is an interesting read for the Looney history.

Boetje's Mustard (2736 12th St.; 309.788.4352), just across the street from Chippiannock Cemetery, is a local institution. Boetje's (pronounced "boat-geez") is a small manufacturer of award-winning stone-ground mustard. They follow the same recipe that Fred Herman Boetje used when he made the first batch in the late 1880s. Tours include an overview of the mustard-making process. Tours can be arranged in summer; call in advance to arrange one at a time that is convenient for them.

Drinking and Dining

Looking for a laid-back place to try something new or enjoy your favorite craft beer? Check out **Radicle Effect Brewerks** (1340-31st St.; 309.283.7605), where you'll find an impressive (and constantly changing) selection of beers from the US.

Enjoy a tasty craft beer at **Wake Brewing** (2529 5th Ave.; 309.558.0878). If the weather is nice (or it's too loud inside), take your beer to the patio.

Located in the middle of The District (downtown Rock Island) in a long and narrow storefront, **Soi 2 Thai Street Food** (1825 2nd Ave.; 309.206.4159) serves some of the tasty noodle and curry dishes one expects from a Thai restaurant, as well as several dishes that you may not have tried before, such as mango chicken.

Where to Stay: Camping

Camelot Campground (2311 78th Ave. West; 309.787.0665), south of I-80 and east of Iowa Highway 92, rents 120 cramped sites, many with full hookups.

Bed and Breakfasts

The **Victorian Inn** (702 20th St.; 309.788.7068) is a cozy bed-and-breakfast in a rambling historic home. Check out the beautiful Fleming tapestries.

Special Events

Bald Eagle Days (QCCA Expo Center, 2621 4th Ave.; 309.794.5338; January, 2nd weekend) in the Quad Cities is part exposition and part eagle watching. The exposition hall has conservation exhibits, animal shows, art, and Native American storytelling and dancing.

See the information for the **St. Patrick's Day parade** on page 245.

If you are into fast cars, albeit small ones, the **Rock Island Grand Prix** (Labor Day weekend) is your event. Professional kart drivers (as in go-karts) from near and far zip around the streets of downtown Rock Island competing for a $25,000 prize. This race is a springboard to NASCAR for many drivers. Seriously.

ARSENAL ISLAND

Attractions

Most of Arsenal Island is a military installation, but there are several sites open to visitors. Just be prepared to complete a screening procedure.

All visitors without an existing military ID must first check in at the Visitors Center at the Moline gate and get a pass. Enter from River Drive in Moline and turn right before you reach the checkpoint, then follow the signs. You will need to show a photo ID and undergo a criminal background check. Once you are approved (the process takes a few minutes but you may have to wait in line for a while), you can enter the Arsenal grounds. You can't get a pass, however, if you are a foreign national (unless you are visiting on official business) or if you are under 18 years of age and not accompanied by an adult. If the criminal background check isn't favorable, you will also be denied access.

Among the first sites you'll pass are the **Rock Island Confederate Cemetery and Rock Island National Cemetery**. The Confederate Cemetery is the final resting place for nearly 2,000 Confederate soldiers who died while imprisoned on the island during the Civil War. The national cemetery began in 1863 as the burial grounds for Union soldiers guarding that same Confederate prison camp. Over 29,000 veterans and their relatives are interred here. Both cemeteries are free and open daily from sunrise to sunset (309.782.2094).

Memorial Field (Rodman Ave. at East Ave.; 309.782.5021) is an outdoor museum featuring a collection of ordnance systems, including artillery pieces and rocket launchers. Most of the weapons on display were manufactured on the island at one time.

The **Rock Island Arsenal Museum** (North Ave.; 309.782.5021) is the second-oldest US Army Museum. It opened in 1905. The collection includes an impressive number and diversity of handguns, rifles, and other small arms.

The **Colonel George Davenport House** (Hillman St.; 309.786.7336), constructed in 1833, was once the center of civic life in the region. Rock Islanders plotted to get the county seat here, towns were platted, and leaders negotiated with railroad executives for a rail port. On July 4, 1845, Colonel Davenport was at home when several men broke into the house. They shot Davenport and mortally wounded him. The murder shocked and angered the community. They launched a massive manhunt and eventually caught six men who were tried and convicted. On October 29, just three months after the murder, three of the men were hanged in a public square before a large crowd. In a bizarre twist, the rope broke for one of the men and the executioner had to reload and try again, while fending off cries from the gallery that the broken rope was a sign from God to halt the execution. Even though several men were caught and executed for the crime, rumors persist to this day that Davenport's murder was part of a larger conspiracy to kill him, although the motivation for such a conspiracy often varies.

At the far end of the island, the **Mississippi River Visitor's Center** (Building 328, Rodman Ave.; 309.794.5338) hosts several displays that highlight Mississippi River ecology and commerce. Check out the cool map embedded in the floor of the lobby. There is also a good vantage point to watch barges pass through Lock #15, which was the first of 29 built that aimed to tame the Mississippi River for navigation. In the Quad Cities, the completion of #15 buried the rapids and created a lake that is popular with recreational boaters. The pool behind this dam is one of the most stable in the system. The water level typically fluctuates just one to three feet, even during floods, an ironic turn of fate—from being one of the most hazardous stretches of the river to being one of the most dependable.

As you exit the visitor's center, look across the street and up at the six-story **Clock Tower**. The tower was built of native limestone and was part of the first structure built for the Arsenal. The clock was purchased from New York-based AS Hotchkiss Company and installed in 1868. Each of the four clock faces is 12 feet in diameter. The minute hands are six feet long and the second hands are five feet long. The clock still has its original parts and still works. If the clock doesn't interest you, the views from the top floor are the best in the Quad Cities. The Corps leads occasional tours through the Clock Tower (check missriver.org for upcoming tours).

MOLINE

Attractions

Who says America doesn't have any cool ruins? The atmospheric setting of **Sylvan Island** (1st Ave. at 2nd St.; 309.736.5714) was the site of the mammoth Republic Steel Works that operated from 1894 to 1956. All that remains is the concrete foundations that ornament the island with post-industrial ruins. If you are lucky, you will be exploring this place on a foggy, slightly cool day around dawn or dusk.

Moline has a cluster of fascinating historic houses to visit. The most impressive ones are the **Deere-Wiman House** (817 11th Ave.) and the **Butterworth Center** (1105 8th St.), and they couldn't be more different. The Deere-Wiman House is an exceptional example of 19th-century Victorian stylings, with gorgeous walnut paneling on the first floor, a music room complete with a pipe organ, and one of the earliest multiple-head full-body showers. And you thought the Victorian era lacked sensuality. In contrast, the Butterworth Center feels like a medieval castle when you enter, an impression that is cemented after entering the stunning library. Like the Deere-Wiman House, the Butterworth Center has a pipe organ, but, then again, whose house doesn't? Both houses are open for guided tours (2:30p W-F, 1st Su, & every Su in July & August; 309.743.2700).

The **Rock Island County Historical Society** (822 11th Ave.; 309.764.8590) is across the street from the Deere-Wiman House. It hosts not only an impressive genealogy and local history collection but also manages a house and a carriage museum. The house itself is not as impressive as the two Deere family houses (there are few original furnishings) but has interesting displays of local history, including replicas of 19th-century dentist's and doctor's offices and an 1840s-era bedroom.

The **Center for Belgian Culture** (1608 7th St.; 309.762.0167) has a small collection of exhibits about Belgian life in the Quad Cities, with displays about homing pigeons, lace, and a game called Rolle Bolle, which you can still play at Stephens Park (15th Ave.

at 7th St.). The Center sponsors a genuine **Belgian waffle breakfast** on the first Saturday of the month at the Friend Circle Hall (701 18th Ave.).

At **John Deere Pavilion** (1400 River Dr.; 309.765.1000), you can climb into the cockpit of a giant harvester and get a new perspective on the world. Different models of tractors, combines, and other giant farm trucks are on display. You are encouraged to touch and climb into the seats of most of them. Just across the street, between the convention center and the hotel, you'll find the sculpture *Spirit of Place* that was installed to mark the site of the first John Deere factory in Moline.

Vibrant Arena at the MARK (1201 River Dr.) hosts national touring shows and musicians in a 12,000-seat arena.

Designed by noted architect Eero Saarinen, who also designed that Arch thing in St. Louis, **John Deere World Headquarters** (1 John Deere Place; 309.765.8000) is the prototypical corporate suburban campus. Then-CEO William Hewitt wanted a building that fit the John Deere corporate image—modern but not flashy. How Midwestern! He got his wishes. The buildings are constructed of Corten steel, a material previously developed for railroads that weathers as it ages, creating a rust-free barrier. Clever. The buildings are private, but you are welcome to drive around the campus. The trip from downtown Moline will only take about ten minutes.

If you haven't had enough of John Deere, take a side trip to the location where it all began. **The John Deere Historic Site** in Grand Detour, Illinois (8393 S. Main; 815.652.4551), a 90-minute drive from Moline. Guided tours lasting an hour will take you around the original homestead of John Deere, where he perfected his self-cleaning plow. The tour includes a replica of John Deere's blacksmith shop.

Getting On the River

It is easier to get near the Mississippi than on the Mississippi in the Quad Cities. The best way to get up close and personal with the river is by riding the **Channel Cat Water Taxis**. Catch a ride at one of the following stops: 1) Moline Landing (Celebration Belle pier), 2) Isle of Capri in Bettendorf, 3) Village of East Davenport, and 4) John Deere Commons in Moline. For $8 you can ride all day. They even have room for a few bicycles. If you do a complete circuit, the ride will take about an hour.

Another option it to ride on the **Celebration Belle** (2501 River Dr.; 309.764.1952), which offers a variety of standard tourist-oriented river cruises, some with food, some without. Sightseeing cruises usually stick to the ten-mile stretch between the locks.

Drinking and Dining

Stop at **Katy's Imports** (2700 7th St.; 309764.8662) to stock up on food from around the world: German mustard, curry ketchup, lefse, chorizo, bangers, black pudding, head cheese, blood sausage! Imagine the fun at your next dinner party.

In 2008, **Lagomarcinos** (1422 5th Ave.; 309.764.1814) celebrated 100 years of making life in the Quad Cities a little sweeter. They are the quintessential soda fountain—they still make sodas with phosphate—but ice cream is their forte. Try a hot fudge sundae and languorously pour the fudge from its own fudge boat onto your ice cream.

Get your caffeine fix at **Dead Poet's Espresso** (1525 3rd Ave.; 309.736.7606), across 15th Street from the John Deere Pavilion, where you can also eat a light breakfast or lunch or snack on a freshly baked pastry.

Milltown Coffee (3800 River Dr.; 309.517.6444) is a fine place to enjoy a latte or sandwich while enjoying good river views through big picture windows.

Bent River Brewing Company (1413 5th Ave.; 309.797.2722) brews a large selection of handcrafted beer (the Uncommon Stout is my personal favorite), good food, live music on weekends that leans toward rock and folk music, and a big patio that is more enjoyable in June than January.

AUTHOR'S PICK: **Lemongrass** (1419 5th Ave.; 309.797.4100) has an impressive menu that includes dishes that cross Asian cultures, including Thailand, Vietnam, and Japan. The food is fresh, delicious, and unlike what you'll find anywhere else in the area.

There are several good Mexican restaurants in the Quad Cities but few are as good as **Coya's Cafe** (4320 4th Ave.; 309.749.7626). Expect juicy tortas, tasty soups (caldo), and a few items you don't typically see in Mexican restaurants in the US.

If you a taste of Latin America other than the standard Mexican American options, check out **Restaurante Sabor Catracho** (2006 16th St.; 309.517.3817), which features dishes from Honduras. Try a delicious baleada or pupusa, or one of their many other satisfying main dishes.

Where to Stay: Lodging

Stoney Creek Inn (101 18th St.; 309.743.0101), a regional chain, offers cozy rooms with a lodge-inspired décor near the river in Moline.

Element Moline (316 12th St.; 309.517.1659) offers 96 rooms in a rehabbed warehouse for visitors who might want to stay longer than a night or two.

EAST MOLINE

Attractions

Campbell's Island State Historic Site (Island Ave.; 309.788.0177) commemorates a skirmish on July 19, 1814, during the War of 1812, in which 16 people were killed by a group of British-allied Sauk and Meskwaki fighters led by Black Hawk. The monument is nothing special but the views of the river are good and you will probably have the place to yourself.

Where to Stay: Lodging

Hyatt Place East Moline (111 Bend Blvd.; 309.755.6000) is right on the river, so of course it offers great views from its modern, comfortable rooms.

HAMPTON

Attractions

The **Brettun & Black Museum** (601 First Ave.; 309.755.6265) recreates a frontier store from the 1840s that served as a critical source of supplies for early residents of northwest Illinois. The museum has displays about local history and a faithfully restored version of the store.

Illiniwek Forest Preserve (309.496.2620) offers several hiking trails and an overlook, which is a five- to ten-minute hike up a steep slope. If you want a little longer hike, turn right at the fork in the trail at the top of the hill, then take every left turn until you get to the overlook, a total of about 20 minutes of hiking up and down several hills.

Where to Stay: Camping

Fisherman's Corner Recreation Area (16123 State Highway 84 North) rents 51 sites with electricity and water and five primitive sites.

Illiniwek Forest Preserve (Illinois Highway 84; 309.496.2620) has 60 sites with electricity and water and 25 basic sites.

John Looney

No city can be truly legit until it has a good villain in its history. Rock Island has John Looney.

He moved to the city in the mid-1880s to work for the Western Union and entered the law profession two years later. He soon founded a newspaper called the *Rock Island News*, which put the yellow in yellow journalism, just without the journalism. He used the paper to extort and control high profile people, like public officials. In 1912, he targeted the mayor, Henry Schriver, with a story headlined:

> "Schriver's Shame! Spent Night and Day in Peoria in Filthy Debauch with Ethel: Deed that Would Shame a Dog!"

The mayor was a bit steamed, so he ordered the newspaper closed and Looney arrested. Looney was not only arrested but beaten severely enough to require medical treatment. Looney's beating sparked two days of rioting that only ended when the Illinois governor declared martial law in Rock Island and sent in troops.

Shortly after this debacle, John Looney was tried in Peoria and convicted of mailing obscene material. He was fined $5,000 and ordered to cease publication of the *News*. Instead of reporting to prison, Looney slipped away to New Mexico. When he returned in 1919, he ramped up his efforts to control the city's vice, expanding his portfolio from the core business of gambling and prostitution to include bootlegging, thanks to Prohibition. A criminal empire of this magnitude requires considerable help, and so it was with Looney. People who were implicated in helping Looney included a former mayor, chief of police, and city attorney, plus much of the Rock Island Police Department.

In July 1922, Looney ordered the murder of tavern owner Bill Gabel, who was set to testify against Looney in federal court. Following Gabel's shooting, a gang war ensued in which twelve people died, culminating with an October attack on Looney himself in which his 22-year-old son was killed.

After a crackdown by authorities, Looney was indicted for a variety of crimes, including the murder of Gabel, and he fled Rock Island again. Two years later he was captured in New Mexico and extradited to Illinois for trial, where a jury found him guilty of Gabel's murder. He ultimately served nine years in Joliet Prison. After he was paroled, he moved to his daughter's house in southern Texas, where he died in obscurity in 1947.

In spite of this remarkable legacy, Rock Island never named anything after Looney. His life has, however, inspired writers. Richard Hamer and Roger Ruthhart wrote *The Citadel of Sin*, the definitive account of his life. Max Allen Collins' graphic novel, *Road to Perdition*, was inspired by Looney, as was my first Frank Dodge mystery, *Rock Island Lines*.

Getting There

Quad City International Airport, founded as Moline Airport, began regular commercial service in 1926. It is on the southern edge of Moline, near the intersection of Interstates 280 and 74. It is served by four airlines: Allegiant, American, Delta, and United.

In Davenport, the Ground Transportation Center (300 W. River Dr.) is the bus terminal for **Greyhound** and **Burlington Trailways**, as well as the local **CitiBus**. National bus lines offer daily departures to other Iowa cities, as well as to Omaha, Chicago, and Indianapolis. In Moline, the bus terminal is at Centre Station (1200 River Dr.); buses from here have daily departures to Chicago, Des Moines, and Indianapolis.

Getting Around

There are many miles of paved bike/pedestrian paths in the Quad Cities. The bike paths along the river are generally flat and take you past a good cross-section of the communities. If you ride away from the river, expect some steep inclines. On the Iowa side, the **Davenport Riverfront Trail** parallels the Mississippi River from Credit Island Park to Bettendorf where it ends at the Isle of Capri Casino. The **Duck Creek Recreational Trail** is another exceptional trail that runs 12 miles through the heart of area from Davenport's Emeis Park to Bettendorf's Duck Creek Park. On the Illinois side, the **Great River Trail** begins in Rock Island's Sunset Park and runs 65 miles to Savanna, Illinois, passing through Moline and East Moline along the way.

From spring through fall, you can **rent (borrow?) a bicycle for free** at Davenport's Union Station (102 S. Harrison) or Moline's Bass Street Landing (1601 River Dr.).

For More Information

There are practical limits to how much I can include in a book, but not with a website! Check out the city profiles on my website to see if they include listings that I couldn't fit in this book.

FOR AN OVERVIEW OF THE QUAD CITIES

MississippiValleyTraveler.com/quad-cities

IOWA COMMUNITIES

Princeton: MississippiValleyTraveler.com/Princeton
LeClaire: MississippiValleyTraveler.com/LeClaire
Bettendorf: MississippiValleyTraveler.com/Bettendorf
Davenport: MississippiValleyTraveler.com/Davenport

ILLINOIS COMMUNITIES

Rock Island: MississippiValleyTraveler.com/Rock-Island
Arsenal Island: MississippiValleyTraveler.com/Arsenal-Island
Moline: MississippiValleyTraveler.com/Moline
East Moline: MississippiValleyTraveler.com/East-Moline
Hampton: MississippiValleyTraveler.com/Hampton
Port Byron: MississippiValleyTraveler.com/Port-Byron

MUSCATINE TO KEOKUK & NAUVOO

Mississippi Harvest; Muscatine, Iowa riverfront

Overview

The river south of the Quad Cities to the Iowa border offers a fascinating mix of towns. The river towns in southeast Iowa were once major industrial centers that employed thousands of people. These communities are in varying degrees of economic health today, but all still have some manufacturing businesses, just with far fewer people working in them than a couple of decades ago. All of these towns are increasingly turning to tourism—river-related tourism, specifically—to help boost their economies.

A small town on the other side of the river with little industrial history—Nauvoo—attracts tens of thousands of visitors every year. Most of them are members of the Church of Jesus Christ of Latter-day Saints (aka, Mormons) who visit Nauvoo for its religious significance. This is an area with a rich history, with the Mississippi River right in the middle of it. You'll find communities that still have strong ties to the river today, but these places remind me of the old saying that the only constant in life is change.

History: Iowa Communities

MUSCATINE

The first Euro-Americans arrived in the late 1820s when Colonel George Davenport dispatched Russell Farnham and two aides to set up a trading post. The first permanent resident was James Casey, who supplied wood to passing steamboats. He wasn't here long, but there's a big rock on the Muscatine riverfront marking "Casey's Landing."

Davenport sold his claim to John Vanata in 1836 and that same year, the city's first plat was finished. The village was called Newburg, but it was soon changed to Bloomington. When Bloomington incorporated as a village in 1839, it had 71 residents and 33 buildings. Those early years were difficult. The winters were long and summer brought diseases such as cholera.

The village had to change its name again in 1849 because their mail was often delivered to Bloomington, Illinois, an inconvenient 160-mile trip to pick up a letter. That's when the village became Muscatine. The origin of the name is a mystery.

In 1855, Sam Clemens moved to Muscatine with his brother, Orion, and their mother Jane. Orion ran a print shop and owned a share of the *Muscatine Journal.* The *Muscatine Journal* published nine letters that young Sam wrote while traveling around the US between 1853 and 1855. The Clemens family lived in Muscatine when a wave of German immigrants was arriving in the city, many of them from Hanover and Hessen. They brought beer with them, a lot of it. In the 1850s, Muscatine had five breweries.

The first growth spurt was fueled by lumber processing, which took off in the 1860s. The industry began in 1838. Many mills were built at the sharp bend in the river that is still mostly industrial to this day. Peter and Richard Musser ran one of the more successful factories. They bought an interest in Northwestern timber and partnered with Frederick Weyerhaeuser for a while. The Musser's businesses got so big (it also included a sash and door factory) that the south part of town became known as "Musserville."

Employees of the lumber mills worked 11-hour days for which they got $1.50 for unskilled jobs or $2 a day for more skilled positions. The last lumber mill closed by 1905, but the sash and door plants kept going. The Musser's sash and door plant survived multiple fires and stayed in business well into the 1960s. Another company, Huttig Building Products, was founded in Muscatine in 1866 as a lumber yard. It is still active today but is now part of the HON Company.

The region's sandy soil, especially on Muscatine Island, proved fertile ground for growing melons, fruit, and vegetables. The agricultural productivity convinced HJ Heinz to open a canning factory in Muscatine, his first outside of Pittsburgh.

Muscatine resident Alexander Clark, Sr. had a big role in desegregating Iowa's public schools. Clark moved to Muscatine at age 16 and worked as a barber and selling real estate. His son, Alexander Jr., graduated from the University of Iowa Law School in 1879, the first African American to do so. Alexander Sr. became the second Black graduate of the law school five years later. In 1867, Alexander Sr. sued the Muscatine Board of Education when his 12-year-old daughter was refused admission to an all-White school. He won and within a few years, all of Iowa's schools were desegregated, nearly 90 years before *Brown v. Board of Education* did the same thing for the rest of the country. Clark Sr. was appointed ambassador to Liberia by President Benjamin Harrison in 1890, where he died the following year.

In the early 20th century, residents could travel from Muscatine all the way to Clinton (65 miles) on the InterUrban rail line. The Muscatine High Bridge opened 1891. It wasn't an especially well-built structure. Spans collapsed in 1899 and again in 1956. The bridge was finally razed in 1973, but one pylon is still standing in Riverside Park. When the bridge was still around, the toll booth also served as a small convenience store that sold lemonade, fireworks, stamps, tobacco, and some sweets.

Pearl Button Manufacturing

While Muscatine had a respectable economy at the end of the 19th century, it hit the big time with its button industry, which boomed due to the abundance of native mussels in the Mississippi. At Muscatine, the river makes a 90-degree turn, which creates an area with a slack current perfect for mussel colonies. At the industry's peak, one-third of the world's buttons came from Muscatine. The industry also became a major battleground in the struggle for fair wages and safe working conditions.

The man who was most responsible for starting the industry was John Frederick Boepple. Boepple was from Ottensen, Germany, where he had worked in the family business—making buttons, of course. High tariffs killed his business, so he left for the United States in 1887 to chase rumors that a large river had a population of mussels that were suitable for button making. He found the mother lode in the Mississippi River and opened the first button factory in 1891.

Boepple took great pride in the craftsmanship with which his workers created buttons. He refused to automate—each button was cut by hand—even as the competition grew more fierce and adopted machinery that improved efficiency. His refusal to keep up with the new machinery was eventually his downfall. His business partners forced him out of the factory, and Boepple went to work buying shells for other companies.

Brothers John and Nicholas Barry were largely responsible for the machinery that sped up the button-making process and made it possible for more factories to get into the game. At its peak, nearly three dozen factories in Muscatine produced 1.5 billion buttons a year. Half of Muscatine's working population worked in the button industry.

The process started with clammers, who harvested huge numbers of mussels from the river, usually between April and November. Hundreds of clammers and their families lived in a camp on the Muscatine riverfront in a community separate from the people who lived in town. The clammers kept to themselves, in part because most people in town didn't want to associate with them.

The mussels they captured had to be cleaned, so they were put in a trough, covered with water, and boiled. The heat coaxed the shells to open up, so the flesh (and maybe a pearl) could be scooped out. The flesh was sometimes saved and used to supplement livestock feed. If you fed it to pigs, though, you had to switch them to a regular diet a few months before slaughter or your pork would taste fishy.

Cleaned shells were transported to the factories, where machines stamped out holes in each shell. The stamping process produced a lot of waste, perhaps 40% or more of the shell. The remnants accumulated in big piles around town and were sometimes disposed of in the river. George Gebhardt found one way to use the waste: he crushed them and sold the powder for use as feed, filler, and fertilizer.

Factory workers endured difficult conditions for low wages. Many were injured (severed fingers were common) and most were paid just enough to survive but not enough to get ahead. Some factories paid workers using a piece-work system in which their pay was based on how many finished items they made. The system was rife with abuse, and many workers were cheated out of a lot of cash. Workers began organizing as early as 1899 but didn't get far until they affiliated with the American Federation of Labor in 1910. Conflict erupted the following year.

Union organizers met in secret—they would be fired if owners knew about their organizing activities—where they decided to spread a rumor that they were going to strike. It was meant as a ploy to get the owners to negotiate, but the owners responded instead

Muscatine to Keokuk Route Map

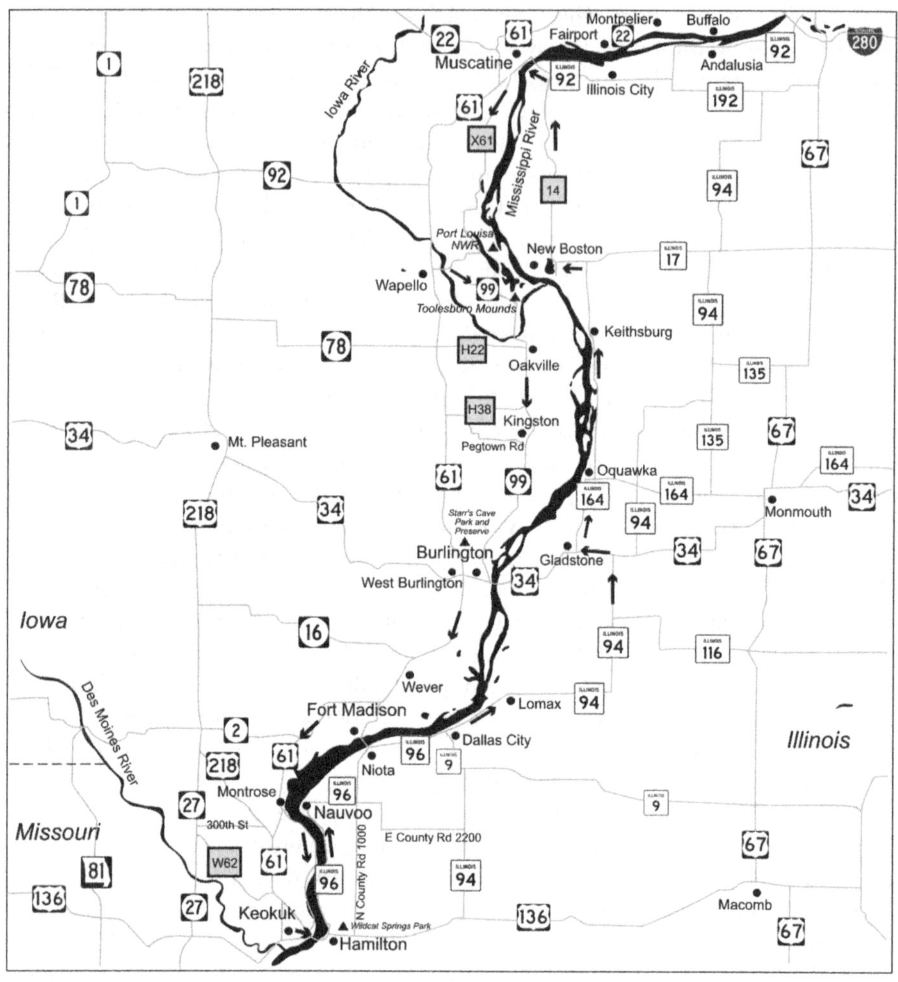

Driving Directions Along the Great River Road

This route follows the Great River Road from Muscatine to Keokuk, then and crosses the river and heads to Nauvoo, Illinois. It's also possible to cross at Fort Madison to visit Nauvoo.

The Great River Road in Iowa (the west side) follows the route below from Muscatine to Keokuk (92 miles):

- South on W. Mississippi Drive (US Business 61)
- Turn left on County X61
- Turn left on State Highway 99, which becomes Main Street in Burlington
- Turn left on Madison Street in Burlington
- Turn left on County Road X62 and follow it to US Highway 61 south

- US 61 bypasses Fort Madison; if you want to drive through town:
  - Exit at 354th Avenue
  - Follow US Business 61 through Fort Madison as it becomes 2nd Street, Avenue H, 20th Street, Avenue L, and Avenue O, then get back on US Highway 61 (it's not as tricky as it sounds)
- After Fort Madison, exit US Highway 61 at Mississippi River Road to Montrose
- In Montrose, follow 1st Street, Water Street, and Elm Street through town, then Mississippi River Road (County X28) to Keokuk
- In Keokuk, follow the road around Rand Park, then turn left on Grand Avenue; it will become N. 5th Street
- At Main Street, turn left, and take US Highway 136 across the river to Hamilton, Illinois, where you can go north on State Highway 96 to reach Nauvoo

To complete the route on the east (Illinois) side (92 miles):

- From US Highway 136 in Hamilton, take State Highway 96 north through Nauvoo
- At Lomax, turn left on County Road 522 (Carmen Road)
- Take US Highway 34 east
- Go north on State Highway 164 through Gladstone
- After Oquawka, turn left on County Road 3 and follow it through Keithsburg; it will become 10th Street
- Turn left on Main Street, then right on 4th Street, which becomes Keithsburg Road after leaving town
- Turn left on State Highway 17 toward New Boston; you can follow this road into New Boston where it ends at the river
- Turn west on Swedtown Road, then north on County Highway 14, which becomes New Boston Road
- Turn left on State Highway 92 and cross the river back into Muscatine

with a lockout. As the factories slowly reopened with replacement workers, sporadic violence broke out, much of it aimed at the replacement workers.

City government openly sided with the owners. At one point, the owners hired an outside security firm to protect their property and harass the strikers. The Pinkerton's were a favorite choice. Their security arsenal included tactics such as kidnappings and beatings to break up unions. In the 1911 conflict, the enforcers were nicknamed "The Sluggers," a brutal group of hired guns—many of them poached from the stockyards of Chicago and St. Louis—who used violence as their first and only means of putting down opposition. When the Sluggers beat an eight-year-old child, public sentiment turned against them. A large crowd swarmed into the city center and surrounded the Commercial Hotel where the Sluggers were staying. They threatened to burn them alive.

The sheriff intervened and promised to kick out the enforcers, which he did. He then called in the state militia, who stayed for four days to keep things quiet. The governor convened a meeting of representatives from owners and workers to meet, which resulted in a few small steps forward. The owners essentially agreed to recognize the union and to adopt a few measures to improve safety. The plants reopened, but the calm didn't last. When conditions in the plants didn't improve, the union called a general strike in the fall of 1911 that lasted for several months.

At the center of many of the battles was a woman named Pearl McGill. Yes, Pearl was her real name (see page 264). For the next 20 years, labor and management fought. By the time they finally made peace, the industry was in decline. Many plants had already closed and the ones that stayed open were switching to plastic, which required far fewer workers. The factories that survived eventually closed as cheap imports flooded US markets. Three companies still made buttons in Muscatine into the 20th century: J & K Buttons, McKee Button Company, and Weber & Sons. All made buttons from plastic. The last pearl button manufacturer, the Ronda Button Factory, closed in 1967.

The process of producing those billions of buttons devastated native populations of fresh-water mussels. Restoration efforts are picking up steam, an exercise that isn't just for grins. Mussels filter water, thus making the river cleaner.

The early leader in the button business didn't fare much better than the mussels. A few years after he was forced out of the factory he founded, John Frederick Boepple worked with the Fairport Biological Station to research ways to replenish the mussel population. In 1911, he walked into a river in Indiana to check out a bed and cut his right foot on a sharp shell, which led to blood poisoning. He was ill for months before finally dying on January 30, 1912, in Muscatine.

Muscatine labor battles weren't restricted to the button industry. In 2009, the Grain Processing Corporation (GPC) locked out 300 employees who belonged to the United Food and Commercial Workers union. The plant makes corn syrup, corn oil, corn-based alcohol products, and other corn-based goodies. The union was locked out after management insisted on new contract language that would have given them the right to replace union workers with non-union workers. The union pretty much lost the fight, as the company brought in replacement workers, anyway. It is a non-union shop today.

Muscatine is home to another industry with a national reach. Two bored friends, Joe Crookham and Myron Gordin, got the idea to build lighting structures for sporting events and venues, so they founded a company called Musco Lighting. It worked out pretty good for them, as their company has built giant light panels for several Olympic Games, NCAA sporting events, and several Super Bowls.

Muscatine also has a surprising international connection. In 1985, a 31-year-old Chinese man traveled with a group to Muscatine to pick up a few tips about hog farming and making the most from a corn crop. That man was Xi Jinping. He's now the president of China and one of the most powerful men in the world. Muscatine has since strengthened its business and cultural ties to China. The upscale Merrill Hotel was funded largely by Chinese investors, and the public library maintains a collection of 500 books about Chinese culture, many of them in both English and Chinese.

BURLINGTON

The area around what we now call Burlington was known to Sauk and Meskwaki people as Shok-ko-kon (Flint Hills). In 1824, when the Sauk and Meskwaki ceded title to lands in Missouri, a special zone of 119,000 acres was created in southeast Iowa. The land was set aside for people of mixed Native and European blood, which is why it became known by an unfortunate name, the half-breed tract. The future cities of Burlington, Fort Madison, and Keokuk were part of this tract. Under the terms of the deal, mixed-race inhabitants could own but not sell the land. Ten years later, the US government granted them the right to sell their property, which triggered a period of chaos and confusion.

Speculators swarmed in and bought land, sometimes for as little as a barrel of whiskey and a pony. Some bought titles from people who claimed to own land they didn't. There were no official land surveys, so boundaries between claims often overlapped. Individual tracts were sometimes sold to multiple people, and squatters moved in to claim a piece of the action, too.

The Wisconsin Territorial Legislature tried to sort it out in 1838 but with little success. Hugh T. Reid believed he bought the whole 119,000-acre claim in a sheriff's sale in 1842 (for $2,884.66), so he sued Joseph Webster in a dispute over 160 acres. The US Supreme Court essentially invalidated Reid's claim in 1850, which meant all the land reverted to the government. A district court divided the land into 101 parcels and divvied it up by partition decree. People with claims drew lots, literally. The parcel each got was determined by a random drawing. One of the attorneys in the case, by the way, was Francis Scott Key, the author of the *Star-Spangled Banner*.

Before all those disputes over land titles, the American Fur Company established a post at Burlington in 1829, staffed by Amzi Doolittle and Sampson White although both probably lived across the Mississippi in Illinois. Just two weeks after the Sauk and Meskwaki ceded six million acres on the west side of the Mississippi River in 1832, Doolittle and White (along with Morton McCarver) made a premature attempt to claim part of the land, even though they could not legally do so until June 1833.

Others tried as well, but were driven out by the army before winter. A persistent group that included McCarver, White, and Doolittle tried to claim a site for a new village—again too soon—but any claim they had was essentially nullified in 1836 when the US Congress passed an act for the platting of Burlington and other towns.

After the act passed, Dr. William Ross was hired to complete the first survey. He is sometimes called the Father of Burlington, not just because of that survey but also because he was the first doctor in town, half of the first marriage, established the first church, the first post office, and probably milked the first cow, too.

John Gray purchased the first lot after the survey was completed. Along with his lot, he got naming rights for the new city—quite a bargain! He went with Burlington be-

A Pearl in the Rough

Ora Pearl McGill was born in rural Louisa County (Iowa) in 1894, one of six children born to James and Eliza Cromer Law McGill. Her father ran a factory that turned raw buttons cut from mussel shells into finished products. When she was 16, she moved to Muscatine to earn money for college. With her father's help, she landed a job at a button factory where the owner used her to spy on his workers. He wanted to know if they were organizing into unions and how productive they were.

What she saw instead shocked her. Men worked long hours for low pay. Many lost fingers and arms in the machinery with only token help provided for job-related injuries. Over time, she became increasingly sympathetic to their plight and began working secretly with the Button Workers Protective Union (BWPU). She was eventually chosen as the union's recording secretary.

During the strike in 1911, she traveled to St. Louis, Boston, and other cities to raise money and support for the striking button workers. In 1912, she moved to Chicago, where she worked with the Women's Trade Union League and organized workers around the country. McGill became one of the most respected organizers for the International Workers of the World.

By 1913, she was ready to give school a try. She moved to Cedar Falls, Iowa, where she started classes to become a teacher, but she didn't have enough money to finish. The following year, she met Helen Keller, and the two became good friends. Keller even gave McGill money to complete her college education.

McGill graduated and found a teaching job at a rural school near Lone Tree, Iowa, but the pay was low and she didn't stay for long. She married Edward Vance in 1917, then got hired to teach in Buffalo, Iowa (just north of Muscatine). She and Vance had a troubled marriage, though. He was emotionally unstable and unreliable, so she divorced him in 1923.

Her life ended tragically not long after that. On April 30, 1924, she was murdered, just a couple months shy of her 30th birthday. Her ex-husband was blamed at first, but some have wondered if she was knocked off by industry bosses, perhaps motivated by rumors that she was considering restarting her activist career. No one was ever charged for her murder.

cause he had previously lived in Burlington, Vermont. His choice wasn't universally loved, but attempts to replace it with a different name ended by 1850. Incidentally, Burlington has had its share of nicknames. One of the most common was Catfish Bend—which wasn't meant as a compliment—but which you'll find today attached to a casino. Presumably the nickname Orchard City pleased more people.

When Burlington incorporated in 1836, some 500 people called it home. The city's initial board of trustees was composed mostly of men looking to make money, a typical setup for pioneer towns. Trustee George W. Kelley, for example, had been a squatter and just wanted to get his claim recognized. The newly formed Iowa Territorial government chose Burlington as its capital in 1838, but the permanent capital was established at Iowa City in 1840.

Many of the early Euro-American residents had pro-slavery views, partly because they maintained trading relationships along the Mississippi with slave-holding states and partly because some had roots in the South. When news trickled upriver that the abolitionist Elijah Lovejoy had been killed at Alton, Illinois, in 1837, a cheer erupted from a crowd on the riverfront.

That may explain why the state did not welcome Black residents with open arms in the early years. Black men couldn't live in Iowa Territory after April 1, 1839, unless they had papers to prove they were free and could post a $500 bond. Like in many other states, Blacks could not vote, could not marry Whites, could not serve in a militia, could not attend public schools, and could not testify in court against a White person.

As Burlington grew, many of the founders moved on, including Doolittle and White. The city they left behind expanded into the surrounding hills. Three hills were named after a cardinal direction (North, South, and West). Vinegar Hill acquired its name when a vinegar factory opened there, but as wealthy people moved in, it became known as Prospect Hill, which sounded like a more pleasant place to live.

Early Burlington was so well known for its pork processing industry that some folks nicknamed it Porkopolis (yet another name for Burlington!). After the railroad bridge was completed in 1868, Burlington lost much of its pork processing industry as live pigs were shipped by rail to slaughterhouses in places like Chicago, St. Louis, and Omaha. The city also had flour mills, lumber mills, wholesalers, carriage manufacturers, shoemakers, a barbed wire manufacturer, and department stores.

While romantic images of river towns persist, life along the Mississippi River in the early days was far from ideal. The Lower Town section of Burlington, like many river towns, was littered with animal feces, broken crates, empty bottles, spoiled and rotting food, discarded animal bones, and other sorts of trash. Hawk-Eye Creek was an open sewer for decades and discharged all that crap into the Mississippi. Passing steamboats dumped their trash on the levee, too. I'll leave it to you to imagine what you might have smelled walking around the city in those days.

In spite of the foul smells and trash, by 1850, Burlington was a major transit center. In the spring of 1851, a thousand wagons ferried across the Mississippi to Burlington. Hundreds of steamboats landed carrying thousands of passengers. The Peoria & Burlington Railroad reached the area in 1855, then merged with the Chicago, Burlington, and Quincy (CB&Q). The railroads brought thousands of immigrants from around the world to Burlington, mostly from Europe, but many from China and Russian, too. Residents of Burlington could go to the train depot to witness the mass migration and enjoy some fascinating people watching.

The railroad was a major employer in the region for decades. The CB&Q built repair yards at Old Leffler's Station, which was renamed West Burlington in 1883. At the time of the name change, West Burlington had more orchards (nine) than houses (eight). The railroad closed the maintenance shops in 2004.

Iowa soldiers assembled at Burlington during the Civil War at Camps Warren and Lauman. The camps were poorly provisioned, though, and often not sanitary. Locals helped supply food and blankets to the soldiers. By 1862, some soldiers had behaved badly often enough that a curfew was imposed for enlisted men. Other soldiers patrolled the streets to enforce it. During the Civil War, all goods that moved through the city were subject to inspection. Any contraband (medical supplies, arms, gunpowder) that authorities suspected was intended for the Confederacy or its sympathizers was seized. Inflation drove up the cost of most goods and a lot of farmers were fighting in the war, so many fields were not planted. Times were hard and food scarce.

After the Civil War, Burlington grew rapidly, from 6,700 in 1860 to nearly 15,000 ten years later. The new arrivals came from diverse backgrounds. Germans were most numerous, but a large number of Swedes also settled in Burlington. Irish immigration peaked between 1860 and 1890, with many of them finding work at the Murray Iron Works or at Embalming Burial Case Company. Congregation B'nai Sholem was founded in 1879 to serve the city's growing Jewish community.

By 1875, Burlington had 300 Black residents. The community grew larger between 1880 and 1920 when some coal and railroad companies brought African Americans from the South to work during strikes. While White residents contributed money to help build some of the city's African American churches, the city's social life was mostly segregated. Black and White patrons had separate sections in the movie theater. Swimming pools and bowling alleys were segregated. Many hotels wouldn't serve Black customers.

In the late 1800s, the most common crime leading to arrest—by far—was drunkenness, but there were other ways to get in trouble, too. In 1872, youthful skinny-dipping and speeding drivers accounted for more arrests than prostitution and gambling.

Other than drinking and skinny dipping, entertainment options in the 19th century included attending lectures (phrenologists, doctors, travel lecturers), going to the circus (it must have been quite a sight to see elephants drinking from the Mississippi!), minstrel shows, magicians, panoramas, masquerades and costume balls, organ grinders, street preachers, fishing, and hunting.

Adults or precocious teens could also head out to a gunboat. From the Civil War until around 1880, gunboats—floating brothels—would tie up at places near Burlington. They served cheap liquor at inflated prices. Prostitutes charged whatever customers would pay. They didn't really answer to anyone. If they ran into trouble, they simply lifted anchor and floated on to a new location. Gunboats often undermined land-based brothels, many of which had worked out good deals with local law enforcement.

Well into the 20th century, Burlington had a stable manufacturing sector, with factories that made spark plugs, backhoes, and batteries. The Iowa Ordnance Plant (later the Iowa Army Ammunition Plant) opened in 1941 on 20,000 acres west of Burlington. At its peak in 1941, the plant employed 12,000 people. It manufactured mortar shells, artillery rounds, and bombs. During its first two years of operation, the plant had two major explosions. The first killed 11 people, and the second killed 21. The plant is still operating today. They built large caliber munitions for the Army, but with fewer fatal explosions, at least at the plant.

Beginning in the 1930s, residents could take the Chicago, Burlington, & Quincy Railroad's four-car *Mark Twain Zephyr*, which zipped along the Mississippi River at 110 miles an hour on its trip south to St. Louis. Each car had a name: the *Injun Joe* carried the mail and the engine; the *Becky Thatcher* carried the luggage; the *Huckleberry Finn* was the dining car; and the *Tom Sawyer* housed the passengers. Service ended by 1960.

Burlington produced several people who had an impact on your life, even if you didn't know it until now. Wallace Hume Carothers (1896-1937) invented the polymer we now call nylon. William Frawley (1893-1966) was an actor whose most famous role was Fred Mertz on *I Love Lucy*. Robert Noyce (1927-1990) was the co-inventor of the semiconductor chip and founder of Intel. Burlington produced quite a nerdlet of scientists! In addition, legendary guitar player Bo Ramsey was born and raised in Burlington.

Burlington native Aldo Leopold (1886-1948) wrote a widely influential book in 1949 (*A Sand County Almanac*) that revolutionized conservation politics and policies. One of his more memorable quotes:

> "We abuse land because we regard it as a commodity belonging to us. When we see land as a community to which we belong, we may begin to use it with love and respect."

In the 1970s, Burlington was home to a variety of manufacturing plants: Chittenden & Eastman Company (mattresses), Winegard Company (antennae), Case Construction (tractors and backhoes), Drake Hardware (wholesaler), Burlington Basket Company, Lehigh-Leopold Company (office furniture), Trane Company/Murray Boiler Division, Champion Spark Plugs, Bonewitz Chemical Services, General Electric, the Burlington Paper Company, and more.

Forty years later, manufacturing remains a key part of Burlington's economy—Case Construction is still turning out backhoes and other heavy equipment and Winegard still makes antennae and satellite dishes—but companies are smaller, the jobs fewer, and most of the remaining manufacturing jobs require more than a high school diploma. Riverboat gambling began (again) in Burlington in 1991, but it has since moved to a land-based casino on the edge of the city. The largest employer in the region today, though, is Great River Medical Center.

FORT MADISON

In 1805, General James Wilkinson, Governor of the new Louisiana Territory and commander of the western army, chose Zebulon Pike to lead an expedition to explore the upper Mississippi. A major focus of Pike's trip was to locate the headwaters of the Mississippi River (he failed), but he was also tasked with identifying locations for forts (he fared better at that). One of the locations he recommended was at a place with a trading post known as Le Moine Factory. When the fort was finally built a few years later, it was initially called Fort Belle Vue, but the name was soon changed to honor then President James Madison.

The Sauk and Meskwaki didn't take kindly to the construction of the fort, however. They believed it violated their territorial integrity under the Treaty of 1804. Black Hawk led an unsuccessful assault against it, but the Sauk and Meskwaki continually harassed the soldiers who lived there.

During the War of 1812, the Sauk and Meskwaki had better luck. A weeks-long siege in July 1813 convinced the soldiers to abandon the fort. The soldiers set it on fire, then escaped down the Mississippi. All that remained of the fort was a stone chimney, which stood for years. That's how the area earned the nickname "Lone Chimney," although the Sauk and Meskwaki called it Po-to-wo-nock (the place of fire). The fort was located about where the Sheaffer Pen parking lot is now (Avenue H between 4th and 3rd).

The land remained under the control of the Sauk and Meskwaki for a while after that, until they were forced to cede it in the aftermath of the Black Hawk War. In anticipation of the treaty, Peter Williams made the first land grab, but he jumped the gun. Soldiers came down from Fort Armstrong and evicted him. When Williams resisted, the soldiers tied him to a tree and destroyed his cabin, then took him across the river to a jail at Commerce (Nauvoo). Williams wouldn't give up, though. He returned in June 1833 and reclaimed the land after it was officially open to settlement. He didn't have much time to enjoy his claim. He died two years later.

NC Steele built one of the first boarding houses in Fort Madison, around 1836. It was a log cabin, just 12 feet by 16 feet. Steele built a clapboard addition for guests. If you wanted to spend the night, you could expect to sleep on a square of canvas that was hung by a rope at the corners of each of four poles. Guests sometimes amused themselves by cutting all the ropes of one bed simultaneously, so the occupant would roll out onto the wood floor. If you got bored cutting bed ropes at the boarding house, you could visit one of the many whiskey shanties along the riverfront.

In 1836, Congress passed an act that called for a town plat and incorporation of Fort Madison. Land sales followed soon after that. In that same year, residents of Fort Madison invited Black Hawk to the 4th of July celebration. Black Hawk lived nearby in a home along Devil Creek two miles west of the city. He greeted the residents of Fort Madison as friends while defending the choices he made, but he focused mostly on reconciliation and looking to the future. He told those gathered:

> "It has pleased the Great Spirit that I am here today. I have eaten with my white friends. The earth is our mother–we are now on it–with the Great Spirit above us–it is good. I hope we are all friends here. A few summers ago I was fighting against you–I did wrong, perhaps; but that is past–it is buried–let it be forgotten. Rock River was a beautiful country–I liked my towns, my cornfields, and the home of my people. I fought for it. It is now yours–keep it as we did–it will produce you good crops. I thank the Great Spirit that I am now friendly with my white brethren–we are here together–we have eaten together–we are friends–it is his wish and mine. I thank you for your friendship."

The speech turned out to be a farewell for Black Hawk. He died three months later.

In 1839, the Iowa Territorial legislature picked Fort Madison as the site for a new prison. The Iowa State Penitentiary has grown quite a bit since that time, but the original 1840 cell house was still used into the 1980s. It's an imposing sight, with rough-hewn limestone walls set into a hill that rises away from the Mississippi. The prison houses Iowa's maximum-security inmates and was the site of many executions (the last one was in 1963—Iowa abolished the death penalty two years after that). It housed about 800 inmates until they were transferred to a new prison in 2015.

Fort Madison grew quickly thanks to milling (lumber and flour), the river trade, and the arrival of immigrants from Germany. By 1850, Fort Madison had 1,500 residents. Early village leaders passed strict blue laws to protect the Sabbath. It was illegal to sell goods, gamble, play any game, shoot guns, or run races for money on Sundays.

Aaron White and Joshua Owens operated the first ferry service. For the trip to Niota, Illinois, they charged 37 ½ cents for a person and a horse and $1 for a wagon and two horses. Ferries couldn't cross the frozen river in winter, but the ice was usually thick enough to form a temporary bridge. Most years one brave person volunteered to test the ice by crossing it slowly, poking the ice to find soft spots and marking the safe route with willows. That person was rewarded with free booze from local saloons.

Fort Madison got its first railroad line in 1856. The city granted a bridge charter and land to the Santa Fe Railroad after officials downriver in Keokuk balked. The railroad also opened yards that brought some 4,000 new residents to the city. The railroad bridge was finally built in 1887. It was replaced in 1927 with a bridge that had a dual rail track on one level and a car deck on another. Its 525-foot swingspan is the largest in the world. It's quite a thrill to drive across (there's a $1 toll for crossing eastbound), but you might want to take it slow.

The railroad triggered rapid population growth in Fort Madison, especially in the area west of 18th street that became known as Santa Fe Town. The new arrivals included Mexican workers enticed to the area by the railroad to fill a labor shortage during World War I. Hundreds settled in Fort Madison, many in a neighborhood called El Cometa near the rail yards between 29th and 33rd Streets. After the area flooded in 1926, most of the community relocated to a nearby area known as El Estafiate (named after a wild herb that grew nearby). Many lived in converted railroad cars before small houses were built. Hundreds of their descendants still live in Fort Madison, and they celebrate Mexican independence with an annual fiesta that goes back to the 1920s.

Ernest Corsepius arrived in Fort Madison in 1901 and started a business that harvested ice from the frozen Mississippi and shipped it to places as far away as St. Louis. He was also a fan of racing. He built a boat called *Minnie C II* that won the 1908 Mississippi Valley championship when it beat the *Independent* from St. Louis.

Walter Sheaffer founded a pen company in 1908. He patented a deflatable rubber sack in the barrel of the pen that was quite an innovation. The Sheaffer Pen Company was a big hit. They built a new factory in 1952, then were purchased by Textron Corporation in 1966 and later by Bic. The Fort Madison factories closed around 2005, but the Sheaffer name is still used for some pens (but they are now made in China).

Fort Madison has lost population in the past few decades, mostly as the railroad cut jobs, but there are still some big manufacturers nearby. Siemens builds wind turbines, and Armour processes meat.

KEOKUK

The first Euro-American to move into the area was apparently Dr. Samuel C. Muir, who built a cabin here in 1820. Muir had been a surgeon in the US Army at Fort Edwards (Warsaw, Illinois), but when the government ordered soldiers to leave their Native American wives, he left the Army instead. Muir moved away after a few years and leased his claim to St. Louisans Otis Reynolds and John Culver, who sent Moses Stillwell upriver in 1828 to set up a trading post. Muir came back in 1830 and took over. He set up a post of his own, but didn't have long to profit from it—he died of cholera in 1832. Stillwell's stone warehouse was wiped away by the Great Ice Gorge of 1832.

For the first several years of its life, the little settlement at foot of the Des Moines Rapids had many identities, going by names like Point, Foot of the Rapids, and Puck-e-she-tuck (which probably means "where the water runs still" but some early Europeans and Americans interpreted it as "the foot of the rapids").

There are a few versions of how the name Keokuk became permanently attached to the place. In one account, a group of rivermen (including Col. George Davenport from upriver) picked the name shortly after the Black Hawk War ended, presumably to honor the Sauk leader. My personal favorite, though, is that nine men met at John Gains' bar in September 1834 to settle the matter. Someone proposed the name Keokuk and all those in favor were instructed to walk up to the bar and drink a shot of whiskey. The vote carried 8 to 1. The lone dissenter was JB Patterson, who had only been in town for a couple of weeks and apparently wasn't too fond of the Sauk leader, or whiskey.

Keokuk was recorded as the village's name in an 1837 plat by Dr. Isaac Galland and David Kilbourne. At the time of the plat, the entirety of the town was a few dilapidated houses known affectionately as Rat Row. These homes were originally built by the American Fur Company but abandoned when the Black Hawk War broke out.

The city incorporated in 1847 and ferry service to Hamilton and Warsaw (Illinois) and Alexandria (Missouri) began soon after that. Keokuk had a reputation for lawlessness in the early years. Boats reportedly preferred to anchor in the middle of the river rather than tie up at town, because they feared being plundered. Englishman Charles Augustus Murray passed through Keokuk in 1835 and wasn't too impressed. He wrote:

> "This village of Keokuk is the lowest and most blackguard place that I have yet visited: its population is composed chiefly of the watermen who assist in loading and unloading the keel-boats, and in towing them up when the rapids are too strong for the steam-engines. They are a coarse and ferocious caricature of the London bargemen, and their chief occupation seems to consist in drinking, fighting, and gambling."

By the 1850s, though, an economic boom transformed the city and new residents poured in and civilized the city. The new arrivals included some of the Clemens family, including the future Mark Twain. Sam Clemens lived in Keokuk for two years, where he worked in his brother's print shop at 202 Main Street. Senator Thomas Rees, the publisher of the *Keokuk Daily Post*, invited young Sam to submit a couple of articles and offered $5 for each. After the first article had been accepted, Clemens asked $7.50 for the second. The publisher deliberated but ultimately agreed to pay it. When Clemens wanted $10 for the third, however, the publisher declined and didn't run any more of his works. Fortunately for us, that decision didn't end Clemens' writing career.

Sam Clemens worked for his brother, Orion, who, with help from Sam and his other brother Henry, published Keokuk's first city directory in 1856. Sam Clemens listed his occupation as "Antiquarian." Orion tried many occupations (lawyer, printer, newspaperman, editor, chicken farmer, silver mine speculator, memoirist, biblical scholar) but didn't succeed at any of them. Later in life, Twain started a novel based on his brother's life that he never finished. He was going to call it *Autobiography of a Damned Fool.* Orion and Sam's mother, Jane Lampton Clemens, lived out their lives in Keokuk. Jane died in 1890, Orion in 1897. Both were buried in Hannibal.

At the time the Clemens family was settling into Keokuk, the city was in the middle of a real estate boom. One person observed that prices were so high in 1856 that "you couldn't reach them with an airship." That all ended in 1857 when the national economy crashed. In Keokuk, land that had been selling for $1,000 barely fetched $10.

Keokuk, as a busy river town, attracted folks from a wide variety of backgrounds. By the mid-1850s, Keokuk's Jewish community was large enough to form a Benevolent Society and to buy land for a cemetery. The first burial was in 1858, young Bertha Aal, who was just over a year old. The community built a synagogue in 1877, Congregation B'Nai Israel. The Romanesque building had an auditorium that could seat 400, a sign of great optimism from the 20 families who were members at that time. The synagogue was decorated with carved white pine, frescoes on the walls and ceiling, and stained-glass windows. The exterior had two octagonal turrets and decorative iron work. Iowa's first synagogue cost about $15,000 to build. The hoped-for wave of Jewish immigrants to Keokuk never materialized, though. The building was sold to the Keokuk Gospel Center in 1933 and torn down in 1957.

A handful of African Americans moved to Keokuk before the Civil War, including Charlotta Gordon Pyles. Charlotta had escaped slavery in Kentucky when her owner, Frances Gordon, moved the family out of state to grant them their freedom. After a dangerous trip in which they had to deal with extortionists and avoid slave catchers, Charlotta, her husband Henry, and several children reached Keokuk and decided to stay. On April 2, 1857, Charlotta and Henry legally married in Lee County, something they had not been able to do in Kentucky.

Charlotta lectured around the country. She met Frederick Douglass and Susan B. Anthony while pleading the abolitionist cause. In six months, she raised $3,000 that she used to buy the freedom of two of her sons-in-law. In Keokuk, even though her family remained poor, she provided a home for her former owner, Frances Gordon, and helped escaped slaves make their way to Canada.

Keokuk sent over 1,300 men to fight in the Civil War (the city's population was about 8,100 in 1860); 158 of them died. Keokuk was the point of embarkation for all of Iowa's Civil War soldiers, some 80,000 men.

The Union Army sent many of its wounded to one of the seven hospitals in the city. The College of Physicians and Surgeons had been training doctors in Keokuk since 1850. The first wounded, 296 men who fought at the Battle of Shiloh, were transported to Keokuk on the *Jerry Deane*, a sidewheel steamboat that arrived on April 20, 1862. Another 300 soldiers arrived three days later.

Although Congress passed legislation in 1862 that authorized a national cemetery in Keokuk, the city donated three acres in Oakland Cemetery rather than take money from the federal government. By the end of the Civil War, 627 Union soldiers were buried in the new national cemetery, along with eight Confederate soldiers. There were also a number of Confederate soldiers who died en route to the prison camp upriver at Rock Island. They were buried in the Mississippi River.

With the Civil War over, the city got back to the business of growing. City leaders believed that bridging the Mississippi was key to making that happen. In 1868, the Hamilton & Keokuk Bridge Company was founded. One of its members was a young Andrew Carnegie. The company succeeded in building a drawbridge that opened for business in 1871. It had a railroad track down the middle, a road on either side for vehicle traffic, and sidewalks outside the vehicle lanes.

In the latter part of the 19th century, Keokuk was the site of so many mercantile companies that supplied folks heading west that the city was nicknamed "Gate City" (not to be confused with the Gateway City further downriver). Keokuk also developed a strong manufacturing base that produced iron works (stoves and locomotives, for example), furniture, and clothing. Because it was close to a lot of farms, Keokuk developed an industry in food processing and canning, too.

In 1868, construction began on a canal that would allow river boats to bypass the Des Moines Rapids. The rapids ran 11 miles from Montrose to Keokuk, dropping 22 feet in elevation in the stretch. Most of the time, the rapids had just three feet of water running over them, which is why so few boats could navigate through them with a full load. The eight-mile canal and its three locks took nine years and $4.5 million to complete (nearly twice the estimated cost), but it allowed boats to get past the rapids without slowing down to unload and reload. The canal became obsolete when the hydroelectric dam was built 30 years later.

Keokuk's rail depot opened in 1891. At its peak, Keokuk was served by seven different lines that ran 20 daily trains. Main Street had an electric streetcar down the middle in early 1900s, and Keokuk was connected to the Illinois cities of Hamilton and Warsaw by streetcar lines (they were all shut down by 1930).

Keokuk was a big enough deal in the 19th century that it attracted a number of celebrity lecturers, including Tom Thumb, Carrie Nation, Mark Twain, President Theodore Roosevelt, and Frederick Douglass.

After the Civil War, a lot of African Americans moved to Keokuk. While many communities along the Mississippi River were just temporary stops for African Americans looking for a new home, many opted to stay when they reached Keokuk.

Like most places in the US, Keokuk operated separate schools for Black and White children. The first school for Blacks was built in 1869 at 11th and Main, but it didn't operate long. In 1875, the Iowa Supreme Court ruled that racially segregated schools violated the state's constitution. Some of the plaintiffs in the suit were from Keokuk.

School integration didn't the generate fierce opposition in Keokuk as it had in other communities. In 1878, William O. Vance became the first African American to graduate from the integrated high school. He would become a doctor and practice medicine in New Albany, Indiana, until his death in 1906. Another one of the early graduates was Geroid Smith (Class of 1880), the grandson of Charlotta Pyles.

Even with school integration proceeding rather smoothly, Keokuk wasn't exactly Utopia for its Black residents. For decades, most Black residents could only find work in unskilled or low-skilled jobs at coal yards or hotels, with the railroad, or as domestic help. In the late 1880s, Dr. William Harper opened a café in Keokuk because no restaurant in town would serve African Americans. He called it Blessed St. Martin, probably after St. Martin de Porres, the patron saint of social justice and mixed-race people.

For the era, though, African American residents in Keokuk had more opportunities than African Americans in many other parts of the country. Some became noted doctors and educators and, perhaps the strongest testament to the life the city offered, many of their descendants still live in Keokuk today.

By the turn of the century, Keokuk's boosters had every reason to feel good about their future. When plans for a long-sought-after hydroelectric dam on the Mississippi moved closer to reality, they could barely restrain their optimism. An editorial in the *Constitution-Democrat* (September 29, 1906) boasted:

Random Fact: The Iowa Theater, a popular movie house on Main Street between 4th and 5th; burned down in May 1975. The last movie shown there was *The Towering Inferno*.

Chief Keokuk

Born around 1780 at a thriving village called Saukenuk (near present-day Rock Island, Illinois), Keokuk (Kiyo'kaga) was rather tall and fat, liked his whiskey, loved the Mississippi River, and loved women. He had several wives. His name has been alternately translated as "one who moves about alertly" and "the watchful fox," although as an older man he called himself "the man who has been everywhere."

While he earned his stripes as a warrior in several battles against Dakota fighters, he was most respected for his skills as a negotiator and peacemaker. He was widely credited with convincing most of the Sauk men to stay out of the Black Hawk War.

He and Black Hawk pursued decidedly different tactics for dealing with the advancing Euro-American settlers. While Black Hawk was ready to fight to remain on traditional Sauk and Meskwaki lands, Keokuk believed that military engagements were pointless. He saw the number of people moving into the area and didn't believe that his group had much a chance to win. Instead, he used his negotiating skills to get the best deal he could.

Still, when the Black Hawk War ended in 1832, Keokuk and others who stayed out of the battles were, like Black Hawk and his followers, forced to sign a treaty surrendering more land. Most of the Sauk and Meskwaki were forced to move to reservation lands in Kansas.

After their removal, Keokuk traveled from his home on his beloved horse. He made regular trips to Osage, Ho Chunk, Ottawa, and Omaha communities. When he visited them, he went in style: riding on a Spanish saddle, dressed in an elegant handmade robe, adorned with a wampum, porcupine quills, and beads, half-moons of silver dangling down his back, wearing a headdress of silver bobs and feathers, and carrying a rifle, scalping knife, tomahawk, pipe, and war club. There wasn't much about him that was subtle.

Keokuk lost favor with many Sauk and Meskwaki as he got older. Many thought he took too big a share of the annuity payments from the American government. He died in April 1848 and was initially buried in Franklin County, Kansas. For a while after his death, his skull was supposedly on the altar of a Masonic lodge, but a doctor who was also a Mason helped to retrieve and replace it with a different skull so it could be buried with the rest of Keokuk's remains. His body was moved to Rand Park in the city that bears his name in 1883, with the approval of Keokuk's son, Moses. A monument was built over the grave, which stands today overlooking the Mississippi River.

> "This work (the power plant and dam), when completed, should cause an immense amount of factory building in this immediate vicinity on account of the cheap power to be enjoyed, and Keokuk is expecting to see a great growth within the next few years."

City leaders had long dreamed about tapping water power for their city, but building a dam was expensive and logistically difficult. Plans picked up steam with the formation of the Keokuk and Hamilton Power Company in 1900, a quasi-public organization initially funded by the cities of Keokuk and Hamilton, Illinois. In 1905, Congress granted the company authority to build a dam. Financing the construction, though, turned out to be a hard sell. Few investors in the US believed in the project, so most of the financing, nearly two-thirds, came from foreign investors (mostly from England, France, Germany, Belgium, and Canada).

With money finally in hand, the company got busy planning the complicated logistics. They had to negotiate with 1,300 landowners whose property would be flooded by the dam, which included parts of the villages of Galland, Sandusky, and Montrose. Railroad lines had to be moved and the sewer system at Fort Madison redesigned. A cemetery at Montrose was relocated. Because the dam would flood the navigation canal around the rapids, the company had to agree to build a lock that would become US government property after completion, which they did.

Construction began in earnest around the end of 1910. Hundreds of workers lived in temporary bunkhouses along the river. For the most part, it went smoothly except for a few anxious moments in the spring of 1912, when flooding nearly washed away parts of the dam. The winter had been harsh, so thick ice covered the river. On March 24, an ice floe broke free and raced down the rapids, piling nearly 30 feet high against a coffer dam. Spectators lined the river banks in anticipation of witnessing a disaster, but the dam held.

The last piece of concrete was placed on May 31, 1913. The lock opened two weeks later. It was the widest dam in the world when it was completed, stretching 4,649 feet across the Mississippi Valley. Construction cost $25 million, a heck of a lot of money in 1913. The first watts of electricity pulsed from the plant on July 1, most of it going to St. Louis but some also supplying nearby cities, including Fort Madison, Dallas City, Nauvoo, Warsaw, and Quincy, in addition to Keokuk and Hamilton.

The 40-mile-long stretch of water impounded by the dam was named Lake Cooper after the engineer who designed the dam (Hugh L. Cooper). It's a popular place for sailboating because it catches the wind easily and there's not much current. In the hundred years since the dam was completed, though, the lake has lost 70% of its capacity as it has filled in with silt trapped by the dam.

The dam didn't bring the prosperity to Keokuk that its boosters had promised. Rather than fueling growth in the Keokuk area, the energy it produced was quickly swallowed up by a rapidly growing St. Louis. Today, all the power (up to 142 megawatts or about 2% of what the St. Louis area uses) generated by the plant goes into the grid for wholesale distribution around the country. Keokuk residents told me that they have the highest electric rates in Iowa, in spite of living next to a hydroelectric plant.

Even though the hydroelectric dam didn't generate the economic boom that city leaders had expected, the city maintained a stable manufacturing economy for generations. In 1940, the city's factories churned out corn starch, cereals, carbides, ferrous alloys, gray iron castings, steel castings, shoes, rubber products, factory trucks, fiber boxes, clothing, electric scoreboards, black powder, corn syrup, trucks, hog rings, and brooms.

The city's population peaked at over 16,000 around 1960 and has declined in every federal census since. The reasons for the decline will sound familiar: consolidation in agriculture that resulted in larger but fewer farms and farm families; the steady loss of manufacturing jobs; and declining retail sales as more people owned a car and could drive to bigger cities like Burlington or Quincy for their shopping. Keokuk has also been hurt, I think, by its location. When river and rails were the primary means for getting around, the city did fine. When cars replaced those options, though, Keokuk suffered, as it wasn't on a highly trafficked route—it's not really on the way to anywhere.

When you drive down Main Street today, with its empty storefronts and buildings in need of some love, it's hard to imagine that this place was once such an important city on the Mississippi. But it was. Perhaps it will be again someday. The city still inspires a core group of fiercely proud residents to fight to turn the city's fortunes around.

History: Illinois Communities

HAMILTON

When New Hampshire native John Gordon built a log cabin around 1833, he and his family were probably the first Euro-Americans to move into the area. A village called Montebello was platted in 1832 at the downstream end of the Des Moines Rapids, not far from the steepest part of the rapids, at an area called the English Chain. Montebello never boomed, but it had a steamboat stop until 1891, a post office beginning in 1830, and ferry service for many years before it faded away. Most of the former village site is under water today thanks to the dam at Keokuk. While the village disappeared, the name Montebello lives on for the township.

In 1852, a group that included John Gordon's son, Samuel, platted a new village. Some of the streets that were part of that original plat were never developed because they flooded regularly. The founders considered and rejected many names for their village, including Bartlett (Bryant Bartlett was an early Euro-American settler who ran a ferry until the bridge put him out of business), Rapid City, Gordon, and East Keokuk. Instead, they picked Hamilton because Artois Hamilton of nearby Carthage was the wealthiest of the early investors, and they hoped he would invest generously in the community. It worked, more or less.

Artois Socrates Hamilton, born in 1795, was a native of Massachusetts. He married Atta Bentley in 1827 and left her in New York and their four children eight years later to find a place out west with better economic prospects. He decided that Carthage, Illinois, was the place to be, so, after several weeks of sleeping in a wagon, he bought a house and sent for his family. Artois did well at farming and used some of his money to buy a house in town in 1836 that he turned into a hotel. It was a big hit.

A few nights before Joseph and Hyrum Smith were murdered, the hotel hosted an event with quite a collection of guests: Illinois Governor Ford, Wilson and William Law, Robert Foster, and Francis Higbee, all of them (except the governor) former Mormons who had became publicly critical of the LDS church. They were joined by Joseph and Hyrum Smith, the founders of the LDS church whom they were all criticizing. How'd you like to have been a dinner guest that night?

> Keokuk was the hometown of a US Supreme Court judge and an eccentric millionaire. **READ MORE** about them at MississippiValleyTraveler.com/Keokuk/

After a mob murdered the Smith brothers in Carthage, Artois Hamilton went to the jail and retrieved their bodies, brought them to the hotel, and built pine coffins for them. He also provided safe haven for another Mormon leader, John Taylor, who had been injured in the attack on the jail but had survived. The next day, Artois joined the procession that took the Smith brothers' bodies back to Nauvoo, a trip that took six hours. He declined compensation for his efforts.

By 1850, Artois was the wealthiest man in the county, but his money didn't protect him from tragedy. In July 1851, an outbreak of cholera erupted at Carthage and hit the Hamiltons especially hard. Artois lost his wife, two children, and a sister. He was sickened, too, but survived. Artois married Susan Smith in 1852 and built a new hotel in Carthage, around the same time that the new village down the road was platted. Artois died on July 4th, 1873, in Carthage, having never lived in the village that bore his name.

The new village of Hamilton got the area's post office 1853 and incorporated the following year. Hamilton got a little bigger in 1859 when it annexed the nearby city of Oakwood, which then became the city's 3rd ward.

Some early residents were eager to keep the wrong kind of people out of town, so on June 8, 1856, a hundred men and women carried out a Carrie Nation-style raid. They met at the post office, hatchets in hand, and stormed the store of Jacob Ryley—a known liquor seller! —and proceeded to destroy his stock. Not satisfied, they next convinced a widow who lived nearby in a tent to sell the barrel of booze that she owned, then they destroyed that barrel, too. None of this stopped liquor sales in Hamilton.

The town started a growth spurt after the Civil War, sprouting industries that included cigar manufacturing, fertilizer production, and lumber mills. The city counted nearly 1,400 residents in 1860 and maintained a population of a thousand or so residents until the 1960s. Nearly four dozen buildings went up between 1887 and 1936 (and many went down in an 1889 fire), mostly in the business district on Main Street and on Broadway. The new businesses included a soda fountain, a jewelry store, quarries, the Gem Theater, and three hotels. Patrons could reach these businesses by walking across the city's wooden sidewalks.

French native Charles Dadant moved to Hamilton in 1863 hoping to grow grapes. When that didn't go as well as he hoped, he turned to bee-keeping. He started a business that is now run by the sixth generation of Dadants. A self-styled "bee-culturist", Dadant tended multiple colonies of bees to produce honey and beeswax. His son, Camille Pierre (CP), ran the company next and was one of the key figures in getting the Keokuk dam built. The Dadant company is still going strong today.

In the late 19th century, the Riverside Sanitarium was a popular spa. For $8-$15 a week, guests could enjoy Swedish baths, magnetic healing, massages, and mineral water cures using water from an Artesian well that was nearly 600 feet deep. The spa closed in 1900. During construction of the Keokuk dam (1910-1913), the former spa buildings housed some of the construction workers. The building burned down in 1913.

Wildcat Springs Park might today be best known for its geodes, but it was busy with Chautauquas in the early 20th century. Chautauquas were traveling shows that featured a variety of educational and entertainment-oriented programs under big tents. Visitors might hear a lecture on women's suffrage or self-improvement, or be entertained by singers, ventriloquists, and magicians. Among the well-known personalities who appeared at a Chautauqua in Hamilton were attorneys Clarence Darrow and William Jennings Bryan.

In the 20th century, the Lakeview Club was a popular place to swim and hang out. Residents went there to dine at the riverfront restaurant, dance, or swim on the beach. The club operated from roughly 1914 to 1960. The building still exists but is part of a private residence now.

Hamilton was a pretty busy place for trains. The Mississippi and Wabash railroad reached Hamilton in 1858, the first of several that passed through. The first river crossing for railroads, the Keokuk & Hamilton bridge, opened in June 1871 and was replaced with a new bridge in 1916. The Keokuk & Western Electric Inter-Urban trolley connected the cities of Keokuk, Hamilton, & Warsaw from 1903 to 1921.

In the 1920s, Alice Green hosted an artist commune in her home south of town known as Ivy Wild. She was known to hold a séance at the drop of a hat. The community included a few artists and painters, one of whom, George Upp, was rather successful. In 1965, Keith Wilkey wrote about a visit he once made to Ivy Wild:

> "This visitor visited Ivy Wild in 1931 and remembers Mrs. Green and the strains of weird music being played on a music saw and vibrations of the tines on a pitchfork in the dimly lighted room filled with animated snakes, stuffed animals and the gutteral raspings of a live parrot."

Hamilton sustained considerable damage on the evening of April 8, 1999, when a tornado ripped through the city of 3,000 residents. The storm destroyed 29 homes and damaged a hundred more.

Hamilton today is mostly a bedroom community, but it still has some industry, including the Dadant Company. Many also know it as a favorite place to hunt for that perfect geode.

NAUVOO

The area around the Des Moines Rapids has a long history of human activity going back at least 12,000 years, from the Sauk and Meskwaki people who moved into the region in the 18th century after the Ho Chunk (Winnebago), Mamaceqtaw (Menominie), and Neshnabé (Potawatomi) had called the area home. At the turn of the 19th century, Meskwaki Chief Quashquema led a village of 500 lodges and several thousand people.

In 1804, a contingent of Sauk and Meskwaki representatives, including Chief Quashquema, went to St. Louis to secure the release of one of their own who had been imprisoned. They also hoped to negotiate a trade deal with terms as favorable as the one given to their rivals, the Wah-Zha-Zhi (Osage). While in St. Louis, the new Governor of Louisiana Territory (and future President) William Henry Harrison took advantage of the situation to induce the group to cede a portion of their ancestral lands, the territory east of the Mississippi River and between the Illinois and Wisconsin Rivers. The US government paid $2,234.50 in goods and cash for the land and promised an annual payment of $1,000 in goods (that the Sauk and Meskwaki would have to pick up at St. Louis). The Sauk and Meskwaki retained hunting rights in the area, though.

In 1805, Indian agent Jean Pierre Chouteau established a trading post that was supposed to supply the Sauk and Meskwaki with goods at reasonable prices. He and his agent, William Ewing, built a two-story log cabin, but it didn't work out, apparently because Ewing wasn't exactly competent. Lieutenant Zebulon Pike met Ewing during his 1805-1806 expedition and called him "utterly unfit" for the work. A few more agents came and went until the cabin was essentially abandoned around 1810.

In 1824, James White bought the claim and the cabin and set up his own trading post. He didn't do much better. He couldn't compete with the American Fur Company, so he closed the post and turned to helping boats transport their goods across and around the Des Moines Rapids, a process called lightering. White also purchased the hunting rights from the Sauk and Meskwaki, who then moved across the river to Iowa.

When the post office was established in 1830 (George Cutler served as postmaster), the community was named Venus. By 1832, Venus counted 62 residents. Cutler died in 1834 and one month later the village's hundred or so residents decided they needed a better name, so they chose Commerce, perhaps hoping the name would be prophetic. It wasn't. Around the same time folks laid out an official plat for Commerce, the financial panic of 1837 devastated the little town and most of its residents moved away.

Commerce Becomes Nauvoo

As the little town of Commerce was growing and shrinking, Joseph Smith was shepherding followers of a new religion that he had founded in 1830. First known as the Church of Christ, we know it today as the Church of Jesus Christ of Latter-day Saints (LDS Church). Smith would eventually leave New York and establish communities of believers—Mormons—in Ohio and Missouri. In both places, they faced considerable hostility from their neighbors and had to move on.

When Smith and his followers were forced out of Missouri in late 1838, some 5,000 refugees crossed the Mississippi into Illinois where they found temporary refuge in Quincy and Adams County. Most were in rough shape after the journey—physically exhausted, hungry, and desperately poor. Illinois residents offered them safety, food, and supplies, which gave the Mormons the space to regroup as they waited for Smith's release from a Missouri jail. Nevertheless, the other church leaders didn't waste time looking for a new home.

The village of Commerce caught their attention because there was a lot of cheap property in the village and it was easy to reach, thanks to its location on the Mississippi River. Sidney Rigdon bought a plot and moved to Commerce on April 1, 1839. Joseph Smith rejoined the group after escaping from jail. He bought land in Commerce and relocated his family there a month later. He observed that the entirety of the village was "one stone house, three frame houses, and two block houses."

Smith and the other leaders executed a new village plat that laid out a street grid over one square mile of land: four-acre lots were platted, each of which was then subdivided into four one-acre lots. Each lot was intended to provide enough space for a home, a garden, and room for domesticated animals to roam. At the end of 1839, Smith renamed the village Nauvoo, a word derived from Hebrew that Smith believed meant "a beautiful location, a place of rest." The change became official the following year when the US Post Office in Washington, DC recorded the new name. It wasn't just a simple rebranding, either. Smith had a vision for the new city that would essentially create a Utopian community, just one that would be built on the doctrine of the new church. Smith wanted to build a Mormon holy city.

At the end of 1840, the Illinois legislature approved incorporation papers for Nauvoo that was based on the charter created for the Springfield, Illinois. The document for Nauvoo granted charters for three entities: one for the city government, one to incorporate a university—the University of the City of Nauvoo—and a third to incorporate a militia, the Nauvoo Legion. The city charter, while not unusual for Illinois at the time, gave Smith the tools to fulfill his vision of establishing an independent government for a community of Mormons that would operate mostly independent of the State of Illinois. Given the hostility Mormons had faced in other places, you could hardly blame him for wanting greater control of the institutions that had often been used against Mormon communities.

One of the powerful tools granted to Smith and Nauvoo was a provision which empowered the city council to determine if Nauvoo residents could be detained for a criminal charge (*habeas corpus*). This provision, in practice, made it nearly impossible to arrest anyone within the city limits without the approval of the city council, which almost never happened, especially if a non-Mormon was trying to arrest a Mormon.

While the original intent of the *habeas corpus* provision may have been to prevent the indiscriminate and unjustified detention of Mormons (in other places, Mormons had often been arrested for frivolous or false charges), in practice the city used the power to free any Mormons arrested anywhere for any cause, including Smith. This would create a perception—justified or not—that Nauvoo had become a haven for criminals and that Mormons could commit crimes with impunity, an issue that grew increasingly contentious with Nauvoo's neighbors.

While the provisions in the Nauvoo charter weren't especially unusual for the time, under Smith's leadership Nauvoo's leaders built a government that eliminated any pretense of separation of powers. Under the charter, the mayor was also the chief justice of the local court, and the board of aldermen served as associate justices. In addition, the mayor was the leader of the local militia, the Nauvoo Legion. The mayor therefore had control of civil government, the court, and a militia. While John C. Bennett served as Nauvoo's first mayor, Smith exercised power behind the scenes. In 1842, Bennett fell out of favor and was excommunicated. Smith became mayor and wielded power openly.

Smith was intent on consolidating the Mormon faithful into a single location. This helped fuel rapid growth at Nauvoo—the city counted 12,000 residents by 1844. Several thousand more Mormons lived outside the city in places like LaHarpe, Lima, Ramus, and a few communities in Iowa. In contrast, most of the non-Mormon communities nearby, places like Pontoosuc and Warsaw, had no more than 300 residents. The new arrivals in Nauvoo included nearly 5,000 English Mormons who emigrated to the US. Most of the English immigrants were former factory workers who were poor and ill-prepared for the rural life of Nauvoo.

Smith's initial plan was that residents would have a home in the city and land to farm outside of it. Smith hoped that wealthy Mormons would purchase the needed land on behalf of the community, then the church would divide up the land according to need, but there were many more needy Mormons than there were wealthy ones. George Miller observed in 1841:

> "Besides these, [others] were crowding in from the States, all poor, as the rich did not generally respond to the proclamation of the prophet to come with their effects."

As Mormons arrived in their new city, they first lived in tents and then log huts, until proper houses were built. In order to expedite construction, the church acquired its own logging camp in Wisconsin along the Black River. It was originally meant to provide building materials for a hotel (Nauvoo House) and for a new temple, but much of the lumber was diverted for home construction. In 1843, the Mormon-run logging camp floated 600,000 board feet of lumber downriver to Nauvoo.

The growing community drained swamps, but many people still died from "swamp fever" (probably malaria). The early economy relied heavily on cottage industries and bartering because there just wasn't a lot of cash. Residents quarried rock from the bluffs and built brick factories to manufacture basic construction materials. Soon they had a fully developed small city with foundries, sawmills, leather shops, wagon makers, lawyers, clothiers, a photographer (who created Daguerreotypes), and much more.

Community life developed quickly, too. Two dozen common schools were established, including the Nauvoo Select School where students studied the classics. Concerts were held regularly, with music from bands such as the Nauvoo Military Band (drums), the Nauvoo Brass Band, and the Nauvoo Quadrille Band (string and reed instruments).

Nauvoo was a tourist hot spot during the years the Mormons lived there. Charlotte Haven arrived in Nauvoo in January of 1843—not the most hospitable time of year—for a lengthy visit. Her initial impressions were fantastic and contradictory:

> "At eleven o'clock we came in full sight of the City of the Saints, and were charmed with the view. We were five miles from it, and from our point of vision it seemed to be situated on a high hill, and to have a dense population; but on our approach and while passing slowly through the principal streets, we thought that our vision had been magnified, or distance lent enchantment, for such a collection of miserable houses and hovels I could not have believed existed in one place."

Josiah Quincy, who reached Nauvoo in May 1844, had a different impression:

> "The curve in the river enclosed a position lovely enough to furnish a site for the Utopian communities of Plato or Sir Thomas More; and here was an orderly city, magnificently laid out, and teeming with activity and enterprise."

Smith often met visitors personally, especially if they were of some importance. Some of those visitors, like renowned priest Samuel Mazzuchelli (see page 183), came to discuss theology with Smith, who readily engaged with them.

At one time, Smith floated a plan to dig a canal that would have run two miles down the middle of town. The city abandoned the plan, though, when they ran into a big bed of limestone at the north end of the route, although some of that limestone ended up being quarried for a grand temple.

Construction of the new temple began in 1841. Smith designed it. When completed (after Smith's death), the temple rose 165 feet from the ground to the top of the tower. It was built of white limestone and of wood harvested from the northern forests. The basement housed a large, oval baptismal font (16 feet by 12 feet and 4 feet deep) that sat elevated on the backs of a dozen life-sized oxen carved from wood (probably later replaced by stone statues). The font was encircled by a seven-foot wall of carved stone. Worshipers climbed steps at either end of the font to enter the basin for baptisms of the dead, the first of which were held in the temple on November 21, 1841.

The temple sat atop the hill at a sharp turn on the river, creating a dramatic new landmark for river pilots. Henry Lewis, who painted one of the popular Mississippi River panoramas in the mid-19th century, included a detailed portrait of the temple in his book, *Das Illustrirte Mississippithal*. By the time Lewis exhibited his rendering of the temple, it had been severely damaged by a fire, probably arson.

The other major building project that Smith envisioned was Nauvoo House, a space that would be part boarding house and part retreat center. Although construction began in 1841, Smith gave up on it in the summer 1843 and instead built a wing on his house that served as a hotel. LC Bidamon, who later married Smith's widow, Emma, purchased the half-built remains of Nauvoo House. He stripped the building to the basement and built a modest house on the foundation. In the 20th century, it was used as a youth hostel for a while. Large groups can rent the space now for overnight gatherings.

Smith pushed for a commercial district on Main Street but a competing one developed up the hill, on Mulholland Street (where it is today), developed by individuals who would later become rivals of Smith. Some of them would be involved in the publication of the *Nauvoo Expositor* that would trigger the conflict that ended Smith's life.

Nauvoo became increasingly insular as its population grew. A small group of church leaders ran the city, and they didn't share the details of their decision-making with the citizenry, which contrasted markedly with the more or less transparent governments of the places around Nauvoo.

Mormons and their neighbors had different approaches to civil government and neighborly relations grew increasingly fraught. One particularly contentious issue related to punishing lawbreakers. County residents were essentially served by separate justice systems. Mormons accused of crimes were tried by Mormon-only juries, and few Mormons served on juries outside of Nauvoo.

The murder of Joseph Smith on June 27, 1844, ultimately marked the end for Nauvoo's Mormon community. The events that led up to his murder reveal much about the state of affairs around Nauvoo at the time.

A schism had developed in the church between Smith and other prominent members over plural marriages, the treatment of women in Nauvoo, and Smith's leadership. The dissident group was eager to start a reform movement, but Smith—the Prophet who was the sole voice through whom God communicated to the community— wouldn't allow other sects to establish themselves, so he waged a campaign to discredit them.

The rebel sect published their grievances on June 7, 1844, in the *Nauvoo Expositor*. Three days later, the city council—at Smith's urging—declared the paper a public nuisance. Smith ordered the destruction of the paper and its printing equipment. The publishers, fearing for their safety, fled to Carthage, where they filed a warrant for Smith's arrest for inciting to riot. On June 11, a Hancock County court issued a warrant for Smith's arrest. Smith turned to Nauvoo's municipal court, which dismissed the charges.

The dismissal excited Smith's detractors in Warsaw and Carthage, who railed against his actions and the unwillingness of the Nauvoo court to arrest him. Smith initially had planned on fleeing to the Rocky Mountains, but after he had crossed the Mississippi River into Iowa, he changed his mind and went back. On June 25, he and his brother Hyrum met with Illinois Governor Thomas Ford in Carthage and agreed to turn themselves in. At their preliminary hearing, they were granted bail of $500, but they were then quickly charged with a new crime: treason. The treason charge grew out of accusations that Smith used the Nauvoo Legion to resist arrest from state law enforcement. Bail wasn't an option for a person charged with treason, so the Smith brothers were jailed in Carthage. Governor Ford authorized an independent militia to protect the Smiths after personally pledging to vouch for their safety.

On June 27, Governor Ford went to Nauvoo to calm tensions, but while he was there, a group of men with their faces painted black (probably from the Warsaw posse) stormed the Carthage jail. The posse had probably pre-arranged help from jail's guards, who did nothing to stop them from entering that evening. The posse shot and killed Hyrum right away. Joseph Smith, wounded in the hail of gunshots, raced to a window and jumped out. Most eyewitnesses testified that Smith did not survive the fall.

Nine men were charged with murdering Smith including Thomas Sharp, the editor of the *Warsaw Signal*, who had written that Smith's murder was regrettable but justified. Five men, including Sharp, were tried in May 1845, but all were acquitted after a sensational trial. The defense benefited tremendously when it managed to get the first jury dismissed and replaced with a new panel that didn't have a single Mormon on it. Besides that, the prosecution's cause got more difficult when all the Mormon witnesses refused to testify. They may have been afraid that they would be the next victims if they did so.

Joseph and Hyrum Smith laid in state at the Smith mansion in Nauvoo; 10,000 people viewed their bodies. Joseph Smith was just 38. His death left a leadership vacuum that Brigham Young eventually filled. Some Mormons thought the rightful heir was Smith's oldest son, Joseph III, but he was only 12 years old at the time.

Smith's widow Emma, worried about the graves being disturbed, buried the Smiths in secret, first under the Nauvoo House, then at another location where they stayed until 1928 when they were reburied in their current crypts.

Young got busy reassuring the faithful of his leadership skills. He pushed ahead with temple construction. The exterior was completed in October 1845. The final cost of construction probably approached a million dollars. Mormons wouldn't use the temple for long, though.

Conflict erupted again between Mormons and non-Mormons in the fall of 1844. A group of Warsaw citizens prodded Governor Ford to expel the Mormons, but Ford said he lacked the authority to do so. After the fall harvest, a few groups advertised a "wolf hunt" in local newspapers, which was a code for a raid on Mormon settlements. After mobs ransacked Mormon-owned farms, Ford brought a militia back to Carthage in late October to keep the peace.

The quiet held through the winter, but the growing hostility toward the Mormon community at Nauvoo spread to the state capital. On January 29, 1845, the Illinois legislature revoked the Nauvoo charter, even though Governor Ford had only supported amending it. Nauvoo's residents hunkered down in the face of the hostility. The Legion was deployed around the city to control entrance to and exit from the city.

When mob violence against Mormons escalated again in the summer of 1845, Mormons organized their own militia—with the help of a friendly county sheriff—and pushed back enough to occupy Carthage. Governor Ford organized another militia to replace the Mormons at Carthage, but by that time he and other state leaders had apparently decided that it was time for Mormons to leave the state.

Facing increasingly intense public pressure, the Mormon leadership announced in September 1845 that they would abandon Nauvoo by the following spring. Unknown to most people, the Mormon leadership had quietly been exploring and preparing for a move west for some time. In February 1846, the first thousand residents moved out, including most of the leadership. Brigham Young left on February 15. Getting everyone out was no small task.

The first group walked across the frozen Mississippi River. In spring, ferries transported thousands of residents across the river to Iowa where many lived in temporary camps. Most had to sell their land and property at deeply discounted prices. Hundreds of Mormons were still in Nauvoo in the summer when violence broke out again, but the Mormons repelled the most serious threats. The so-called Battle of Nauvoo was fought on September 12, 1846, which consisted of an hour of gunfire between 700 anti-Mormon agitators and 300 residents of Nauvoo, most of them Mormons.

That incident motivated most of the remaining Mormons to leave. The small number who remained in Nauvoo were no longer perceived as a threat. Most of Joseph Smith's family stayed put: his mother Lucy; his sisters and their families; his widow Emma, and their four sons and adopted daughter. Joseph Smith III would later become the leader of a separate branch of Mormons called the Reorganized Church of Jesus Christ of Latter-day Saints, today known as the Community of Christ. He assumed the leadership in 1860 and later moved its headquarters to Independence, Missouri.

The Mormons left behind a lot of infrastructure: a thousand log houses, nearly 300 brick homes, and 300 frame houses. In 1845, Hancock County was the most populous county in Illinois, with 22,559 residents, and Nauvoo was the largest city with just over 11,000 residents. Just five years later, the entire county had 14,652 residents and Nauvoo just 1,200. Charles Lanman, who passed through Nauvoo after the exodus, wrote:

> "The Mormon City occupies an elevated position, and, as approached from the south, appears capable of containing a hundred thousand souls. But its gloomy streets bring a most melancholy disappointment. Where lately resided no less than twenty-five thousand people, there are not to be seen more than about five hundred; and these, in mind, body and purse, seem to be perfectly wretched...When this city was in its glory, every dwelling was surrounded with a garden, so that the corporation limits were uncommonly extensive; but now all the fences are in ruin, and the lately crowded streets actually rank with vegetation. Of the houses left standing, not more than one out of every ten is occupied, excepting by the spider and toad. Hardly a window retained a whole pane of glass, and the doors were broken, and open, and hingeless."

In 1848, the Mormon temple was partially destroyed by a fire that was later blamed on arson. The remaining bits were destroyed by a tornado in 1850.

Sorting through the events at Nauvoo is a difficult task. Nauvoo remains a revered place for Mormons. The story of Mormon Nauvoo is both inspiring and tragic, a place where the community came together in the face of violent opposition, but also the place where its founder was murdered. Besides that, many key theological concepts of the church were developed here, like baptism of the dead. For this reason, some historical pieces written by Mormons are focused more on myth-making than a fair accounting of events. On the other hand, many of those involved in expelling the Mormons from the area downplayed the hypocrisy and cruelty of their own actions.

Ultimately, it seems that much of the opposition to the Mormons arose primarily from civil and not religious concerns, even though some Mormon practices (like polygamy) undoubtedly aroused strong opposition. Accusations of crimes committed by Mormons that went unpunished fueled opposition, even if it's hard to figure out today how widespread those criminal acts actually were.

But accusations of lawlessness were only part of the dynamic. People who settled on the frontier strongly valued the democratic process. They were egalitarian in orientation and tended to value the rights of the individual over communal rights.

Joseph Smith's Nauvoo represented very nearly the polar opposite of these frontier values. He had established a community ruled by a small group of religious elites who demanded that community members conform to the dictates of the leaders. Smith's opponents decried the concentration of power into the hands of just a few people. In 1844, the *Quincy Whig* printed an anonymous letter that summed up these feelings:

> "The spectacle presented in Smith's case—of a civil, ecclesiastical, and military leader, united in one and the same person, with power over life and liberty, can never find favor in the minds of sound and thinking Republicans."

The whole setup was perhaps far too similar to the old-world governments that many on the frontier thought they had left behind, and the size of the Mormon population aroused fears that Mormons would impose a similar style of government on everyone, regardless of their religion.

John Hallwas, who has extensively researched the events at Nauvoo asserted that the whole affair was an ideological conflict in which both sides ditched their commitment to pluralism in favor of self-interest. Mormons suppressed internal opposition even as they trumpeted their commitment to liberty, while their non-Mormon antagonists trumpeted their commitment to democracy even as they resorted to mob violence to drive out the Mormons. He makes a compelling case.

Whatever the causes, they were complex and marked by attempts from many people to push a narrative that favored one side over the other when, in fact, there was plenty of blame to go around. It all makes for one heck of a story, though.

More Utopians Move to Nauvoo

After the Mormons were forced to leave Nauvoo, Etienne Cabet, another idealist with big plans, founded a new Utopian community in the same place. He lead his followers across an ocean and up a river to establish the community of his dreams, even if he was slow to embrace the work required to make it happen.

The French-born Cabet was a visionary and anti-monarchy activist prone to getting in trouble with the powers-that-were. In 1834, he was convicted of printing accusations that were "an affront to the king." For his punishment, he was allowed to choose between five years in exile or two years in prison. He chose exile and went to England. He put his time to good use. In 1839, he published a novel called *Voyage en Icarie* (*Voyage to Icaria*), a romance influenced by Thomas More's *Utopia.*

In the novel, William Carisdall, an English nobleman, sailed to an island nation off the coast of east Africa. The residents had built a new society after kicking out their last dictator. In his place, they let a benevolent dictator named Icar rule until his death, then they became a democracy. In the book, the residents of this fictional island lived without money. The community owned everything. Cabet's central premise was that the major cause of misery and conflict in the world was private property ownership.

The book inspired quite a following. Shortly after its publication, Cabet's exile ended, and he went back to France where he advocated non-violent reform and organized three dozen Icarian chapters around the country. France soon sank into economic depression, though, and political turmoil led to a repression that did not spare the Icarians.

Cabet wasn't about to let go of his dreams, though, so he decided to start an Icarian community in the US. He announced it with great fanfare on the front page of his newspaper, *Le Populaire*, on May 9, 1847: Allons en Icarie! (Let's go to Icaria!). In spite of Cabet's enthusiasm, most French Icarians weren't crazy about starting a new community on the other side of the Atlantic. They preferred to stay in France and fight.

Cabet really didn't have the foggiest idea about how to get the new community going. He agreed to a land deal where the Icarians had a chance to take ownership of 3,000 acres along the Trinity River in Texas for nothing. All they had to do was build 3,000 homesteads by July 1, 1848. The parcels, however, weren't contiguous, which made a nearly impossible task even harder.

Nevertheless, he organized a group of 69 people that left France for Texas on February 3, 1848. Each person paid Cabet 600 francs to join the exodus. Cabet was not among the first to go. He remained in France where he tried to aid the revolution, but when public opinion turned on everyone who had once supported any form of communist ideology, Cabet had to flee France for his own safety.

Those first Icarians reached New Orleans about seven weeks after leaving France. An advance guard quickly set out for Texas but the trip from New Orleans was much harder than anyone anticipated and the land itself was barely habitable. A few cabins were built by July 1, but malaria and cholera took a heavy toll. In August, four people died, which was enough hardship to convince the group's physician to desert.

The whole party soon decided to give up and trudged back to New Orleans to join the larger body of Icarians that had since grown to 480, still without Cabet. When Cabet finally joined his fellow Icarians in New Orleans on January 19, 1849, he found a restless group, many of whom were ready to call it quits. In spite of the hardships, though, a majority voted to continue with the mission. Most of the rest (218 people) sailed home with a full refund. After they reached France, they sued Cabet for fraud.

A couple of weeks after the vote to forge on, another advance team returned to New Orleans with news that they had found a promising site for the new community, at the (mostly) abandoned city of Nauvoo, where land could be purchased for just the cost of back taxes. Two weeks later, the group was on a steamboat heading upriver, all 280 of them (142 men, 74 women, and 64 children).

They arrived in Nauvoo on March 15, 1849, and bought property around the temple square (that included the ruins of the former Mormon temple), plus 2,000 acres of nearby farmland. The community came together quickly. In a short time, they had a mill and a distillery running and had opened retail shops in Keokuk and St. Louis for the flour they milled and the whiskey they distilled. (Their whiskey was quite popular.)

The Icarians wanted to convert the Mormon temple into a meeting house, but a tornado in 1850 destroyed what was left of the building. Instead, they used some of the stone to build other structures, including a school where they hung their motto over the door: "From each according to his talent, to each according to his needs."

Cabet, like the fictional Icar, was the benevolent dictator of the community, acting as the sole, undisputed leader until it was stable enough to select its own government. He handed out work assignments and made all the major decisions. He formed a governing body that gave women a partial voice—they could express their views but still weren't allowed to vote on many issues.

Life wasn't too bad. The workday began at 6am. Men woke up with a shot of whiskey and went to work, then took a break at 8am to have breakfast with their families. The work day ended at 6pm. Free education began at age four. The community had a 36-member orchestra that played every Sunday afternoon and a performing arts theater, both of which were popular with non-Icarians, too. In the 1850s, the Icarians claimed the largest library in Illinois, some 4,000 volumes in total.

By 1855, six years after settling in Nauvoo, the Icarian community had grown to 469 people. (They were never more than 25% of the city's total population, though; most of Nauvoo's residents were not Icarians). It wasn't all peaches and cream, however. Some Icarians complained about the food (more peaches and cream!), and several people complained that Cabet was spying on them.

Cabet had to return to France in the summer 1851 to defend himself against the dissidents' charges of fraud. He was acquitted, but he stayed in France for another year. In his absence, the Nauvoo Icarians loosened up the strict rules that Cabet had insisted on. When Cabet got back to Nauvoo, he tried to restore his system by pushing through a new set of rules, but his efforts weren't popular. A majority of Icarians pushed back, charging Cabet with incompetence and challenging his leadership. Cabet wasn't pleased.

The community muddled through for a couple more years, but Cabet's decision to push for an amendment to the governing charter in December 1855 would split the community. Under the existing charter, the president–Cabet–and directors served one-year terms, with half of the directors facing elections every six months. Cabet proposed changing the charter so that the president would serve a four-year term and would be empowered to appoint the directors. When Cabet proposed the change in 1856, some members reminded him that constitutional changes were allowed only in odd-numbered years. When Cabet failed to win re-election as president on August 3, open conflict erupted. Non-Icarian neighbors had to call the sheriff to intervene.

Cabet shouldered much of the blame, so the Nauvoo mayor told him to get out of town. He was formally expelled from the Icarian community in October 1856. He took 71 men and 44 women with him and settled near St. Louis, where they were ready to build a new Icaria. Cabet, however, suffered a stroke on November 7 and died the next day. The group that had followed him from Nauvoo rebuilt their community, but after four years of suffering through dysentery and other diseases they were forced into bankruptcy. The St. Louis colony formally disbanded in January 1864.

Back in Nauvoo, productivity declined and creditors stalked the community, so in 1860, they sold their holdings and moved on, too. They took the $20,000 they got for the property—just one-third of what they hoped to get—and moved to Adams County, Iowa, to an area where a few Icarians had moved in 1852. They struggled for a while, but when the Civil War erupted, some of their products (including wool) were in demand from Union soldiers. They made enough money to pay down most of their debts.

Many aspects of life changed for the Icarians as their group shrank. They evolved into a loosely affiliated agricultural commune, with weak leadership and families living in their own houses. Their children even went to public schools. Fresh converts arrived from France in the mid-1870s, committed communists who weren't too happy with the state of affairs they found in Iowa. The old and new guard eventually sued each other and dissolved into separate communities. The new bloods didn't do well—they lacked leadership, too, and weren't fond of farming—so a couple dozen relocated to Sonoma County, California, before that group fell apart, too.

As for that older group—the last Icarians standing—they built another new community about a mile away from where they first settled in Iowa, but with no new members joining them, they got smaller and smaller throughout the 1880s. The last eight surviving Icarians got together in 1898 and formally dissolved the community.

Remnants of Icarian life lingered into the 20th century. The last of the Icarian home foundations at Nauvoo was removed in 1952. The school was razed in 1972. Some Icarians stayed in the Nauvoo area, and descendants can still be found, like the Baxters, who have been running a winery since 1857.

Cabet's attempt to translate his Utopian ideals failed for many reasons. For one thing, he had imagined an urban Utopia, which is why the group was composed primarily of middle-class and well-educated people, many of them artists. The community at Nauvoo, however, was primarily agricultural, so the Icarians didn't really have the experience and skills they needed to succeed under those conditions. Ultimately, though, it seems the community failed because of struggles over leadership and influence. Even though most members shared Cabet's vision for the community, they had a hard time agreeing on how to make it work.

Nauvoo after the Mormons and Icarians

Nauvoo had plenty of life after the Mormons and Icarians left. The city had a reasonably busy port in the 19th century. A ferry operated between Nauvoo and Iowa from 1834 to 1946. The last one, the *City of Nauvoo*, transported people and their goods across the Mississippi from 1884 to 1946.

After the Icarians left, German and Swiss immigrants moved in. For 50 years, until World War I, Nauvoo had the largest number of German speakers of any place in Illinois. The new residents transplanted much of their culture, including grapevines from home that led to a robust wine-making business in Nauvoo.

Grape-growing and wine-making go back to Nauvoo's earliest days, however. Father John Alleman cultivated grapes in Nauvoo as early as the 1840s. He later bought a bell for Saints Peter and Paul Church that included grape vines as a decorative element.

In 1866, Nauvoo had 250 vineyards and dozens of wine cellars, including the Rheinberger vineyards that were planted in 1851 and are still productive today. The wine-making industry did well until Prohibition. Only a few vineyards survived after that as much of the land that had been dedicated to grape cultivation was converted to other uses.

After Prohibition, Nauvoo residents who enjoyed sipping wine had the pleasure of pairing it with a well-regarded local cheese. In the late 1930s, Oscar Rohde opened a factory in town that produced blue cheese from homogenized cow's milk instead of the sheep's milk that was typically used. He set up shop in the former Schenk Brewery, where he took advantage of the limestone vaults for storing and aging the cheese.

Rohde died in 1965 but his family continued to run the operation for many years. His company's cheese was selected as the best blue cheese in the US in 1983 and won an international competition the year after that. The plant changed hands a couple of times until it was purchased by Con Agra in 2000, which closed it just three years later and sold the brand names (Treasure Cave and Nauvoo) to Saputo Inc. of Montreal. Con Agra then sold the property to the LDS Church for $100,000—one-tenth of the asking price—who subsequently tore it all down for a parking lot. There have been a couple of attempts to revive production of Nauvoo blue cheese, but so far it hasn't worked out.

Five Benedictine sisters arrived in Nauvoo in 1874 and opened a school for girls where the Mormon temple once stood. The sisters named the school St. Mary's Academy and went about educating girls for the next 100 years, until boarding schools lost their popularity. The Academy closed in 1997, and the sisters sold the property to the LDS Church, which razed the complex to clear land around the temple. The sisters used the proceeds from the sale to build a new, eco-friendly home in Rock Island in 2001.

Nauvoo had its ups and down in the 20th century. An explosion in 1909 destroyed some downtown buildings and killed a young child. When the dam was completed at

Keokuk, water levels rose some 30 feet, submerging two blocks of the old city. In 1934, the First Trust and Savings Bank went under, taking with it the savings of many locals.

After a couple of generations of distance, a few Mormons returned to Nauvoo to visit or preach. In 1903, the LDS Church bought the Carthage Jail where Joseph and Hyrum Smith were killed. In 1909, the Community of Christ (formerly the RLDS church) started buying up the property that had once belonged to Joseph and Emma Smith. In the 1930s, the LDS Church bought a small lot near the site of the Temple, and over the years bought additional parcels as they became available.

Soon after that, restoration of the surviving buildings began, starting with the home of Heber Kimball, one of the Twelve Apostles in the early church, by his Utah-based great grandson, Dr. J. LeRoy Kimball. Interest in wholesale preservation took off after that. Kimball and the LDS Church started buying up land and transferring it to Nauvoo Restoration, Inc. in 1962. The church now owns over 1,000 acres in Nauvoo and has renovated dozens of buildings.

Nauvoo today draws thousands of Mormon visitors who come to explore the city's past and their connection to it. The steady tourism business has both helped the town financially and irritated some long-time residents who feel that much of Nauvoo's past has been overwhelmed by the efforts of the LDS church to preserve Mormon history.

I find Nauvoo a fascinating place. In Nauvoo's history, there are important lessons about the shifting struggle to balance civil government with deeply held religious beliefs, as well as the dangers to civil society when tolerance and respect for others break down. As someone who isn't Mormon, I also find it fascinating to watch how a new religious group actively shapes its mythology. (Getting all of the historical details just right isn't the priority.) Nauvoo's sites may be of greatest interest to Mormons, but even those who are not members of the LDS Church will be fascinated by the Beautiful City.

Explore Down the West Bank (Iowa)

MUSCATINE

Attractions

Wildcat Den State Park (1884 Wildcat Den Rd.; 563.263.4337), just north of Muscatine, has hiking trails that wind through the forest and bluffs. The park is also home to the **Pine Creek Grist Mill**, built by Ben Nye in the mid-1800s.

Weed Park (1 Park Dr.), named for James Weed (he donated the land), is a popular spot for summer fun, with a nice overlook of the river, rose gardens, and Indian mounds, plus the usual park amenities. It's in the northeast part of the city.

For a nice view of the river and Muscatine, drive up to the **Mark Twain Overlook** (2nd St. at Highway 92).

Riverside Park (Mississippi Dr.) runs along the Mississippi River near downtown, home to Erik Blome's monumental tribute to the city's past, *Mississippi Harvest*, a moving 28-foot tall bronze sculpture of a clammer. Walk a couple of minutes south, then stop for a selfie next to the **World's Largest Slice of Watermelon**!

Musser Park (Oregon St.) covers 11 acres on the southeast part of town, with a skate park and some good views of the Mississippi.

The **Running River Trail System** currently has ten miles of paved, multi-use paths that aren't all connected but someday will be. You'll find one trailhead at Musser Park. Other sections run along the river.

The **Muscatine Art Center** (1314 Mulberry Ave.; 563.263.8282), housed in the former Laura Musser Mansion, contains period furniture and hosts rotating art exhibits.

The **National Pearl Button Museum** (117 W. 2nd St.; 563.263.1052) chronicles the city's pearl button industry in fascinating detail, while also showcasing other major employers in the city's history.

The current **St. Mathias Catholic Church** (215 West 8th St.; 563.263.1416) is an ornate and architecturally eclectic building. It is the heir to the much simpler original church designed by frontier priest Father Samuel Mazzuchelli (see page 183). For a fun study in contrasts, visit the old church first—it's on the front side of the complex—then tour the new building.

Drinking and Dining

Big Cat's Café (101 W. Mississippi Dr.; 563.261.7458), located in a historic building along the riverfront, serves coffee and tea, plus a few options for breakfast and lunch.

The **Coffee Belt** (210 E. 2nd St.; 563.264.6963) can also supply your caffeinated beverage of choice, which you can enjoy in the inviting space or take with you.

Grab some local flavor at **Contrary Brewing Company** (411 W. Mississippi Dr.; 563.261.7446), a craft brewery with good views of the river. You can sample their beers with a snack or pizza.

Miss'ipi Brewing Company (107 Iowa Ave.; 563.262.5004) is a large and sometimes boisterous place that buzzes on weekends, and rightly so. The food is good, and there's a nice selection of beers that actually taste like beer.

I could call the **Yacky Shack** (163 Colorado St.; 563.264.8007) Korean-Chinese fusion, but it wouldn't explain the tacos or General Tso's chicken sandwich. The place serves an unusual mix of menu items, including the namesake Yacky, which is a delicious fried dumpling stuffed with an ingredient of your choice.

Salvatore's (313 E. 2nd St.; 563.263.9396) is run by sweet people who know how to make good pizza, salads, and sandwiches.

If you're looking for a splurge with a view, **Maxwell's On the River** at the Merrill Hotel and Conference Center (119 W. Mississippi Dr.; 563.263.2600) can satisfy both. The menu consists mostly of steaks and fish, with solid choices for sides and salads, all of which you can enjoy with those scenic river views.

Where to Stay: Camping

Just east of Muscatine along Iowa Highway 22, there are several state and federal campgrounds right next to the river, including **Shady Creek Recreation Area** (3550 State Highway 22; 563.262.8090), **Fairport State Recreation Area** (3280 Highway 22), **Clark's Ferry Recreation Area** (3680 Sunset Beach; 563.381.4043), and **Buffalo Shores County Park** (Buffalo: 1433 W. Front St.; 563.328.3281). Each has sites that can accommodate RVs, some with electricity. These are popular campgrounds, so advance reservations are a good idea. Of the four, **Fairport State Recreation Area** (3280 Highway 22) is the closest to Muscatine; it offers sites with electricity and a shower house.

Wildcat Den State Park (1884 Wildcat Den Rd.; 563.263.4337) is also near Fairport and offers two dozen basic sites in a shady area; no showers.

Bed and Breakfasts

Strawberry Farm Bed & Breakfast (3402 Tipton Rd.; 563.262.8688) offers five guest rooms in a country retreat a few miles outside of Muscatine.

Lodging

The **Muskie Motel** (1620 Park Ave.; 563.263.2601) offers no-frills budget rooms that are clean and in good shape.

If you're looking for a night (or more) of pampering, look no further than the **Merrill Hotel & Conference Center** (119 W. Mississippi Dr.; 563.263.2600). Rooms are modern and elegant, and many have views of the Mississippi River. Relax in the saltwater pool or sip a cocktail in the lounge while watching the river flow by.

Special Events

The Muscatine **farmers market** runs on Saturday mornings (7:30am-11:30am) on the corner of 3rd & Cedar Streets.

BURLINGTON

Attractions

Starr's Cave Park and Preserve (11627 Starr's Cave Rd.; 319.753.5808) is a peaceful wooded area along scenic Flint Creek north of town with a nature center and a couple of miles of hiking trails. Its rock formations are rich with fossils and with a type of unique flint that was once widely traded among indigenous people in North America. The namesake cave is now closed to protect the habitat of its resident bat population.

Crapo and Dankwardt Parks (2900 S. Main) are a couple of delightful city parks atop the bluffs at the south end of town. Among their 150 acres, you'll find an arboretum, the **Hawkeye Log Cabin**, a band shell, hiking trails, and a swimming pool.

Mosquito Park (North 3rd and Franklin Streets) is a small patch of grass atop a bluff at the north end of town that has a pretty darn good view of the Mississippi. **South Hill Park** (Elm St. at S. 6th) also has a good overlook.

The **Flint River Trail** is a multi-use trail that connects downtown Burlington to Big Hollow Recreation Area 20 miles to the northwest. Some portions of the trail currently run along highways.

The **Des Moines County Heritage Museum** (501 N. 4th St.; 319.752.7449), in the ornate former public library, showcases the county's history in nine rooms spread across three floors. Expect exhibits on agriculture, the military, and Native American art.

The **Garrett-Phelps House Museum** (521 Columbia; 319.752.7449), built in the mid-19th century for William Garrett, has many original furnishings and also hosts a display of medical treatment artifacts (the house was converted to a hospital at one time) and the occasional rotating exhibit.

At the end of the 1800s, three German immigrants (Charles Starker, George Kriechbaum, and William Stehy) planned a street they hoped would provide an easy way to navigate the steep slope from Lower Town to Upper Town. **Snake Alley**—the "Crookedest Street in the World" according to *Ripley's Believe It or Not*—opened in 1894. It twists and turns its way down 275 feet from Columbia Street to Washington Street with five half-curves and two quarter-curves. It turned out to be less practical than hoped, so the city scrapped plans to build more like it, but this one is still around. It's a one-way street. Enter from Columbia Street and descend slowly.

The **Art Center of Burlington** (301 Jefferson St.; 319.754.8069) features rotating exhibits that highlight the work of local and regional artists.

Burlington by the Book (301 Jefferson St.; 319.753.9981) can set you up with a good read, including books by local and regional authors.

Take in a game of the **Burlington Bees**, the city's professional baseball team that plays in the Prospect League (Community Field: Mt. Pleasant St. just east of US Highway 61; 319.754.5705).

The Washington (306 Washington St.; 319.758.9553) is a fine venue to catch regional and national touring acts in an intimate setting.

The Art déco **Burlington Capitol Theater** (211 N. 3rd St.; 319.237.1099) hosts performing arts events, movies, and concerts. Hang out at the **Night Cap Listening Lounge** at the Capitol for a chill evening enjoying good music with your favorite drink.

There's truth in advertising at **Weird Harold's** (411 Jefferson; 319.753.5353), and it sure is a fun place to explore. Inside you'll find costumes to rent, artwork, CDs, creative greeting cards, cassette tapes, and 50,000+ vinyl LPs. They have a good selection of music made by local and regional artists. You aren't likely to leave empty-handed.

For something a little different, go find Burlington's **two historic bells**. In 1839, Father Samuel Mazzuchelli (see page 183) founded St. Paul the Apostle Church. He supervised construction of a building the following year. In 1842, he bought a bell for the church. Two buildings and 170 years later, that bell is still calling out to parishioners at **Saints John and Paul Church** (508 N. 4th St.).

The other bell is at **Parkside First Baptist Church** (300 Potter Dr.) in a cloister behind the building. The bell was purchased by two formerly enslaved people, Aunt Kitty and Uncle Ben Sandridge. While enslaved in Kentucky, the two asked a Burlington man, a Mr. Wallis, to buy their freedom and take them to a free state, promising to pay him back. He agreed and took them to Burlington. They paid him back in full in three years. When Aunt Kitty died in 1863, she left a bequest to purchase a bell for her church, calling it her Liberty Bell. The bell was installed in 1865.

Our Lady of Grace Grotto at Saints Mary and Patrick Catholic Church in West Burlington (420 W. Mount Pleasant St.) was the Depression-era brainchild of two Benedictine priests, the Reverends MJ Kaufman and Damian Lavery. They created an impressive grotto dedicated to the Blessed Virgin Mary using rocks donated by people from around the world and built with volunteer labor.

Catfish Bend Casino (3001 Winegard Dr.; 866.792.9948) moved from a riverboat to a strip mall a few years ago. Aside from the usual gambling options, the complex has an auditorium for concerts, a spa, and an amusement park called **FunCity**.

Toolesboro Mounds State Preserve (State Highway 99; (319) 523-8381) features a cluster of Indian mounds built about 2,000 years ago. Many of the mounds started with a single burial but were expanded over time with additional burials. The people who built the mounds probably lived nearby in the rich bottomlands around the confluence of the Iowa and Mississippi Rivers.

Getting On the River

Port Louisa National Wildlife Refuge (319.523.6982) spreads over 1,700 acres south of Muscatine. Much of the refuge is only accessible by boat, but there are many access points and good paddling in the backwaters (check out the Odessa Water Trail). If you didn't bring a boat with you, **River Basin Canoe & Kayak** north of Burlington (13038 US Highway 61; 319.752.1857) can help you out. Call ahead to reserve a boat.

Tours

Get a close look at the process of assembling a backhoe at the **CNH Industrial** factory in Burlington. Tours run the first Thursday of the month at 9:30. Visitors must be at least 12 years old and must wear closed-toe shoes. Call to reserve a spot (319.754.3000).

Drinking and Dining

The **Bean Counter Coffeehouse** (212 Jefferson; 319.850.1939) is a good option for coffee and locally made snacks (or panini), especially if you'd like to hang out for a while. The interior is cozy and inviting with plenty of room.

For classic diner fare in a cozy setting, grab a counter seat at **Jerry's Main Lunch** (501 S. Main St.; 319.752.3750), which has been pleasing Burlingtonians since 1946.

Wake N Bake Breakfast Company (713 Jefferson St.; 319.754.0494) is another popular option for breakfast or brunch. Get some donuts to go or enjoy biscuits and gravy on the large patio when the weather cooperates.

You won't find a restaurant with better views of the river than **Martini's Grille** (610 N. 4th St., 4th floor; 319.752.6262). The food is on the pricey side and while good, not quite what it aspires to be, but with those views you won't really care. It's also a good choice if you just want a couple of cocktails.

The classic Italian food at **La Tavola** (316 N. 4th St.; 319.768.5600) receives consistently rave reviews. The make a tasty pizza and offer an extensive selection of Italian entrêes. It's a small place, so it's a good idea to make a reservation in advance.

Where to Stay: Camping

Tucked into a compact area on the dry side of the levee, the **4th Pumping Plant Recreation Area** (319.753.8260) has 22 sites with electric, a couple dozen primitive sites, and a playground. Drive Highway X99 for 20 miles north of central Burlington, then go five miles east on Pumping Station Road.

Just south of Burlington, **Spring Lake Campground** (3939 Spring Lake Rd.; 319.752.8691) is full-service camping community, offering a variety of full hookups to primitive sites. Amenities include a shower house and a swimming beach.

Bed and Breakfasts

Squirrel's Nest B&B (500 North St.; 319.752.8382) rents three rooms, including a penthouse suite with great views of the river. Guests rave about the full breakfast and the views.

Lodging

Arrowhead Motel (2520 Mt. Pleasant St.; 319.752.6353) offers clean, well-kept affordable rooms close to US Highway 61 that are just ten minutes from downtown and the river. You can even walk to a baseball game. All rooms come with a small fridge, microwave, and adjacent parking.

Special Events

Look for the Burlington **farmers market** downtown along Jefferson Street on Thursdays (4:30-7:30).

On Memorial Day weekend, bicyclists race up, down, and around Burlington, including up the crooked street that lends its name to the event, the **Snake Alley Criterium**.

The **Snake Alley Festival of Film** showcases short films from around the world (Capitol Theater; June).

Artists' booths wind their way up and down the crooked street for the annual **Snake Alley Art Fair** (mid-June).

The **Des Moines County Fair** kicks off in late July (West Burlington: 1500 Agency Rd.), complete with carnival rides, livestock judging, and fried foods.

In late September, **Burlington Heritage Days** celebrates the city's past with music, food, and historical reenactments (319.752.6365).

FORT MADISON

Attractions

The **Daniel McConn Barn** (2095 354th Ave./US Business 61), one of the largest barns you'll ever see, was built in 1857 with native limestone and a heck of a lot of timber. It has three levels inside and three cupolas outside. It is still a working barn, so regular tours are not offered, but it is easily visible from the highway. McConn was one of the first Euro-Americans to live in the area and became one of the wealthiest.

Riverview Park (5th St. and Avenue H) is a pleasant place for an easy stroll along the river or to sit and watch the river roll by. In the park, you'll find the Lone Chimney Memorial, a replica of the remnant chimney that stood in the area for many years after the fort burned. The replica was built in 1908 to mark the 100th anniversary of the construction of Fort Madison.

Old Fort Madison, also in Riverview Park (319.372.6318; open April-October), is a reconstruction of the original 1808 fort. It was built using materials and methods that would have been used in the early 19th century.

The **Sheaffer Pen Museum** (627 Avenue G; 319.372.1674) has an impressive collection of pens manufactured by the former Sheaffer Pen Company, as well as several machines that were used to make them. The museum has limited hours, so call ahead to verify when they are open.

The **Fort Madison Area Arts Association** (825 Avenue G; 319.372.3996) maintains a storefront gallery that showcases the works of local and regional artists.

Lee County has **two county seats** (Fort Madison and Keokuk) and both are on the eastern edge of the county. The curious arrangement dates to 1847. Fort Madison was initially designated the county seat in 1838 but fights over the location continued for a decade. It was nearly moved to the village of West Point in 1844 but West Pointians failed to build a courthouse. As Keokuk grew in population and influence, though, its residents made a play for the county seat, which they eventually got, sort of. In 1848, the state legislature created a second county seat for Lee County and put it in Keokuk. Lee County still has those two county seats today, the only county in Iowa with such an arrangement. While there has been talk in recent years of consolidation, the issue remains divisive for the county's 35,000 residents, who have grown accustomed to the arrangement.

Fort Madison's share of county government services are housed in the **North Lee County Courthouse** (Avenue F at 7th St.), a Greek Revival structure with four imposing columns in front. It opened in 1842 and was designed by frontier priest Father Samuel Mazzuchelli (see page 183). The exterior remains much as he designed it.

The modest stone building next door to the courthouse is the **Old Lee County Jail.** Built in 1867, it is the oldest existing jail in Iowa (and was used well into the 1960s). The upstairs had room for 24 male inmates in six cells and two female inmates in another cell. The first floor had several cells for solitary confinement, which look like good reasons to avoid getting arrested. If you want to tour the old jail, visit the North Lee County Historical Museum (see below) and ask.

The **North Lee County Historical Museum** (810 10th St.; 319.372.7661), located in the old Sante Fe Railroad depot (built for the Atchison, Topeka, and Sante Fe Railroad in 1911), houses displays about the railroad (naturally), Fort Madison and the Civil War, the state prison, and local industries including Sheaffer Pens. Outside of the museum, you'll find a big old steam engine (the 2913) that ran the rails between Fort Madison to Los Angeles for 11 years.

Brush College, built in the late 1870s, is a stout one-room schoolhouse preserved and managed by the local historical society (tours by appt; 319.372.7661).

Appleberry Orchard (2469 Highway 2; 319.372.1307), the descendant of long-time favorite, Faeth Orchards, grows quite a bit of fruit, especially apples, and runs a good-sized market that sells locally made jams, pies, syrups, and more. They also set up a corn maze and a pumpkin patch in the fall, so that's pretty cool.

Tours

Few of us these days have spent any time on a farm, so maybe it's time to correct that. Just 20 minutes west of Fort Madison, **Hinterland Dairy** (2149 Franklin Rd.; 319.470.3919) produces artisan cheese and offers a peak at how they do it. They will also lead guided tours of their farm with advance notice. At the very least, visit the on-site store to find some tasty cheese to take home.

Drinking and Dining

Faeth's Cigar Store (832 Avenue G; 319.372.2792) has provided a friendly place to sip on a soda and chat for the past 90 years. If you need a new gun, ammo, or fishing supplies, you can buy those, too.

Commercial fishing on the Mississippi isn't what it used to be, but there are still a few places where you can get a fresh catch of the day, including **Quality Fisheries** (2617 240th St.; 319.372.8750). The choices vary from day to day but often include fresh or smoked catfish, buffalo fish, sturgeon, and carp. And before you sneer, smoked carp is a delicious and inexpensive treat. Try some!

Swed & Co. Coffee (702 Avenue G) will satisfy your desire for a tasty cup of coffee and a snack, and maybe some good conversation, too.

The **Fort Diner** (801 Avenue H; 319.372.1949) is as classic as a diner can be, with legit roots to the 1930s and a hard-workin' deep fryer. The space is tiny and they close early, but you'll glad you had the experience.

Horan's Cabaret Irish Pub (1337 Avenue G; 319.372.2556) is a popular local eatery, with satisfying food and a good beer selection.

A bite and a local brew at the **Lost Duck Brewing Company** (723 Avenue H; 319.372.8255) come with good views of the riverfront.

Where to Stay: Camping

Fort Madison runs two campgrounds. Expect RV sites with full hookups at the **Fort Madison RV Park** (Rodeo Park, 2103 303rd Ave.; 800.210.8687) and 20 sites with electric and showers at the **Fort Madison City Campground** (2134 302nd Ave.).

Lodging

The Kingsley Inn (707 Avenue H; 319.372.2144) sits in a great location in downtown Fort Madison and next to the riverfront in a historic warehouse. The large rooms are decorated with Victorian flair. The rate includes a full breakfast.

Special Events

Fort Madison hosts a **farmers market** on Mondays (4-6) at the old depot (Avenue H at 10th St.)

The **Charlie Korschgen Kiddie Parade** (July 4) began in 1913 when Fort Madison's Charlie Korschgen noticed that neighborhood kids didn't have much to do on the Fourth of July. His answer was to hand out small flags to a few of them, strap a snare drum around his neck, and lead them in a march around the block. His idea gradually caught on and is now held downtown and involves the whole city. When Korschgen died in 1966, he had led the parade for a remarkable 53 years!

The **Fort Madison Tri-State Rodeo** (September) has been packing in the crowds for over 65 years. It all began in 1948 when the city needed something to replace the annual Labor Day festivities, which were at risk of fading away with the railroad craft unions that had been a major supporter. Town leaders saw an opportunity when they realized that singer/rancher Gene Autry rested his livestock at Fort Madison every year as they traveled from Texas to New York City for a rodeo at Madison Square Garden. They convinced Autry to lend his support to a new rodeo in Fort Madison and committed the required local resources to make it happen. That first year, Autry was the main entertainment and the new arena was filled to the gills with 10,000 spectators. It's never really slowed down. Every year, the rodeo draws popular entertainers, top-notch professional cowboys, and enthusiastic fans.

Several generations of Mexican Americans have called Fort Madison home, and they and their ancestors have thrown a big party nearly from the beginning. The first **Mexican Fiesta** (September) was celebrated in the 1920s and is still a lot of fun, with traditional dance, dress, and food, plus carnival games. The festival takes place on Avenue Q at 34th Street.

KEOKUK

Attractions

Rand Park (15th to 17th Sts.; Grand Ave. to Orleans Ave.) is the place where folks in Keokuk gather for major events or just to hang out. Aside from the lovely gardens, disc golf course, and amphitheater, the park is home to the Chief Keokuk Monument and has great views of the river.

Head to the **Keokuk-Hamilton Dam Museum** (428 Main St.; 319.524.2102) for exhibits that overview the history and construction of what was once the widest dam in the world. Take the virtual reality tour for an inside look at the dam's construction. Call ahead to confirm they are open.

Part of the old river bridge was converted to a **walkway and observation deck** with great views of the river and the lock and dam (N. 1st St. at Lucas Ave.).

Victory Park (foot of Main St.) also hosts a number of festivals and is another good place to watch the river.

Just south of Victory Park, the landlocked **George M. Verity River Museum** (319.524.5599) is a former paddlewheeler that was built in 1927 and pushed barges on inland rivers until 1960. The boat hosts historical displays on the upper Mississippi and life on a riverboat.

Keokuk Historic Union Depot (117 S. Water St.) is a striking example of Romanesque Revival architecture, with its angular roof covered in red clay tiles and a beautiful wood ceiling inside. Built in 1891, it was a busy place at its peak, with seven rail lines running 20 daily trains to Keokuk. Passenger rail service ended in 1967. The City of Keokuk took ownership in 2011 and a foundation has been renovating the building since. It's now used for concerts and special events.

The home of Supreme Court **Justice Samuel Miller** (318 N. 5th; 319.524.5599) is now a museum that features exhibits on local history (including elastic starch manufacturing) and the Miller family. One of the more unique items in the collection is a pair of overalls made in the 1940s for the world's heaviest man, Robert Earl Hughes.

Sprawling on the southwest part of the city, historic **Oakland Cemetery** (1802 Carroll St.; 319.524.5813) is a fascinating place to take a walk, strolling among the hills dotted with memorials to earlier generations. At the south end of the cemetery and toward the middle, you'll find the old Jewish section. Coming in from 18th Street, you can quickly access **Keokuk National Cemetery** (1701 J St.; 319.524.1304).

The historic **Grand Theatre** (26 N. 6th St.; 319.524.1026), built in the 1920s on the footprint of the Opera House that had burned down, showcases performing arts, with an emphasis on live theater and music.

The area around Keokuk attracts a lot of **geode** hunters. The best ones are found within a 35-to 50-mile radius of the confluence of the Mississippi and Des Moines Rivers. You can see some good samples at the **Keokuk CVB Office** (428 Main St.; 319.524.5599), including a few available for purchase. **Callie-Co Gems and More** (714 1/2 Main St.; 319.670.9162) also sells geodes in various sizes and colors.

Drinking and Dining

Keokuk has a couple of good options for coffee. I enjoy them both! The **Lost Canvas Coffee** downtown (719 Main St.; 319.331.2164) offers tasty coffee drinks in a historic downtown space. A few blocks west, **Java River Coffeehouse & Bakery** (2528 Main St.; 319.524.2586) is the place for your caffeine fix and fresh pastries.

Chill with your favorite drink at the **Southside Boat Club** (625 Mississippi Dr.; 319.524.7122) and enjoy it on the inviting outdoor patio next to the river. They sometimes offer food, too, but call ahead to make sure if you're hoping to eat.

Ever popular **Angelini's** (1006 Main St.; 319.524.9009) serves good pizza and Italian fare in an atmospheric space.

The **Hawkeye Bar and Grill** (105 N. Park Dr.; 319.524.7549) is a solid choice for hearty and consistently good Midwestern fare. The extensive menu includes burgers, steaks, pork tenderloin, sandwiches, and salads.

Where to Stay: Camping

Hickory Haven Campground (2413 353rd St.; 319.524.8459) offers sites with full hookups in a private, shady campground north of Keokuk.

The City of Keokuk (319.524.4765) manages two small camping areas on the riverfront: **Victory Park** (at the foot of Main St.) has five sites with water and electric and **Hubinger Landing** (Mississippi Dr.) has 16 sites with water and electric.

Lodging

Pelican Peg's in nearby Montrose (3046 Koehler Lane; 319.463.5955) can accommodate up to four people in a small house next to the river. It includes a private bath, a deck with river views, and a continental breakfast.

The Chief Motel (2701 Main; 319.524.2565) offers 18 no-frills, clean budget rooms in good shape.

Special Events

Look for the Keokuk **farmers market** on Saturdays (7am-11am) at River City Mall (300 Main St.)

Explore Up the East Bank (Illinois)

HAMILTON

Attractions

Wildcat Springs Park (840 N. 7th St.) can be a fun place to search for geodes or to stretch out and enjoy a picnic or play a round of disc golf.

Where to Stay: Camping

Wildcat Springs Park also has 16 campsites, 12 of which have electric, in a shady but compact area.

Special Events

Hamilton's **farmers market** runs Thursdays (3p-6p) at City Park (142 N. 9th St.).

NAUVOO

Attractions

The **Weld House Museum** (1380 Mulholland St.; 217.453.6590) explores the breadth of Nauvoo's history with exhibits on the Mormon era, the Icarian community, the Mississippi River, and also showcases farm life and shopping in a small-town store.

Located in the heart of town, **Nauvoo State Park** (217.453.2512) has a campground, a 1 1/2-mile hiking trail, and the **Rheinberger House Museum** (217.453.6590). The museum presents a wide swath of Nauvoo's history, from Native Americans who lived in the area to Nauvoo's famous blue cheese. The original house was built during the Mormon era, then in 1850, Liechtenstein natives Alois and Margretha Rheinberger bought it. The Rheinbergers eventually added four rooms to accommodate their large family (they had 10 children), plus a wine cellar, press room, and carriage house. Alois planted his first Concord grapevines on three acres in 1851; they are still productive.

For a quick overview of the LDS Church and its history in Nauvoo, head to the **Historic Nauvoo Visitor Center** (350 N. Main St.; 217.577.2603). Don't be surprised if a young missionary strolls over to say hi. While the LDS Church downplayed evangelizing in the early years of re-establishing a presence in Nauvoo, that's no longer the case. Communicating the LDS vision is part of the experience at the historic sites they manage. The visitor center also shows short and feature-length films that present the sanctioned version of their history.

The **Nauvoo Restoration Area** comprises some 20 restored historic properties in the flats near the Mississippi River. Actors in period dress bring the past to the present and demonstrate 19th-century crafts.

While the vast majority of Mormons left Nauvoo in the mid-1840s, the family of the church's founder, Joseph Smith, stayed put. They went on to found a spin-off sect that is now known as the Community of Christ. They own the former home of Joseph Smith in Nauvoo and lead guided tours of the house and associated sites. Stop in at the visitor center for the **Joseph Smith Historic Site** (865 Water St.; 217.453.2246) where you can sign up for a short film followed by the guided tour.

The **Old Nauvoo Cemetery** (East Mulholland St) contains monuments to many early residents of Nauvoo, including Seymour Brunson. It was at Brunson's funeral that Joseph Smith introduced the concept of baptizing the dead.

In 2002, the LDS church completed a replica of Smith's **Nauvoo Temple**, which took three years and about $30 million. A spire rises high above the temple, topped with a golden sculpture of the angel Moroni. The building (50 N. Wells St.) is only open to Mormons in good standing, but everyone else is welcome to walk around the grounds.

At the south end of town, the **Stone Arch Bridge** spans a canal dug by the Mormons in the 1840s that was used to drain some of the swamps in the area.

The **Carthage Jail** (310 Buchanan St.; 217.357.2989), built in 1839, is where LDS founder Joseph Smith and his brother, Hyrum, were murdered on June 27, 1844. The LDS Church has owned and maintained the site since 1903. The site today is devoted to honoring the slain Smiths, whom Mormons view as religious martyrs. It's a half-hour drive southeast of Nauvoo.

Drinking and Dining

Baxter Vineyards (2010 E. Parley St.; 217.453.2528) traces its origins to 1857 when Emile Baxter planted the first grapevines. The family had moved to Nauvoo in 1855 to join the Icarian community but stuck around when the rest of the community splintered and moved away. Baxter's has a tasting room where you can sample their products.

Hotel Nauvoo (1290 Mulholland St.; 217.453.2211) specializes in comfort food that you can order from the menu or enjoy at the popular buffet. It's a deceptively large place. The dining rooms can seat 300 hungry people. Fried chicken and desserts are especially good. The price is reasonable but don't be surprised when they automatically add in a tip. People tend to dress a little nicer for dinner here, but it's not a necessity.

Where to Stay: Camping

Nauvoo State Park (217.453.2512) rents 105 sites including 35 with electric that are rather close together but heavily shaded. There is a shower house on site.

Bed and Breakfasts

Sample Victorian elegance for a night or two at **The Nauvoo Grand** (2015 E. Parley St.; 801.499.6636). Guests choose from six rooms, including a cozy attic space to a basement apartment, each with its own bath and fully decked out in Victorian splendor. Room come with a full breakfast.

The **Willard Richards Inn** (950 White St.; 801.416.4470) offers five rooms in a solid brick, historic home on a shady acre and a half. Rooms are simple and well-cared for. Three rooms have en suite bathrooms; the other two rooms share a bathroom. Room rates include a full breakfast.

Lodging

Four generations of Krauses have run the **Hotel Nauvoo** (1290 Mulholland St.) in a building that traces its roots to the 1840s. All rooms are on the second floor and evoke a simple, period feel but are modern and clean. The two suites are large enough for a family. The same owners offer similar rooms but at ground level at the **Motel Nauvoo** (1610 Mulholland St.). For both, they take reservations by phone only (217.453.2211).

Special Events

For about four weeks each summer, actors perform an elaborate show called the **Nauvoo Pageant** (July) that tells the origin story of the Mormon religion in a big way, with colorful banners, singing, dancing, and children skipping across stage. The Nauvoo Pageant alternates with the British Pageant, which tells the story of the journey of thousands of British converts to the US and Nauvoo with colorful banners, singing, dancing, and children skipping across stage.

At the end of the summer, Nauvoo hosts its annual **Grape Festival** (Labor Day weekend), which it celebrates with wine, live music, and arts and crafts.

Getting There

Amtrak offers service to both Burlington and Fort Madison. The *California Zephyr* route between Chicago and Oakland, California, has one daily stop in the morning at Burlington for trains headed to Chicago and a daily stop in the evening for the train coming from Chicago.

Amtrak's *Southwest Chief* between Chicago and Los Angeles has one daily stop in Fort Madison. The train heading to Chicago stops in the morning, while the train from Chicago stops in the evening.

For More Information

There are practical limits to how much I can include in a book, but not with a website! Check out the city profiles on my website to see if they include listings that I couldn't fit in this book.

Muscatine: MississippiValleyTraveler.com/Muscatine
Burlington: MississippiValleyTraveler.com/Burlington
Fort Madison: MississippiValleyTraveler.com/Fort-Madison
Keokuk: MississippiValleyTraveler.com/Keokuk
Hamilton: MississippiValleyTraveler.com/Hamilton
Nauvoo: MississippiValleyTraveler.com/Nauvoo

And as long as you're in the area, check out these places, too:
Montrose: MississippiValleyTraveler.com/Montrose
Warsaw: MississippiValleyTraveler.com/Warsaw
Dallas City: MississippiValleyTraveler.com/Dallas-City
Lomax: MississippiValleyTraveler.com/Lomax
Gladstone: MississippiValleyTraveler.com/Gladstone
Oquawka: MississippiValleyTraveler.com/Oquawka
Keithsburg: MississippiValleyTraveler.com/Keithsburg
New Boston: MississippiValleyTraveler.com/New-Boston

There's no shortage of stories about the Great River, which is why I started the **Mississippi Valley Traveler podcast**. In each episode, I go deep into a topic about the river's culture, history, and natural world. It helps the miles fly by as you drive the Great River Road. Find it everywhere podcasts are available, including Spotify, Apple podcasts, and YouTube.

HANNIBAL & QUINCY

Mark Twain on the Hannibal riverfront

Overview

These two old river towns may be neighbors, but they are quite different places. The storied imagination of a native writer crafted Hannibal's fame, while Quincy built its own reputation brick by brick. Hannibal rightly draws a lot of tourists eager to step into the world created by Mark Twain. Don't overlook Quincy, though. It's a friendly city with a history and collection of buildings that span time and trends.

History

HANNIBAL

Salt deposits in the area attracted a few Euro-Americans to Bear Creek, but no permanent community developed until Moses Bates organized a group of St. Louis residents to leave and start a new town. After poling a keelboat for 16 days against the current, the group reached Bear Creek and got to work building a few cabins.

When Bates met Thompson Bird, Bates saw an opportunity to kick start his community and to make some money. Thompson's father, Abraham Bird, possessed a New Madrid Certificate, which was like gold at the time. In 1815, the US Congress passed a relief act that granted 640 acres to landowners who suffered losses from the New Madrid earthquakes. Certificates could be used to buy any land in Missouri that had not already been claimed. Bates convinced Bird to use the claim for the area around Bear Creek, which he did. Bird then gave Bates one-eight interest in the property and sold half of the claim to a St. Louis investor.

The new village was surveyed in 1819, and Bates probably named it Hannibal because that's the name Don Antonio Soulard used for the creek when he surveyed it in 1800. (Later residents called it Bear Creek.) Bates, who brought enslaved Blacks with him, opened a trading post, but business wasn't great for the first few years. Some families left, including Bates. In 1821, he moved to Galena to build keelboats for the Galena-St. Louis run. Four years later, he launched the *General Putnam*, the first steamboat to run regularly between Galena and St. Louis. Hannibal was one of its stops.

The city took root in the 1830s, after disputes over land titles were settled. Some of the early businesses included a pork packing plant, a sawmill, and cooper shops. In 1831, the city got its first ferry, a flatboat powered by oars that had just enough room for a team of horses and a wagon.

In the 1830s, an east coast investor founded Marion City about 12 miles upriver of Hannibal. He didn't realize that most of the area was marshy, though. He lost much of his investment when folks gave up after a big flood in 1836 and moved to Hannibal, which helped the city grow from just 30 residents in 1830 to a thousand a decade later.

During those years of rapid growth, Jane and John Marshall Clemens moved to Hannibal with their six children, one of whom, four-year-old Samuel Langhorne Clemens, would later immortalize the town in his books and short stories. The year after the Clemens family arrived, a measles epidemic swept through town and killed 40 people.

Hannibal's early fortunes were deeply tied to the river. In 1847, the city recorded over a thousand steamboat landings. Many of those boats carried surplus wheat to market, as well as hemp and tobacco. Commercial fishing thrived for a while, until native fish stocks were nearly depleted. The city also suffered through major floods in 1844 and 1846. The river giveth and the river taketh away, too.

After the Civil War, logging boomed in the forests of northern Minnesota and Wisconsin, and many of those logs were floated to Hannibal for processing. In the 1870s, Hannibal grew into the fourth largest producer of finished lumber in the US.

The logging boom was over by 1900, and the city's sawmills shut down. Hoping to reboot Hannibal's economy, the city bought up old factory lots and offered free land to new companies. In some cases, they even covered up to half of new construction costs. These incentives helped land a big shoe factory (Roberts, Johnson & Rand, which later became the International Shoe Company) and soon the industrial corridor along Bear Creek filled in with a variety of factories (cigars, steel, metal products).

South of town, Atlas Portland Cement Company opened a big factory in 1901. The town that grew up around it became known as Ilasco, which was an acronym created from the ingredients used to manufacture cement (iron, lime, aluminum, silica, coal, oxygen). The village quickly grew to 1,500 people (and topped out at 3,000), many of them recent immigrants from Europe. The village was dissolved in 1963, but the cement plant is still going.

A small Jewish community grew in Hannibal in the early 1900s. Temple Israel was dedicated in 1935 and remained active until it merged with Temple B'Nai Shalom in Quincy in the 1960s. Lester Gaba was part of the small Jewish community of that era. He worked in his father's retail store when he was growing up. After graduating from high school, he found fame designing retail window displays. He was also a gifted artist. He worked with soap for a while (he sculpted a cameo of Mark Twain for the local museum), then became an adept painter later in life. His brother, Mark, was a local tennis star who was killed in the Philippine Islands at the end of World War II.

Like most of the US, Hannibal lost manufacturing jobs beginning in the 1980s. Hannibal still has a significant manufacturing base, though. General Mills is the region's largest employer. Health care and education also employ a lot of people, and tourism is also a big deal, obviously.

Like every river town, Hannibal has lived through its share of flooding. Building a barrier wasn't a cheap proposition, though, so it wasn't until 1993 that a flood wall was completed (where Front Street used to be), just in time, as it turned out. The Great Flood of 1993 crept high up the new wall, but it held. Subsequent major floods in 2008, 2013, 2014, 2018, and 2019 have tested the wall again and again.

QUINCY

In 1820, John Wood and Willard Keyes passed through west-central Illinois and liked the area so much that they came back to put down roots. Keyes returned in 1822 and built a cabin, while Wood came back shortly after and squatted near the current village of Atlas, Illinois. Wood was a New York native who left quite a mark on his new home.

He fought an initiative to legalize slavery in Illinois. That measure lost in a statewide vote in 1824. He served three terms as mayor of Quincy, then was later elected as state senator, lieutenant governor, and governor (winning election in 1860). He left the governor's office in 1861 and served in the Civil War, first as Quartermaster General for Illinois, then—at 65-years old—as commander of the 137th Illinois Infantry.

Wood pushed for the creation of Adams County and got his wish in 1825. Quincy, his hometown, won the county seat but had to fight to keep it. On August 2, 1841, voters approved moving it from Quincy to Columbus. Curiously, 200 more votes were cast for the county seat question than for the congressional candidates in that same election, so Quincy interests naturally assumed fraud was involved. County commissioners refused to move, even after Judge Stephen A. Douglas upheld the validity of the results.

The case was appealed to the state supreme court but before they could reach a decision, the Illinois legislature crafted a political solution. They voted to create a new county by lopping off the ten eastern townships of Adams County, which just happened to include the city of Columbus. The residents of the affected counties didn't get to vote on the issue, however. The new county was first called Marquette then renamed Highland, but what they really should have called it was Unworkable. The new county flopped—it was too small to be viable—so in 1848, it was reunified with Adams County but with Quincy as the seat of government. In 1875, Quincy faced another challenger, but this time voters safely rejected a proposal to relocate the county seat to Coatsburg.

Quincy's early years were often difficult. In 1833, cholera killed 43 of the town's 400 residents. Another cholera epidemic in 1849 killed 400 people, including the mayor, Enoch Conyers. Life wasn't always grim, however. Corn husking parties gave people joy. Pairs of men and women teamed up to rip the husks off of corn in someone's barn. If a woman's husking revealed a red ear, she got a kiss from every man at the event. Men likewise got the same privilege if they found a red ear, a kiss from every man. Just kidding. They got kisses from every woman. Once all the ears were husked, a violin player got busy playing, and they danced until the sun came up. The farmer who got all that corn husked for free, meanwhile, danced to the bank.

> **RANDOM FACT:** Some streets you drive in Hannibal today are topped with asphalt that was laid over cobblestones that were placed atop wood planks.

When folks weren't husking corn or dodging cholera, they might have been busy exterminating the local wildlife. Native species of fauna were considered a great inconvenience by many people at the time, as those critters sure liked to eat the crops the farmers grew. Ring hunts were a popular way to make a big dent in the wildlife population. Someone would start by driving a pole into the ground on top of a hill to mark a spot. Men and boys from the area would gather into a circle around a perimeter as wide as 40 square miles, and they'd begin walking and making enough noise to scare out the wildlife and drive it toward the pole. When the ring was finally small enough, the huntsman blew a horn and then the real fun began as those men and boys would get busy killing as many animals as they could, with guns if it was safe or by clubbing or stabbing with pitchforks, if shooting was a bad idea. One of these hunts near Quincy reportedly killed 60 bears, 25 deer, 100 turkeys, and many more small mammals and rodents.

The single biggest force in the city's early economy was the Mississippi River. Keelboats were the primary means of moving goods until the early 1830s when steamboats took their place. By 1853, Quincy was averaging about five steamboat landings a day during the ten-month long navigation season, but steamboat landings grew steadily until the Civil War.

Residents of Quincy initially welcomed Mormons as they fled persecution in Missouri. Mormon refugees reached the city in the winter of 1838-39. Even though 6,000 people poured into the city of 1,600 residents, Quincyans found a way to meet their basic needs. Most of the refugees moved on to Nauvoo to build a new Mormon holy city. In spite of the initial welcoming, however, public opinion in Western Illinois turned against the Mormons a few years later. Many Quincyans were among those who joined the militias that drove the Mormons out, while other residents helped negotiate a deal that ensured the Mormon community would have a peaceful exit from Illinois.

On October 13, 1858, Abraham Lincoln and Stephen A. Douglas squared off for their sixth and next-to-last debate in the Illinois US Senate campaign. The debate was a major social event, preceded by parades and picnics that culminated with 12,000 people packing into Quincy's Washington Park to listen to the two men speak, primarily about slavery. The debate was quite a spectacle, but at that time, state legislators chose US Senators, not the popular vote. In the end, the Illinois Legislature, with its newly elected Democratic majority, picked fellow Democrat Stephen A. Douglas for the Senate seat.

While the river played a major role in the city's early economy, railroads were a major force after the Civil War. The Chicago, Burlington, & Quincy completed the first tracks to Quincy (in 1856), but eventually the city would be served by eight different railroads. The first railroad bridge across the Mississippi at Quincy was built in 1868. It served rail traffic until 1960, when a new bridge replaced it.

The city's industrial base expanded rapidly after the Civil War and so did its population. The city grew from 14,000 residents in 1860 to 36,000 in 1900. Some of the largest industries produced stoves, elevators, carriages, bricks, tractors and other farm equipment, pickles, and limestone (but no pickled limestone). In 1879, the largest industry was tobacco processing, which employed nearly 1,200 people.

Beer was also a big deal. Multiple breweries offered steady employment. The Dick Brothers ran one of the most successful breweries. The three brothers who left Ger-

Much of the Lincoln-Douglas debate in Quincy focused on slavery and the future of African Americans. **Read more** about it at MississippiValleyTraveler.com/Quincy.

many in 1852—Matthew, a cooper; John, a baker; and Jacob, a salesman—moved to Quincy in 1856 and opened a brewery at 9th and York. They were attracted by the clear, cold water they saw bubbling out of a local spring. For decades, the Dick Brothers sold their beer throughout the Midwest. They even reopened after Prohibition, although they were far less successful. They survived bankruptcy in 1937 but had to close for good in the early 1950s.

Quincy's first Jewish residents probably arrived in the late 1840s. Within a decade, the community was large enough to establish B'Nai Avraham Temple. It opened on December 14, 1856, with 23 members. A few members broke away in 1864 to start a Reform Congregation called B'Nai Shalom, then the two synagogues merged in 1872.

Temple B'Nai Sholom (427 N. 9th St.), was dedicated on September 8, 1870. It was an optimistic venture, with room to seat over 600 people. In the front lobby of the temple, there's a chart that shows the original seating arrangement when the Temple opened. While there were 500 members at the time the building was completed, membership hasn't been that large since, dropping quickly in the ensuing years. By 1935, there were just 35 families and 110 dues-paying members. Even after absorbing the small Jewish congregation of Hannibal, membership remained modest in size. The synagogue closed in 2019.

In 1860, a group of Franciscan friars arrived in Quincy from Germany and founded St. Francis Solanus College. The first building constructed is now the eastern-most section of Francis Hall. The college specialized in training Franciscan priests in the early years, but over time, its mission has shifted with its name. In 1970, the school closed its seminary and renamed itself Quincy College and focused on providing a liberal arts education. In 1993, it added a few graduate degree programs and became Quincy University. While all of the classes were taught by friars when the school was founded, few friars are part of the faculty today.

Both of Quincy's primary founders, Keyes and Wood, were strong abolitionists, which may be part of the reason that the city had a number of Underground Railroad sites. As African Americans moved into Quincy—many before and during the Civil War—they founded churches (including the First Baptist Church at 8th and Elm), a baseball league, and fraternal organizations. African American migration to Quincy picked up in the years right after the Civil War and again around World War I.

The first African American priest in the United States, Father August Tolton, led his first mass at Quincy's St. Boniface Church. Augustine Tolton was born April 1, 1854, in Ralls County, Missouri. Both of his parents were enslaved. His father Peter Paul probably fought with the Union Army during the Civil War. His mother Martha escaped to Quincy with their children. Tolton attended school at St. Boniface for a brief time but apparently had to leave because some people objected to having a Black child attend classes with White children.

In 1878, Tolton enrolled in Quincy College, thanks to the help of Father Anselm Mueller. The college refused to admit Tolton into the seminary, however. He was eventually admitted to the College of Sacred Propaganda in Rome in 1880. Tolton was ordained on April 24, 1886, and said his first mass (in Quincy) on July 18, 1887.

In the early 20th century, several small companies built boats in Quincy. Cliff Padgett built racing boats, many dubbed *Miss Quincy*, which he numbered by version: *Miss Quincy I* rolled out in 1918. OF (Chris) Christner ran Quincy Welding and Marine (later Quincy Precision Machine) from the late 1940s until 1984. He transformed the world of boat racing with his innovative approaches to improving the motors. His first breakthrough was a modified Mercury outboard motor, but he later designed and built outboard motors from scratch, such as the Quincy Looper he introduced in 1963. Christner was an accomplished racer himself. He won a race in 1948 with another boat called *Miss Quincy*.

The railroad continued to serve a central role in Quincy's life in the 20th century. One of the more memorable trains to serve the area was the sleek, Art déco-inspired *Mark Twain Zephyr*. It began its service in October 1935, running along the Mississippi River between St. Louis and Burlington, Iowa, with stops in river towns including Hannibal, Quincy, Keokuk, and Fort Madison. The *Zephyr* ended its run in May 1963.

Like many other Midwestern cities, Quincy struggled with the loss of manufacturing jobs beginning in the late 1970s. Motorola closed a plant in 1978, which eliminated 3,500 jobs. Three years later, the Electric Wheel plant closed and cut another 1,500 jobs. The county unemployment rate jumped from 5.5% in 1979 to 12.6% in 1982. That was the worst of it, though, as the city's economy has steadily diversified. While health care and education employ the largest number of people in Quincy today, manufacturing is still robust with companies such as Knapheide (truck bodies and truck beds), Titan Wheel (off-highway wheels), and ADM (food processing).

Explore on the West Bank (Missouri)

HANNIBAL

Attractions

AUTHOR'S PICK: If you're going to visit Hannibal, you may as well go full Mark Twain. Start at the **Mark Twain Boyhood Home & Museum** (120 N. Main St.; 573.221.9010). One ticket buys admission to several buildings, including the main museum, the home where Sam Clemens grew up, and the Huckleberry Finn and Becky Thatcher Houses. The museum gives a good overview of Twain's life and why we still read his books. His boyhood home is a couple of blocks down the street and is a well-preserved middle-class dwelling from the era.

Richard Garey's **Mark Twain Himself** is the actor's take on Twain's famous lectures. He performs at the **Planters Barn Theater** (319 N. Main St.; 573.231.0021).

As you visit Twain sites around town, see how many **statues of Mark Twain** you can find (Hint: look on the riverfront and in Riverview Park).

Jim's Journey: The Huck Finn Freedom Center (509 N. 3rd St.), housed in a historic stone house built by enslaved people, relates stories of African American history in Hannibal with photographs of residents, documents, and items from everyday life.

As you roam around town, you might even come across **young Tom Sawyer and Becky Thatcher**. If you do, don't be shy about posing for a picture with them.

You can't miss **Cardiff Hill Overlook Park** (505 N. 3rd St.); it's the small park north of downtown with the lighthouse in the middle of it. When Sam Clemens was a boy, it was known as Holliday Hill, but in the *Adventures of Tom Sawyer*, he called it Cardiff Hill. Because of the book, so many visitors asked to see Cardiff Hill that the city eventually changed its name.

Mark Twain Cave (7097 County Road 453; 573.221.1656), just south of downtown, offers a one-hour tour that explores more Twain mythology, but this time in an underground setting. Jim Waddell also performs **Mark Twain 'Live'** at the cave complex from April through December.

Hannibal Map

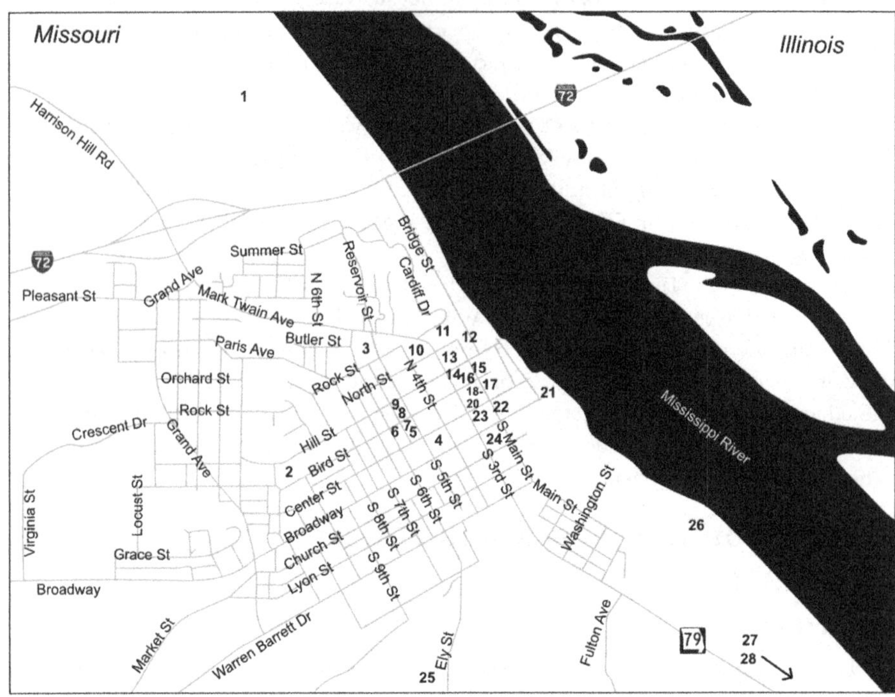

Attractions

15. Art Gallery 310
11. Cardiff Hill Overlook Park
24. Hannibal Arts Council
17. Hannibal History Museum
10. Jim's Journey
26. Lovers Leap
13. Mark Twain Boyhood Home
22. Mark Twain Museum
28. Mark Twain Cave
14. Mark Twain Himself/Planters Barn
21. Mark Twain Riverboat
3. Molly Brown Birthplace and Museum
1. Riverview Park
2. Rockcliffe Mansion
25. Sodalis Nature Preserve

Where to Eat and Drink

23. Brick Oven Pizza
27. Cave Hollow West Winery
4. Farmers Market
12. Friendship Brewing Company
16. Great River Brewing Company
19. Java Jive
5. LaBinnah Bistro

Where to Stay

6. Belvedere Inn
7. Dubach Inn
8. Garden House B&B
20. Main Street B&B
28. Mark Twain Cave Complex
9. Reagan's Queen Anne B&B
2. Rockcliffe Mansion
18. Travelers Rooming House

> Mark Twain returned to Hannibal two times as an adult. What did he think of his hometown? **Read about** his experiences at MississippiValleyTraveler.com/Mark-Twains-Hannibal.

Believe it or not, Hannibal has a few attractions that aren't directly related to Mark Twain. **Riverview Park** (2000 Harrison Hill) offers 465 shady acres on a bluff in north Hannibal overlooking the river, with walking trails, picnic shelters, and monuments.

The Hannibal History Museum (200 N. Main St.) features exhibits on the city's history that isn't necessarily connected to its most famous resident.

Hannibal native Margaret Tobin Brown, better known as Molly Brown, was one of the lucky people who survived the sinking of the *Titanic.* The modest **Molly Brown Birthplace and Museum** (600 Butler St.; 573.221.2477) showcases her remarkable life.

Spread out on top of a hill above downtown, the 13,500-square foot **Rockcliffe Mansion** (1000 Bird St.; 573.221.4140) reeks of gilded age opulence. The house, Georgian Revival in style with Art Nouveau accents, was completed in 1900 for the John J. Cruikshank family. Mr. Cruikshank made a lot of money from the lumber business in Hannibal. The house is open for guided tours from mid-April to mid-November.

The **Hannibal Arts Council** (105 S. Main St.; 573.221.6545) showcases the work of local and regional artists and hosts a few performances a year, as well.

Local artists offer their works for sale at **Art Gallery 310** (310 N. Main St.).

A couple dozen **murals** decorate the walls of buildings around downtown and the historic district. Many, of course, feature themes from the works of Mark Twain. You can pick up a list at the visitor center (925 Grand Ave.) or online (VisitHannibal.com).

A third of America's endangered Indiana bats inhabit an abandoned limestone mine near downtown. **Sodalis Nature Preserve** (819 Ely St.) protects their home and the homes of five other bat species. Two miles of paved trails run through the property. Gates prevent access to the mine, but you may see bats flying out just before sunset.

Lovers Leap (Highway 79 south of downtown) rises about 300 feet above the Mississippi River. The park at the top provides great views up and down river.

Getting On the River

The **Mark Twain Riverboat** in Hannibal (300 Riverfront Dr.; 573.221.3222) offers one hour sightseeing cruises, as well as longer cruises with a meal.

If you want to travel the river under your own power, the **Mississippi River Water Trail** (mississippiriverwatertrail.org) runs 121 miles from Saverton (just south of Hannibal) to St. Louis. Highlights include islands and backwaters, the historic villages of Louisiana and Clarksville, and the confluence of the Mississippi and Missouri Rivers.

Tours

The **Hannibal Tour Company** (220 N. Main St.; 573.231.1000 takes guests on a relaxing one-hour driving tour of the sights around town.

You can pick up a couple of **self-guided tours** of the city's historic homes at the visitor center (925 Grand Ave.).

For a different kind of experience, **Haunted Hannibal Ghost Tours** (573.248.1819) takes guests around Hannibal in a shuttle to introduce them to the specters and undead who still roam the city. Tours begin at the Hannibal History Museum (200 N. Main St.).

Drinking and Dining

Java Jive (211 N. Main St.; 573.221.1017) is part coffee shop and part café, with fresh pastries, salads, and sandwiches served in a historic storefront.

Hannibal has two places to sample locally brewed beer: **Friendship Brewing Company** (422 N. Main St.; 573.600.9091) offers a good range of beers in its taproom, as well as barbecue specialties to fill your belly. **Great River Brewing Company** (219 N.

Main) operates from a cozy space downtown and serves a rotating selection of beers; they sometimes host live music.

Relax while sipping wine at **Cave Hollow West Winery** (300 Cave Hollow Rd.; 573.231.1000) down near Mark Twain Cave.

The **Brick Oven** (205 Center St.; 573.221.1288) bakes tasty pizza in a wood-fired oven in a lovely old commercial building.

LaBinnah Bistro (207 N. 5th St.; 573.221.8207) is a good choice for Mediterranean-inspired fine dining in an intimate yet casual setting.

Where to Sleep

Camping

South of Hannibal, the campground at the **Mark Twain Cave Complex** (300 Cave Hollow Rd.; 573.231.1000) offers 99 campsites from tent sites to full RV hookups, all next to caves that fired up Mark Twain's imagination.

Bed and Breakfasts

Mark Twain slept here and so can you! Located just outside of town, **Garth Woodside Mansion** (11069 New London Gravel Rd.; 573.221.2789) offers eight rooms, three cottages, and 36 acres of quiet space to enjoy.

Mark Twain spoke here, and so can you! That impressive estate on the hill, **Rockcliffe Mansion** (1000 Bird St.; 573.221.4140), not only offers tours but rents rooms for overnight stays. Guests enjoy a nightly wine and cheese reception, great views of town and the river, and plush accommodations.

The **Dubach Inn** (221 N. 5th St.; 573.355.1167) rents three suites in an Italianate mansion built in 1871.

The **Belvedere Inn** (521 Bird St.; 217.799.6086) rents six rooms in another Italianate mansion, this one built in 1859.

The **Garden House B&B** (301 N. 5th St.; 573.221.7800) is another Queen Anne beauty and comes with views of the river. They rent four rooms.

In the heart of downtown, the **Main Street B&B** (201 N. Main St.; 573.406.3892) rents three thematically decorated rooms.

The Travelers Rooming House (213 N. Main St.; 573.600.9401) offers four rooms and two suites in a rehabbed former boarding house above a downtown storefront; guests get a voucher for breakfast at a local restaurant.

Special Events

Check out the Hannibal **farmers market** on Saturday mornings and Tuesday evenings (Central Park; 5th & Broadway).

Hannibal's annual **Twain on Main Festival** (573.795.6233) celebrates Mark Twain's writings. Events take place over the Memorial Day weekend and include re-enactors roaming the streets, live music, arts and crafts vendors, and a memorial lantern float on the Mississippi River.

Juneteenth is the annual event marking the day Abraham Lincoln issued the Emancipation Proclamation. In Hannibal, most of the events take place at Jim's Journey: The Huck Finn Freedom Center (509 N. 3rd St.).

National Tom Sawyer Days (573.795.6233) is Hannibal's big festival of the year, as it has been since 1956. Look for events such as fence painting, frog jumping, fireworks on the 4th of July, and plenty of places to buy stuff from local vendors. You'll also find young Tom and Becky wandering around town to say hi and to pose for photos.

Explore on the East Bank (Illinois)

QUINCY

Attractions

Housed in the imposing Newcomb-Stillwell mansion, the **Quincy Museum** (1601 Maine; 217.224.7669) is several attractions in one. The first floor is maintained as a historic house, complete with gorgeous woodwork and elegant 19th-century craftsmanship. The second floor has rotating displays on the region's history, while the third floor is set up with exhibits on natural history and Native American history.

The former mansion of **Governor John Wood** (425 S. 12th St.; 217.222.1835), completed in 1835, has 14 rooms of faithfully maintained Greek Revival architecture, complete with some original furnishings and many others from the period when the Woods occupied the house. The house was originally built across the street, so when Wood wanted to build a new mansion, this house was cut in half and moved (and carefully raised over a flower bed that Mrs. Wood wanted to protect). Wood built a cool octagonal mansion on the old site of the house and his son occupied the relocated mansion. While the original, Greek Revival mansion has survived, the octagonal mansion has not.

Tucked away in an old part of the Illinois Veterans Home, the **All Wars Museum** (1707 N. 12th St.; 217.222.8641) preserves artifacts from every war the US has ever fought in. The impressive collection includes original flags, uniforms, prints, and dedicated volunteers who keep it going (open March to late Nov.).

Dr. Richard Eells was an anti-slavery activist who risked his own life and fortune to help hundreds of enslaved people escape to freedom. Tours of the **Quincy Underground Railroad Museum** (415 Jersey St.), built in 1835, describe Eells' life and role with the secret network of freedom advocates. The home has been restored to its 1840-era appearance, and tours also highlight the building's architectural influences. Call for tour times (217.223.1800).

The Dick Brothers name may no longer be associated with beer production, but the brewery complex they built has found new life. The **Dick Brothers Brewery Museum** (917 York St.; 217.242.9567) features a few exhibits about the brewery's past, plus you can take a guided tour through the caves and hallways of the old complex.

The **Quincy Art Center** (1515 Jersey St.; 217.223.5900) presents rotating exhibits that showcase the works of local and regional artists.

Washington Square (Maine at 4th Street) was the site of the sixth Lincoln-Douglas Debate and continues to be the site of community events to this day. Across the street, the **Lincoln Douglas Debate Interpretive Center** (128 N. 5th St.; 217.223.5099) features educational panels on the content and context of the debate.

The **History Museum on the Square** (332 Maine; 217.214.1888) took over the space vacated by the Gardner Museum of Architecture, which is also the old city library. The museum inherited some architectural artifacts, but most of the museum's exhibits focus specifically on Quincy history and are time-limited.

Villa Katherine (532 Gardner Expressway; 217.224.3688) is one of the unique treasures of the Great River Road. Avid traveler George Metz designed the Moorish-inspired house from sketches he made adventuring around the world. (He named the house after his mother). He lived in the house for 12 years before selling it to a railroad that considered building a switching yard on the site. The yard wasn't built, and the house survived multiple ownership changes before it was purchased by preservationists

Quincy Map

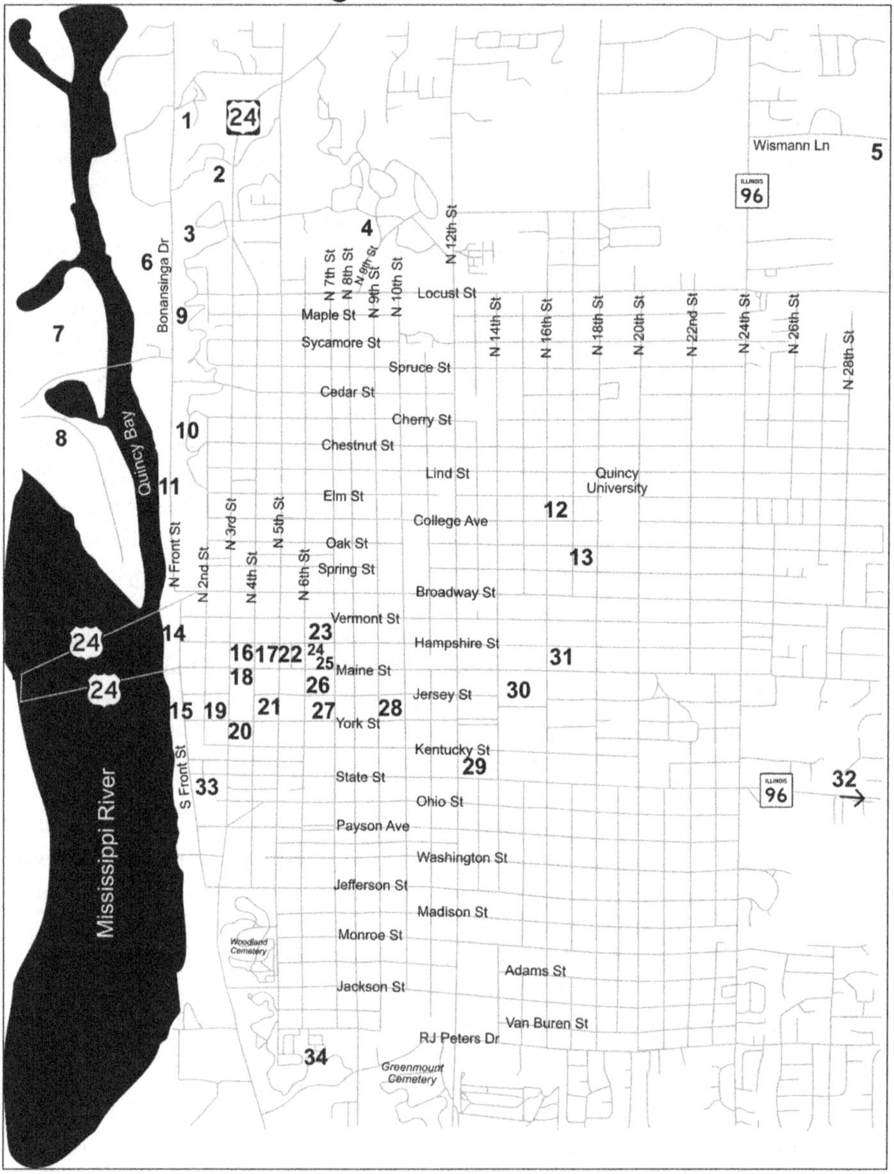

Go deeper into the world of the Mississippi with my other guide: *The Wild Mississippi: A State-by-State Guide to the River's Natural Wonders.* The *Wild Mississippi* describes the river's main ecosystems, the plant and animal life supported in them, and lists 166 places (public lands) to be near the river.

Quincy Map Index

Attractions

6. All America Park
4. All Wars Museum
14. Clat Adams Bicentennial Park
28. Dick Brothers Brewery Museum
21. Quincy Underground Railroad Museum
15. Edgewater Park
3. Gardner Park
29. Governor John Wood
18. History Museum on the Square
34. Indian Mounds Park
11. Kesler Park
22. Lincoln Douglas Debate Interpretive Center
20. Oakley Lindsay Center
2. Parker Heights Park
8. Pioneer Mississippi Valley Village
30. Quincy Art Center
31. Quincy Museum
33. Quincy Visitors Center
7. Quinsippi Island
10. Riverview Park
9. Sunset Park
33. Villa Katherine
17. Washington Square

Where to Eat and Drink

25. Electric Fountain Brewing Coffee Bar
17. Farmers Market
24. Quincy Brewing Company
28. Ratskeller/Dick Brothers Brewery
19. Riverside Smokehouse
13. The Abbey
26. The Maine Course
23. Thyme Square Café
16. Tiramisu
12. Underbrinks Bakery

Where to Stay

1. Driftwood Campgrounds
32. Lighthouse Lane B&B

Other

5. Amtrak
27. Burlington Trailways/Greyhound Stop

DRIVING BETWEEN HANNIBAL AND QUINCY

This chapter follows a simple circular route. The entire drive is about 50 miles.

- From Quincy, follow US Highway 24 across the river to the west (Missouri) side, then follow US Highway 61 south to Hannibal. (Alternately, you can detour along winding and scenic Missouri Highway 168 to stay on the signed Great River Road.)
- At Hannibal take Interstate 72 to Missouri Highway 79 to reach downtown Hannibal and the main tourist sites.
- When you're ready to leave, take Interstate 72 to the east side (Illinois), then follow Interstate 172 north; exit at State Highway 57 and follow it back to Quincy.

in 1978. It now serves as **Quincy's Visitor Center**. You are welcome to wander around most of the first floor (don't miss the courtyard and reflecting pool).

The **1930s Ag Museum** (1435 Boy Scout Rd.) houses a private collection of vintage John Deere farm equipment and artifacts of rural life in the early 20th century. Call to arrange a visit (217.430.3036).

One hundred thirty-acre **Quinsippi Island** once had a "Sky Cruiser" aerial tram that ran a one-mile round trip to the island from the city. The tram is long gone, but today you'll find the **Pioneer Mississippi Valley Village**, a marina, and good river views.

Quincy has a string of parks along the river and Quincy Bay, including:

- **All America Park** (Front & Cedar Sts.) north of the bridge
- **Kesler Park** (Bonansinga Dr. north of Clat Adams Park), which has a boat ramp, a couple of murals, and a display showing historic river crests for Quincy
- **Clat Adams Bicentennial Park** (Front & Hampshire Sts.), named for the long-time riverfront store owner, has great views of the river and Quincy's bridges and is the site of many community celebrations, including the 4th of July
- **Edgewater Park** (Front and York Sts.), which also has good views of the river

There are also several scenic parks on top of the bluffs:

- **Parker Heights Park** (North Bottom Rd.) is closed to auto traffic and the old roadway has been integrated into the **Bill Klingner Trail** system
- **Gardner Park** (3rd St.) is adjacent to Sunset Park and is fine place for a stroll or picnic lunch
- **Sunset Park** (3rd and Cedar), between Gardner and Riverview Parks, has a good overlook of the Mississippi River
- **Riverview Park** (2nd and Chestnut), just south of Sunset Park, has a good overlook and a statue of George Rogers Clark
- **Indian Mounds Park** (5th and Harrison) sprawls over 37 hilly acres and has a couple of overlooks, a swimming pool, and plenty of places to picnic; the park also preserves several historic mounds as part of an interpretive trail that traces the region's history from the last ice age to the arrival of Euro-Americans

Getting on the River

Rent a kayak (with paddles and life jackets) at a self-service kiosk and paddle around Quincy Bay. You'll find them in Kesler Park (800 Bonansinga Dr.; 800.978.4748).

Tours

Stop by the **Quincy Visitor Center** (532 Gardner Expressway; 217.214.3700) and pick up a **self-guided tour** of the city's impressive architecture and historic sites.

Drinking and Dining

AUTHOR'S PICK: **Thyme Square Café** (615 Hampshire St.; 217.224.3515) is a gem. The proprietors take pride in the food they put out and pay attention to the smallest of details to make it all work. They purchase most of their raw materials from folks in the area and turn them into delicious made-from-scratch entrées for breakfast and lunch. My personal favorite is corned beef hash, which is cooked with big, juicy chunks of their rich house-made corned beef. I get hungry just thinking about it. If that's not good enough, their space in a renovated storefront is a joy to dine in.

If you're looking to relax with a pint of locally brewed beer, head on over to the **Quincy Brewing Company** (110 N. 6th St.; 217.214.5512). They have as many as 16 different beers on tap. They don't serve food, but you are welcome to bring your own or order food from a local restaurant and have it delivered to the brewery.

Sip a pint or two in the atmospheric **Ratskeller** at the historic Dick Brothers Brewery (917 York St.; 217.242.9567).

Underbrinks Bakery (1627 College Ave.; 217.222.1831) has been pleasing Quincyans since 1929 with baked goods like cakes, bread, and pies. They are especially beloved for their angel food cupcakes.

Electric Fountain Brewing Coffee Bar (625 Main St.) serves house-roasted coffee in a historic building with exposed brick walls and wood floors near downtown. The entrance is off the alley in the back in the building.

Riverside Smokehouse (222 S. 3rd St.; 217.214.7675) can satisfy your crave for smoked meat. They offer generous meat platters with good sides at reasonable prices.

The Abbey (1736 Spring; 217.228.8868) is a busy neighborhood tavern/restaurant near Quincy University with an extensive menu, ranging from sandwiches and salads to steak and seafood entrées.

Tiramisu (131 N. 4th St.; 217.222.9560) serves good Italian dishes from pizza to pasta in a historic downtown building. They can be busy on weekend nights.

At **The Maine Course** (626 Maine; 217.222.6244) the emphasis is on fresh, so the menu changes frequently. You can count on fine dining in a relaxed setting with friendly and attentive service without pretense.

Where to Sleep

Quincy has the usual chain hotels. Pick your favorite brand and go there.

Camping

Driftwood Campgrounds (2300 Bonansinga Dr.; 217.222.7229) caters primarily to RVs (many sites have full hookups), but they have room for tents, too. The campground is located in a scenic spot at the foot of a bluff and across the road from Quincy Bay.

Bed and Breakfasts

Lighthouse Lane Bed & Breakfast (3404 State St.; 217.257.5101) began life as a farmhouse in the 19th century. Today, you can rent one of the two spacious rooms accented with plenty of country charm.

Special Events

The Quincy **farmers market** runs Saturday mornings (Washington Park, 4th & Maine).

The Standing Bear Council sponsors a **Winter Gathering** in Quincy that focuses on Native American cultural traditions (January; Oakley Lindsay Center, 300 3rd St.). The event is open to the public, but it still feels a bit like a big family reunion, which just adds to its charms.

One of Quincy's signature events, the **Dogwood Festival** (217.222.7980) includes block parties, amusement park rides in Washington Park, and a grand parade down Maine Street in May.

Getting There

Amtrak runs two daily trains between Chicago and Quincy. The *Illinois Zephyr* (not to be confused with the Zephyr of old) has a scheduled departure from Quincy early in the morning and departures from Chicago to Quincy leaving Union Station in the evening.

The *Carl Sandburg* departs from Quincy in the evening for Chicago, while trains bound for Quincy leave Chicago's Union Station in the morning. The trip between Quincy and Chicago takes about 4 ½ hours. Check with Amtrak for the latest schedule information, though. Quincy's Amtrak station is a brick gazebo on the edge of town (Wisman Lane at N. 30th St.). Buy tickets in advance.

Quincy and Hannibal are also served by **Burlington Trailways/Greyhound** buses. In Quincy the buses pick up passengers at the transit station at South 7th and Jersey Streets. In Hannibal they stop at a Burger King along the Highway 61 corridor (4811 McMasters Ave.). You should purchase tickets in advance.

For More Information

There are practical limits to how much I can include in a book, but not with a website! Check out the city profiles on my website to see if they include listings that I couldn't fit in this book.

Hannibal: MississippiValleyTraveler.com/Hannibal
Quincy: MississippiValleyTraveler.com/Quincy

Snapshot: Mark Twain Days

Hannibal celebrates the Fourth of July by throwing a big party called National Tom Sawyer Days that celebrates an innocent, wholesome interpretation of Mark Twain's books. Two local children are crowned Tom and Becky. Popular events include a craft show, mud volleyball, and a fence whitewashing contest.

ALTON TO GRAFTON

Looking north up the Great River Road from Alton, Illinois

Overview

With majestic limestone bluffs rising next to the river, the drive along the Mississippi between Alton and Grafton is one of the most scenic stretches of the Great River Road. The communities along the way are worth some of your time, too. Alton was once a battleground in the fight over slavery. Godfrey was home to agricultural innovators. Elsah is one of the best-preserved 19th century villages in the Midwest. Grafton is a popular spot to enjoy the river with a drink or food. Many people enjoy this stretch as a day trip, but there's enough to do to keep you happy and busy for longer.

History

ALTON

Today's Alton was once six separate communities: Alton, Upper Alton, North Alton, Hunterstown, Salu, and Milton Heights. Colonel Rufus Easton laid out Alton in 1817. He named it after his oldest son, then he named some streets after his other children. The original Alton is now the downtown area. It eventually absorbed two other towns and incorporated in 1837.

Early Alton had a mix of residents from around the US, including many who relocated from the South. When Elijah Lovejoy moved from St. Louis to Alton in 1835 to print his abolitionist newspaper, *The Observer*, some folks weren't too happy. A mob stormed his office before he could get the first issue printed and threw the printing press into the Mississippi River. That was his second press. A mob in St. Louis had destroyed his first one. Lovejoy bought another press and published for about a year until that one was also destroyed. Not easily deterred, he bought a fourth press and stored it in a warehouse near the river. When news leaked about the replacement, a mob assembled again and raced to the warehouse in the middle of the night to confront Lovejoy. They ransacked the warehouse and destroyed the press, then killed Lovejoy. In spite of the number of witnesses, no one was successfully prosecuted for the murder.

The issue of slavery didn't go away with Lovejoy's murder. When Abraham Lincoln and Stephen Douglas met for their seventh and final debate in a US Senate contest, slavery was still the central issue. Both men arrived in Alton at dawn on October 15, 1858, on the steamer *City of Louisiana.* Later that day, thousands of people turned out to hear the two men exchange views. Douglas later won the Senate seat when Democrats won a majority in the state legislature and chose their candidate to fill the US Senate seat. Lincoln had to settle for the US Presidency two years later.

Abe Lincoln had one other connection to Alton, one he rarely talked about. In 1842, he publicly chided James Shields, then the Illinois State Auditor, about Shields' role in a plan to close the failing Illinois State Bank. Lincoln wrote a letter to the editor of the *Sangamo Journal* under the pen name Rebecca, in which he assumed the persona of a distressed farmer and attacked Shields' politics and his character. Lincoln showed the letter to Mary Todd, and a couple of days later, she wrote an anonymous letter of her own, apparently without Abe's knowledge.

Shields was not amused. He found out who was behind the letters and demanded that Lincoln write a retraction. When Lincoln refused, Shields challenged him to a duel, naturally. As the one who was challenged, Lincoln got to choose the weapons. He chose broadswords. Lincoln was six feet, four inches tall, a full seven inches taller than Shields and had a much wider wingspan. He hoped that choosing swords would encourage Shields to change his mind. It didn't.

On September 22, the two met in Alton, then traveled downriver to Bloody Island at St. Louis to swing their swords at each other. (Dueling was illegal in Illinois but not Missouri.) They stood face-to-face with a plank marking the line between them. Lincoln swung his sword above Shields' head and sliced off a tree branch. That demonstration apparently sobered Shields, who—at the encouragement of friends—agreed to a truce. Shields accepted a muted apology from Lincoln, and the two men put the swords down and went their separate ways.

They would meet again, though. During the Civil War, Shields was a Brigadier General in the Army of the Potomac. After Shields' forces defeated Stonewall Jackson at the Battle of Kernstown, Lincoln promoted Shields to Major General, so the two men had apparently moved past their previous differences.

Illinois built its first state prison in 1833 in Alton. The prison was a regular target of criticism from reform advocates, including Dorothea Dix, in part because the site was a notorious vector for spreading deadly diseases. The prison closed in 1860 after the new Joliet prison opened, but two years later it saw new life during the Civil War as a detention center for captured Confederate soldiers. During the war, nearly 12,000 Confederate prisoners were incarcerated at the prison alongside a few civilians—men and women—arrested for treason or for committing acts of terrorism.

The Alton prison was deadlier than the average Union prison, mostly because diseases like dysentery and pneumonia were common. When a small pox epidemic erupted in the winter of 1862, three hundred prisoners were moved to an island across the river for quarantine where most of them died and were buried. At least 1,500 Confederate soldiers died in the prison. Most were buried in North Alton. The prison closed again on July 7, 1865, and was torn down gradually. Most of the stones were re-used in construction of buildings around town.

Alton's early fortunes were closely tied to the Mississippi River. In 1841 alone, Alton counted 1,100 steamboat landings. River traffic was so central to the city's life that some homes and businesses were built with special platforms at the top from which folks could watch for approaching steamboats.

By 1850, Alton had grown to 3,500 residents, five percent of whom were free Blacks. The first African Methodist Episcopal Church was established in 1839 in Lower Alton to serve the growing community.

Factories grew as steamboating declined. The city's first grain mill opened in 1831. Alton still has an active grain processing facility today. One of the largest employers was the Illinois Glass Company. It grew from a modest operation with 74 employees in 1873 to a giant with 3,200 people working there 30 years later. The company employed nearly half of the city's workforce at that time and was once one of the largest manufacturers of glass bottles in the world. In 1929, the company merged with the Owens Bottle Company of Toledo. The factory closed in 1984.

Apart from the glass company, Alton once had factories that produced lead, steel, chemicals, and box-board. In addition, the quality of the local clay supported several potteries for a while.

Altonians have survived and rebuilt after many floods. One of the worst was in 1844, before the city had a large population. Steamboats floated across flooded fields far away from where the main channel would normally have been. In modern times, the flood of 1993 was the most damaging, but the Mississippi River has stretched into town several times since then.

Robert Wadlow was one of the city's beloved residents. After an unassuming birth on February 22, 1918, Wadlow began to grow at an unusually fast rate. When he started kindergarten, he was already 5' 6" tall, and by ten years of age, he had soared past six feet in height. An exceptionally active pituitary gland was responsible. His size made life a challenge at times. He had to custom order his clothes and had to climb stairs sideways because his feet were so big (size 37 AA).

Still, he never complained. He lived his life with grace. He traveled with his father for a while, which gave him a chance to see the country. While visiting Manistee, Michigan, in 1940 with his father, he developed a blister on his foot that became infected. Doctors couldn't get it under control. He died a few days later. Wadlow was just 22 years old. At the time of his death, he was 8' 11" tall and weighed 490 pounds, the tallest man who ever lived. Five thousand people turned out at his funeral to say goodbye.

GODFREY

The town takes its name from one of its earliest residents, Captain Benjamin Godfrey. Born in Chatham, Massachusetts in 1794, Godfrey began a career at sea when he was just nine years old. He enlisted in the Navy in 1812 and by 1819, two years after marrying Harriet Cooper, he had won command of his first merchant ship. He made and lost a lot of money a couple of times before moving to Alton in 1832 as a wealthy man.

Godfrey's life stayed bumpy after he moved. He went into business with Winthrop Gilman, an old friend from his days at sea. They ran a warehouse and shipped products (furs, food) directly to New Orleans. In November 1837, he let Elijah Lovejoy store his fourth printing press in his warehouse, which is where Lovejoy was killed by a pro-slavery mob on November 7. He also took a financial hit in the Panic of 1837.

Harriet died in 1838, which left Benjamin to parent six daughters and two sons by himself (five of their children were under 12 years of age). A year later, he married Rebecca Emeline Pettit. They had three more children.

In 1838, Godfrey founded Monticello College and Preparatory School for Girls, because he had the radical idea that women were entitled to the same education as men. The college opened with a curriculum modeled after a program at Yale University. Students took classes that covered a broad range of topics, including geometry, philosophy, geology, chemistry, history, and music.

The college educated thousands of young women during its 130+ years. When it shut down in 1971, Lewis and Clark Community College bought the campus. The former Monticello College used the proceeds from the sale to create the Monticello College Foundation, which now offers college scholarships to women instead of teaching them directly. In addition to the college and the town that later carried his name, Benjamin also had a hand in getting the Alton & Sangamon Railroad on track.

Benjamin Godfrey died on August 13, 1862. During his life, Benjamin hinted that he felt ashamed of something from his younger days. There's no record that he confided in anyone about what bothered him, but contemporary researchers uncovered a detail that might explain his feelings. When he was younger, he had captained several ships that transported enslaved Africans from Baltimore to New Orleans, eight of them, in fact, between 1819 and 1822. Given the life he led after he moved to Illinois, one surrounded by staunch abolitionists, it's a good bet that he later felt remorse about those trips.

A small village called Monticello developed around the women's college, but local folks eventually started calling it Godfrey. The area remained primarily agricultural well into the 20th century. Many of the early residents were migrants from the East Coast and strongly opposed to slavery. Several Godfrey residents were active in the Underground Railroad, especially those who lived around Rocky Fork and the current Warren Levis Boy Scout Camp.

Emil A. Riehl was another early resident who left a mark. He was an innovative horticulturist. One of his breakthroughs was a hybrid chestnut that combined the size of the large Italian chestnut with the depth of flavor of the much smaller American chestnut. After a few years of experimenting, he grew the first successful hybrid chestnut in 1915. Those nuts provided the Riehls a steady income, right through the tough years of the Great Depression.

Riehl was quite a tinkerer, too. He built a water tower for his house and connected it to a system of pipes that provided the Riehls with running water in their kitchen, a rarity at the time. He also designed a skiff for use on the Mississippi River that was far more maneuverable than the standard skiff of the day. Emil Riehl also donated money to build a church, even though he wasn't a churchgoer himself. He told folks that he "found communication with God through nature."

Asparagus was a major crop in the Godfrey area for a while. One of the first to grow it was Theodore Nicholas Droste, an immigrant from Westphalia. Other immigrants from Germany, Louis Stiritz and his cousin John Gottleib Stiritz, brought grapevines from their home region in the Nekar River valley and planted them at Clifton Terrace. They built stone terraces from 1852 to 1865 to support their grapevines; some of those terraces are still visible today in Clifton Terrace Park.

Clifton Terrace was once a popular tourist draw. Folks arrived on steamboats to drink wine, eat hearty meals, and enjoy the river views and a good swim. The town had two competing hotels early on, but both eventually burned down, one in the early 1900s and the other in 1959. Clifton Terrace is now part of Godfrey.

Godfrey didn't incorporate until 1991. The first mayor was Lars Hoffman, a political science professor at Lewis and Clark College. During his two terms, he helped organize the city's new government and positioned the town to take advantage of its location along the Great River Road. The city today spreads out over 37 square miles, the second largest city in Illinois (by area).

ELSAH

A visit to Elsah feels a step back in time to the 19th-century. Elsah was built into a ravine along Askew Creek at the base of the bluffs. Around 1847, Addison Greene built a home near the creek and made a living by selling cordwood to passing steamboats; folks called this spot Jersey Landing. Six years later, General James Semple, a US Senator from Illinois with Scottish roots, bought the land and moved in. He offered free plots of land in a town he called Elsah to anyone who would agree to buy stone from his quarry. The town's name might be derived from Ailsa Craig, which is a rocky island off the southwest coast of Scotland and is one of just two places in the world where you'll find the right kind of rock to make curling stones.

The town soon had the usual mills, plus a distillery. For a brief time, Elsah was a busy port for shipping local agricultural products to markets down river. The town was also a site of much speculation, briefly, when railroad baron Jay Gould unveiled plans to build a bridge across the Mississippi River at Elsah. Alas, Gould was merely threatening to build a bridge as leverage to drive down the value of the Eads Bridge at St. Louis, which he was trying to buy. After he closed on the Eads Bridge, he dropped plans for the Elsah bridge.

Because of the limitations of its geography, Elsah didn't get much bigger beyond that initial burst of settlement. The townsfolk have lived through many floods, the worst in 1993, but rebuilt and moved on each time. Elsah today is a quiet village that is home to just under 700 people.

CHAUTAUQUA

A Chautauqua is as much an aspiration as it is a place. The word is derived from an Algonquin language and supposedly means a lake or a community by a lake. At least, that's what the New Yorkers who started the first one believed. In 1874, a few members of the Methodist Episcopal Church in New York created a retreat for Sunday school teachers at Chautauqua Lake. Once assembled, they would have the chance to better themselves by attending lectures on topics in the social sciences and humanities. At other times of day, they could attend music or art lessons. The whole experience was all about personal improvement, and it was all grounded firmly in Methodist Episcopal spirituality.

The idea found a receptive audience in post-Civil War America. In 1885, the Sunday School Conference of Southern Illinois and the Methodist Episcopal Church Conferences of Southern Illinois and St. Louis teamed up to bring the idea to the heartland. They founded the Western Chautauqua, as it was first called, on ideas similar to the New York progenitor, "to maintain a summer resort for literary, scientific, and religious instruction and culture." They held their first camp in August 1885, and by the next year had raised enough money to buy 580 acres in Babb's Hollow for a permanent home.

In the early years, guests traveled to the Chautauqua by buggy, steamboat, or train.

Round-trip steamboat fare from St. Louis cost 75 cents in 1891 or 50 cents from Alton. Once at the site, guests rented a tent for the duration of the Chautauqua. You could rent a 10'x12'x3' tent with two cots, sheets, and pillows for $15 for 30 days. The largest tent, 14'x24'x6', was yours for $23.50 for a month and came with five cots. If you wanted any other furnishings, you could bring them yourself or pay to rent them.

While the earliest Chautauquas were just one week long (in August), they eventually extended to a full month. In the early 20th century, a typical schedule included time for prayers, Sunday school lessons, lectures, roundtable discussions, and a sermon or a song (or both). In 1890, guests learned about immigration and citizenship, but they could also attend interesting lectures called "Wise and Otherwise" and "Tramps and their Kin." In 1896, a lecture by a famous preacher of the day, Dr. Talmage Day, drew 3,000 people. Williams Jennings Bryan spoke four times over the years.

The site took on a feeling of permanence in the late 1890s when a hotel was built. Cottages gradually went up, too. But even as folks got used to the idea of spending a chunk of every summer at Chautauqua, the threat of disruption loomed. The association had survived bankruptcy in 1908, but in the 1950s, a bigger threat emerged. The US government was looking for a site to build an Air Force Academy and selected Chautauqua as one of three finalists. Eventually, though, Colorado Springs was chosen and Chautauqua carried on.

Over time, the cottages of Chautauqua transitioned from rentals for transient guests to private vacation homes owned primarily by local families who spend the bulk of their summers in them. Chautauqua still hosts performances and lectures today, but it is essentially a private community now. You can visit if a resident invites you, but otherwise only members of the community can get in.

GRAFTON

Grafton sits at the confluence of the Illinois and Mississippi Rivers. The rivers gave Grafton life, and the town has deep and enduring ties to them. Before the Illinois River was thoroughly sculpted into a barge canal, it had a different character. The *WPA Guide to Illinois*, written in 1939, noted the following about its confluence with the Mississippi:

> "Save in extremely rainy weather, the Illinois retains its naturally clear beauty and refuses, for several miles, to mingle with the mud-stained waters of the Mississippi. Thus for a considerable distance there is presented the spectacle of two great rivers flowing side by side in the same channel, each retaining its identity."

Grafton didn't get off to a fast start. In the 1830s, the land owned by James Mason was little more than a post office and a tavern. Mason died in 1834, but his widow Sarah and brother Paris platted the village and called it Grafton in honor of the Massachusetts town where James was born.

A decade later, its economy boomed, as hundreds of people—including German and Irish immigrants—moved to the area to work in nearby quarries, to build boats, and to catch fish. After work, those folks relaxed and partied in the dozen or so saloons in town. Much of the stone they removed built structures in the region, including the Eads Bridge and the Old Cathedral in St. Louis.

The Rippley Boat Company began building ferries, skiffs, and paddlewheelers at the end of the 19th century. They also built a thousand life boats for the military during

World War I. The company became the Grafton Boat Works in 1923 and continued the boat-building tradition until they closed in 1978. Grafton also had a pearl button manufacturing plant that used mussels harvested from the Illinois River. The city expected an economic boost when a series of locks and dams were built on the Illinois River beginning in the 1920s, but the dams never delivered the promised benefits.

Grafton's population hovered around a thousand people for a long time, but the 1993 flood took a heavy toll. A third of the town's pre-flood residents moved away. Grafton today depends heavily on tourism, although there are still a handful of commercial fishing operations in the area.

Explore on the East Bank (Illinois)

SOUTH OF ALTON

Attractions

The **National Great Rivers Museum** at the billion-dollar Mel Price Locks and Dam (618.462.6979) showcases the history of navigation on the Mississippi River. Guided tours lead visitors all the way to the top of the structure.

On the other side of the Clark Bridge, **Riverlands Migratory Bird Sanctuary** is an excellent spot for waterfowl viewing, especially during the spring and fall migration seasons, with flat trails through prairies and woods and several viewing platforms overlooking wetlands. The **Audubon Center at Riverlands** (301 Riverlands Way; 636.899.0090) hosts wildlife exhibits and special events and is a good place to start.

ALTON

Attractions

Alton was one of the sites for the famous Lincoln-Douglas debates. Check out their statues in **Lincoln Douglas Square** (100 Market St.). Read a transcript of the debate at: https://www.nps.gov/liho/learn/historyculture/debate7.htm.

Jazz legend Miles Davis lived a chunk of his life in Alton, which is why the city placed a statue of him downtown on 3rd Street in **Miles Davis Memorial Plaza**.

The unique collection at **The Soul Asylum** (301 E. Broadway; 618.468.1051) mixes stories and artifacts about Alton history with replicas of ancient torture devices and local hauntings. Not a combination one sees everyday but fitting for a museum in the ill-fated Mineral Springs Hotel.

Further down Broadway, the **Jacoby Arts Center** (627 E. Broadway; 618.462.5222) hosts rotating exhibits that feature the work of local and regional artists, plus they occasionally host concerts.

The **Argosy Casino** (1 Piasa St.; 800.711.4263), one of the first gaming boats on the river when it opened in 1991, is also one of the last Mississippi River casinos that still floats, although the casino no longer takes excursions.

A column in **Alton City Cemetery** (5th St. at Monument St.) honors the memory of slain abolitionist Elijah Lovejoy, who was murdered by a pro-slavery mob in 1837. **Alton National Cemetery** is located in the northeast corner of the same cemetery. It is the final resting place for about 500 veterans who served from the Civil War to Vietnam.

You can see a piece of a **Lovejoy press** in the lobby of the Hayner Public Library's Genealogy and Local History Library (401 State St.). It was salvaged from the Mississippi River in 1915.

Alton to Grafton Route Map

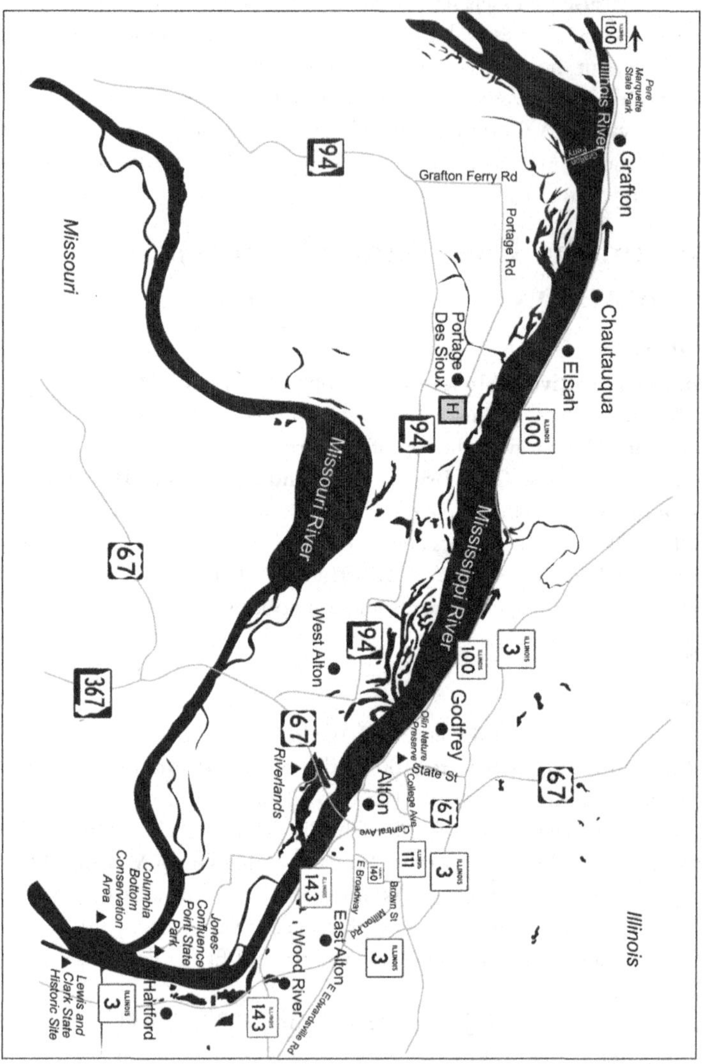

The sights on this route are on the east side of the river, mostly along Illinois Highway 100 between Alton and Grafton, one of the prettiest 15 miles of the Great River Road anywhere. If you want to continue past Grafton, consider taking the (free) Brussels Ferry across the Illinois River, then take your time driving around rural Calhoun County (an especially appealing diversion during harvest season).

To drive a complete route (63 miles) without backtracking, go north from Alton on the east side and drive toward Grafton, then take two ferries—the Brussels Ferry (free) north of Grafton and the Golden Eagle Ferry (not free) from Calhoun County to the west side and Missouri's St. Charles County (see page 330 for more details on the ferries). Once on the Missouri side, you can take County Highway B east to Highway 94. Go east on Highway 94 and take the Clark Bridge to return to Alton.

Think you're tall? Stand next to the life-size statue of **Robert Wadlow** (2810 College Ave.), the world's tallest man, and see how you compare.

Check the calendar at **Alton Little Theater** (2450 N. Henry St.; 618.462.3205) for an evening of live theater.

Head up to **Riverview Park** (450 Belleview St.; 618.463.3580) and enjoy the views of the Mississippi River from the overlook.

Another tall monument honors the Confederate soldiers who died in Alton while imprisoned during the Civil War. The **North Alton Confederate Cemetery** (635 Rozier) is a five-minute drive from downtown.

Heading north on the Great River Road, you'll notice a bird-like image painted on the side of a bluff. In 1673, Father Jacques Marquette and Louis Joliet passed a similar cliff painting near present-day Alton. Marquette wrote:

> "While Skirting some rocks, which by Their height and length inspired awe, We saw upon one of them two painted monsters which at first made Us afraid, and upon Which the boldest savages dare not Long rest their eyes. They are as large As a calf; they have Horns on their heads Like those of a deer, a horrible look, red eyes, a beard Like a tiger's, a face somewhat like a man's, a body Covered with scales, and so Long A tail that it winds all around the Body, passing above the head and going back between the legs, ending in a Fish's tail. Green, red, and black are the three Colors composing the Picture. Moreover, these 2 monsters are so well painted that we cannot believe that any savage is their author; for good painters in France would find it difficult to reach that place Conveniently to paint them."

Marquette and Joliet were the only Europeans to see the painting and write a description of it. A modern interpretation of the **Piasa Bird** image is now painted on a bluff just north of Alton along Highway 100.

There are miles and miles of dedicated bike paths in this area, including two trails along the Mississippi: the 20-mile **Sam Vadalabene Trail** that runs from Alton to Pere Marquette State Park, and the 21-mile **Confluence Bike Trail** from Alton to Hartford.

Tours

Rumor has it that there are a lot of tortured spirits stuck in Alton. If you want to get in touch with these haunted souls, one of these tours may help you reach them:

- The **McPike Mansion** (2018 Alby St.; 618.830.2179), built in 1869, has held a spot in purgatory since it was last occupied in the 1950s. Many local tours take guests here to show off its haunted nature, but you can tour just the mansion one Saturday a month from April through September, or on weekends in late September through Halloween.
- **Alton Hauntings** (217.791.7859) leads ghost tours around town from April through November on Saturday evenings (7pm).
- **Alton Odyssey Tours** (618.208.7765) takes guests to haunted sites around town in a presumably non-haunted trolley (Oct, Nov).

For non-ghost-themed tours, check out the options offered directly from **Great Rivers and Routes Tourism Bureau** (618.465.6676), such as the Fall Foliage and History tour, the Freedom to Equality tour that highlights African American history in the region (usually on the 3rd Saturday of the month in season), and the mid-winter eagle tours. Purchase tickets in advance for these tours (www.riversandroutes.com).

You can also take a tour of Alton's Underground Railroad sites. **J.E. Robinson Underground Railroad Tours** (618.465.6676) highlights Altonians' history of helping enslaved people reach safe havens. **Great Rivers and Routes Tourism Bureau** offers monthly Underground Railroad tours (800.258.6645).

Drinking and Dining

AUTHOR'S PICK: **Old Bakery Beer Company** (400 Landmarks Blvd.; 618.463.1470), housed in an old commercial building on the riverfront, brews some fine beer, and they put as much skill into the food, too. The sandwiches are delicious and the sides creative. They also host live music on some nights.

Get a cup of coffee at **Maeva's Coffee** (1320 Milton Rd.; 618.581.7510) and sip it in a converted turn-of-the-century schoolhouse.

Germania Brew Haus (617 E. Broadway St.; 314.667.4751) is another good option for coffee. Their building once housed a bank and still has the original vault. They also have a self-service beer tap and occasionally host live music.

Duke Bakery (819 Henry St.; 618.462.2922) has been pleasing palates since 1951. They have a nice selection of fruit tarts, in addition to donuts, cannoli, and cream horns.

Fast Eddie's Bon Air (1530 E. 4th St.; 618.462.5532) is the sprawling complex famed for cheap food, good drinks, and live music. They get crazy busy on weekends.

My Just Desserts (31 E. Broadway St.; 618.462.5881), housed in a 19th-century storefront downtown, offers healthy choices for lunch, as well as delicious, sweet treats to balance out that healthy food you just ate.

The **Brown Bag Bistro** (318 E. Broadway; 618.433.9933) is another fine choice for a tasty lunch that you can enjoy on the patio or take with you. They offer a good range of salads, hearty sandwiches, and soups. They can be very busy at times.

Johnson's Corner (2000 State St.; 618.465.5640) is a good choice for pizza or a big and tasty pork tenderloin.

Gentelin's on Broadway (122 E. Broadway; 618.465.6080) has been pleasing Altonians with fine dining for a decade. Enjoy peppered ribeye or wild mushroom ravioli with a glass of wine and a good view of the river.

Where to Stay: Camping

5 Diamond Campgrounds (Hartford: 429 Confluence Tower Dr.; 618.257.8423) rents 49 sites in a compact location next to the levee. The sites vary in size but many include full hookups. The campground is about 10 minutes south of Alton.

Bed and Breakfasts

A stay in one of the rooms at the 10,000-square-foot **Beall Mansion** (407 E. 12th St.; 618.474.9100) is a step back in time, but one where you get to take modern luxuries with you, and you can pretty much eat all the chocolate you can handle.

The **Tiffany Inn** (410 E. Broadway St.; 618.462.4145), a bed-and-breakfast downtown above a stained-glass studio, offers three art-inspired rooms.

Lodging

Lodging at the **Alton Cracker Factory** (205 E. Broadway St.; 618.917.4466) comes with great views and beautiful, contemporary rooms.

Special Events

You'll find the **farmers market** on Saturday mornings and Wednesday evenings in the parking lot at the corner of Landmarks Boulevard and Henry Street.

The **Alton Memorial Day Parade** is the oldest such parade in the US. Alton staged its first parade in 1868 when the holiday was called Decoration Day. The route begins at Alton Middle School and follows College Avenue to Washington, then loops around the square and back to Washington before ending at Upper Alton Cemetery.

In September, Alton puts on a river-themed celebration called the **Mississippi Earthtones Festival**. The event features art and craft vendors, booths of organizations that offer nature-based activities, and live music (Liberty Bank Alton Amphitheater).

Alton stages a popular **Halloween parade**, a tradition that dates back to 1916.

GODFREY

Attractions

Benjamin Godfrey founded Monticello College and Preparatory School for Girls in 1838. That former campus is now home to **Lewis and Clark Community College** (5800 Godfrey Rd.), but several sites related to Monticello College are still around.

The majestic **Benjamin Godfrey Chapel** dates to 1854. The Greek Revival building, a style that was popular in New England when Godfrey lived there, has served as a chapel for the college and a Congregational Church. It can seat up to 500 people. The building was moved in 1991 from its original location across the street to the current on-campus location.

The **Monticello College Foundation** occupies an Italianate building known as the Evergreens that was built in 1856 as housing for the president of Monticello College.

Look for the **statue of Sacajawea** in the historic quadrangle around Baldwin and Caldwell Halls. Glenna Goodacre created the bronze tribute. She also designed the image of Sacajawea featured on a dollar coin.

Further down the road, the original **Godfrey Mansion** (6722 Godfrey Rd.), built in 1831, is still standing. Godfrey bought it in 1834 from Captain Calvin Riley and enlarged it. It's an impressive Greek Revival structure, with thick limestone walls, impressive balconies, and 14 rooms. The building now houses administrative offices for Lewis and Clark Community College.

Godfrey once had an emergency landing strip for the airmail route between St. Louis and Chicago. In the mid-1920s, one of the pilots on that route was a young Charles Lindbergh. The little **supply shack** (stocked with oil, gas, and a telephone.) that Lindbergh visited a few times was moved from its original location at the northern end of Airport Road (the site now has a Walmart Supercenter) to a new home near Godfrey Village Hall (6810 Godfrey Rd.). It was restored in 2001.

AUTHOR'S PICK: **The Nature Institute's Olin Nature Preserve** (2213 S. Levis Lane; 618.466.9930) offers lovely hikes along several trails, some of which follow a serene creek that flows over a limestone bed. The trails are often framed by steep rocks and some pass through restored prairies. The terrain is hilly and always beautiful.

Hoffman Gardens at Great Rivers Park is a memorial to Godfrey's first mayor, Lars Hoffman. The park is 4 ½ miles north of Alton along Route 100.

Drinking and Dining

Josephine's Tea Room and Gift Shops (6109 Godfrey Rd.; 618.466.7796) occupies buildings that were once part of Monticello College. The delightful Tea Room (open M-Sa for lunch) serves satisfying fresh soups, sandwiches, and salads (save room for pie!), so you can fuel up before making your way through the adjacent gift shop.

Pick up a fresh baked good or something sweet at **LuciAnna's Pastries** (1020 W. Delmar.; 618.433.9395) or stick around for a tasty lunch, maybe a savory quiche.

Illinois' One-Horse Towns

Many communities on the east side of the river around St. Louis developed as single industry towns. Big companies bought land in Illinois to avoid the taxes and regulations of St. Louis, built a factory, then incorporated a city the company controlled. East St. Louis started as a railroad town. National City was home to the stockyards and meat-packing plants. Several single-industry towns developed near Alton, too.

East Alton

East Alton traces its roots to 1809 when Walter Seely and John Wallace laid out a town called Milton along Wood River Creek. In 1893, Vermont-native Franklin Olin built a factory to manufacture blasting powder, the Equitable Powder Manufacturing Company. Olin made a lot of money, so four years later he built the Western Cartridge Company next door to manufacture small arms. The factory typically employed 2,500 people but that number soared to 15,000 during World War II. If you just happened to walk past the factory in the daytime back then, you could hear machine guns being tested. Western Cartridge Company is still in business today as a subsidiary of Olin Corporation but with far fewer employees. Learn more about their history and the community at the **East Alton History Museum** (211 N. Shamrock; 618.216.2781). Call for hours.

Wood River

In 1908, Standard Oil built a refinery near the location where the Lewis and Clark expedition camped in the winter of 1803-04. Construction of the refinery triggered the growth of three new communities: Wood River, East Wood River, and Benbow City. The early years were marked by a frontier lawlessness common to mining towns.

Wood River and East Wood River merged in 1911, but Benbow City's founder, Amos Edward Benbow, wasn't interested in joining the party. Benbow was a force to reckon with. He weighed over 200 pounds and proved every bit as stubborn as he was large. He was a long-time power broker in Democratic politics in Madison County and in the state and had held a few local government positions.

He built his city at the same just as Standard Oil built their refinery. Benbow's little kingdom was barely more than a single street but it was lined with bars and brothels that served the booming population of single (or single-acting) men hired to work at the refinery. Shortly after incorporating in 1908, Benbow City counted 19 bars (12 of them owned by Anheuser-Busch) but only 75 residents.

Standard Oil wasn't too keen on having Benbow City as a neighbor, so in 1909, they ran their own candidate for mayor against Benbow. The election was a complete mess, tainted by allegations of voter fraud and inconsistencies in the count. The election was eventually decided in Benbow's favor, even though he wasn't even a resident of the city—he lived in Alton. But, hey, it was Benbow's town.

Standard Oil eventually wore Benbow down in the 1910s. It's also likely that Benbow himself saw the end coming and wanted to get as much out of the city as he could, especially with the country racing toward Prohibition.

Life settled down in Wood River after that. Children visited their fathers at the refinery for lunch and played games around the pipes and fumes. The new community, though, lacked sufficient housing, so Standard Oil ordered a bunch of houses from the Sears catalog. They were built along 7th, 8th, and 9th Streets, and many are still there today.

While the refinery provided hundreds of jobs in the beginning, not everyone was impressed by it. In 1938, Englishman Rowland Raven-Hart paddled a canoe from Hannibal to Baton Rouge. After passing by Wood River, he wrote: "The river was oily there, and filthy so after Wood River came in, so that we had to take soap and water to get hull and paddles clean that evening: it was here that the Rogers-Clark expedition camped, in their great Western expedition of 1804—they wouldn't want to camp here now."

In 1956, Standard Oil became Amoco and kept the refinery going until 1981. The company closed the Wood River chemical additives plant in the 1990s. In 1998, Amoco merged with British Petroleum. In the time since the refinery closed, the company has spent tens of millions of dollars cleaning up environmental pollution.

Two museums document the history of this area. The **Wood River Refinery History Museum** in Roxana (900 S. Central Ave.; 618.255.3718) presents the history of the Shell/Phillips 66 refinery, with displays about the refining process. The **Wood River Museum** (Wood River: 40 W. Ferguson Ave.; 618.254.1993) houses exhibits on the town's early history, the Standard Oil Refinery, and Lewis and Clark. Call ahead for hours.

Hartford

In 1910, the future site of Hartford consisted of just six houses. Life changed nearly overnight when the International Shoe Company chose the area for a large tannery in 1916. The plant employed about 900 people during the 1930s who processed up to 28,000 tanned hides every week. The process of turning a raw animal hide into finished leather required 110 different steps over 37 days in the 1930s, but it was eventually reduced to a ten-day process. Finished hides were shipped to a different factory and assembled into shoes.

Workers got paid about $1/hour in the early years, but the company kept a motel on campus, so employees could sleep close to work during the week. Many of the workers lived far away, and transportation options at the time weren't good enough to go back and forth on the same day. (At least food was cheap. In the 1940s, you could get a burger, a soda, and a Twinkie for 15 cents at Jones' Café.) The company was also known for its mature work force. In 1962, only 45 of its 305 employees were under the age of 45. The tannery closed in 1964.

In 1918, the Wood River Refining Company built a plant (not to be confused with that other Wood River Refinery). It went through a few ownership changes: Sinclair Oil (1949), Clark Oil (1965), Apex Oil (1968), and Premcor Refining Group (1988). The refinery employed nearly 400 people at its peak.

The refinery turned out to be a difficult neighbor. Gasoline and oil leaked from pipelines, which contaminated groundwater and land. Both Apex and Premcor reached multi-million-dollar settlements with regulatory agencies to clean up the mess they created. The refinery closed in 2017.

Special Events

Check out the performance schedule at **Hatheway Cultural Center** (618.468.4222) at Lewis & Clark Community College (5800 Godfrey Rd.).

ELSAH

Attractions

Elsah is easy to miss from the highway. Tucked into a narrow valley, the village boasts a modest but well-built collection of buildings in a variety of architectural styles. You'll feel like you are walking the streets of a 19th-century village when you visit.

The Village of Elsah Museum (26 Lasalle St.; 618.374.1059; Apr-Oct) hosts exhibits that document the town's history from its founding in the 1850s to today.

Elsah General Store (22 Lasalle St.; 618.556.0709) recreates a small-town store from the past. Stop in to stock up on honey, homemade jams, and nostalgia.

Principia College (1 Front Gate Rd.; 618.374.2131) sits atop a bluff near Elsah. The college was founded in 1898 and built in the 1930s to educate Christian Scientists, who still make up all of the student body. Visitors may take a quick drive around campus, but there are rules about when and how you are allowed to do so. Check in with the security guard at the entrance.

Where to Stay: Bed and Breakfasts

The **Green Tree Inn** (15 Mill St.; 618.374.2821) rents five cozy rooms, plus a room that is available specifically for people traveling with pets.

The **Maple Leaf Cottage Inn** (12 Selma St.; 618.374.1684) rents five adorable rooms, plus the two-bedroom Buggy Shop House.

Special Events

Elsah's **Home for the Holidays** (December) is a great time to tour the town's historic homes and see them all dressed up for the holidays.

GRAFTON

Attractions

The **Grafton Welcome Center** (950 E. Main St.; 618.786.7000) hosts a few exhibits about local history, plus stacks of brochures to help you plan your stay.

Raging Rivers Water Park (100 Palisades Pkwy.; 618.786.2345) is a good place to cool down on a hot day.

Take a scenic ride above Grafton to Aerie's Winery on the **SkyTour** (3 W. Clinton St.; 618.786.8439). You can choose a specific boarding time and either an open chair or enclosed gondola.

Live music is pretty easy to find at bars on weekend nights. The **Loading Dock** (401 Front St.; 618.786.3494) is a popular choice.

A few miles north of Grafton, 8,000-acre **Pere Marquette State Park** (13112 Visitors Ln.; 618.786.3323) has good (and moderately challenging) hiking trails, some of which come with expansive views of the Illinois River Valley. The park also has a 1930s-era lodge that offers food and lodging. See the lodging section below.

Two Rivers National Wildlife Refuge (618.883.2524) has multiple tracts throughout the area. One of them, the **Gilbert Lake Division**, has a three-mile walking trail through a floodplain forest along the Illinois River which is a good place for bird watching. Gilbert Lake is three miles north of Grafton along Highway 100.

Getting On the River

You can get on the river by taking a **river cruise** on the *Hakuna Matata*. Cruises board at Grafton Harbor (215 W. Water St.; 618.786.7678).

Or maybe you'd prefer to rent a pontoon boat or runabout at **Grafton Harbor** (215 W. Water St.; 618.786.7678).

Another great option is to take a ride on one of the area's **river ferries** (see p. 330).

Drinking and Dining

Grafton has a lot of places to satisfy your thirst or hunger. While most offer some variation on the bar food theme, most do it well, so it's hard to make a bad choice. Here are a few places to consider.

If you brought a cooler along (and who doesn't travel with one?), pick up some freshly caught river fish at **Beasley Fish Stand** (1512 W. Main; 618.786.3697).

Aerie's Winery (600 Timber Ridge Dr.; 618.786.7477) cornered the market on great views, and you can enjoy them with a glass of wine or a beer. They also serve food, most of which is light fare like flatbread, salads, sandwiches, and small plates.

Abigail's Tap Room at the historic Ruebel Hotel (217 E. Main St.; 618.786.2315) features a standard burger and sandwich menu, but they also make schnitzel, catfish, and pasta. Check out the elegant wood bar that was salvaged from the 1904 World's Fair in St. Louis.

The **Loading Dock** (401 Front St.; 618.786.3494) serves traditional bar food that is best enjoyed on the riverside patio.

The **Grafton Oyster Bar** (215 Water St.; 618.786.3000) features New Orleans-inspired Cajun and Creole dishes, including fresh oysters, po boys, and blackened meats.

Upriver a bit, **Pere Marquette Restaurant** (13653 Lodge Blvd.; 618.786.2331) in the historic park lodge serves pleasing dishes that lean into comfort food.

Where to Stay

There are a lot of vacation rentals in Grafton. If you prefer a different option, the places below are good choices.

Camping

The campground at **Pere Marquette State Park** (618.786.3323), just south of the main park entrance, offers 80 sites with electric and a separate area for tents.

Bed and Breakfasts

Located high atop the bluff above Grafton, **Tara Point Inn & Cottages** (1 Tara Point Dr.; 618.786.3555) offers luxury accommodations and a million-dollar view.

Lodging

The historic **Ruebel Hotel** (217 E. Main St.; 618.786.2315) has been offering overnight accommodations since 1879, more or less. Rooms have been thoroughly updated, of course, while retaining the feeling of a historic inn.

The lodge at **Pere Marquette State Park** (13653 Lodge Blvd.; 618.786.2331) dates to the 1930s but is equipped with all the modern conveniences. It's a relaxing place to stay for a night or two, with several hiking trails in the park and a full-service restaurant on site (and Grafton is just a few minutes away).

Special Events

Stop by Grafton on a Thursday evening from late May through August for **Music in the Park**, a series of live concerts in The Grove Memorial Park (Market & Main Sts.).

Getting Around

Rivers define this region but there aren't many bridges, so residents rely on a tried and tested mode of river transportation: ferries. The seasonal **Grafton Ferry** (618.465.6676) connects the town to rural St. Charles County, Missouri (for a fee). Access it from the ramp near the lighthouse at the end of Market Street.

Just one mile west of Grafton along Highway 100, the **Brussels Ferry** 618.465.6676) connects Illinois's Jersey and Calhoun Counties, and it's free. The ferry occasionally closes if conditions are dangerous, but otherwise it operates all day every day.

If you're driving through Calhoun County, you can cross back to Missouri on the **Golden Eagle Ferry** (618.535.5759). There is a fee, but the ferry runs all year. It shuts down at 9pm during the week and at 2am on Friday and Saturday nights. To reach the ferry from the Brussels Ferry in Illinois, follow Illinois River Road to Centerville, then follow Gun Club Road to Ferry Road. (Or just follow the signs.) On the Missouri side, take County Highway B. Golden Eagle Ferry Road is a mile west of Kampville.

Getting There

Amtrak offers daily service to Alton Station (1 Golf Rd.) with multiple trains a day running between Chicago and St. Louis.

For More Information

There are practical limits to how much I can include in a book, but not with a website! Check out the city profiles on my website to see if they include listings that I couldn't fit in this book.

Alton: MississippiValleyTraveler.com/Alton
Godfrey: MississippiValleyTraveler.com/Godfrey
Elsah: MississippiValleyTraveler.com/Elsah
Chautauqua: MississippiValleyTraveler.com/Chautauqua
Grafton: MississippiValleyTraveler.com/Grafton

There's no shortage of stories about the Great River, which is why I started the **Mississippi Valley Traveler podcast**. In each episode, I go deep into a topic about the river's culture, history, and natural world. It helps the miles fly by as you drive the Great River Road. Find it everywhere podcasts are available, including Spotify, Apple podcasts, and YouTube.

Snapshot: Robert Wadlow

Robert Wadlow grew up (and up and up) in Alton, ultimately reaching 8 feet, 11 inches tall, the tallest man to have ever lived, as far as we know. The city honors its famous residents with a life-sized statue that rises in a park (2810 College Ave.) next to a replica in bronze of a chair made just for him.

ST. LOUIS

The Eads Bridge at St. Louis, Missouri

Overview

"First in booze, first in shoes, and last in the American League."

We still have the booze (and a National League team, the Cardinals) and so much more now! You'll find a lot of attractions along the Great River Road through St. Louis, but there is a lot to explore throughout the region. This guide will introduce you to the city's river corridor, but I hope you'll stick around for a few days (or come back for another visit) and get to know the city that looks east, opened the West, yet feels a whole lot southern.

St. Louis History

The area where the Mississippi and Missouri Rivers meet has long been an attractive place to live. One of the great cities in North America grew up across the river a thousand years ago, home to thousands at a place we call Cahokia today. Even before Cahokia emerged, the site of today's St. Louis has been home to hundreds of years of settlements. Some of those communities built earthen mounds near the river, which is why the city was nicknamed Mound City (most have long since been destroyed).

French-Canadian missionaries established a presence in Illinois in 1699 and called their community Cahokia (no relation to the mounds) in the same year that the village of Williamsburg, Virginia, was founded. It would be a while, though, before Euro-Americans lived on the west bank of the Mississippi River.

In August 1763, Pierre Laclède left French New Orleans with 24 men to establish a treading post. By the time Laclède laid out the new village, though, France had ceded the territory to Spain. Laclède's new city would feel French but its citizens would live under Spanish rule.

Laclède chose to build his post on a terraced piece of land on the west bank of the Mississippi River 12 miles south of the Missouri River. The founders of St. Louis had considered building a post at the confluence of the two rivers, but the area was too marshy. The early city got a quick boost in 1763 when England took control of France's Illinois Country. Many French families moved to St. Louis from places like Cahokia and Kaskaskia. In 1772, St. Louis counted just over 600 residents, about a third of whom were enslaved (mostly enslaved Africans but a few enslaved Native Americans, too). The city was also home to a few free Blacks, and Native Americans from various tribes came and went regularly during the early years.

Laclède laid out the early boundaries of the city but didn't live long enough to see it prosper. He traveled to New Orleans in 1777 to straighten out his financial affairs but became ill and died during the return voyage. Leadership of the city passed to Auguste Chouteau, the son of Laclède's lover, Madame Marie Thérèse Chouteau. Chouteau would go on to make a lot of money from the fur trade and other ventures and would become the city's most influential early leader.

The city's thousand residents, most of them French, became part of the United States in 1804 with the Louisiana Purchase. The newly American St. Louis must have been an exciting place to be. Living on the edge of the US—the last American outpost—the city's residents outfitted Meriwether Lewis and William Clark's expedition west in 1804 and Zebulon Pike's 1805 expedition north.

Irish immigrants had a hand in building early St. Louis. John Mullanphy left Ireland at a time when Catholics had few opportunities in the Emerald Isle. Under British rule, they couldn't own land or send their children to school and were excluded from many occupations. When Mullanphy reached St. Louis, he took a long drink of water from the Mississippi River, which tasted like freedom and opportunity (but probably also rather gritty). He made a fortune selling cotton at the end of the War of 1812 and used his wealth to influence the development of St. Louis. He funded start-ups and donated land and money for a hospital, an orphanage, and a seminary. His son, Bryan, served a term as mayor of St. Louis. John Mullanphy also raised and educated seven daughters who built their own legacies, even if their husband's surnames were the ones memorialized around town (Chambers, Biddle, Clemens).

In 1817, the first steamboat reached St. Louis, the *Zebulon Pike*. Steamboats reduced the travel time between St. Louis and New Orleans from months to days. This watershed event heralded dramatic growth for St. Louis as it evolved into one of the most important ports in the US. Those boats connected St. Louis to markets in New Orleans and around the world. By the 1850s, hundreds of steamboats made three thousand annual landings. Steamboats regularly packed the mile-long levee. Roustabouts cargo stacked high on the levee as they busily loaded and unloaded the boats.

Missouri entered the US in 1820 as a slave state. As a result, Missouri's population was bolstered by the migration of many enslavers from bordering southern states. They were joined by thousands of immigrants, including the 7,000 Germans who arrived in the 1830s and Irish emigrants who had arrived earlier. By 1836, there were enough Jews in St. Louis to hold the first prayer meeting. The city also counted among its residents thousands of enslaved Blacks and a small community of free Blacks.

St. Louisans developed a reputation as a hostile place to live if you were Black, though, whether you were free or enslaved. William Wells Brown, a man who had escaped slavery, wrote in his autobiography:

> "Though slavery is thought, by some, to be mild in Missouri, when compared with the cotton, sugar and rice growing states, yet no part of our slave-holding country, is more noted for the barbarity of its inhabitants, than St. Louis."

Brown may have been influenced by one incident in particular. On July 9, 1841, four Black men were hanged on Duncan Island (the island no longer exists). They were accused of killing two men during a robbery. One of the hanged men was Charles Brown, a well-known abolitionist who was probably targeted for his political views. The hanging had been widely advertised, so it drew a crowd of 20,000 spectators, including a steamboat full of people who traveled down from Alton eager to watch it. After the execution, the heads of the four men were displayed in the window of Corse's Drug Store.

Still, free Blacks did what they could to build a life. John Berry Meachum, who had bought his way out of freedom by mining and selling saltpeter, moved to St. Louis around 1815 and set up a business as a carpenter and cooper. He earned enough money to buy freedom for his wife and children and nearly two dozen other enslaved people. He was ordained as a Baptist minister and was one of the original founders of the First African Baptist Church. In the basement of that church, he established one of the few schools for free and enslaved Blacks in St. Louis.

In 1847, Missouri outlawed education for Blacks, whether free or enslaved. Schools for Blacks closed, including one run for Black girls by the Sisters of St. Joseph of Carondelet. Meachum, however, as the story goes, moved his school to a steamboat, so he could continue teaching kids on the river and out of the reach of Missouri law.

Two major disasters in 1849 reshaped the city: a cholera epidemic that killed 7,000 people (10% of the city's population!) and a major fire that wiped out much of the core of the city. As a result, the city greatly improved its sanitation systems and required masonry construction for new buildings. Still, these were boom times for St. Louis thanks to the river. Every day, hundreds of steamboats loaded and unloaded their cargo on the city's levee.

With civil war under way in 1861, Union Captain National Lyon moved to secure the weapons at the St. Louis Arsenal and to impound weapons from pro-Confederate state militias. The aggressive move secured St. Louis for the Union and spooked St. Louis residents who held pro-Southern views. Some 17,000 people fled the city, many of whom joined the Confederate Army. The city also attracted new Black residents as they fled slavery and war in the South. The African American population in St. Louis grew from 3,000 in 1860 to over 20,000 twenty years later. St. Louisan James B. Eads, a self-taught engineer, built five iron clad boats for the Union's combat efforts on the Mississippi and adjoining rivers that were instrumental in Union victories.

From 1860 to 1900, the population of St. Louis exploded from 160,000 residents to 575,000. Chinese immigrants arrived beginning in 1869 and built a community where Busch Stadium is today. Thousands more Germans and Irish moved to St. Louis. Slovaks, Croats, Bohemians, and Lebanese settled in the city's Soulard neighborhood. Poles found homes on the near north side. In the 1880s, Italian men moved to the area around the brick factories and clay mines of southwest St. Louis. They settled in and helped their families immigrate to the neighborhood, The Hill, which has retained its Italian identity to this day.

After the Civil War, manufacturing expanded rapidly. St. Louis had nearly 90 brickyards producing the vibrant red bricks that still define the city's appearance today. Flour mills and iron foundries employed thousands of people. At the same time, railroads replaced steamboats for long-distance transportation, which diminished the importance of the Mississippi River to the city's economy.

Beer was another major industry, thanks to abundant clean water and a natural cave system that brewers used to keep their finished product cool. Forty breweries were active after the Civil War. Most of them were small operations that served just their immediate neighborhoods, but as two local companies moved toward mass production, beer grew into big business.

Adam Lemp was one of the first to brew lager beer in the US. By the 1870s, the Lemp Brewery was the largest in St. Louis and later became the first beer company to develop a national distribution network. They introduced their flagship brand, Falstaff, to Americans from coast to coast.

In the 1870s, Adolphus Busch rolled out the first cans of Budweiser and began an aggressive marketing campaign to challenge the Lemp's dominance. Adolphus married into a beer family when he wedded Lily Anheuser in 1861. Anheuser-Busch grew into a national brand thanks to their early adoption of refrigerated railroad cars and pasteurization to lengthen the shelf life of their beer. The company also built taverns around town like the Stork Inn, Feasting Fox, and Bevo Mill, to dominate the St. Louis market.

Sales of Lemp beer declined in the early 1900s, then Prohibition killed the brewery. Anheuser-Busch survived by selling products such as brewer's yeast and an alcohol-free beer called Bevo. After Prohibition, Anheuser-Busch grew phenomenally. The company became the largest US brewer in the 1950s. In 2008, they were bought by an international company, InBev, but kept its North American headquarters in St. Louis. The conglomerate is now the largest beer maker in the world.

Goodness, there are a lot of stories about these two companies and the people who ran them, far more than I can cover in this book. If you'd like to read more, check out *St. Louis Brews: The History of Brewing in the Gateway City* by Henry Herbst, Don Roussin, Kevin Kious, and Cameron Collins.

At the end of the 19th century, St. Louis grew into one of the world's largest manufacturers of shoes. In 1905 alone, the city's factories churned out 48 million pairs of shoes, which was one-sixth of all the shoes produced in the country. The St. Louis shoe business grew because cheap labor (women and children, mostly) was easy to find thanks to the large immigrant population, and railroads made it easy to ship the shoes all over the US.

The industry developed along Washington Avenue in a row of solid brick and stone buildings. Twenty companies operated plants in St. Louis at one time, including big names like Brown Shoes and the International Shoe Company. Those companies eventually moved much of the production to rural areas where the factories grew more specialized and the workforce less likely to be unionized. Following a few lucrative years of government contracts during the war years, production dropped and factories closed. Most of the production moved out of the US where labor was cheaper yet again. The old factories of Washington Avenue have since been converted into trendy lofts and restaurants.

St. Louis may have reached its cultural zenith in 1904. Basking in its status as the fourth largest city in the US, St. Louis hosted three prominent events: a World's Fair to celebrate the Centennial of the Louisiana Purchase, the summer Olympic Games, and the Democratic Party convention.

St. Louisans today are still nostalgic about that World's Fair, and rightly so. Some 20 million people visited the fair in just seven months, quite a crowd for a city of 600,000 residents. Visitors viewed exhibits that highlighted the best in early 20th-century science, culture, and the arts. A guy named Thomas Edison helped with the electrical exhibits. Along the Pike, native people from around the world, such as people from Central African tribes derisively called pygmies, lived in exhibits meant to recreate their homes (and highlight their inferiority to modern White Americans).

The first Olympic games on American soil drew 651 athletes from 12 countries. Those games featured what was perhaps the most memorable marathon in Olympic history. Frederick Lorz crossed the finish line first, but somehow none of the officials noticed that he had dropped out after running just nine miles. (He had hitched a ride in a car the rest of the way.) The truth surfaced shortly after he was awarded the first-place medal, and he was then banned from competition for a year. In his defense, he must have been a pretty good runner, as after the ban ended, he won the Boston Marathon.

Thomas Hicks was the real winner of the marathon. He was a British native who competed under the US flag. He won because of—or maybe in spite of—trainers who gave him a neurotoxin called strychnine sulfate. It was supposed to act as a stimulant to keep him going, but the trainers also fed him a little brandy—probably to numb the pain from the strychnine—which must have confused his body. Hicks was too weak to cross the finish line on his own. His trainers had to carry him. At least they helped him once. In spite of the strychnine, brandy, and running 26 miles, he survived and won.

In 1916, St. Louis voters approved a referendum that codified housing segregation. It banned anyone from buying a house in a neighborhood where 75% of the residents were of a different race. The US Supreme Court tossed out the law the next year, but determined St. Louisans turned instead to using racial covenants, contracts in which individual homeowners agreed they would not sell their property to someone of a different race. (It was always White property owners who agreed they wouldn't sell to African Americans.) In 1948, the US Supreme Court ruled that racial covenants violated the constitution, too. The case, *Shelley v. Kraemer*, originated in St. Louis.

As neighborhoods became more integrated, White families moved out of the city en masse. From 1950 to 1970, the White population fell from 700,000 to 365,000, while the African American population rose from 153,000 to 250,000.

A few entrepreneurs and artists managed to find success in the Jim Crow era. Annie Turnbo Malone, whose parents had been enslaved before the Civil War, developed a line of cosmetics and hair products for African American women. She began by selling the products door-to-door (and demonstrated them at the 1904 World's Fair) and eventually sold them across the country. She got pretty rich in the process—probably the first Black woman in the US to be worth a million dollars—but she lived modestly and donated a lot of money. One of her favored causes was an orphanage that is now called the Annie Malone Children and Family Service Center. They now sponsor an annual parade to celebrate African American history and to raise money for their operations.

Scott Joplin moved to St. Louis from Sedalia in 1901. Joplin's early music training was influenced by European classical music, but he gained fame as a composer of ragtime. His first big hit, *Maple Leaf Rag*, generated enough in royalties to enable him to focus on teaching and composing music full-time. Some of his other famous works include *The Entertainer* and an opera called *Treemonisha*. Joplin did pretty well financially, but he never accumulated much wealth, as he usually re-invested his earnings in new projects.

Electric lights began to systematically replace gas lamps in 1923. Their light was sometimes needed during the day when dense smoke blanketed the city, a product of the furnaces that burned the soft bituminous coal mined from neighboring Illinois. Pollution was so bad at that time that the Missouri Botanical Garden considered moving out of the city. They bought land 35 miles from the city in Gray Summit, Missouri. They ultimately stayed put and developed the new land into the Shaw Nature Reserve. It wasn't until the late 1930s that the city began to address air pollution.

St. Louisans suffered more during the Great Depression than other places. In 1931, the national unemployment rate was 16%, but in St. Louis it hit 24%. Some of the city's shoe factories had moved to small towns, while the breweries had been devastated by Prohibition. Most trade unions at the time didn't allow African Americans to join, which contributed to the elevated unemployment rate for Black workers (43%).

As legal barriers to segregation broke down, some institutions moved faster than others to integrate. In 1947, Cardinal Joseph Ritter ordered integration of Catholic schools in St. Louis, seven years earlier than the city's public schools. In addition, Saint Louis University was the first university in a former slave state to integrate. It did so in 1944.

The city's population peaked in 1950 at a whopping 856,796 but rapidly declined after that. The end of legal segregation was an important factor. White families fled to the suburbs, aided by the construction of interstate highways and federal policies that gave generous incentives to new home construction while ignoring older buildings.

Through much of the 20th century, St. Louis attracted few immigrants. That changed in the 1970s, as resettlement programs steered refugees to St. Louis for its low cost of living and the availability of jobs. Refugees from Vietnam were among the first to resettle, followed by tens of thousands of Bosnians in the 1990s. Most Bosnian families settled in the neighborhoods around Bevo Mill and nearby south St. Louis County. Today, the city welcomes people from Afghanistan, Eritrea, Iraq, and many other places.

The city's population decline has slowed considerably. St. Louis City counts about 300,000 residents today, while the metropolitan region overall is home to nearly three million people. About 130,000 of the region's residents were born outside of the US, primarily in southeast Asia, Latin America, and Haiti and the Caribbean. The region as a whole has grown into a giant land lover, though. From 30 square blocks laid out by Pierre Laclède in 1764, St. Louis now sprawls over 8,600 square miles.

St. Louis seems to have weathered the worst of the decline and is a city on the rise. Sure, there's still plenty to fix, but there are many hopeful signs, including a booming craft beer scene, new chefs gaining national acclaim, new construction all over, and renewed interest in that big river that started it all.

HISTORY: ILLINOIS COMMUNITIES

East Carondelet

Like its neighbors at Dupo and Cahokia, East Carondelet is in an area that has probably been continuously inhabited for thousands of years. The first Euro-Americans to move in were French, who began farming and living in the area near the Prairie du Pont common fields at the end of the 18th century.

The village had previously been known as Morganville and Henryville but incorporated in 1876 as East Carondelet, probably because it was the site of a busy ferry service across the Mississippi River to Carondelet (now part of St. Louis). That ferry service didn't end until 1944 when the Jefferson Barracks Bridge opened.

The village had some bad luck with early buildings. A hotel that opened in 1872 burned down in 1875. A flour mill was completed in 1876 but burned down in 1880. Even the Catholic church didn't fare well. It was built in 1873 but was destroyed by a storm in 1876. Meier & Company managed to hold out longer. They ran a blast furnace that employed 300 people. Their chimneys were once the tallest in the US. They were built from a million bricks and rose 203 feet above the floodplain.

The village had the usual businesses in the 1800s: a wagon shop and blacksmith, a boarding house, an ice harvesting company, and seven saloons. In 1881, a major flood swamped the homes and businesses of its 400 residents. East Carondelet today is a residential community in the floodplain separated from the river by a tall levee.

Dupo

In 1765, fourteen French families moved from Cahokia to the other side of a small bridge and into an area known as Prairie du Pont. By 1780, Antoine Girardin had led a successful effort to formally separate Prairie du Pont from Cahokia, although the villagers remained under the jurisdiction of the same court.

The small community focused on agriculture for generations and never gained the momentum to formalize local government. Residents incorporated a school district in the 19th century, but it took them 20 years after that to get around to building a school. In 1880, Prairie du Pont had just 50 residents, ten of whom were African American.

The area changed dramatically in the early 1900s as railroads set up shop. In 1903, the St. Louis Iron Mountain Railroad established a base in a neighboring village called Bixby, then became part of the Missouri Pacific Railroad.

The companies attracted residents, which created a need for housing. In those early years, the village had more taverns than grocery stores. When the village incorporated in 1907, railroad executives wanted a simpler name than Prairie du Pont. A local resident, Louis Dyroff, came up with the idea for shortening it to Dupo. In 1910, Missouri Pacific moved its main operations from Bixby to Dupo and built the expansive switching yards that still dominate the area today.

The trains and their coal-fired engines spewed thick layers of smoke around town. If you hung your clothes out to dry, there was a good chance that they would turn several shades darker. The rail yards are still active but without all that smoke, thanks to the introduction of diesel engines in the 1940s.

Dupo has avoided the crippling population losses of many of its neighbors. The area where the old Prairie du Pont settlement was located is between the canal and the railroad tracks, and people still live there. In spite of its proximity to St. Louis, Dupo has retained a small-town vibe.

Cahokia

Many of the communities on the Illinois side of the Mississippi were founded by a single company looking to buy cheap land and to escape regulations. When those companies closed or cut back, the towns suffered tremendous losses. Cahokia is the exception to these one-industry towns. Established by French-Canadian missionaries in 1699, Cahokia was the first Euro-American community on the Mississippi River—it is older than New Orleans and St. Louis.

Cahokia was already home to 47 families by 1715, but attacks from Dakota and Meskwaki fighters made life challenging. After France ceded the Illinois territory to England, many families moved to St. Louis. In 1790, forty families still lived in Cahokia, though, and the town would build an impressive log church in 1799 that is still in use.

In 1950, Cahokia was still a remote village of only 794 residents, but by 1960, the population had exploded to 15,829 due to the availability of affordable tract housing and highways to reach them. It is largely a bedroom community today, but one that has preserved some impressive architectural links to its past.

Sauget

When Monsanto Corporation was looking to build a new facility, executives searched for a place where taxes were low (or nonexistent) and where no one would ask what the company dumped on the land and in the water. They found their spot just south of East St. Louis and created a village they called Monsanto. Other companies liked the low-regulation business climate and located there too, including a huge Union Electric power plant, refineries, and a fertilizer manufacturer.

The city didn't attract many residents, though. Leo Sauget served as the first mayor for the handful of people who lived there. Leo's father Ludwig used to hunt on the land that became Monsanto with John Queeny, the founder of Monsanto Corporation. The village called Monsanto was later renamed after its most prominent political family.

Sauget today remains a refuge for businesses that are often shunned by other communities. Apart from the power plant and refineries, the city is also home to a zinc smelter, a waste transfer station, a toxic waste incinerator, and a couple of strip clubs, as well as 150 residents.

East St. Louis

East St. Louis is often derided for its contemporary corruption (or perception of corruption), but the reality is that the city is in the shape it is today because of corruption and poor management that stretches back to the city's founding.

In 1795, James Piggott inaugurated ferry service from St. Louis to the east bank of the river. Samuel Wiggins bought an interest in the ferry in 1819, and later persuaded the Illinois legislature to grant him a monopoly, which is part of the reason that the Wiggins Ferry Company operated until the 1930s. In 1808, a small village called Illinois City was founded, but, in 1818, the newly platted village was called Illinoistown. In 1821, the small community counted a hundred residents.

When no bridges spanned the Mississippi River, railroad tracks from the east terminated at the river. The railroad industry, with its growing size and influence, pushed to create a new town at the site. They got their way in 1861 when Illinoistown and the town of St. Clair were combined into a new city and given the name that the railroads had already been using informally: East St. Louis. Railroad tracks eventually covered a substantial area of the city and its streets. (There's an old story that East St. Louis never had a single bank robbery because the railroad tracks blocked the escape routes.)

The first mayor of East St. Louis was a lawyer with ties to the big transportation companies. He drafted incorporation papers, the city charter, and land boundaries. For the first 20 years, the wealthy industrialists, most of them based in the East or North (Carnegie, Mellon, Gould, Morgan, Vanderbilt, Morris, Armour, Swift) battled with local merchants for control of the city government. Big business ultimately won and in the process convinced city politicians to keep business taxes low. Since the city raised little money from the big companies, it was forced to rely on tavern licenses as its main source of revenue.

In 1877, a disputed election resulted in two separate groups claiming victory. Unable to resolve the issue quickly, the town had two mayors, two city councils, and two police forces–for two years! The conflict exploded in violence on June 30, 1878, when the two police forces shot at each other. Two marshals died in the fight.

Monroe Stephens was elected mayor in 1887 and presided over 22 years of relative calm and stability. His administration floated a bond issue to build new roads that were supposed to be high enough to stay dry during floods. Unfortunately, the construction costs were well beyond the city's financial means, so East St. Louis could only afford to make interest payments on the bonds–for decades. It didn't help that city officials stole money from the public coffers while accepting bribes from businesses and individuals.

Blacks from the south began migrating to East St. Louis in the early 20th century, encouraged by companies like the Aluminum Ore Company (now called Alcoa) to fill jobs vacated by White employees who had gone on strike. Thousands responded, and racial tensions rose. Newspapers inflamed the tensions by writing stories that exaggerated the role of Blacks in criminal activity, and White elected officials fed into the hysteria. Politicians and business leaders colluded to keep Blacks in segregated neighborhoods. If a Black person moved too close to a White neighborhood, they could lose their job.

In the mid-1910s, unions complained local companies were attempting to break them by importing African Americans as replacement workers. Unfortunately, the unions directed their anger more at the Black workers than the companies. Tensions rose as community leaders called for vigilante groups to drive Blacks out of town for good. On May 28, 1917, violence erupted when news circulated that a Black man robbed a White man and killed him. A crowd formed and people clamored to lynch the Black man. The mob crowded the downtown streets and attacked any Black person they encountered, injuring several people. By the time the National Guard arrived, the mob had settled down.

Tempers seethed under the surface for the next month. White workers at the Aluminum Ore plant frequently harassed and beat Black coworkers. By the end of June, White residents circulated rumors that Blacks were preparing an armed attack on them on July 4. On the night of July 1, a couple of cars drove through Black neighborhoods and fired at the homes of Black residents. Shortly after that, another car, identical to one of the earlier ones, drove through the same area. Black residents responded this time by shooting at it. Unfortunately, the two occupants of that car were plain clothes police detectives Samuel Coppedge and Frank Wadley. Both were killed.

The next morning, the city displayed the damaged car in front of the police station where everyone could see the bullet holes and blood-stained upholstery. A local attorney offered to represent anyone who would avenge their deaths. The attack on the detectives' car fueled fears of the rumored July 4 uprising. Mayor Fred Mollman requested National Guard troops, but the Governor only sent one company instead of the six the mayor expected. Around 10am on July 2, a mob of armed White residents marched downtown and attacked every Black person they encountered, including women and children. The mob torched Black-owned homes and businesses, then regrouped downtown around 6pm when the chaos reached its peak. Black people begged for their lives, but rioting Whites maimed and murdered them, anyway. White rioters burned some Blacks alive and hanged others from street lamp posts.

The National Guard gradually reestablished order. The St. Louis Fire Department rushed to help the East St. Louis firemen quell the flames. St. Louis police were stationed on the Eads Bridge to prevent White rioters from crossing into Missouri. In the end, property damage was nearly $400,000 and some 300 buildings and 44 railroad cars were destroyed. The official death toll was eight White and 39 Black people, but most estimates put the actual death toll in the hundreds, almost all of them Black. Few White residents expressed regrets about the riot.

Even in the best of times, East St. Louis was never a wealthy community. By 1920, poverty was endemic. It was the second poorest city in the US with at least 50,000 residents. Even though the city had a large number of factories and jobs were plentiful, industries kept wages low by flooding the market with cheap labor in the form of new immigrants and Blacks from the South. In 1920, the annual income for a resident of East St. Louis was one-fourth of that for the average Illinois resident. Because of the number of low paying jobs, the city never developed much of a middle class.

With few sources of revenue, the city still relied heavily on saloon licenses in the 20th century, half of the city budget in some years. The saloons developed into havens for illegal gambling, prostitution, and bootlegging. The neighborhood between East St. Louis and National City had so many saloons that folks called it Whiskey Chute. Illegal gambling persisted well into the 1950s, and brothels operated freely until the 1940s.

Brothels might have lasted longer if not for World War II. During the War, nearby Scott Field had one of the highest rates of venereal disease in the United States. The Army was not keen on this and threatened to make East St. Louis off-limits to its soldiers if the city didn't act. Fearing the loss of revenue from one of the city's most important customer bases, the mayor reluctantly shut down the brothels.

East St. Louis also developed into a haven for organized crime. The city produced gangsters such as Frank "Buster" Wortman, who controlled a crime network from Peoria to Cairo. Criminal gangs became established during Prohibition, expanded into gambling and prostitution, then later got involved with some labor unions.

The city's population peaked in 1950 at 82,295 but decline set in swiftly as industries abandoned East St. Louis and its neighbors. In the 1950s, the Aluminum Ore Company laid off 25% of its workforce, and the Armour meatpacking plant closed a few years later. In the 1960s, job losses accelerated when big companies like American Zinc, Darling Fertilizer, and Swift shuttered their factories. Employment at the National Stock Yards dropped from thousands to just 375 by 1965.

Even as the US economy was going strong during the Vietnam War, unemployment in East St. Louis hit 21%. Not surprisingly, the residents began to follow the jobs out of the city. Between 1950 and 1970, the city lost 30% of its population. Unemployment reached staggering levels for those who stayed in the city—by the end of the 1960s, 36% of households did not have a single person employed. Declining revenues lead to substantial reductions in city services, and crime skyrocketed. Elevated highways cut through city neighborhoods and the riverfront, further damaging the city.

East St. Louisians today haven't given up, though, even as plans to help the city back on its feet never seem to gain traction and rarely attract the resources to make change possible. A core group of dedicated folks continues to work hard to turn things around.

National City

The St. Louis National Stock Yards and adjacent meatpacking plants filled up the floodplain north of East St. Louis (and outside of the city limits) at the end of the 19th century. In 1907, the enclave incorporated as National City in order to maintain a corporation-friendly civil government. East St. Louis agreed to provide some services to the area (like fire protection) and promised not to annex it. National City never had more than a token residential base. It was a shell of civil government created by and for the meat-packing companies that operated here, including Morris (1889-1935), Armour (1903-1959), Swift (1893-1967), and Brooklyn Packing Company (which later became Hunter and closed in 1982).

In 1900, the stockyards employed 1,200 people and processed 50,000 animals every week. The Armour and Swift plants each employed about 4,000 people at their peak. National City never had more than 300 residents, though, all of whom leased their homes from the St. Louis National Stock Yards.

Long after the packing houses closed, in 1996, a fire (probably arson) destroyed city hall and the police station. Soon after that, the city ordered the few remaining residents to move out. National City officially dissolved, and neighboring Fairmont City annexed the land. The extant structures were demolished when the Stan Musial Veterans Memorial Bridge was built in the 2010s.

Brooklyn

Driving through Brooklyn today, there's barely a hint of the town's long history as a enclave for African American freedom. The town was founded around 1830 when "Mother" Priscilla and John Baltimore led a group of 11 families—some free Blacks and some enslaved people on the run—across the Mississippi River. It is arguably the oldest Black majority town in the US.

In 1837, five White men platted the town and named it Brooklyn, but the area grew into a biracial community with a Black majority population. The city grew by providing a refuge for formerly enslaved people and by attracting White laborers. In 1850, the town, still unincorporated, had 300 residents, 60% of whom were Black.

Brooklyn incorporated in 1873, but the post office referred to it as Lovejoy. The name came from the first school in the city, which was named in honor of the abolitionist leader, Elijah P. Lovejoy, who was killed by a pro-slavery mob in Alton, Illinois. Because another town in Illinois was called Brooklyn, the post office stuck with Lovejoy.

For the first 13 years after incorporation, White residents held a majority on the Board of Trustees, even though they were a minority of the town's residents. In 1886, John Evans led a successful campaign for the Black majority to win control of the Board. He became the city's first Black mayor in the process. The city's population grew to 1,577 in 1910 (88% of whom were African American), thanks to migration from the South, which included a disproportionate number of single men. In the 20th century, White residents slowly moved out and Brooklyn evolved into an all-Black community.

City leaders never had much luck attracting business, even as new factories sprung up around them. Between 1875 and 1919 (an era of rapid industrial), 47 new factories opened in the area—not one of them in Brooklyn. Instead, Brooklyn became primarily a residential community for the Black employees of neighboring factories.

Brooklyn today is a struggling community where half the residents live below the poverty line and where the major industry is adult entertainment. In spite of their challenges, residents have taken up efforts to recognize and publicize the town's unique heritage in the hopes that it can be used as a foundation to turn their fortunes around.

Venice

Venice got its name from the fact that, in the days before levees were built, its streets flooded regularly. The city dates back to a ferry landing that began operating in 1804. Its streets were laid out in 1841 and Venice was incorporated in 1873. In 1891, a major railroad switching yard was built for the new Merchants Bridge, which attracted some residents. Still, Venice remained something of a backwater outpost. One writer described early 20th-century Venice as the "Least prepossessing of the Tri-Cities." He added that it "...lies amid industrial sites and mazes of railroad tracks." Not exactly Chamber of Commerce-quality advertising copy.

Even though Venice was a small community, railroad tracks divided its northern and southern areas. North Venice was part of the Madison school district and had a Madison address, but it got fire and police protection from Venice. The Lee Wright housing project was built on the west side of north Venice. All of the residents were African American, but the rest of north Venice, which also bordered the African American neighborhoods of West Madison, was exclusively White. North Venice began to integrate in the late 1950s, while south Venice stayed exclusively White until the early 1970s.

Venice established two high schools in 1917, one (Venice High School) for White students and another (Lincoln High School) for Black students. Venice slowly desegregated its schools, integrating one grade each year beginning with the 1963-64 school year. Both high schools had success in basketball before integration (each won a few district titles), but after integration, the school did very well, winning two state championships. The city, though, couldn't afford to keep Venice High School open as people moved away and enrollment dropped; it closed in 2004.

Only recently did the federal government disclose that a whole bunch of uranium was processed in the St. Louis area from the early days of nuclear weapon development. One of the processing facilities was the Dow Chemical plant on the Madison/Venice border. From 1957 to 1961, the plant processed uranium for Mallinckrodt on behalf of the US Atomic Energy Commission. The same factory built tanks during World War II. Dow purchased it from the government after the war.

The plant produced more waste than it could burn, so the company buried tons of radioactive sludge in fields near the plant. They also dumped as much as 50 pounds of radioactive sludge a month directly into the sewers. Beginning in 1989, Dow and Consolidated Aluminum (Conalco, the building's owner at that time), quietly cleaned up the site. In three years, they dug up 105,000 tons of soil contaminated with radioactive thorium and shipped it by rail to a radioactive waste facility in Utah. Many people who live near that old processing facility believe they were exposed to radiation.

Venice today has lost most of its industrial base (it never had much retail) and nearly three-quarters of its population. The city today is overwhelmingly African American, with nearly 40% of the population living below the poverty line.

Madison

The Madison Land Syndicate, a partnership between the St. Louis-based Merchant's Exchange and east side coal interests who were unhappy with the high cost of moving their product across the Eads Bridge, incorporated Madison in 1887. They ultimately pushed construction of a new rail bridge in 1890, the Merchants Bridge.

In 1891, the American Car and Foundry Company opened a plant, then built adjacent housing that wasn't built to last. One person wrote that they were "Two rows of flimsy, box-like houses erected near the foundry... Home of mill workers, the community rises or falls with the fortunes of the steel industry."

Granite City

Granite City was (is) a steel town. It was named after the first major industry in town—granite ware. While a few folks moved here from neighboring states as early as 1815, not much growth took place until nearly 1900. In 1891, William F. Niedringhaus of St. Louis bought 3,000 acres where he built a plant for the National Enameling and Stamping Company. He also built a rolling mill and a lot of two-family flats for employees.

In 1893, American Steel Foundry opened a plant. Unlike other industrial barons, the Niedringhauses worked with unions instead of trying to destroy them. Employees orga-

ST. LOUIS ROUTE MAP

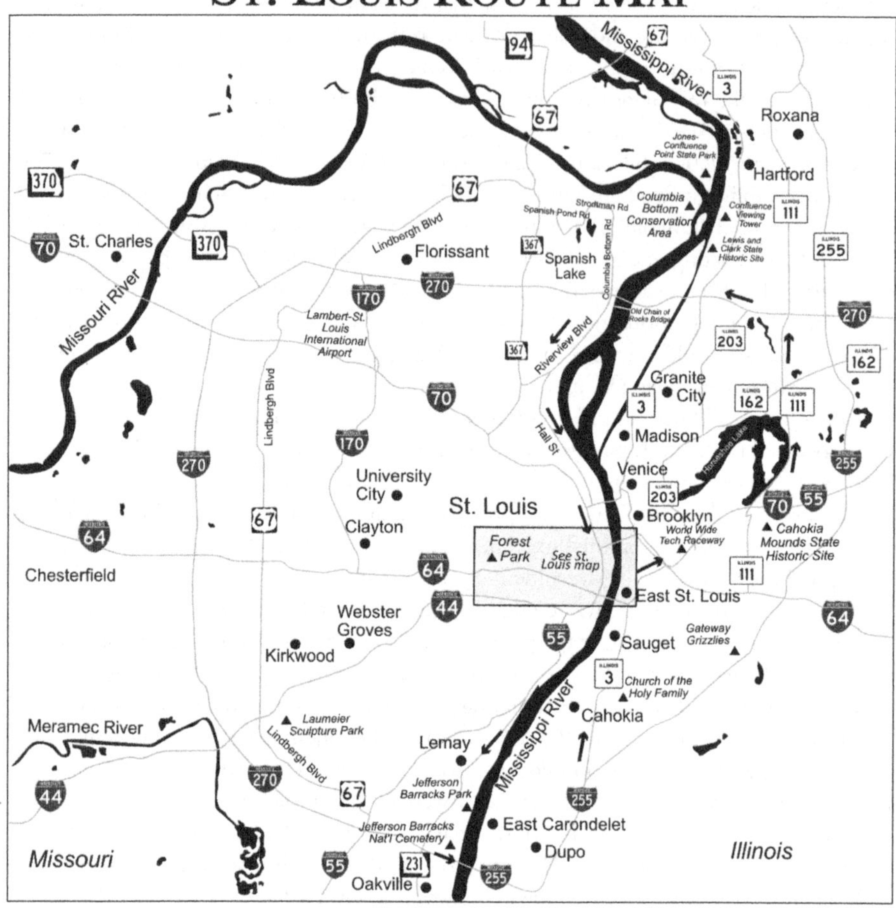

DIRECTIONS FOR THE GREAT RIVER ROAD IN ST. LOUIS

If you want to drive a loop on the Great River Road, I recommend a route bounded by the Chain of Rocks Bridge (I-270) in the north and the Jefferson Barracks Bridge (I-255) to the south. The entire route covers 40 miles.

DOWN THE WEST BANK (MISSOURI):

- Head south on Riverview Boulevard from Interstate 270
- Follow Riverview Boulevard south to County Road H, aka Hall Street, and turn left at the light. Follow Hall Street for 3.5 miles, turn right on Adelaide Ave, then take Interstate 70 east toward downtown; exit at Broadway
- Follow Broadway through downtown and to the city limits (11 miles) where it becomes Kingston Road, then Telegraph Road in St. Louis County
- Take I-255 east across the Jefferson Barracks Bridge into Illinois, then continue on I-255 north

UP THE EAST BANK (ILLINOIS):

The official route is outlined below. As an alternative, you could follow Illinois Route 3 back to Interstate 270, which would take you through the old east side industrial corridor north of East St. Louis (whose towns are profiled above). Neither route is all that scenic, and you won't see much of the river either way.

- From Interstate 255 north, take exit 10 to Illinois Highway 3 north toward Cahokia/East St. Louis; follow it for 6 ½ miles until it merges with Interstate 55
- Once on Interstate 55, if you follow the signed Great River Road, you will take I-55 North for six miles to Exit 6, then go north on Illinois Highway 111 toward Pontoon Beach
- Follow Illinois Highway 111 north for 7 ½ miles to Interstate 270
- Take Interstate 270 westbound back across the river to St. Louis

MISSISSIPPI RIVER BRIDGES

- The uninspiring Chain of Rocks Bridge, which opened in 1966, carries Interstate 270; it connects north St. Louis County to Granite City, Illinois.
- The old Chain of Rocks Bridge opened in 1929 and served as a river crossing for Route 66 for many years. The 30-degree turn mid-river no doubt induced white knuckles for many drivers, especially if a truck was coming from the other direction. The bridge closed to auto traffic in 1968 and sat abandoned for decades, a magnet for crime but also for a few scenes in the movie *Escape from New York*. In 1999, the bridge reopened for pedestrians and bicyclists, thanks to a massive effort led by the group Trailnet.
- The McKinley Bridge, built in 1910, connects Salisbury Street in St. Louis to Illinois Highway 3 at Venice, Illinois. It was named for William Brown McKinley, who was president of the Terminal Railroad Association when the bridge was built.
- The newest bridge is officially called the Stan Musial Veterans Memorial Bridge, but the "Stan Span" is catching on! The cable-stayed suspension bridge opened in 2014 to carry Interstate 70 between St. Louis and St. Clair County, Illinois.
- The Martin Luther King Memorial Bridge between St. Louis and East St. Louis opened in 1951 as the Veterans Memorial Bridge; it was renamed in 1972. On the East St. Louis side, the King Bridge connects with St. Clair Avenue/Illinois Highway 3 north, Interstate 64, Interstate 55, US Highway 40 and ML King Drive. From downtown St. Louis, the bridge is accessed from Convention Plaza.
- The historic Eads Bridge opened in 1874. It connects Washington Avenue in downtown St. Louis with River Park Drive in East St. Louis near the Casino Queen and has a protected lane for bicycles and pedestrians.
- The Poplar Street Bridge (PSB), another modern bore, opened in 1967. It is officially called the Bernard F. Dickman Memorial Bridge, but nobody calls it that. The PSB is the interstate highway bridge for Interstates 64 and 55 and connects St. Louis and East St. Louis. During rush hour, take the Stan Span across the river instead of the PSB.
- The two spans of the Jefferson Barracks bridge opened in 1983 (westbound) and 1992 (eastbound). The bridges both use a steel arch construction in which the road deck is suspended from the superstructure on steel cables. They carry traffic for Interstate 255 between south St. Louis County and Monroe County, Illinois.

nized as early as 1899, and unions grew from there. The two sides apparently figured out a way to live with each other, as strikes were rare. These factories needed quite a lot of skilled labor, which may have been a factor in their strategy to accept unionization.

Granite City incorporated in 1896, and the city boomed. Many foreign-born residents found their first place to live in the Lincoln Place neighborhood. They often struggled to make ends meet, so the area became known as Hungry Hollow.

Granite City Steel has been on a roller coaster ride, though. National Steel purchased the plant in 1971, then in 2003, after National Steel went bankrupt, it became part of US Steel. Some 2,000 people worked at the plant in late 2015 when the company announced it was laying off most of its workforce. In 2018, the company brought hundreds of workers back, but the future of the plant remains murky.

Granite City still relies on the steel industry, although the factories employ a lot fewer folks than they once did. Other active businesses in town include Precoat Metals, Kraft Foods, Heidtman Steel, Prairie Farms, and American Steel. Still, the city's population has been steadily shrinking since 1970 when it peaked at 40,000 residents, or about 10,000 more people than today.

Explore Down the West Bank (Missouri)

This guide sticks to the river corridor, but St. Louis obviously has many attractions beyond the river. I'll mention some of them briefly later in the chapter. For attractions near the Mississippi River, we'll start in Missouri around Interstate 270 and go south.

Attractions North of Downtown St. Louis

Twenty miles north of St. Louis, the two largest rivers in North America merge into one. The Missouri river ends its 2,341-mile journey and combines its muddy flow of prairie dirt and mountain gravel with the relatively clear water of the upper Mississippi River. Access to the **confluence** has really opened up to visitors in the past 20 years, so there are now four places to view it, two on each side of the river.

Edward "Ted" and Pat Jones Confluence Point State Park (1000 Riverlands Way; 636.899.1135) is perhaps the best place to experience the sublime merging of North America's two largest rivers. You can straddle a triangular sliver of land where you'll have a different river on each side of you. The park also has a couple of short hiking trails and restored bottomland habitats that attract a lot of birds. High water sometimes closes the park, especially in spring.

The 4,300-acre **Columbia Bottom Conservation Area** (801 Strodtman Rd.; 314.877.6014) offers another great view of the confluence, plus hiking trails and a boat ramp. The confluence viewing platform is about five miles from the entrance. The last mile of road to the viewing area has been closed since 2019 because of flood damage. Park at the lot next to the closed gate and walk one mile (each way) to reach it. Once you are there, you can get a sense of the magnitude of big floods by standing under the 15-foot pole at the head of the walkway.

Chain of Rocks Park (10840 Riverview Dr.) offers easy access to the old Chain of Rocks Bridge. Park in the secured lot and you're just a few steps from walking on the famous bridge. (See page 364 for more about the bridge.)

The **Griot Museum of Black History** (2505 St. Louis Ave.; 314.241.7057) tells stories of African American history through wax figures, artifacts, and art. The exhibits emphasize people from the region who made an impact.

Attractions in Downtown St. Louis

The **Mississippi Greenway** runs 16 miles on a paved path from just south of the Arch to the Chain of Rocks Bridge. It passes by the Arch, through an industrial corridor, and by the **Mary Meachum Freedom Crossing** along the way. The flat elevation makes for an easy bike ride or walk. There is a small parking lot for the trail where Biddle Street ends at the river (next to the old power plant).

Laclede's Landing (just The Landing to St. Louisans) contains several square blocks of 19th-century buildings, a fragment of St. Louis' old riverfront commercial district. Although the Landing has some office space, it is primarily an entertainment district, with a casino, restaurants, and bars. Take a walking tour along the cobblestone streets and brick and among the stone buildings. One of the outstanding structures is the Cast Iron building, (712 N. 2nd St.) which dates to 1872 and features a beautiful cast iron facade. For something completely different, tour the **Laclede's Landing Wax Museum** (720 N. 2nd St.; 314.241.1155) and pose for selfies next to your favorite celebrities, including some who are truly out of this world.

The **Eads Bridge** frames the southern boundary of the Landing. It was one of the first bridges to span the Mississippi and is now the second oldest still standing. The bridge was the first in the world to use steel in its construction, and the first in the US to use pneumatic caissons that allowed the crew to work underwater and sink piers down to bedrock. On July 4, 1874, some 200,000 people—two-thirds of the city's population—turned out for the bridge's dedication. Rail traffic moved on the lower deck, while carriages and pedestrians crossed on the upper deck. Both decks of the bridge are still in use today. The road deck has a separate lane for pedestrians and bicyclists.

The **Gateway Arch National Park** (314.655.1600) commemorates the Louisiana Purchase and the role of St. Louis in the growth of the US west of the Mississippi River. The centerpiece of the park, the 630-foot-tall stainless steel Arch, was the brainchild of Eero Saarinen. It is the tallest structure in St. Louis and will remain so until the city repeals a law that prohibits construction of anything taller. The newly freshened up park grounds stretch from the riverfront to downtown, complete with gently sloping walkways dotted with interpretive markers.

The park has several attractions in the rooms under the Arch. You must pass through a security screening (which includes metal detectors) to get in. The new entrance is on the east end of the park facing the Old Courthouse. Once through security, the **tram ride** to the top should be on your must-do list. Some people find the tram cars a bit too cozy, but the reward for squeezing in is a memorable ride and expansive views of St. Louis. If you don't want to ride the tram, go to the middle of the lobby where you'll find a replica of the keystone section from the top of the Arch. It is outfitted with a webcam, so you can check out the view virtually. The **museum** under the Arch highlights the role of St. Louis in the westward expansion of the US, the city's deep French roots, and the diverse group of people who lived in the area. You can also watch *Monument to the Dream*, a documentary about the construction of the Arch.

Once you're outside again, walk down the steps facing the river and check out the 1840s-era **cobblestone levee**. For decades, roustabouts, steamboat passengers, and enslaved people mingled on the levee, especially when steamboats landed. (In St. Louis, boats literally "landed" on the levee rather than docking at it.). Cruises on the *Tom Sawyer* or *Becky Thatcher* riverboats leave from here; purchase tickets at the Arch. Waiting times for attractions can be long in summer, so it's best to book ahead.

Destroying a City to Save It?

I love the Arch. As a monument, it's elegant, striking, and helps define St. Louis as a unique place. On the other hand, St. Louis sacrificed so much to build it, I'm not sure if we're ultimately better off. Let me explain.

At the turn of the 20th century, the St. Louis riverfront was showing its age. As the city expanded away from the river that gave it life, the buildings on the riverfront didn't look as nice as the new ones going up in other parts of the city. As early as 1907, civic leaders proposed a plan to demolish 30 blocks of riverfront property and replace it with 12 massive warehouses and a park that connected the riverfront to the old courthouse. There was no money for that plan, however, nor the one proposed by Pierre Chouteau, a descendant of the city's first family, to mark the centennial of the Louisiana Purchase by recreating the original colonial village on the riverfront.

In 1933, Mayor Bernard Dickman hosted a meeting with civic leaders where he floated the idea of creating a memorial to Thomas Jefferson. Dickman, who had spent his career in real estate, was more concerned about protecting property values, especially downtown, than honoring the third president, but a memorial would provide good cover. The business leaders formed a group called the Jefferson National Expansion Memorial Association and got to work looking for money to pay for it.

The outline of the plan moved along swiftly. In June 1934, President Franklin Roosevelt signed a bill that created the United States Territorial Expansion Memorial Commission (USTEMC). On May 1, 1935, the USTEMC approved a general plan that outlined the boundaries, a theme, and proposed a budget of $30 million, although no money was actually allocated for it. A few months later, St. Louis voters approved a $7.5 million bond issue that would fund a local match even though no federal money had yet been approved.

Not everyone was on board with the plan, though. An analysis by the *St. Louis Post-Dispatch* (whose editorial board had supported the memorial) uncovered widespread fraud in the election. Sure, 71% of voters had voted for the initiative, but the newspaper found instances of ballot stuffing (in one district, 100% of votes cast were in favor). The newspaper also estimated that there were 46,000 false registrations for the election.

Some business and cultural leaders also criticized the destruction of so much tax-generating property. Even though advocates of the plan insisted the area was run down, ugly, and plagued by high vacancy rates, a study by the Chamber of Commerce found otherwise. They surveyed 37 blocks and counted 5,000 people living in the district and 290 functioning businesses (printing companies, fur and wool traders, seed and feed distributors, and wholesale grocers). Just 2% of the buildings were vacant. The Chamber did conclude, however, that demolishing five million square feet of industrial space would raise property values throughout the city. (It would also eliminate $200,000 a year in property taxes generated by the district.)

Other critics noted that the district included many historically significant buildings, including some that were built with a cast iron construction that was unique to St. Louis. Saving architectural treasures wasn't a priority at city hall, though.

Congress finally approved $6.75 million to clear the site, which St. Louis matched with $2.25 million. Demolition work began on October 9, 1939, and by 1941 all 37 blocks had been leveled. The only buildings spared were the Old Courthouse, the Old Cathedral, and the Old Rock House, a warehouse build by fur trader Manuel Lisa in 1818 and the oldest existing building in the city at that time. (The Old Rock House would not survive, either, though. It was torn down in 1959 to make way for a railroad tunnel.)

The cleared land then sat vacant for decades as city leaders tried to figure out what kind of redevelopment plan would attract funding. The long gap led many people to propose using the site for some other purpose, like a stadium, a new high-density downtown, or an airstrip for small planes. Instead, it served as a parking lot. Even after Eero Saarinen won a design competition in 1948, it took another decade to raise the $36 million to build it, which was 20 years after the district's buildings were razed.

I wonder what the city would be like today if those buildings were still standing. Sure, there's no guarantee that the district would have survived later urban renewal fads. It probably wouldn't have, given the fervor with which St. Louis (and other US cities) embraced a slash and burn approach to stopping the population loss to the suburbs.

But imagine if the district had survived, if St. Louis today had 37 blocks of stout brick and cast-iron buildings filled with tax-paying residents and businesses next to the Mississippi River. Might St. Louis have its own French Quarter today? It could have been the kind of neighborhood that today's city planners dream of recreating.

Random Fact: The Old Chain of Rocks Bridge is one of many St. Louis sites that stood in for post-apocalyptic New York City in the movie *Escape from New York*.

The **Old Courthouse** (11 N. 4th St.; 314.655.1600), which is part of the Gateway Arch National Park, dates to the 1820s, but it has been expanded and renovated many times. In its early history, enslaved Blacks were sold at auction on its steps when their enslavers had died without a will. Dred Scott and his family initiated their battles for freedom here. The courthouse hosts exhibits on the Dred Scott case, as well as on early St. Louis history. [**Note**: The Old Courthouse is closed for renovations until 2025.]

The **Basilica of St. Louis, King of France** (209 Walnut St.; 314.231.3250)–the Old Cathedral as it is known locally—is one of only two structures that survived the massive demolition project that made room for the Arch. Situated on the very spot originally set aside for a church by Pierre Laclède in 1764, the lovely Greek Revival building was completed in 1834. The church also has a small museum with exhibits on early church history.

Just west of the Old Courthouse, **Citygarden** is a fun and inspiring sculpture garden/playground spanning two city blocks along Market Street from 8th to 10th Streets.

St. Louis doesn't get enough credit for its musical roots (especially its early blues history), but that might change now that the city is home to the **National Blues Museum** (615 Washington Ave., 314.925.0016). The museum's exhibits cover the big and broad history of the music that emerged from the oppressive social conditions of the South.

Downtown has several architectural gems. The massive Second Empire **Old Post Office** (815 Olive St.) opened in 1884 as a federal court and custom house. A proposal to raze the building in the 1960s helped start the modern preservation movement in the United States and made the Old Post Office the first structure placed on the National Register of Historic Places. The building today houses government offices, a library branch, and college classes, but feel free to walk around the public areas.

The **St. Louis Public Library** (1300 Olive St.; 314.241.2288) is another architectural gem. Designed by renowned architect Cass Gilbert, the library opened in January 1912. A top-to-bottom restoration at the end of the building's first century freshened up the inside and out, so the beauty of the building really shines. Volunteers lead free tours (314.338.7792 for tour information) of the building on Mondays (11a, 12:30p) and Saturdays (11a, noon, 1p).

When monumental **Union Station** (1820 Market St.) opened in 1894, it was the largest and busiest rail station in the world, capable of handling 260 trains and 100,000 passengers every day. Designed by noted architect Theodore Link, some aspects of the design may have been influenced by the famous Bavarian castle Neuschwanstein, most notably the double-barrel tower. Rail service at the station ended in 1978. The building now houses a hotel and an aquarium, but most of it is still open to the public. Highlights include the Whispering Arch, the Allegorical Window made of Tiffany glass, and the Grand Hall with its barrel-vaulted ceiling (now the lobby for the hotel).

Part of the station houses the **St. Louis Aquarium** (201 18th St.; 314.923.3900) and its exhibits featuring over 250 aquatic species. Many of the exhibits showcase creatures that are native to the regions' rivers, such as ancient sturgeon, alligator gar, and bowfin.

When you're done in the aquarium, step outside for a relaxing ride on the **St. Louis Wheel** (201 S. 18th St.; 314.923.3960. You'll get a new perspective on St. Louis from the safety of an enclosed gondola as it carries you 200 feet above the ground.

AUTHOR'S PICK: The **City Museum** (701 N. 15th St.; 314.231.2489) is an amazing place that grew out of the imagination of the late Bob Cassilly. Housed in the former International Shoe Company factory, the museum is a playground for adults and their children and is an experience that will inspire more than one a-ha moment. Check out the mosaics on the floors, secret caves, multi-floor slides, and the architectural graveyard. And don't miss the circus, either.

The **Campbell House Museum** (1508 Locust St.; 314.421.0325) is the last remnant of an exclusive neighborhood that was called Lucas Place. A tour of the home, built in 1851, offers a peak back at an upper-class lifestyle from the mid-19th century. Many of the furnishings are original to the Campbell family.

The **Scott Joplin House State Historic Site** (2658 Delmar Blvd.; 314.340.5790) preserves the residence and legacy of the prolific ragtime composer and musician. Visitors can tour the apartment where Joplin lived from 1900 to 1903, which is presented as it would have looked in Joplin's day. In the music room, player pianos perform ragtime tunes, including some by Joplin.

The **Field House Museum** (634 S. Broadway; 314.421.4689) showcases the life of the Field family. Roswell Field served as Dred Scott's lawyer, and his son Eugene was a famous children's poet. The museum's exhibits include an impressive collection of antique toys, as well as objects that belonged to the Field family.

Attractions South of Downtown St. Louis

The **Soulard Historic District** is the oldest residential neighborhood in St. Louis, dating to 1841. Early residents were mostly working-class immigrants (Germans, Czechs, Syrians, Hungarians) who toiled in the factories nearby. Soulard today is part residential district and part entertainment district, akin to New Orleans' French Quarter, just without the nudity. The neighborhood has a bustling market, good restaurants, and music clubs. If you're here in February, grab your beads (and coat) and enjoy **Soulard Mardi Gras**, one of the largest in the country. Otherwise, park and walk. Soulard's buildings come in many different architectural styles, from rowhouses to mansions.

With an abundance of natural caves and a plentiful supply of laborers, the brewing industry grew rapidly in south St. Louis. Of the 30 breweries that once called Soulard home, the largest were Eberhard Anheuser's Bavarian Brewery and Adam Lemp's Western Brewery. **ABInBev Brewery**—home of Budweiser and Clydesdales—is the only one left. It anchors the southern end of Soulard. Free brewery tours are offered year-round, which includes visits to the beautiful 19th-century brewhouse and a stable with Clydesdales. At the end of the tour, persons over the age of 21 get free beer samples. Start at the visitor's center (1200 Lynch St.).

The **Chatillon-De Menil House** (3352 DeMenil Place; 314.771.5828) was built in two phases. Henri Chatillon, a guide and hunter in the fur trade, built a four-room brick home in 1848. He sold the home in 1856 to Dr. Nicholas De Menil and his wife, Emile Sophie Chouteau, a descendant of the founding family of St. Louis. Their Greek Revival renovation was completed in 1863. Guided tours are available Wednesday, Thursday, and Saturday (11a, 12:30, 2p), but the museum is closed in January and February.

The Italianate **Lemp Mansion** is next door (3322 DeMenil Place; 314.664.8024). Jacob Feickert built the 33-room manse in 1868, and William Lemp, from St. Louis' other beer baron family, bought in 1876. Three members of the Lemp family—William, Sr., William, Jr., and Charles—committed suicide in the house. Highlights include African mahogany mantels, a ceiling fresco, a glass-enclosed marble shower, and tortured souls. The best way to see the house is as a guest, either by staying at the bed-and-breakfast or eating a meal in the restaurant. Seasonal **ghost tours** are available; call to find out when.

As you travel on Broadway through the southern reaches of the city, you'll enter the **Carondelet Historic District**. It's long been a working-class area and was an indepen-

St. Louis Map

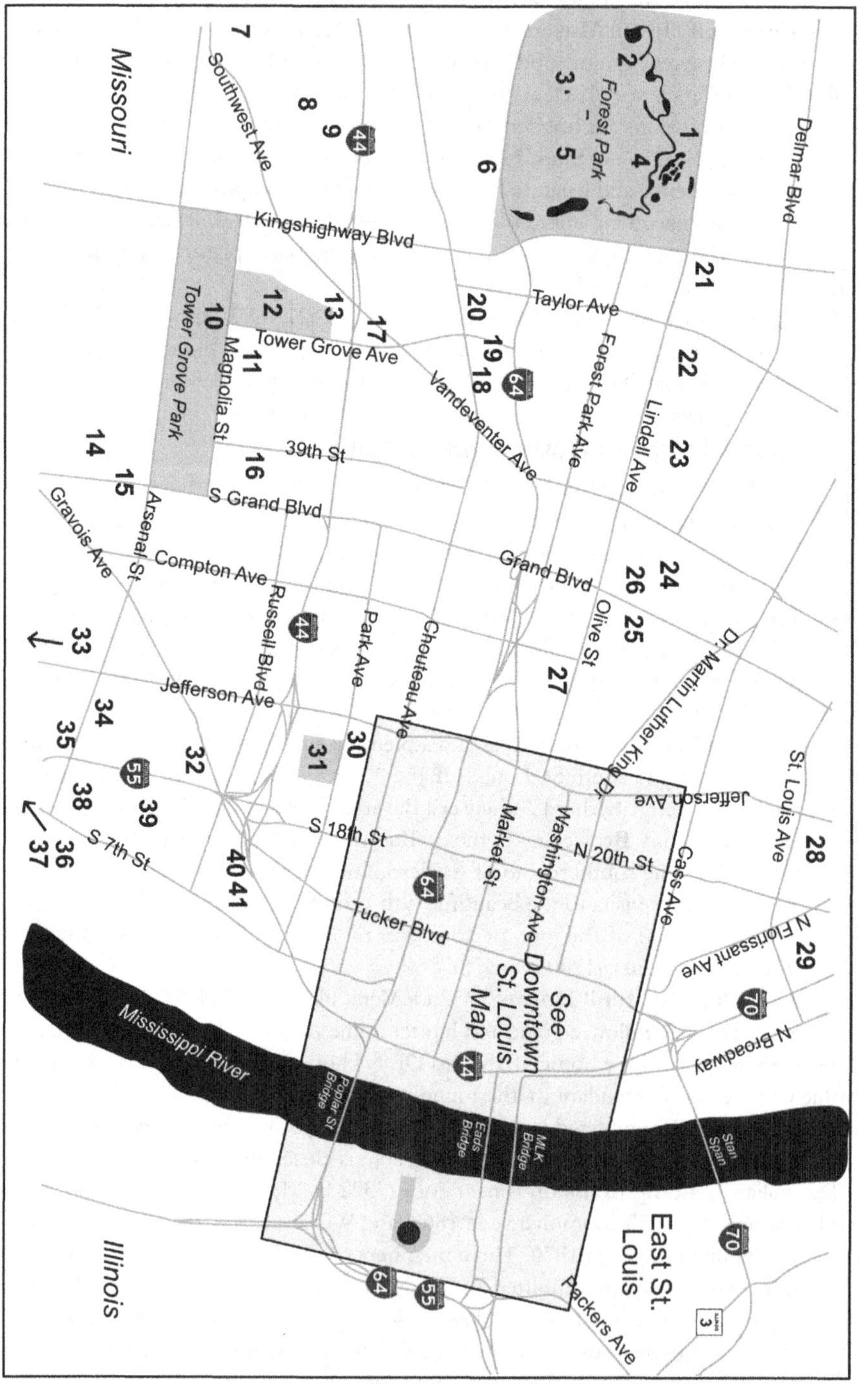
Missouri
Illinois
Forest Park
Delmar Blvd
Southwest Ave
Kingshighway Blvd
Taylor Ave
Tower Grove Ave
Vandeventer Ave
Forest Park Ave
Lindell Ave
Tower Grove Park
Magnolia St
39th St
S Grand Blvd
Grand Blvd
Gravois Ave
Arsenal St
Compton Ave
Russell Blvd
Park Ave
Chouteau Ave
Olive St
Dr. Martin Luther King Dr
Jefferson Ave
St. Louis Ave
S 18th St
N 20th St
Market St
Washington Ave
Cass Ave
S 7th St
Tucker Blvd
N Florissant Ave
N Broadway
See Downtown St. Louis Map
Mississippi River
Poplar St Bridge
Eads Bridge
MLK Bridge
Stan Span
East St. Louis
Packers Ave
44
64
55
70
3
1 2 3 4 5 6 7 8 9 10 11 12 13 14 15 16 17 18 19 20 21 22 23 24 25 26 27 28 29 30 31 32 33 34 35 36 37 38 39 40 41

St. Louis Map Index

Attractions

38. ABInBev Brewery
22. Cathedral Basilica of Saint Louis
37. Chatillon-De Menil House
26. Fabulous Fox Theatre
28. Griot Museum
5. Jewel Box
31. Lafayette Square
36. Lemp Mansion
12. Missouri Botanical Garden
1. Missouri History Museum
4. Muny Theater
39. Soulard Historic District
2. St. Louis Art Museum
6. St. Louis Science Center
3. St. Louis Zoo

Where to Eat and Drink

9. Adriana's
14. Black Thorn Pub
32. Blues City Deli
40. Bogart's Smokehouse
29. Crown Candy Kitchen
18. Gramophone
35. Gus' Pretzel Shop
16. Ice's Plain and Fancy
36. Lemp Mansion
7. Lou Boccardi's
27. Pappy's Smokehouse
8. Pizzeria da Gloria
41. Soulard Farmers Market
15. South Grand Boulevard
33. Sump Coffee
10. Tower Grove Farmers Market
17. Union Loafers
20. Urban Chestnut Brewing Company
19. Vincent Van Doughnut
13. World's Fair Donuts

Where to Stay

25. Angard Arts Hotel
34. Benton Park Inn
11. Casa Magnolia
23. Central West Inn Bed & Breakfast
24. Grand Center Inn
30. Lehmann House B&B
36. Lemp Mansion
21. Royal Sonesta Chase Park Plaza

Downtown St. Louis Map

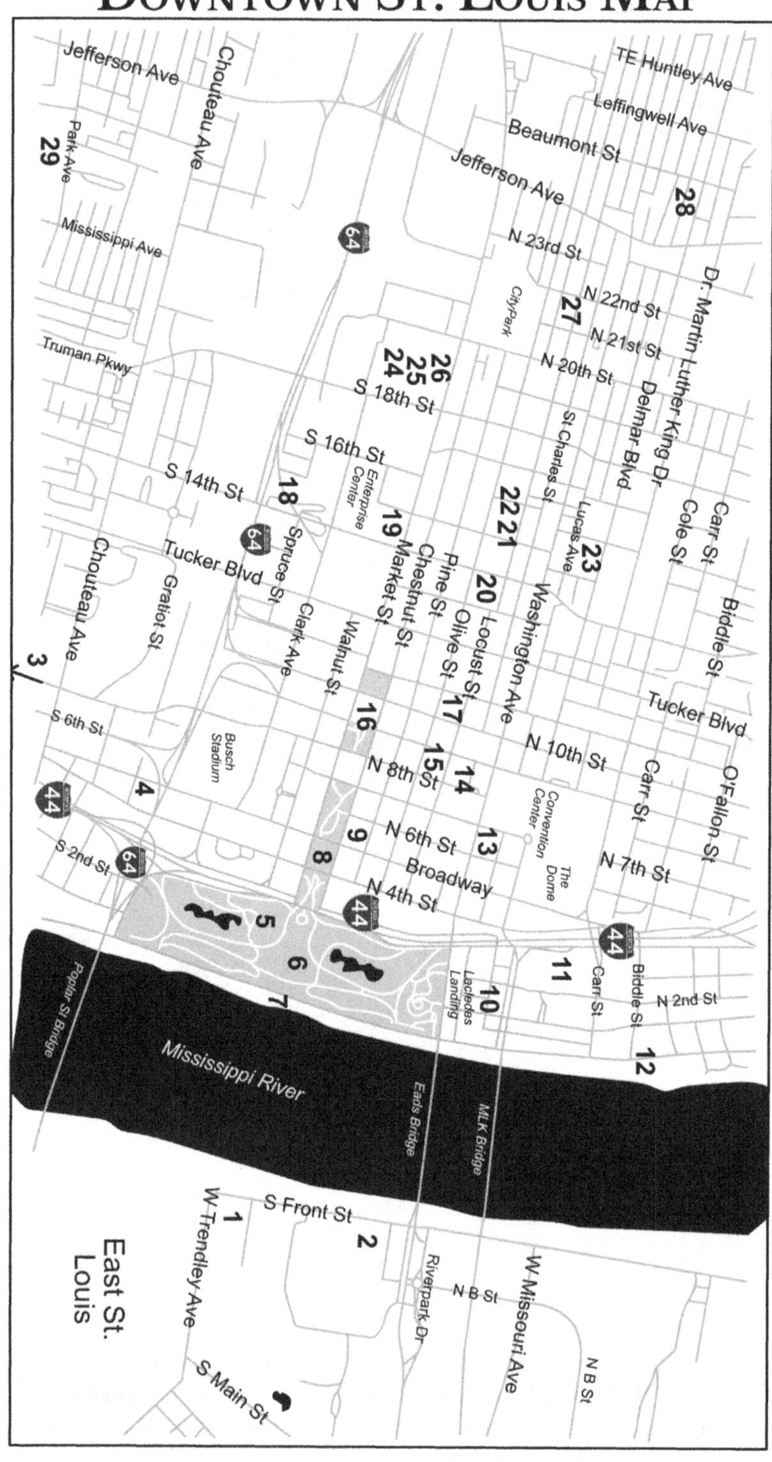

Downtown St. Louis Map Index

Attractions Downtown

5. Basilica of St. Louis, King of France
21. Campbell House Museum
23. City Museum
16. Citygarden
7. Cobblestone Levee
4. Field House Museum
6. Gateway Arch National Park
11. Horseshoe Casino
10. Laclede's Landing Wax Museum
29. Lafayette Park
12. Mississippi Greenway Trailhead
13. National Blues Museum
8. Old Courthouse
15. Old Post Office
28. Scott Joplin House
25. St. Louis Aquarium
20. St. Louis Public Library
24. St. Louis Wheel
19. Stifel Theatre
26. Union Station

Attractions in East St. Louis

2. DraftKings at Casino Queen
1. Malcolm Martin Memorial Park

Where to Eat and Drink

3. Four Hands Brewing Company
9. Chili Macs Diner
17. Park Avenue Coffee/Downtown
27. Schlafly Tap Room

Where to Stay

22. 21c Museum Hotel
2. DraftKings Campground
14. Magnolia Hotel

Other

18. Gateway Transportation Center (Amtrak/Buses)

The story of Dred and Harriet Scott's pursuit of freedom is one of the most significant in American history. But who were they? What were their lives like? **Read about them** at MississippiValleyTraveler.com/Dred-and-Harriet-Scott.

dent city until 1870. The village went through several names before the residents settled on the current one, which honors the man who was the Spanish Governor of the Louisiana territory at the time, the Baron de Carondelet, Francisco Luis Hector.

Carondelet's initial growth was similar to St. Louis. The village got a boost from an influx of French residents from the Illinois towns of Cahokia and Kaskaskia who did not want to live under British rule. The village had 250 residents when it was absorbed into the United States in 1804. Early on, Carondelet was nicknamed *vide poche*, which means "empty pockets." It is not clear if the nickname was meant to describe the economic status of the town folk, or a visitor's economic status after engaging residents of Carondelet in games of chance.

Carondelet was incorporated in 1832. Twenty years later, its population had grown to 1,200. During the Civil War, many of the ironclad boats designed by James B. Eads were built in a riverfront factory. St. Louis annexed the area in 1870 through an act of the Missouri Legislature. The citizens of Carondelet did not get to vote on the matter.

Carondelet was a multicultural community from the beginning. Many of the original Creole residents were married to Native American women. Some residents brought enslaved Blacks. It was not unusual for the French to free enslaved laborers after some period of service, so Carondelet's residents included both free and enslaved Blacks. In the 1840s, Winston Early (from the fledgling African Methodist Episcopal Church) visited Carondelet and held services for resident Blacks—free and enslaved together, a risky thing to do in a slave state.

After the Civil War more Blacks migrated into Carondelet in search of work, leading to a large enough population to found the Carondelet Chapel African Methodist Episcopal Church (225 Bowen St.) in the 1870s. The church, now the Quinn Chapel AME Church, is still active. It was named in honor of William Paul Quinn (1788-1873) who founded the African Methodist Church in St. Louis in 1840.

The neighborhood received a large influx of European immigrants in the 19th century, primarily Germans. In the early 1900s, Carondelet welcomed immigrants from Spain. The Spanish Society at 7107 Michigan is still active.

For an overview of the neighborhood's history, visit the **Carondelet Historical Society** (6303 Michigan Ave.; 314.481.6303; open W, F, Sa 10-2), which is housed in the very schoolhouse where Susan Blow founded the first public kindergarten in America.

South St. Louis Square Park (7701 S. Broadway St.) features the limestone house Anton Schmitt built in 1859. It was moved to the park after years of sitting in lonely isolation on the grounds of Monsanto's Carondelet plant.

Just past the city's southern boundary, **Jefferson Barracks County Park** (345 North Rd.; 314.544.5714) sprawls over 425 acres of a former military installation. From 1826 through World War II, the US Army operated an important base along the Mississippi River. Most of that land is now part of the park, although a small section is still used by the Missouri Air National Guard and the Missouri Army National Guard.

The park offers plenty of outdoor fun, with space to picnic and walk around, plus good views of the river. While the park has the expected amenities, what sets it apart is its collection of museums. The **Powder Magazine Museum** hosts exhibits on the military history of Jefferson Barracks, while the **Old Ordnance Room** hosts rotating exhibits. The **Missouri Civil War Museum** (222 Worth Rd.; 314.845.1861) hosts permanent and rotating exhibits on the people and events of the Civil War, with an emphasis on Missouri connections. The **Jefferson Barracks Telephone Museum** (12 Hancock

Ave.; 314.416.8004) preserves just what you'd think it does (thanks to volunteers who used to work for the phone company), with cool exhibits of old equipment and helpful explanations about how those things actually work.

Jefferson Barracks National Cemetery (2900 Sheridan Rd.; 314.845.8320) is just south of Jefferson Barracks Park. It is the second oldest national cemetery and at 331 acres, one of the largest. Established in 1826, the first recorded burial occurred in 1827 when Elizabeth Ann Lash, the infant child of an officer, was interred. Over 163,000 people are buried in the cemetery. You can pick up a map at the office.

Getting On the River

AUTHOR'S PICK: There's no better way to get close to the Mississippi River than on a guided canoe trip with **Big Muddy Adventures** (2muddy.com). They offer several different options, most of them in 29-foot-long voyageur-style canoes, including full moon floats that include a paddle and a gourmet meal on an island. If you want to put together a trip on your own, they can help with that, too.

You can also take a narrated **day cruise** on the river on the *Becky Thatcher* or *Tom Sawyer*, replicas of old-style steamboats. Buy your tickets on-line (www.GatewayArch.com) or at the Arch ticket windows. Cruises leave from the levee below the Arch.

Tours

The Missouri History Museum's **See STL** tours (314.746.4599) offer a refreshing take on the city's big and broad history. All tours run two hours but some are walking tours around a neighborhood (or topic), while others take guests on a bus to cover a larger area. Check their website for current offerings (mohistory.org/learn/see-stl).

Explore downtown with a guide from the **Landmarks Association** and go deep into St. Louis architecture (Sa 9am from Apr-Oct; landmarkstours-stl.org).

Attractions in St. Louis Away from the River

Neighborhoods

St. Louis is a city of neighborhoods, and there are many worth exploring:

- **Lafayette Square** is known for its collection of colorful Victorian homes; take a drive or walk along Park Avenue just east of Jefferson.
- **Cherokee Street** between Lemp and Gravois is a fun mix of antique shops, Mexican-American businesses, and hip bars and restaurants.
- The **Central West End** is the upscale heart of the central corridor; take a walk along Euclid Avenue to see the range of restaurants and shops in the area.
- Many of the city's performing arts venues are in **Grand Center** (Olive St. and N. Grand Blvd.), including the **Fox Theater**, the **St. Louis Symphony**, and **The Sheldon** concert hall. The neighborhood is also home to two museums that focus on modern art—the **Contemporary Art Museum** and the **Pulitzer Foundation for the Arts.**
- **The Grove** offers an eclectic mix of bars and restaurants surrounded by a booming residential population. It is centered along Manchester Avenue between Vandeventer Avenue and Kingshighway Boulevard.
- **The Hill** has retained a strong Italian American identity; the neighborhood has a high concentration of restaurants and small Italian grocers where you can stock up on speck and Parmigiano-Reggiano.
- The neighborhoods around 289-acre **Tower Grove Park**, a Victorian gem, have a solid mix of old brick architecture and small businesses. The business district

The Great Mississippian City of Cahokia

Mississippian people created a sophisticated social order with advanced science and art and built connections to much of North America via a vast trade network. If they had built with stone instead of dirt, their civilization would be as famous as the Mayans and Egyptians, and the sites where they thrived would draw crowds of tourists like Angkor Wat.

Beginning around 1,200 years ago, the population in the American Bottom boomed. We don't know if these people—whom we call Mississippians—came from somewhere else or were descended from earlier people in the area. Corn was king, perhaps the single most important food product. White-tail deer were also abundant. Mississippians didn't waste a single part of the deer. They ate the flesh and carved the antlers into arrowheads and tools. Bones were transformed into awls, fishhooks, and scrapers. Hooves were ground up and used for medicine and glue. Even the brain had a special use. It was mixed in with other liquids to soften the hide, making it more flexible.

The area where they put down roots also had relatively easy access to other key resources that fueled their growth. The Ozark mountains to the southwest provided chert for arrowheads, hoes, and other tools. The prairies to the north and west produced grasses that were harvested for building construction. Forests to the east provided a bounty of nuts, berries, and game, plus hardwood trees for tools, fuel, and building materials. The bottomlands had salt licks, edible plants (such as cattails), and tall trees for dugout canoes. The river itself yielded a bounty of fish and waterfowl.

What Mississippians lacked nearby they traded for: copper from the upper Great Lakes, seashells from the Gulf Coast, mica from Appalachia. At their peak, their culture spread throughout the Mississippi Valley and the southeast US. Mississippians built satellite communities from Minnesota to Florida.

The main city didn't grow haphazardly. It was carefully planned into areas designated for specific purposes. The core city was laid out in a diamond shape that spread over five square miles with Monk's Mound in the center. Land that flooded regularly wasn't developed. At its peak, some 20,000 people lived in the city, with many more in other cities in the area. Cahokia proper may have had a population density as high as 4,000 people per square mile, which is just a little less than Miami (4,323) and Philadelphia (4,337) have today.

Mississippians concentrated the most important monuments and neighborhoods in the city center, including a large plaza where people gathered for public events, games, markets, and festivals. Other neighborhoods radiated out from there, each anchored by a plaza of its own. Walkways connected the different parts of the city.

Mississippian agriculture was so successful that they fed thousands of people and still had surplus crops to trade. With a reliable food source, they had spare time to develop art (including music and dance), to play games like chunkey, and to develop new technologies and more complex religious rituals. Mississippians made extensive use of pottery. They created vessels for different purposes and added mussel shells as a tempering agent. Tattooing was common for men and women. If they had a writing system, we haven't found it yet.

One of their more remarkable feats was their ability to organize thousands of laborers for construction projects, most notably for earthen mounds (or pyramids; they are basically the same). Workers excavated soil with hand tools, then carried dirt in baskets to the construction site. Cahokia once had 120 mounds, which is a heck of a lot of dirt to move! Sixty-eight mounds survive today. The Mississippians built three types of mounds: conical, ridgetop, and platform.

Conical mounds were generally used to bury elite members of the society. Regular folks were buried in cemeteries. Of the six surviving ridgetop mounds, four appear to mark boundaries. The excavation of one—Mound 72—revealed the remains of an elite leader who was laid to rest on top of thousands of shells arranged in the shape of a falcon. Dozens of other remains were found in the same mound, people who had probably been killed as part of ritual sacrifice.

Platform mounds are one of the defining features of Mississippi culture. They usually had a structure on top of the highest level—a building for religious ceremonies, homes for leaders, or buildings where the dead were prepared for burial (charnel houses). The grandest structure, Monk's Mound, dominated the central city. It was built and expanded a few times over three centuries and is remarkable not only for its scale but also for the engineering required to pull it off. It's not just a bunch of dirt piled high and compacted. Mississippians used different types of soil in different places to maximize drainage and stability.

Area rivers played an important role in the lives of Mississippians. Apart from the food they provided, the rivers offered a reliable means of getting around. Cahokia Creek, which is barely noticeable today, once provided a water connection to the Mississippi River. Mississippians navigated the rivers in dugout canoes that ranged from 12 to 70 feet long. They were usually carved from a single bald cypress, poplar, or cottonwood tree.

While Cahokia was the center of Mississippian culture, they built satellite communities nearby, including at St. Louis and East St. Louis. The central city was later enclosed with a wall. Mississippians built palisades around other communities at the same time, which suggests that the leaders felt a need to defend themselves from something, but there's no evidence that the city was ever attacked.

By 800 years ago, Cahokia had lost steam, although there's no obvious reason for the decline. There is no evidence of a major precipitating event like an epidemic, invasion, or natural disaster. It's likely that the city's population just grew too big and exhausted the resources in the area.

Ultimately, it looks like people just gradually moved away. By 600 years ago, the city was a shell of its former self. Mississippians didn't disappear, though. Even after Cahokia's decline, Mississippian communities thrived in other places. When Hernando de Soto invaded North America, he and his marauders encountered indigenous people who were clearly part of the Mississippian tradition. Natchez Indians were also part of the Mississippian tradition. They survived until the French essentially wiped them out in the 1730s. It's likely that many Mississippian people dispersed and joined other communities.

along South Grand Avenue between Arsenal and Gravois is home to perhaps the widest range of culinary options in the city.

- **The Loop** is a lively mix of restaurants, shops, bars, and music venues that draws a diverse group of people. The main strip runs on Delmar Boulevard east of Big Bend to just east of Skinker Boulevard, encompassing parts of St. Louis City and University City. The strip also features the **Walk of Fame**, sidewalk plaques that pay tribute to St. Louisans who made a difference.

Museums and Parks

Forest Park, the 1,371-acre jewel west of downtown, has plenty of room to spread out, throw down a blanket and nap, do a few laps, or set up a picnic. It's also home to several of the best attractions in the area, including: the **St. Louis Zoo** (314.781.0900), the **St. Louis Science Center** (314.289.4400), the **St. Louis Art Museum** (314.721.0072), the **Missouri History Museum** (314.746.4599), the **Muny Theater** (314.361.1900), and the Art déco **Jewel Box** (314.531.0080), a greenhouse filled with seasonal flowers. All offer free general admission except the Jewel Box, which charges a buck. Each place charges a fee to view special exhibits, however. You can even see a show at the Muny without paying for a ticket: The last nine rows are free on a first-come, first-served basis.

The world-class **Missouri Botanical Garden** (4344 Shaw Blvd.; 314.577.5100) is the oldest continuously operated botanical garden in the US and a quiet sanctuary in the middle of the city. The gardens are divided into themes, including the Japanese Garden and the tropical greenhouse known as The Climatron.

For a big-picture perspective on the many ways that we've invented to get around, spend a couple of hours at the **National Museum of Transportation** (2933 Barrett Station Rd.; 314.965.6212). The collection of railroad cars is worth the visit alone.

Historic Sites

The **Cathedral Basilica of Saint Louis** (4431 Lindell Blvd.; 314.373.8200), or the New Cathedral to locals (it opened in 1914), is renowned for the astounding mosaic art that covers its walls and ceilings. The building features a mix of Byzantine and Romanesque influences with an eye-catching dome centered between two towers. The flat gray stone on the exterior contrasts sharply with the bright, detailed mosaics that line nearly every inch of the interior. More than 41 million pieces of tesserae glass cover 83,000 square feet, a project that took decades to finish (the last tiles were placed in 1988). Dozen of skilled artists placed those tiles, including father and son Paul and Arno Heuduck. Pick up a guide and explore the images. If you have limited time (or attention), stand under the central dome and look up at the Apocalypse-themed images. The four anchor images represent the Holy Trinity, the prophets Ezechiel and Elijah, and Woman of the Apocalypse Clothed in the Sun, all against a striking red background. At the right time of day, the light from the surrounding images gives the mosaics a heavenly sheen.

The Busch family estate is the site of a popular attraction known as **Grant's Farm** (10501 Gravois Rd.; 314.843.1700). It is located on land once owned by the 18th President. The site includes a petting zoo, a tour through a park with exotic animals like zebras and bison, US Grant's restored cabin, and a beer garden. Fun for the whole family!

As long as you're in the area, stop by the **Ulysses S. Grant National Historic Site** (7400 Grant Rd.; 314.842.1867). The site preserves White Haven, the family home of Grant's wife, Julia Dent. Grant met Dent at White Haven in the early 1840s when he was stationed at Jefferson Barracks. They lived in the house for a few years in the 1850s.

Sporting Events

For a taste of life as a local, take in a **St. Louis Cardinals** baseball game at Busch Stadium or a **St. Louis Blues** hockey game at Enterprise Center, both downtown. You can also watch **St. Louis City SC** compete in Major League Soccer at CityPark (2100 Market St.) just west of downtown.

Six Flags St. Louis (4900 Six Flags Rd.; 636.938.5300) is the area's major theme park. It is 30 miles southwest of downtown St. Louis in Eureka, Missouri.

Arts

The **Fabulous Fox Theatre** (527 N. Grand Blvd.; 314.534.1678), **Stifel Theatre** downtown (1400 Market St.; 314.499.7600) and the **Touhill Performing Arts Center** on the UM-St. Louis campus (1 University Blvd; 314.516.4949) host performing arts and concerts. **Chaifetz Arena** (1 S. Compton Ave.) hosts some live concerts, too, as well as home basketball games for Saint Louis University.

Laumeier Sculpture Park (12580 Rott Rd.; 314.615.5278) hosts permanent and temporary installations in a beautiful outdoor setting.

The **Black Rep** has been showcasing the work of Black playwrights since 1976. They perform at the Edison Theatre on the campus of Washington University (6445 Forsyth Blvd.; 314.534.3810) and a couple of other venues around the city.

Casinos

- **Horseshoe Casino**, St. Louis: 999 N. 2nd St.; 314.881.7777
- **River City Casino**, St. Louis: 777 River City Casino Blvd.; 888.578.7289
- **Ameristar Casino Resort & Spa**, St. Charles: 1 Ameristar Blvd; 800.325.7777
- **Hollywood Casino**, Maryland Heights: 777 Casino Center Dr.; 800.855.4263

Drinking and Dining

St. Louis is a big city, so there's no shortage of good places to eat. Read about the latest St. Louis dining in *Sauce Magazine*.

Beer. When you think of St. Louis and beer, you might think of Budweiser, but the beer scene has grown far beyond the place with the Clydesdales. St. Louis now counts over 30 craft breweries. The **Schlafly Tap Room** (2100 Locust St.; 314.241.2337) started it all when they opened in 1991, and they're still a great option. Other popular places include the neighborhood-based **Civil Life** (3714 Holt Ave.), the German influenced beers of **Urban Chestnut Brewing Company** (check out their big beer hall at 4465 Manchester Ave.), **4 Hands Brewing Company** (1220 S. 8th St.; 314.436.1559), and the Belgian-style beers at **Perennial Artisan Ales** (8125 Michigan Ave.; 314.631.7300).

St. Louis food specialties include **toasted ravioli** (which are deep fried and delicious), **gooey butter cake** (which is as good as it sounds; get at a sample at one of the **Park Avenue Coffee** locations, such as downtown at 417 N. 10th St.), **concretes** (frozen custard worth every minute of the wait at **Ted Drewes**: 6726 Chippewa St.; 314.481.2652), and **pork steaks** (which you won't see on many menus).

St. Louis also has its own style of **pizza**: a cracker-thin crust with a sweet tomato sauce topped with Provel cheese, a local invention. It's a processed cheese made from a combination of Swiss, cheddar, and provolone. St. Louis natives love it. The rest of us usually aren't impressed. Still, give it a try, maybe at the local chain that specializes in it, Imo's, or a better version at **Lou Boccardi's** (5424 Magnolia Ave.; 314.647.1151).

If that St. Louis-style pizza doesn't sound all that appealing, don't fret—there are many great options. The **Black Thorn Pub** (3735 Wyoming St.; 314.776.0534), a neighborhood tavern, offers deep dish to thin crust. **Pizzeria da Gloria** (2024 Marconi Ave.; 314.833.3734) cooks up tasty wood-fired pizza in the Hill neighborhood, which you can enjoy on their beautiful patio. Step into the past (and down into the basement) at **Monte Bello Pizzeria** (3662 Weber Rd.; 314.638.8861), which has been serving pizza since 1950. Thin crust pizzas are baked and served on cookie sheets. They also make tasty toasted ravioli.

If you're game to try food you won't find anywhere else, get a **St. Paul sandwich**—basically egg foo young on white bread with mayo and lettuce. You'll find it in many of the city's chop suey joints, but **Mai Lee** (Brentwood: 8396 Musick Memorial Dr.; 314.645.2835) makes an especially good one.

For a hearty meal, try a **slinger**, which usually starts with chili, eggs, and a hamburger piled on top of hash browns but may grow from there. I like the versions at **Chili Macs Diner** downtown (510 Pine St.; 314.421.9040) and **Southwest Diner** (6803 Southwest Ave.; 314.260.7244).

St. Louis is in the midst of a **barbecue boom**, which is a good thing. **Pappy's Smokehouse** (3106 Olive St.; 314.535.4340) started the trend, but there are many other good options in the area, including **Bogart's Smokehouse** in the Soulard neighborhood (1627 S. 9th St.; 314.621.3107).

We're pretty big on **donuts**, too. **World's Fair Donuts** (1904 S. Vandeventer Ave.; 314.776.9975) is a long-time favorite. **Vincent Van Doughnut** (1072 Tower Grove Ave.; 314.339.5440) offers a modern twist on the donut concept.

We've got a whole bunch of great **sandwich** shops. **Blues City Deli** (2438 McNair Ave.; 314.773.8225) serves hearty po' boys and muffulettas. **Union Loafers** (1629 Tower Grove Ave.; 314.833.6111) specialized in artisan sandwiches on fresh bread. The **Gramophone** (4243 Manchester Ave.; 314.531.5700), a self-described sandwich pub, offers a crazy number of options. **Adriana's** (5101 Shaw Ave.; 314.773.3833) specializes in Italian-themed sandwiches.

But wait! There's more. Below are a few other places to drink and eat that stand out from the crowd.

AUTHOR'S PICK: If you ever find a better cup of coffee than at **Sump Coffee** (3700 S. Jefferson Ave.), please tell me where you went. This place is absolutely devoted to crafting the perfect cup of coffee, and I'm not one to argue with perfection.

At **Gus' Pretzel Shop** (1820 Arsenal St.; 314.664.4010), you can get a warm pretzel to snack on or better yet, an Italian Sausage wrapped in a pretzel bun. Yum!

Crown Candy Kitchen (1401 St. Louis Ave.; 314.621.9650) has been pleasing St. Louisans since 1913 with their malts, chocolates, and hearty food. They serve up affordable lunches (get a BLT!) and do a brisk business in chocolates.

On Sundays, the **Lemp Mansion** (3322 Demenil Place; 314.664.8024) hosts an all-day family-style dinner featuring fried chicken and all the appropriate sides (11:30am to 8pm). It's a great way to eat good food and to get a peek inside the (in)famous house where three Lemps ended their own lives. If you can't make it for the Sunday dinner, they are also open for lunch during the week.

St. Louis has several restaurants that serve Bosnian cuisine. **Balkan Treat Box** in Webster Groves (8103 Big Bend Blvd.; 314.733-5700) serves tasty traditional dishes such as cevapi, but check out the daily specials, too.

If you aren't sure what you're in the mood for, head to **South Grand Boulevard** between Arsenal and Utah Streets, where you can sample food from around the world.

AUTHOR'S PICK: If you've never had ice cream made to order, well, what are you waiting for? **Ice's Plain and Fancy** (2256 S. 39th St.; 314.601.3604) takes the raw ingredients (including liquid cream) and magically freezes them before your very eyes to create a unique made-to-order (and delicious) treat.

Where to Stay: Lodging

Downtown St. Louis is a convenient place to stay, but the rooms tend to be expensive and the properties are mostly chain hotels. If you are looking for something with more personality, consider these options:

21c Museum Hotel (1528 Locust St.; 314.940.2333) turned an old YMCA into a lovely boutique property. The rooms are stylish and well-appointed, but the most unique feature is the way the hotel integrates art and rotating art exhibits into its décor. The former gym and swimming pool have been restored and are almost too beautiful to use.

Another fine option is the **Magnolia Hotel St. Louis** (421 N. 8th St.; 314.436.9000), with its 182 boutique rooms, stylish bar and restaurant, and pet friendliness.

These places offer good alternatives to staying downtown:

Swing into style at the 1920s-era **Royal Sonesta Chase Park Plaza** (212 N. Kingshighway Blvd.; 314.633.3000), the Art déco gem in the heart of the Central West End and next to Forest Park.

The **Lemp Mansion** (3322 Demenil Place; 314.664.8024) rents four suites for overnight guests just south of downtown.

The **Angad Arts Hotel** (3550 Samuel Shepard Dr.; 314.561.0033) is a delightful place to stay in the middle of the Grand Arts District and within walking distance of venues including the Fox Theater and the St. Louis Symphony. Rooms come in a variety of configurations (and colors) that can accommodate singles to families.

The **Moonrise Hotel** (University City: 6177 Delmar Blvd.; 314.721.1111) wears a modern coat. It is close to restaurants, bars, music venues, and great people watching.

Bed-and-Breakfasts

The **Benton Park Inn** (2017 Arsenal St.; 314.669.6196) rents three lovely rooms in a historic house near the Anheuser-Busch Brewery and the Cherokee Street district.

Get a taste of life in one of the city's historic Lafayette Square mansions at the **Lehmann House Bed & Breakfast** (10 Benton Place; 314.422.1483). Eight of the house's 26 rooms are set aside as guest bedrooms, five with king-sized beds. All have en suite bathrooms, and stays include a full breakfast.

Smack in the middle of the city's arts district, the **Grand Center Inn** (3716 Grandel Sq.; 314.533.0771) rents seven modern rooms and suites in a historic building.

Casa Magnolia (4171 Magnolia Ave.; 314.664.8702) occupies a formidable red brick beauty across the street from Tower Grove Park, one of the city's premier parks. The three spacious guest rooms have en suite bathrooms and come with a full breakfast.

The **Central West Inn Bed & Breakfast** (4045 Washington Blvd.; 314.535.7900) offers seven modern rooms on the perimeter of the Central West Inn, each decorated with a theme, like the Kaleidoscope and Reflections rooms.

Special Events

Like any big city, St. Louis throws a lot of good parties and special events throughout the year. Below are a few you might want to check out.

The **Soulard Farmers Market** (730 Carroll St.; 314.622.4180; W-Sa) is one of the oldest public markets in the US and is a fun place to shop and people watch on a busy

Saturday morning. The market includes vendors who sell fresh, local produce and some selling wholesale produce from elsewhere, as well as delicious prepared foods.

The **Tower Grove Farmers Market** takes over the middle of Tower Grove Park on Saturday mornings, filled with vendors selling fresh produce and handmade items (soaps, jewelry). Food trucks will make sure you don't go hungry while shopping.

St. Louis has one of the best-attended **Mardi Gras parades** in the country, even though February in St. Louis isn't the optimal time of year for frolicking outdoors. Still, the grand parade on the Saturday before Fat Tuesday draws a big crowd, as does the pet parade on the Sunday before the grand parade. If you visit during Mardi Gras, book a room early and bring plenty of patience.

The Ancient Order of Hibernians sponsors a popular **St. Patrick's Day Parade** (March 17) that winds through the crowded streets of the Dogtown neighborhood.

The Missouri Botanical Garden (4344 Shaw Blvd.; 314.577.5100) hosts the **Whitaker Music Festival** on Wednesday evenings in summer (concerts begin at 7pm, with free entry to the garden beginning at 5pm). It's a great chance to hear great regional musicians. You can even bring food and drinks into the garden (just don't bring glass).

The annual **Shakespeare Festival** takes place in Forest Park on a hill near the Art Museum (6604 Fine Arts Dr.). The company generally stages nightly performances in June (except for Tuesdays). A preview show begins at 6:30.

St. Louis hosts **PrideFest** the last full weekend in June, which fills the downtown streets with 300,000 or more people. The biggest event is the parade on Sunday, which steps out at noon.

Celebrate St. Louis is the city's annual Fourth of July party. After a morning parade, festivities culminate with a fireworks display backdropped by the Arch.

In late August, the International Institute of St. Louis sponsors the **Festival of Nations** in the eastern portion of Tower Grove Park (Grand Ave. between Magnolia Ave. and Arsenal St.). The event includes food and craft vendors from around the world, plus dance and musical performances.

St. Louis honors its blues heritage with the **Big Muddy Blues Festival** (bigmuddybluesfestival.com) on Labor Day weekend. Shows take place around Laclede's Landing.

In October, the Missouri Botanical Garden (4344 Shaw Blvd.; 314.577.5100) and the Shaw neighborhood team up to offer a taste of local food and art. The Garden hosts the **Best of Missouri Market**, a cornucopia of Missouri food and beverages, while the adjacent neighborhood hosts the **Shaw Art Fair**, which features mostly local and regional artists (Flora Place at Tower Grove Ave.).

EXPLORE UP THE EAST BANK (ILLINOIS)

East Carondelet

The **Martin-Boismenue House State Historic Site** in East Carondelet (2110 First St.; 618.332.1782) is one of the oldest surviving residences in Illinois. The French Creole-style house was built around 1790 by Pierre Martin using the *poteau sur solle* (post-on-sill) technique common at the time. Call ahead to schedule a tour.

Cahokia

AUTHOR'S PICK: The Village of Cahokia has some outstanding buildings from the French colonial period built in a style called *poteaux-sur-sol* (post-on-sill), in which logs are aligned vertically on a horizontal beam. The **Church of the Holy Family** (E. 1st and Church Streets; 618.337.4548) is spectacular example. The congregation dates to

1699. In 1799, they built a permanent church using timbers of native black walnut. The gaps between the logs were filled with material called *pierrotage*, a mix of stone rubble and lime. Note the 85-foot-long timber that helps support the ceiling; it was cut from a single tree. The church is open for tours during the summer.

In 1810, Nicholas Jarrot built a mansion next door to Holy Family Church. The **Jarrot Mansion** (124 E. First St.; 618.332.1782) is the oldest brick structure in Illinois and represents a style that some have called Frontier Federal. During its restoration, several horse heads were discovered inside walls. No one knows why there were put there. The interior of the house has been painstakingly restored to its original appearance. Call ahead for information on when the house is open for tours.

Cahokia Courthouse State Historic Site (107 Elm St.; 618.332.1782) is another example of the post-on-sill construction style. Built originally as a private residence around 1737, the building served as a courthouse for part of the Northwest Territory from 1790 to 1814. The current structure with its double-pitched roof is a faithful restoration built with some original materials.

Sauget

The **Gateway Grizzlies** play baseball in the Frontier League, a professional association with no ties to Major League Baseball. They play home games at GCS Credit Union Ballpark in Sauget (2301 Grizzlie Bear Blvd.; 618.337.3000).

East St. Louis

Malcolm Martin Memorial Park (185 Trendley Ave.) features the best view of the Arch and downtown; head to the top of the **Mississippi River Overlook.**

The **Katherine Dunham Museum** (1005 Pennsylvania Ave.; 618.795.5970) preserves the private collection of African and Caribbean art of the famed dancer, as well as memorabilia from her career. It is currently open for tours by appointment only.

If you enjoy the casino life, check out **DraftKings at Casino Queen** (200 S. Front St.; 800.777.0777).

Where to Stay: Camping

The RV park closest to downtown is just across the river at the **DraftKings at the Casino Queen** (200 S. Front St.; 800.777.0777). The casino manages a secured RV park that offers full hookups.

Cahokia Mounds State Historic Site

One of the greatest cities in North America once existed in the wide plain south of the confluence of the Missouri and Mississippi Rivers. The city was the center of a civilization that archaeologists call Mississippians, whose influence stretched far along the Mississippi River and into the eastern half of North America. The city peaked 800 to 1,000 years ago when it was home to at least 20,000 people who built 200 earthen mounds, which was just a portion of a larger culture in the area that consisted of tens of thousands of people spread over several square miles (see pages 358-9 for more).

The site of the main city is preserved today as **Cahokia Mounds State Historic Site** (Collinsville: 30 Ramey St.; 618.346.5160). It is a UNESCO World Heritage Site. The interpretive center features displays that recreate village life and includes some remarkable artifacts. Time has erased many of the physical reminders of the civilization, but audio tours bring it to life. One of the highlights is a walk to the top of Monk's Mound, the largest remaining structure from the old city. [**Note**: The visitor center will be closed through most of 2024 for renovations.]

Cahokia Mounds SHS also hosts a number of events throughout the year. Some celebrate celestial milestones such as the equinox and solstice, while others highlight Native American culture. In the past, they have hosted an event that showcases the skill of throwing the ancient weapon known as the atlatl (cahokiamounds.org/events).

Granite City

The **Old Six Mile Museum** (Granite City: 3279 Maryville Rd.; 618.225.1452) preserves the Emert-Zippel House, which dates to the 1830s. Walk through to get a taste of mid-19th century farm life.

The **Old Chain of Rocks Bridge** once served vehicles that traveled famed Route 66. Opened in 1929, the bridge is about a mile long and has a trademark 22-degree bend about halfway across, a turn that reportedly scared the heck out of people driving across. The bridge closed in 1968 and deteriorated for decades until it was repurposed for pedestrians and bicyclists. It now connects the Mississippi Greenway in St. Louis with the Madison County Confluence Trail in Illinois. The views from the bridge are outstanding. From Route 3, go west on Chain of Rocks Road and follow the road until it ends. You may have a bit of a wait at the stoplight that controls the flow of traffic across the one-lane bridge over the navigation canal.

When you look south from the bridge, you'll notice two structures that look like small castle turrets. They are **water intake towers** built in 1894, an era when people believed that something as mundane as water intake towers should be beautiful. Just south of the towers you will see a rare stretch of Mississippi River rapids, the **Chain of Rocks**. The rapids are not exactly navigation friendly, so the ten-mile Chain of Rocks Canal was built to bypass them. It opened in 1953. For a close look at the Chain, turn right from the bridge's parking lot and follow the gravel road to the river.

A few miles north of the bridge, the **Lewis and Clark State Historic Site** (Hartford: 1 Lewis and Clark Trail; 618.251.5811) marks the area where Lewis and Clark wintered before beginning their journey to the Pacific Ocean. The site includes a replica of Camp DuBois and one the expedition's keelboats. The current site of the museum is not exactly in the same spot as the original Camp DuBois, because that pesky Missouri River changed course and now has its confluence with the Mississippi River about three miles further south than in 1803. Nearby, you'll find two places to view the confluence of the Missouri and Mississippi Rivers. Follow Lewis and Clark Trail west until it ends at a small memorial and a good view of the confluence. Then go back to Illinois Route 3 and drive north to the 180-foot-tall **Lewis and Clark Confluence Tower** (Hartford: 435 Confluence Tower Dr.; 618.251.9101), two towers connected by viewing platforms that offer a bird's-eye view of the confluence.

Drinking and Dining

The Illinois side of the river consists mostly of suburban and old industrial communities with a lot of chain restaurants, but Granite City has a couple of good options.

For a bit of pampering, head to the **Garden Gate Tea Room** (839 Niedringhaus Ave.; 618.452.0539) for lunch or schedule a time for High Tea for Two.

Ravanelli's in Collinsville (26 Collinsville Dr.; 618.343.9000) offers a nice range of traditional Italian fare.

Lodging

In Illinois, you'll find chain motels in Granite City (mostly budget motels), Collinsville, and Fairmont City.

If you'd like to retreat to a quiet country setting after a day in the city, **Along the Way Bed and Breakfast** (Mitchell: 152 Mitchell Ave.; 618.931.1537) just might be your place. They rent three rooms in a modern country home on 75 acres near Granite City.

Attractions in Illinois Away from the River

World Wide Technology Raceway in Madison (700 Raceway Blvd., 618.215.8888) hosts major auto racing events.

Special Events

Collinsville hosts the annual **International Horseradish Festival** on the first weekend in June. You'll be surprised at the variety of ways in which the spicy root can be used.

Getting There

St. Louis Lambert International Airport is located northwest of downtown along Interstate 70. It takes 20-30 minutes to drive from the airport to downtown or just a little longer via the Metro Red Line light rail.

Amtrak offers daily service to Chicago and Kansas City. The Gateway Transportation Center (430 S. 15th St.) is a little hard to find, but look for it under the elevated highway at 15th and Poplar Streets. **Greyhound/Burlington Trailways and Megabus** also serve St. Louis. They board at the Gateway Transportation Center, too. Purchase tickets in advance. For Megabus, you must buy tickets in advance through their website.

Getting Around

Metro operates the local light rail and bus system. Red line trains run from St. Louis Lambert Airport (with stops at both Terminals 1 and 2) to the University of Missouri-St. Louis and downtown, cross the river into Illinois on the Eads Bridge to East St. Louis, then continue on to Belleville and Scott Air Force Base. The blue line runs from Fairview Heights, Illinois, to Shrewsbury, with stops in downtown Clayton and at Washington University. The two lines split at the Forest Park-DeBaliviere station. The Laclede's Landing station is the stop closest to the Arch.

For More Information

There are practical limits to how much I can include in a book, but not with a website! Check out the city profiles on my website to see if they include listings that I couldn't fit in this book.

MISSOURI

St. Louis: MississippiValleyTraveler.com/St-Louis

ILLINOIS

Cahokia: MississippiValleyTraveler.com/Cahokia
Sauget: MississippiValleyTraveler.com/Sauget
East St. Louis: MississippiValleyTraveler.com/East-St-Louis
National City: MississippiValleyTraveler.com/National-City
Brooklyn: MississippiValleyTraveler.com/Brooklyn
Venice: MississippiValleyTraveler.com/Venice
Madison (for much more history): MississippiValleyTraveler.com/Madison
Granite City: MississippiValleyTraveler.com/Granite-City

Kimmswick Detour

Kimmswick is a charming and compact old river town, popular with shoppers looking for unique items and tasty treats. It's an easy day trip from St. Louis, just a half-hour drive from downtown.

People have lived in the area for at least 12,000 years. Clovis-era people hunted mastodons, while later Native Americans processed salt from the mineral springs around the Mississippi River and Little Rock Creek. In 1850, Theodore Kimm, a well-off merchant from St. Louis, moved to the area. He platted the village nine years later along the new St. Louis & Iron Mountain Railroad. The new village attracted middle-class St. Louisans, most of them German immigrants, who opened stores, a brewery, mills, a copper shop, and greenhouses that sent fresh flowers up to St. Louis. The town eventually grew to include 1,500 residents, then fell back.

Old buildings fell into disrepair until Lucianna Gladney-Ross used her wealth and influence (her father, Frank Gladney, was one of the founders of 7Up) to shepherd preservation of what was left. In 1970, she began a determined and ultimately successful effort to buy and restore buildings in town. Kimmswick today retains its small town feel even as clusters of subdivisions have surrounded it.

Kimmswick is best explored on foot. The **Kimmswick Historical Society** (6000 3rd Ave.; 636.464.8687) maintains several displays on the town's history. The most impressive object is an old watchmaker's cabinet, whose drawers are still filled with all the objects needed to build or repair a watch.

Tour the riverside estate of **Mabel-Ruth and Fred Anheuser** (6000 Windsor Harbor Ln.), descendants of St. Louis beer royalty. The century-old home overlooks the Mississippi River and is filled with family heirlooms and antiques. Guided tours run on Thursdays from noon to 4 from April through November.

Just a few miles northwest of Kimmswick, **Mastodon State Historic Site** (1050 Charles J. Becker Dr.; 636.464.2976) tells the story of the beasts that once roamed the area. Excavations from a nearby quarry provided the first solid evidence that humans co-existed with and hunted mastodons 12,000 years ago.

In June (the first weekend), the **Strawberry Festival** showcases the many creative ways to enjoy the dimpled fruit and also features art and craft vendors.

Come back the last weekend in October for the uber-popular **Apple Butter Festival**, which draws tens of thousands of visitors who stock up on homemade apple butter, shop the rows of vendor booths, and enjoy live music. The town's narrow streets are closed to auto traffic for the weekend. While you can park along Highway K near town, your best bet is to park at Windsor School just off Highway 61/67 (Imperial: 933 Windsor Harbor Rd.) and take a shuttle into town.

When you're hungry, check out the **Blue Owl Inn** (6116 2nd St.; 636.464.3128). They have been pleasing diners since 1985, especially with their pastries and pie. They are open for lunch only.

LaChance Winery of Kimmswick (6035 2nd St.; 636.223.0453) is another fine option for a good meal. The menu changes offers something tasty for everyone, and if the weather is nice, you can enjoy your meal on a lovely patio. If you just want to sip some wine, for $10 you can sample four varieties.

FRENCH COLONIAL RIVER

Bauvais Amoureux House; Sainte Genevieve, Missouri

Overview

It's been 250 years since France governed the Mississippi Valley, but French culture is still alive and well in a few communities along the Mississippi River between St. Louis and Sainte Genevieve. Some of these towns pre-date New Orleans and have preserved impressive reminders of their earlier days. It's possible to take a day trip through this area and see most of the sites, but two days would be a more rewarding pace, especially if you're interested in sampling the local wine.

This route begins in Sainte Genevieve, which is a one-hour drive from St. Louis. If you start in St. Louis, I suggest you also visit the French Colonial sites near St. Louis, especially The Church of the Holy Family in Cahokia. See page 364 for more details.

History

At the time the first French missionaries came to the area, there were few resident Native Americans, although Wah-Zha-Zhi (Osage) people occasionally hunted in the area. Small groups of Shawnee, Kickapoo, and Lenape (Delaware) people also called the area home around the time the first French moved in. Before that, Mississippian people built settlements in this area. Early Euro-Americans found eight large platform mounds around the future site of Sainte Genevieve. Those mounds have been nearly erased over time by continual cultivation of the land. Late in the 18th century, some Native Americans conducted occasional raids on Euro-American villages, but the spoils of the fur trade relationships eventually blunted much of the hostility.

French-Canadian missionaries arrived in the mid-Mississippi River Valley in 1698 and established a settlement at Cahokia the following year, the same year that the village of

Williamsburg, Virginia, was founded. The Jesuits left Quebec on a mission to convert Tamaroa Indians to Christianity.

Other settlements sprang to life in the rich bottomlands along the Mississippi River in the same general period: Kaskaskia (1703), St. Anne's (1719), St. Philippe (1723), Prairie du Rocher (1721), and Sainte Genevieve (1749). These settlements were compact in size with small populations organized around agriculture. Each family farmed its own plot but shared common fields for grazing cattle and harvesting wood. The residents of these communities often included Blacks—some free, some enslaved—and a substantial number of Native Americans. Brief summaries of the main communities follow.

COMMUNITIES ON THE WEST BANK (MISSOURI AND ILLINOIS)

SAINTE GENEVIEVE

Sainte Genevieve was founded around 1749 by French-speaking farmers who relocated from Kaskaskia, Illinois. Nearly three centuries later, the center of town still resembles a French colonial village. The town's namesake, a 5th century Parisian named Geneviève, is the patron saint of those seeking protection from floods and disease, which given the town's early history, was a good choice.

The village got a boost around 1763 after Britain gained control of France's Illinois country. Many French families relocated across the Mississippi River to avoid British rule. In 1773, Sainte Genevieve counted 676 residents, 276 of whom were enslaved Blacks. Forty percent of families enslaved at least one person.

The first farmers built on the floodplain two miles south of the current town. After a major flood in 1785 (*l'année des grandes eaux*), most of the residents relocated to higher ground (*les Petites Côtes* or little hills) where the city is today. Residents lived in town while farming long, narrow lots in fields on the edge of town. Tobacco, maize, and wheat were the most common crops. Folks made a pretty good living, but they also knew how to have fun. The village had three billiard halls in the 18th century, and gambling was popular, especially on Sundays after church.

By 1800, Sainte Genevieve's population had grown to 1,100 residents, which included a growing number of English-speaking Euro-Americans; nearly one-third of the population was enslaved. The famous naturalist and artist John James Audubon moved to Sainte Genevieve in 1811 to set up a mercantile business with his friend, Jean Ferdinand Rozier. Rozier took to the business world well (and still has many descendants in the area). Audubon did not, but he later found his niche drawing and studying wildlife.

German Catholics began moving to Saint Genevieve around 1840. They built sturdy masonry structures with locally fired bricks, including the Firmin Rozier Store (c. 1850) and the John Hael house (c. 1860). By the mid-1800s, there were more people in town with German than French ancestry. For a brief time, Ste. Genevieve did a brick business shipping iron ore from Missouri mines on the Mississippi, as well as granite and marble, but railroads eventually captured that business.

After the Civil War, newly freed African Americans settled in the south part of the city. In the 1920s, a small wave of African Americans migrated to the city from the South to work at the lime factory. In 1930, three of the newer residents were accused of robbing and killing two White men. The three were arrested and jailed in St. Louis, but that wasn't enough for a group of White vigilantes, who stormed Black neighborhoods and went door-to-door ordering everyone to leave town. Virtually all did. The state sent in the National Guard to restore civil order, and long-time Black residents were invited to come back (but not the newer migrants). Many returned, but most no longer felt welcome and didn't stay. By 1960, the city's Black population had declined from 200 to just 16. It has rebounded somewhat since and now numbers around 70 people.

Ste. Genevieve threw a big party in 1935 to celebrate its bicentennial, back when most people identified the founding year as 1735. Dignitaries from around the country visited the city. Even President Franklin Roosevelt called to congratulate residents. The highlight was a live show called *Fair Play*, which was written and directed by a priest from nearby Perryville, Missouri, the Reverend JB Platisha. The city dammed Valle Spring to create a lake for the production and built a 14,000-seat arena around it. In the middle, they built a triangular stage with a model of the old village. The show premiered on July 27, 1935, with a cast of 1,200— yes, 1,200! During the show, the little island was covered with water to simulate the 1785 flood. The whole celebration was a big hit. The Frisco line ran a charter train from St. Louis, and thousands of people rode it every day. The event helped to establish Ste. Genevieve as a tourist destination. Tourism plays an important role in the city's economy, as does lime processing, which is still going strong.

KASKASKIA

Kaskaskia has had a long, curious, and unusually mobile history. A community called Kaskaskia has been located in six different places. The first one—a village of Illini Indians—was founded on the upper reaches of the Illinois River in 1673 near the present town of Utica. In 1691, the community moved downriver near today's Peoria.

By 1700, the village had moved again but much further south, to the junction of the River Des Peres and Mississippi River at St. Louis. Three years later, they moved south again to the west bank of the Kaskaskia (formerly known as the Metchigamia) River about four miles from its confluence with the Mississippi, to join a small community of Native Americans, French traders, and their families. In 1719, most of the Native Americans moved further up the Kaskaskia River and started a new village because they thought the old village had become overrun with French settlers. Their new home was sometimes called Indian Kaskaskia. It remained an active community until the 1790s.

Meanwhile, the village the Native Americans left behind—French Kaskaskia, as it was known then—was growing into an important agricultural and administrative center. Canada governed Kaskaskia until 1717, then the monarchy switched governance to Louisiana. The residents developed an economy centered around agriculture and trade with Native Americans. Enslaved laborers—Black people, mostly, but a few Native people, too—were a part of the local economy from the earliest days. (Catholic missionaries probably brought the first enslaved people to Illinois country.)

In December 1718, the area's new commandant arrived, Pierre Boisbriant, with 100 soldiers and a support team. Boisbriant got to work building Fort de Chartres and asserting control over Kaskaskians. It was a prosperous period for the village, as it grew into the breadbasket for lower Louisiana (including New Orleans) and also profited from nearby mining (lead). By 1720, there were 80 houses in the village.

The city thrived, which caught the attention of King Louis XV. In 1741, he donated a church bell to the town to recognize its prosperity. That bell would toll from the tower of the Church of the Immaculate Conception until 1873.

The boom years under French rule ended around 1763, when France lost a war to England and ceded the Illinois territory to the British. A lot of French families didn't want to see what life would be like under British rule, so they left. About 50 families moved from Kaskaskia to a little village called St. Louis.

Those who moved probably had the right idea. Kaskaskia didn't do well during the years of British governance, as there just wasn't much governance. The population fell, and the economy tanked. The people who remained had a hard time making a living.

During the American Revolution, George Rogers Clark led a surprise attack on the village (July 4, 1778). He didn't meet much resistance, because the French and Native American residents had no desire to fight for the British. In the aftermath, though, civil control in Kaskaskia was nearly absent, so the region descended into lawlessness. Theft, assault, and murder were common. It took a decade to reestablish civil control.

When the US created the Northwest Territory in 1787, Kaskaskia fell under its jurisdiction. The Territory banned slavery, though, so slave-owners moved across the river to Sainte Genevieve, New Madrid, and St. Louis. By then, French influence was in sharp decline. In the decade of the 1780s, the number of French households dropped from 194 to 44 and continued to fall after that.

As late as 1800, the village was mostly a collection of single-story frame buildings. The lone brick structure was built in 1750. The village did well in the early part of the 19th century. Its population peaked between 1810 and 1820 around a thousand people. Farms did well, and the village was the center of government for the region.

Kaskaskia served as the capital of Illinois Territory from 1809 to 1818, and as the seat of Randolph County from 1795 to 1848. Shadrach Bond, the first governor of the newly minted State of Illinois, was a resident of Kaskaskia. Kaskaskians had better luck building a government than bridges, though. In 1824, a new bridge opened across the Kaskaskia River, but it washed out a couple of years later. Construction started on another bridge in 1840, but it collapsed before it was finished.

Ultimately, the village's location in the floodplain would be its undoing. Major floods in 1766 and 1785 damaged the town around the edges, but the big flood of 1844 convinced many people that the village didn't have a bright future. The town's population fell below 500 as folks moved Chester, Sainte Genevieve, and other places.

The Mississippi River crept closer and closer to the town, eventually washing away the home that had once belonged to Governor Bond. When the Mississippi River flooded again in 1881, the consequences were more dire. On the evening of April 18, the Mississippi cut across a narrow strip of land and captured the channel of the Kaskaskia River. Two days later, steamboats were making their way down the new channel and soundings revealed a depth up to 66 feet. The town's 300 or so residents suddenly found themselves living on an island and on the Missouri side of the channel. (When Kaskaskia was founded, the Mississippi was three miles away.)

By 1894, what was left of the town had to be abandoned. Kaskaskians relocated the cemetery atop Garrison Hill. The old church was razed before the river took it. Villagers laid out a new community 2 1/2 miles to the south—the sixth site for Kaskaskia—and moved a few buildings there. In 1900, the village's population was down to 170. A few stragglers stayed at the old village site. The remains of the old village washed away in the next few years, though.

The new location hasn't really been a lot better. Kaskaskia took another big hit in the 1993 flood. Many of the remaining residents decided that they'd had enough and left. Kaskaskia today is even smaller than a hundred years ago. In fact, it's hard to image it getting much smaller. In 2020, the village's official population was just 21.

COMMUNITIES ON THE EAST BANK (ILLINOIS)

CHESTER

In 1829, Samuel Smith built a cabin next to the river, opened a small hotel, and initiated ferry service to Missouri, which is why the place was first called Smith's Landing. Smith's wife, Jane Thomas, was from Chester, England, which is apparently the source of the town's current name.

Chester's first important product was castor oil, which it produced in large quantities and shipped up and down the Mississippi. Nathan Cole opened a grain mill in 1837. His company was later powered by an electric generator that produced more electricity than it needed, so the company directed the extra power to the city's street lights, making Chester one of the first cities to enjoy the luxury. The company is still operating today as Ardent Mills, which is part of food giant ConAgra.

The Menard Correctional Center has also provided a steady source of employment. It opened in 1878 and has housed some of the state's most notorious criminals, including serial killer John Wayne Gacy.

By the end of the 19th century, the city began expanding away from the riverfront and up to the top of the bluffs. The International Shoe Company built a factory on the hills above the river, but the city lost many of its manufacturing jobs in the 1960s.

Popeye creator Elzie Segar was born and raised in Chester. Many of the characters from his cartoon strip are based on people he knew growing up. Chester's economy today is driven mostly by the prison, a mental health center, and light manufacturing.

FORT DE CHARTRES

When the new French Commandant of French Illinois country, Pierre Boisbriant, arrived in Kaskaskia in 1718 with 100 soldiers and a support team, he put them to work building a fort. He named it after the Duke of Chartres—son of the French regent—probably to gain his favor. The wooden structure was completed in 1721.

Thirty years later, Chevalier de Makarty rebuilt the fort with stone. The French didn't get to enjoy it for long. The English defeated the French in the Seven Years' War/ French and Indian War and took possession of the territory where Fort Chartres was located. Still, it took two years for the first British troops to occupy it.

The British may have felt buyer's remorse, though, because in 1772 they abandoned the fort, as the Mississippi River crept ever closer to the fort's walls. When the fort was completed in 1721, the Mississippi was a mile away, but by 1770 it was practically next door. The British moved to Fort Kaskaskia, which they renamed Fort Gage.

Not long after Fort de Chartres was completed, a small village sprung up just outside its walls called St Anne (after the Jesuit church, St. Anne de Fort Chartres) or New Chartres. In 1764, forty families lived in the village, mostly soldiers and their families and the merchants who served them. After the British took control of the territory, folks moved to St. Louis and Sainte Genevieve and St. Anne faded away.

In 1817, forty years after the fort had been abandoned, Judge Brackenridge visited the area on a tour. He wrote that the fort "is a noble ruin, and is visited by strangers as a great curiosity…The outward wall, barracks, and magazine are still standing. There are a number of cannon lying half buried in the earth with their trunnions broken off."

The US government finally disposed of the land in 1849, and a local man took over. He built a cabin and farm buildings within the old fort walls. The State of Illinois later purchased the property and opened it as a state park in 1913. The powder magazine, the only surviving structure, was repaired shortly after that. The fort submerged under 15 feet of water in the 1993 flood, but a concerted effort from volunteers and the state cleaned it up and put it back together. The fort today is preserved as a state historic site.

PRAIRIE DU ROCHER

One history book asserted that Prairie du Rocher "never grew to any great size, and no event of importance seems to have marked its history." That's rather harsh for a community that has existed since 1722. The town's name (Rock Prairie) references the rocky bluffs nearby. Jean St. Therese Langlois, nephew of Fort de Chartres' Commandant Boisbriant, founded the village. It started as an agricultural community loosely associated with the fort. Like most French colonial towns, Prairie du Rocher had a common field (three square miles of it) where livestock grazed. The village was home to 22 French Canadian families in 1766, plus a few Native Americans and enslaved Blacks.

When Britain took control of the Illinois country, many of the town's French residents moved across the Mississippi River to St. Louis or Sainte Genevieve. The town attracted a few new residents, so by 1800, 200 people called Prairie du Rocher home. Still, by 1840, the town had just one general store to go with its flour mill and saw mill.

The first Church of St. Joseph in Prairie du Rocher was built in 1734 and replaced in 1858. In 1881, it got a steeple and a new addition on the front. In the latter half of the 1800s, the church celebrated mass in French, German, and English.

Residents tried to incorporate in 1825 and 1835, but neither effort took. Prairie du Rocher did not become an incorporated village until 1871. Farming was the main occupation among its residents, but a few folks also worked in a nearby quarry.

The village survived a close call with the Mississippi in the Great Flood of 1993. The levee district's late-night decision to blow an extra hole in the upstream levee probably made the difference. The hole diverted water back into the river and away from town.

Prairie du Rocher today still has a dozen buildings that date to the 1700s, including the Melliere House (built in 1735). A New Year's Eve tradition known as *La Guillannée* also dates to the earliest times. To this day, some locals dress in 18th-century garb and go door-to-door singing an old French song of that name.

Explore Down the West Bank (Missouri/Illinois)

SAINTE GENEVIEVE

Attractions

Sainte Genevieve has an impressive collection of **French colonial architecture**. Remarkably, nearly three-quarters of the buildings that existed in 1832 are still standing today. The most common types of construction were post-on-sill (*poteaux sur solle*) and post-in-the-ground (*poteaux en terre*). In both cases, logs were aligned vertically instead of being laid flat like American log cabins of the era. The homes that are open to the public are managed by the National Park Service, the State of Missouri, or private parties.

The US Congress created **Sainte Genevieve National Historic Park** in 2020. Start at the Welcome Center that the NPS shares with the City of Sainte Genevieve (66 S. Main St.; 573.880.7189). While you're there, spend a few minutes taking in Lewis Pruneauthe's impressive diorama of Sainte Genevieve in 1832.

The park service owns several historic buildings in town; three are currently open to the public. Across the street from the Welcome Center, the **Jean Baptiste Vallé House and Garden** (99 S. Main St.) occupies a prominent corner in town. The Vallés made lots of money from businesses that included salt and lead mining and also from the free labor they got from their slaves. The Vallés served as representatives to Spanish crown when the territory was ruled by Spain. The inside isn't open to the public (the Park Service maintains their offices in the house), but feel free to walk around the gardens. The **Bauvais-Amoureux House** (327 St. Mary's Rd.) is one of only five remaining post-in-the-ground houses in the US. Jean Baptiste St. Gemme Bauvais built it in 1792. The nearby **Green Tree Tavern** (244 St. Mary's Rd.), probably the oldest structure in town, dates to 1790. It has served as a Masonic Lodge and a tavern and tobacco shop.

The **Centre for French Colonial Life** (573.883.3105) is another group that preserves the built and cultural history of the town. Their museum features rotating exhibits about the French Colonial period, and their guides lead tours of the **Bolduc and Bolduc-LeMeilleur Houses** (123 S. Main St.). The Bolduc house was originally built in 1770 in the lowlands but Monsieur Bolduc rebuilt it in the post-on-sill style in its current location in 1792-93. The house has been restored to its late 18th-century appearance, and includes a few furnishings original to the Bolduc family.

In 1824, Felix Vallé purchased Jacob Philipson's six-year-old federal-style home and turned it into a trading post. The Felix Vallé House is now part of the **Vallé State Historic Site** (198 Merchant St.; 573.883.7102). Inside the building, you'll find period furniture and a recreation of a general store from the era.

Sainte Genevieve Museum Learning Center (360 Market St.; 573.883.3466) showcases the village's broad history, with exhibits on the Native Americans who lived in the area, as well as the region's French and German influences, but the life-sized models of dinosaurs draw most people in.

If you're traveling with children, make a stop at **Hands-On History at the Linden House** (116 S. Main St.; 573.880.4123), where the little ones can feel history.

Several artists formed a colony in Sainte Genevieve in the 1930s, and the Art Guild carries on the tradition. Stop in to the **Sainte Genevieve Art Center and Art Museum** (310 Merchant St.) to see a few pieces from the colony's past, then check out the gallery of contemporary art from regional artists. When you're done, pick up a guided walking tour that highlights outstanding art around town, including local painter Martyl Schweig's mural in the post office and a painting from 1821 called *Sainte Genevieve Receiving the Veil* in Sainte Genevieve Catholic Church.

Catholics have worshiped in Sainte Genevieve since the mid-18th century. The current **Sainte Genevieve Catholic Church** (49 DuBourg Pl.; 573.883.2731) dates to 1880 and is the third church to occupy the site. The brick Gothic Revival building is in great shape and filled with beautiful art, including Schweig's painting mentioned above. Pick up a guide inside the church near the doors.

Enjoy a night out at the historic **Orris Theater** (291 Merchant St.; 573.883.7211). They host live shows and musical acts throughout the year.

Magnolia Hollow Conservation Area (573.290.5730) offers hiking through 1,740 lush acres of bluff and floodplain forests along the Mississippi River. There's also a nice overlook of the river that's an easy walk from the parking lot. This conservation area is bright with colors in fall (but make sure it's not hunting season before you visit). Take I-55 north to County O at Bloomsdale, then go north on US 61 to County V to Magnolia Hollow Drive to the entrance.

French Colonial River Route Map

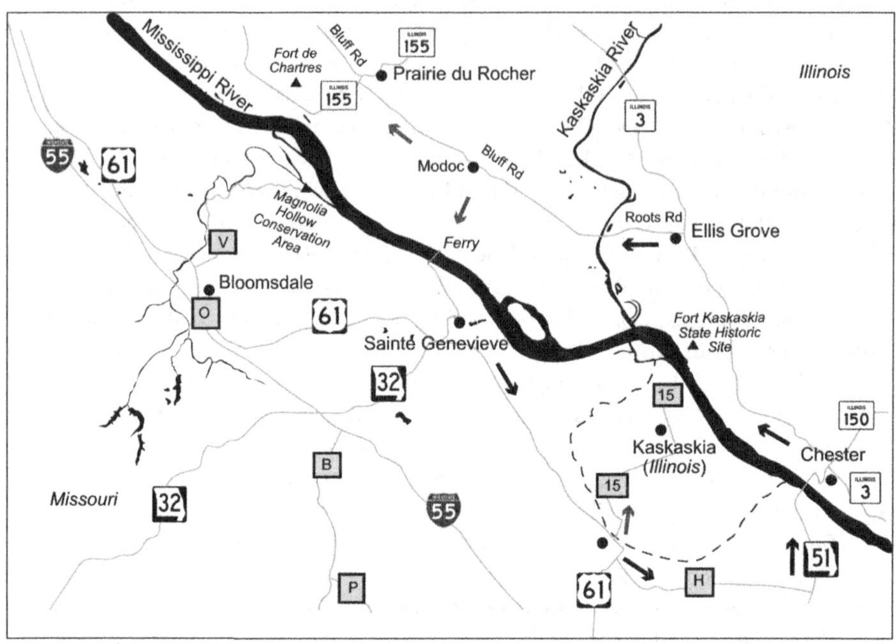

DRIVING DIRECTIONS

This is not a circular route, but you can easily turn it into one (46 miles). There are river crossings at Chester (a bridge) and Sainte Genevieve (a ferry) that you can use to get back and forth across the river.

When you are finished in Ste. Genevieve, go south down the west bank on US Highway 61 to St. Mary. At St. Mary, turn left on County Highway H and follow that road to State Highway 51. Go left and cross the bridge to the east bank (Illinois) and Chester.

Once you're done in Chester, head north on Illinois Route 3. Turn left on Roots Road after Ellis Grove, then right on Bluff Road. After Prairie du Rocher and Fort de Chartres, you can either continue to St. Louis by following Bluff Road and then Route 3 or double back to Modoc and take the ferry across to Sainte Genevieve and back to the west bank.

Drinking and Dining

Oberle Meats (21529 Missouri Highway 32; 573.883.5656) has been producing tasty smoked sausages and meats for five generations. Pick up something for a picnic later.

The baristas at **Common Grounds Coffee** (10 3rd St.; 573.880.7092) can prepare your favorite coffee drink and sate your hunger in the morning or for lunch. Common Grounds opened specifically to give opportunities to individuals with disabilities.

Pat's Pastries (123 Merchant St.; 573.608.5002) bakes tasty sweets and prepares fresh sandwiches. They also sell locally produced beer and wine.

Sirro's Restaurant (261 Merchant St.; 573.883.5749) is a popular choice for pizza and sandwiches.

Stella and Me Café (198 N. Main St.; 573.883.3078) is a satisfying choice for soup, salad, or a sandwich, plus a little something sweet at the end.

At the **Anvil Saloon** (46 S. 3rd St.; 573.883.7323), dine on classic American cuisine in a warm, cozy space; folks love their onion rings. For something different, try the liver dumplings, a local specialty. The bar was salvaged from a 19th-century steamboat.

Just outside of town, the **Inn at Weingarten** (12323 Rottler Lane; 573.883.2505) specializes in elevated dining that features seasonal ingredients (Saturday evenings only).

The rolling hills around Sainte Genevieve are home to several wineries. Some make beverages besides wine and also serve food.

- The **Grapevine Grill at Chaumette Winery** (24345 State Route WW; 573.747.1000) emphasizes fine dining with local, seasonal ingredients, often with a hint of Cajun or Southwest influence (open for lunch F-Su, dinner F, Sa).
- **Charleville** (16937 Boyd Rd.; 573.756.4537) produces wine and brews craft beer, so there's something for everyone. I'm a fan of their Hoptimistic IPA.

Where to Sleep: Camping

Hidden Valley RV Park (Bloomsdale: 5000 Hidden Valley Dr.; 314.324.9901) offers 17 sites with full hookups. It is 12 miles north of Ste. Genevieve.

Timber Run Campground (Perryville: 300 Lake Dr.; 573.547.8303), a full-service campground 20 miles south of Ste. Genevieve, offers 77 sites with full hookups plus room for tent campers.

Bed and Breakfasts

The Inn St. Gemme Beauvais (78 N. Main St.; 573.880.7505) is an elegant, mid-19th century mansion maintained as a time capsule of that era. The eight, reasonably priced rooms and carriage house are tastefully furnished with a few antiques.

Charleville (16937 Boyd Rd.; 573.568.8165) rents two bed-and-breakfast rooms in a restored dog-trot cabin on the winery grounds.

Lodging

For something completely different, stay in a tiny house in the woods at **Getaway St. Francois** (getaway.house/st-louis/). Getaway is a national chain that manages similar properties around the country. The St. Francois location is just a few miles north of Ste. Genevieve. The 40 small cabins are well-spaced and offer many of the conveniences of modern life, including a big bed, bathroom with shower, and small kitchen.

Originally built as a hotel in 1882, **Main Street Inn** (221 N. Main St.; 573.880.7500) rents eight recently renovated rooms that offer plenty of modern touches.

The building that houses **Audubon's Hotel** (9 N. Main St.; 573.883.2479) has been accommodating guests since 1904. Today, the hotel offers seven tasteful and modern rooms in the heart of old Ste. Genevieve.

The **Villages at Chaumette** (24345 State Route WW; 573.747.1000) is a collection of 26 modern country villas on the grounds of the Chaumette Winery that come complete with fireplaces and full kitchens. A continental breakfast is included, but more elaborate breakfast options are available for an additional fee.

Special Events

Pick up some fresh, local produce at the Sainte Genevieve **farmers market**. Vendors set up in the parking lot at 600 Market Street on Saturday mornings.

The biggest annual celebration in Sainte Genevieve is **Jour de Fete** (August). Vendor booths line streets that snake their way around the old town and bands perform, too.

One old French cultural tradition that has survived in Ste. Genevieve (and Prairie du Rocher) is **La Guillannée** (pronounced as gee-oh-nee with a hard "g"), a tradition that goes back to Medieval times (or earlier) in which folks dress up in costumes—some of them quite unique—and roam the city's streets on New Year's Eve, singing songs and begging for favors. It's quite fun. Visitors are welcome to follow the celebrants around town. The fun usually begins in the evening.

KASKASKIA (ILLINOIS)

Welcome to Illinois, even though you haven't crossed the Mississippi! If you aren't sure how that happened, read about Kaskaskia's history above. There's not much left of the old village, and what remains today is only accessible from St. Mary, Missouri. Take Highway 15 across the slough and onto **Kaskaskia Island**, then follow the signs to the **Liberty Bell of the West** and **Immaculate Conception Chapel** (203 1st St.; 618.615.5747). The bell was a gift to the village from King Louis XV in 1741. It rang out from the church steeple until it was replaced in 1873. Inside the church, there is a display of photographs of the island during the 1993 flood. The church altar dates to the 1730s. It was hand-carved out of black walnut and cottonwood native to the region.

Explore Up the East Bank (Illinois)

CHESTER

Attractions

It's a bit afield from Chester, nearly a half-hour-drive south, but **Piney Creek Reserve Nature Preserve** (618.826.2706) is worth a detour. The preserve is home to the largest collection of rock art (petroglyphs and pictographs) in Illinois, some of which are 1,500 years old (but not always easy to identify). Besides that, it's a darn pretty place to hike, thanks to the deep ravine and limestone-lined creek. From Chester, take Highway 3 south for 11 miles, then go east on Hog Hill Road to Rock Crusher Road. Turn left on Piney Creek Road; the parking lot will be on the right after a private driveway.

Just south of Chester, the 2,000-acre **Turkey Bluffs State Fish and Wildlife Area** (4301 S. Lake Dr.; 618.826.2706) has several miles of hiking trails and a good overlook.

The **Randolph County Court House Annex** (1 Taylor St.; 618.826.5000, x112) is the only remaining section of the second Randolph County courthouse. It was built in 1864 and now houses a museum. Its star attraction is the old electric chair from Menard prison, which was last used for an execution in 1938. The museum also has a lot of interesting exhibits and photographs of Kaskaskia. The fifth floor of the current courthouse (next door) has a good view of the Mississippi River and the floodplain. You'll have to pass through security to get to it.

A series of **Popeye-themed statues** pay tribute to Elzie Segar. The original Popeye statue was installed in 1977 in Segar Park next to the Mississippi River bridge. In 2006, the city began memorializing other Popeye characters with statues of their own. As of 2023, there are nineteen. A new statue is unveiled at the annual Popeye Picnic.

You didn't come all this way to go home empty-handed, so make time to scan the shelves at **Spinach Can Collectibles** (1001 State St.; 618.826.4567), which has a fun collection of Popeye-themed merchandise.

AUTHOR'S PICK: The French Creole **Pierre Menard Home State Historic Site** (4230 Kaskaskia Rd.; 618.859.3031) is a must-see site if you're interested in the area's French Colonial history. Menard moved to Kaskaskia in 1790 and made a good living running a trading post. He later served as Indian agent, was selected for the Indiana and Illinois Territorial legislatures, and was chosen Illinois' first Lieutenant Governor. He built the house in the 1810s, a magnificent example of frontier Creole architecture. It's a 15-minute drive north of Chester.

Fort Kaskaskia State Park (Ellis Grove: 4372 Park Rd.; 618.859.3741) sprawls over 200 acres atop a bluff along the Mississippi River. The small fort—it only had a three-room barrack and a kitchen—was built around 1759 to defend the village of Kaskaskia but was probably never completed. The site of the old fort has great views of the river and of the location where the old village of Kaskaskia once thrived. The park has plenty of room to picnic and walk around.

Drinking and Dining

Reid's Harvest House (2440 State St.; 618.826.4933) is popular for their delicious, buffet-style food; the options change every day.

Barb's Bounty (832 Lehmen Dr.; 618.826.7600) has been pleasing locals for years, with their (mostly) made from scratch dishes. The food may remind you of your grandmother's cooking. They have just a few seats inside, so you might want to get it to go.

At **St. Nicholas Landmark** (111 Ferry St.; 618.826.7150), you can enjoy a craft beer and a hearty sandwich in a historic riverfront building along the Mississippi.

Where to Sleep: Camping

The campground at **Fort Kaskaskia State Park** (Ellis Grove: 4372 Park Rd.; 618.859.3741) has 32 sites with electricity and basic sites for tents.

Special Events

The **Popeye Picnic** in Chester takes place the weekend after Labor Day and features a grand parade and the unveiling of a new Popeye-themed statue.

PRAIRIE DU ROCHER

Attractions

Just south of Prairie du Rocher on Bluff Road, a marker commemorates the **Modoc Rock Shelter,** a site where people have sought short-term sanctuary for 9,000 years.

The **Creole House** in Prairie du Rocher (Market St.; 618.214.1284) dates to 1800 and is a bit of an architectural mash-up, with part of it built using old European half-timber construction and part built using American frontier style methods with studs instead of posts. The house is now owned by the Randolph County Historical Society; call ahead to set up a tour.

Fort de Chartres State Historic Site (1350 State Route 155; 618.284.7230) preserves the partially reconstructed ruins of the original 18th-century fort. The original powder magazine was restored a century ago. It is probably the oldest building in Illinois. In the 1930s, crews with the Works Progress Administration rebuilt the gateway and a couple of other buildings. Exhibits describe life in the 18th century. The best time to visit is during a special event, such as the annual Rendezvous (see below). Follow Highway 155 southwest from town to get to the fort.

At **Fults Hill Prairie Nature Preserve** (618.826.2706), follow a 1.5 mile hiking trail that loops up from a bottomland forest to a blufftop prairie and back down. It is a moderately difficult hike to the top, but it comes with good views of the river valley. The site is 1.5 miles south of Fults. The parking lot is on the bluff side of Bluff Road, about seven miles north of Prairie du Rocher.

Where to Stay: Bed and Breakfasts

Conner House Bed & Breakfast (315 Main St.; 618,284.8752) offers four comfortable rooms in a gorgeous, historic Victorian mansion; a stay includes a full breakfast.

Special Events

The annual **Rendezvous** at Fort de Chartres (1350 State Route 155; 618.284.7230) is a good opportunity to buy traditionally made items such as pots, pans, and knives, as well as to watch reenactments of French colonial military parades and battles. Look for it the first weekend in June.

Like Ste. Genevieve, Prairie du Rocher carries on the old tradition of **La Guillannée** in which folks dress in costumes and parade the city's streets on New Year's Eve, singing songs and begging for favors. The fun usually starts in the evening.

Getting Around

One of the few remaining Mississippi River ferries connects Sainte Genevieve with rural Illinois. The **Ste. Gen-Modoc Ferry** (sometimes called the French Connection) is a nice way to get some river time (for a fee; no credit cards). In Sainte Genevieve, follow North Main Street (which becomes Little Rock Rd.) until you reach the river.

For More Information

There are practical limits to how much I can include in a book, but not with a website! Check out the city profiles on my website to see if they include listings that I couldn't fit in this book.

Sainte Genevieve: MississippiValleyTraveler.com/Sainte-Genevieve
Kaskaskia: MississippiValleyTraveler.com/Kaskaskia
Chester: MississippiValleyTraveler.com/Chester
Prairie du Rocher: MississippiValleyTraveler.com/Prairie-du-Rocher
Fort de Chartres: MississippiValleyTraveler.com/Fort-de-Chartres

CAPE GIRARDEAU & SOUTHERN ILLINOIS

A flood wall mural at Cape Girardeau, Missouri

Overview

It's as far south as you can go and still call it the upper Mississippi River, and you'll notice some big changes. The air may feel warmer and thicker. The bluffs give way to delta plains, and the pace of life feels less harried.

This chapter introduces you to some old river towns, including the largest city in the region, Cape Girardeau. It also dips into the tip of southwest Illinois—Little Egypt—where you can experience bits of the old cypress swamps that once dominated the area. Enjoy the sites of the small cities, then lose yourself in the forest or swamp, and work your way through the tasting rooms of the region's wineries.

Sure, you could tour this area in a (long) day, but as usual, you'll have a better experience if you take your time and explore the region's pleasures over two or three days.

History: West Bank Communities (Missouri)

CAPE GIRARDEAU

A city was bound to rise where Cape Girardeau is today. The river makes a big turn here and throws the force of its current at the base of a prominent formation known as Cape Rock. That makes for an easy-to-spot landmark and a good place to land a boat. It also helped that the views from the top of the rock were expansive. A person can see for miles up and down the river.

The origin of the city's name is a bit of a mystery, but it probably comes from a soldier, Jean Baptiste Girardot, who set up a trading camp at this point around the middle of the 18th century. He apparently didn't stick around all that long, but other people remembered he was here and named the place after him.

It wasn't until 1793 that anyone tried to establish a more permanent Euro-American settlement. Don Louis Lorimier got permission from the area's Spanish commander to set up a trading post along the El Camino Real, a road that connected the Spanish settlements of St. Louis and New Madrid. Lorimier built the post to establish trading relationships with Native Americans in the area.

Lorimier was born near Montreal in 1748. A gifted polyglot, he traded with Native Americans most of his life and married a Shawnee woman, Charlotte. He wasn't too fond of the Americans he met. In 1778—during the American Revolution—he led a raid that captured Daniel Boone. The Americans eventually caught up to him at Vincennes and drove him across the Mississippi River into Spanish territory.

The Spanish authorities then realized that he spoke many languages, so they put him to work as a translator and mediator. Grateful for the help, the Spanish Governor Baron de Carondelet gave Lorimier 6,000 acres, which included present-day Cape Girardeau. He built a home known as the Red House that served as his trading post and a gathering place for the small community. On the eve of the Louisiana Purchase, a census of the entire district counted 545 White men, 481 White women, 90 enslaved men, and 80 enslaved women. After the territory joined the US in 1804, Lorimer donated four acres for a Common Pleas Court House and got a temporary appointment as a judge.

In 1806, Lorimier's secretary, Barthelemi Cousin, laid out a village. Only a few lots were sold, in part because Lorimier was reluctant to part with much of his land. As a result, people who moved into the area generally staked out claims in the surrounding countryside. Lorimier died in 1812 and left behind a lot of confusion about who owned what. The US government had initially refused to recognize his Spanish land grants, which clouded titles. The government didn't formally recognize his land claims until 1826. As a result, the county seat moved to Jackson, and the town didn't grow much until the 1830s. In 1818, the town had just two stores and 50 houses.

Major Stephen Long passed through the area in 1820; he wrote...

> "The town comprises at this time about twenty log cabins, several of them in ruins, a log jail no longer occupied, a large unfinished brick dwelling falling rapidly into decay and a small one finished and occupied, it stands on the slope and part of the summit of a broad hill elevated about 150 feet above the Mississippi and having a deep primary soil resting on a strata of compact and sparry limestone. Near the place where boats usually land is a point of white rock jutting into the river and at very low stage of water producing a perceptible rapid...The streets of Cape Girardeau are marked out with form of regularity intersecting each other at right angles but they are in some parts so gullied and torn by the rains as to be impassable; others overgrown with such thickets of gigantic vernonias and urticlas as to resemble small forests."

By the 1830s, steamboat traffic was growing and providing a big economic boost for the city, enough to spur other developments. In 1838, the Congregation of the Mission (better known as the Vincentians) established St. Vincent's Male Academy, which would later become St. Vincent's College. While the campus included a seminary to train priests (it moved to St. Louis in 1893 and was renamed Kenrick Seminary), the Vincentians also founded a secular educational institution at a time when such schools were rare. The Vincentians owned several enslaved laborers in the school's early years, but probably began selling them to local Catholics after a decree from Pope Gregory XVI in 1839 that condemned the slave trade.

By 1830, there were over a thousand enslaved Blacks in Cape Girardeau, but that would swell to over 1,500 by the Civil War. Just 20 free Blacks lived in all of Cape Girardeau County in 1850. The local powers-that-were passed a series of increasingly oppressive laws to keep the enslaved population under control, including one measure in the 1840s that authorized patrols to prevent enslaved people from gathering in groups.

Cape Girardeau was a city with divided loyalties during the Civil War. Many early residents had migrated to the city from the South, but the city also had a large population of pro-Union German immigrants. The Union Army took control of the city on July 10, 1861, and never relinquished it. As a result, many Confederate sympathizers fled, some to join the Confederate Army.

General Ulysses S. Grant took command of the district in September 1861 and ordered construction of four forts to protect the city. Once it became clear that no Confederate attacks were imminent, the army turned to raiding the countryside to neutralize support for the Confederacy.

The city's economy picked up again after the Civil War. Industries such as logging and sawmills, cement manufacturing, quarries, mills, pottery and cigar factories employed large portions of the population.

In 1873, Southeast Missouri State College was founded as a normal school (educating future teachers). It would later become Southeast Missouri State University.

Cape Girardeau grew quickly in the early part of the 20th century. In 1900, the city counted just under 5,000 residents, but by 1940, it was home to nearly 20,000 people. One reason was the presence of the largest factory in the International Shoe Company portfolio. The factory opened in 1907 as the Roberts, Johnson & Rand Shoe Company. By the 1950s, the plant employed nearly 1,400 people and turned out 8,000-9,000 pairs of shoes a day. The plant was later assigned to the company's Florsheim Shoe division, which built a new facility in 1984. The company gradually cut jobs at the plant as competition from international markets increased, then closed it altogether at the end of 1999, at which time the remaining 300 employees lost their jobs.

Living near major industries in the 1930s came with significant challenges. Celeste Beatrice Stanton remembered visiting her aunt Josephine Brown, or Aunt Phene, who lived on South Fountain Street next to a gully that trains ran through. Every time a train approached, the family sprang into action closing up the house to protect it from the train's soot.

> "When Aunt Phene heard the train whistle blow in the near distance, she'd shoosh me into the house and everyone would hurridly slam down the open windows and shut all the doors to prevent the acrid, black soot billowing out of the train's stack from permeating the insides of the home. Once the train passed and the soot settled, the doors and windows would be re-opened and Aunt Phene would see to it that the soot was wiped from items on the porch, and the porch and steps were swept clean."

Jazz pianist Jess Stacy grew up in Cape Girardeau. During his long and successful career, he played with Benny Goodman Orchestra and many other well-known musicians. Stacy was born in 1904 in a converted railroad box car near Bird's Point, Missouri. One of his first jobs was working for the Illinois Central Railroad on a ferry that moved rail cars to and from Cairo, Illinois. He moved to Cape Girardeau in 1918, and two years later heard Fate Marable and Louis Armstrong play on the excursion boat *St. Paul* during a stop in Cape Girardeau.

A year later, he was hired as a musician on the *Majestic.* In 1923, he got a job playing with Tony Catalano's Famous Iowans. One of his responsibilities was to play what he called "the damn calliope." He was part of the Benny Goodman Band when they played Carnegie Hall in 1938, the first jazz performance in that famed venue. During that show, Stacy played a two-minute improv solo that jazz lovers still rave about today. He played with many of the greatest jazz musicians, and even worked for gangsters Al Capone and Bugs Moran at one time. Still, he had a hard time making a living as a jazz pianist. He played shows in piano bars—he hated doing it—and took a job with Max Factor in Los Angeles delivering company mail for ten years. He died in 1995.

Cape Girardeau today is still attracting new residents. Its population is around 40,000 now. Southeast Missouri State University remains an anchor. Health care is a major employer, as is Proctor and Gamble.

History: East Bank Communities (Illinois)

GRAND TOWER

Named for the big rock on the other side of the Mississippi (Tower Rock), the site drew its first Euro-American settlers in the early 1800s, including Daniel Boone's nephew, William Boone. A boatyard operated near where the power plant is today, and coal mining picked up around 1810.

The most significant boost to the area was the founding of the Grand Tower Mining, Manufacturing, and Transportation Company (GTMMT), which opened just after the Civil War. The company built coke ovens and produced pig iron—oblong blocks of rough iron that were shipped to other foundries for final processing. The company grew big enough to keep a hundred coke ovens burning and even built their own barges.

The company platted a town in 1867 and named it Grand Tower. The village incorporated in 1872. The company built houses for some of its employees and painted them all red, so the neighborhood naturally become known as Red Town. A tornado in 1890 wiped out much of the neighborhood.

A national recession in the 1870s took a toll on the town, as did a series of floods and fires. Still, iron processing remained a steady employer, enough to attract the attention of Andrew Carnegie who considered opening a big steel factory near Grand Tower. Lime manufacturing picked up in the 1880s, and the town got a small boost from sawmills and wood processing, too.

Grand Tower grew big enough that its opera house drew nationally known performers. The town had three hotels, plus a floating hotel on the converted steamer *RL Woodward.* Traveling circuses made regular stops. Watching those performances inspired a local kid—Tommy Halligan—to join the Barnum and Bailey Circus as the Flying Irishman.

Random Fact: The suspension bridge at the north end of Grand Tower carries a gas pipeline. It was completed in 1955.

By World War II, however, the town's fortunes were on the decline. Even the construction of a big levee in the 1950s didn't make much difference. Grand Tower today is a quiet river town of about 600 people.

THEBES

A small cluster of houses that had initially been known as Sparhawk's Landing (after George and Martha Sparhawk, prominent landowners in the area), became Thebes in 1843 and had enough pull to win the county seat shortly after that.

Not everyone was impressed with the new Thebes. In an 1883 history of the area, William Perrin wrote:

> "It was named, perhaps, in honor of Thebes, the ancient capital of Upper Egypt, but differs from its ancient namesake in that the latter stood upon both sides of the river Nile, while our Thebes sometimes has a river on both sides of it. Ancient Thebes began to decline 800 years B.C.; our Thebes when the county's capital was removed to Cairo. The ruins of ancient Thebes are among the most magnificent in the world; these of our Thebes are only equaled by a half-score of other towns in Alexander, Union and Pulaski Counties. Troja fuit! [Troy has perished!]"

With the county seat came a need for a courthouse. Henry Ernst Barkhausen got the contract to build it, and he got to work at the end of 1845. The Greek Revival building was constructed on top of the bluff using local limestone for the exterior walls. The courtroom was on the second floor, while the first floor housed a couple of dark cells and offices. As you traveled along the river, the courthouse really stood out among the forested banks of the river. In 1859, though, the county seat was moved to Cairo.

Berkhausen was a native of Prussia. He came to the US in 1835 and settled near Thebes two years later, where he sold wood to passing steamboats. He also ran a ferry from Thebes to the Missouri riverbank. He was apparently not content with designing an iconic building, so he began to study medicine at the same time he was supervising the courthouse construction. He spent most of the next 30 years tending to the medical needs of Thebans.

Thebes saw limited economic activity outside of the courthouse. An iron ore mine operated for a bit, and the town had a flour mill, a general store, and two sawmills nearby. Some Thebans worked in river-related occupations, while others farmed. Thebes population has been pretty stable since 1960, hovering around 450 people.

CAIRO

The confluence of the Ohio and Mississippi Rivers has long been an important crossroads. Native American communities thrived for thousands of years. Descendants of the Mississippian people who built Cahokia lived in the area for centuries. A vast, bottomland forest dominated by cottonwoods, sycamores, maples, and boxwoods spread along the Ohio and Mississippi River. Wild game was plentiful.

The forest was barely 300 feet above sea level, so it flooded often, which made it a difficult location to build permanent structures. Both French and British settlers attempted to establish a presence at the confluence. They failed.

Late in the 18th century, General George Rogers Clark built Fort Jefferson on the east bank of the Mississippi River about five miles downstream of the confluence, where the land didn't flood as often. The resident Chickasaw people weren't too happy about the influx of new people, so they attacked the fort. After six days, the Chickasaws relented, then most of the Euro-American settlers gave up and left, too, including Captain James Piggott who moved upriver and founded what later became East St. Louis. When Enoch Swarthouse passed by in 1809, hardly anyone lived at the confluence. He saw a hut on stilts, a "water-logged canoe" and a few stakes driven in the ground to tie up to.

Interest in establishing a city at the confluence grew with steamboat travel. Just four days after Henry Shreve's steamboat the *Washington* completed a 25-day round trip from Louisville to New Orleans in 1817, William and Thompson Bird bought 318 acres at the southern end of the peninsula. Around the same time, John Gleaves Comegys bought 1,800 acres nearby.

Comegys, unlike the Birds, had grand plans. He convinced the Illinois Territorial Legislature to pass a bill incorporating the City of Cairo and a bank in 1818. He apparently chose the name because he thought the area resembled the Nile River's delta. He promoted the heck out of his plan, but he died before he could develop anything. The land reverted to the control of the US government just as Illinois became a state.

The Birds didn't build anything until 1828 when they brought their enslaved laborers across the river and built a tavern and a store. When Alexander Phillip Maximilian, Prince of Wied-Neuwied, passed by in 1832, Cairo was just that store and tavern, plus a few houses at a place known simply as "Mouth of the Ohio."

Judge Sidney Breese tried to resurrect the Comegys plan. He organized a group of investors who hoped to build a railroad to Cairo. Darius Blake Holbrook emerged as the primary marketer and ran much of the day-to-day show. In 1835, the investors bought all of the land at Cairo except for the Bird's plots. Two years later, the Illinois legislature approved the incorporation of the Cairo City and Canal Company. Holbrook took the lead, and the group managed to get financing from London's John Wright & Company. The financiers sent representatives to look at the site and were impressed. In their December 1838 report, they wrote:

> "the whole peninsula is covered with a growth of forest trees many of which are 3 to 8 feet in diameter: The cottonwood, sycamore, mulberry, maple and boxwood, abound over the surface...The railroad now constructing by the State of Illinois is already at this point; the route is cleared of the timber and the depot is laid out on the Ohio river front...There is not in any quarter of the globe a situation so commanding and replete with every kind of produce and material to promote the prosperity of the merchant, the skill of the mechanic, and the growth of a great city."

The company ran elaborate ads in London papers and attracted a lot of investors. They used some of the money to build a small v-shaped levee to protect the town from the big rivers, and a few businesses moved in: a planing mill, an iron mill, sawmills, a brickyard, and shipyards. Dozens of homes were built, and the town quickly attracted hundreds of new residents.

Holbrook had a hard time convincing the new residents to stick around, however. The conditions were unpleasant. Summer heat bred intolerable swarms of mosquitoes and flies, while winter meant plodding through muddy streets. Besides that, Holbrook owned everything, so new residents were forced to lease property from him, an arrangement that bred discontent. One resident, Moses Harrell, complained that:

> "even personal liberty and freedom of thought were brought in direct antagonism to this singular undertaking. ... At no price, in no shape or form, could a resident of this city . . . become a freeholder. He could not purchase, he could not lease ... a single foot of ground within the proposed city ... he lived in it only during the pleasure of this 'Lord of the manor'."

The chickens came home to roost in 1840. The State of Illinois had halted construction for the railroad in 1837, but Cairo survived, at least until the London bondholders went bankrupt in 1840. The Cairo bank failed quickly after that, and within a few months businesses closed and residents got the hell out. A flood in 1842 washed away a few abandoned buildings and made the rest look even worse. When writer Charles Dickens passed by the remnants of Cairo on April 9, 1842, he wasn't impressed:

> "At the junction of the two rivers, on ground so flat and low and marshy, that at certain seasons of the year it is inundated to the house-tops, lies a breeding-place of fever, ague, and death; vaunted in England as a mine of Golden Hope, and speculated in, on the faith of monstrous representations, to many people's ruin. A dismal swamp, on which the half-built houses rot away: cleared here and there for the space of a few yards; and teeming, then, with rank unwholesome vegetation, in whose baleful shade the wretched wanderers who are tempted hither, droop, and die, and lay their bones; the hateful Mississippi circling and eddying before it, and turning off upon its southern course a slimy monster hideous to behold; a hotbed of disease, an ugly sepulchre, a grave uncheered by any gleam of promise: a place without one single quality, in earth or air or water, to commend it: such is this dismal Cairo."

After the crash of 1840, a few dozen people stuck around to run taverns and supply passing boats. Those folks did okay. Miles Gilbert arrived in 1843 to oversee the interests of the Cairo City and Canal Company and built a third levee that connected with the other two, so the city was finally protected all around. Those levees were even high enough to protect the small city during the Great Flood of 1844.

By 1848, the city had about a hundred residents and steamboat landings were picking up. Along the Ohio levee, the wharfboats *Cairo*, *Louisville*, and *Ellen Kirkman*, did a brisk business by selling groceries to passing steamers and offering temporary storage and lodging. Gambling halls did well in Cairo, too, although that didn't please everyone.

Around 1851, momentum picked up for another effort to develop Cairo with the incorporation of the Illinois Central Railroad. Cairo was chosen as one terminus of the new cross-state railroad. The trustee for the Cairo City Property Trust, S. Staats Taylor, traveled west from New York City to Cairo to manage the company's investment. Once there, he evicted people from the land that his company had just bought. When the company took its time selling property, the riverfront filled with floating houses and businesses until land became available for purchase at the end of 1853.

The railroad construction attracted a lot of transient workers, which just added to the town's already rough reputation. The riverfront boomed with taverns and brothels that catered mostly to construction workers and steamboat passengers.

The first train finally left from Cairo on November 22, 1854. The trip to East St. Louis took 12 hours. That same year, Cairo counted 3,798 steamboat arrivals, or 700 more than St. Louis. The village incorporated in 1855 and one of the council's first official acts was to ban steamboats from dumping sick and dying passengers in the city, something boats had been doing for a long time.

By 1856, the city's population had reached a thousand again, but not everyone who arrived was welcome. Because of the city's location as the first slice of free territory, it was attracting a growing population of free Blacks and runaway slaves. In 1856, one of the city's papers, the *Weekly Times and Delta*, wrote that the city is "almost entirely overrun with free niggers." A few months later, White mobs went on a four-day rampage kidnapping free Blacks and trying to sell them into slavery in Missouri. They drove other free Blacks out of town at gunpoint.

Runaway slaves found little safety in Cairo. One enslaved man who escaped recalled that "...though Cairo was free in name, it was one of the most active depots of the Negro catchers [who] made quite a large income by returning [slaves] to their masters under the sanction of the Fugitive Slave Law."

The city voted overwhelmingly for Stephen Douglas in the 1860 election (347 votes to just 76 for Lincoln) but became a Union stronghold almost as soon as the Civil War began. Just one week after the Confederacy attacked Fort Sumter, Secretary of War Simon Cameron ordered soldiers to Cairo to protect the strategic location.

Within a few weeks, 5,000 troops occupied makeshift Camp Defiance at the confluence, backed up by three packet boats retrofitted with guns. In September 1861, Ulysses Grant set up headquarters in the city and a short time later raided Confederate territory.

Shipyards at nearby Mound City and (and in St. Louis) built iron clad boats and other warships. Thousands of Blacks fleeing slavery ended up in Cairo, where they lived temporarily in a "contraband" camp. Many chose to settle in Cairo after the war ended.

Cairo was a key base for Union forces as they fought to gain control of the Mississippi River. Residents of the city probably didn't mind all that much. In fact, they did quite well. Many profited handsomely by selling supplies to the Army and its troops. Still, the war interrupted the flow of cargo on the river and the shift to railroads would prove to be permanent.

After the Civil War, the city boomed. Its population jumped from 2,188 in 1860 to 6,267 in 1870, even after a series of fires in 1865. New factories opened, including a brass foundry, a steam engine plant, a vinegar factory, a boiler works, and machine shops. Five newspapers kept residents informed (more or less), including one German-language paper. Cairo built its first sewer system in 1866 and installed some wooden sidewalks. The boom times weren't easy to sustain, though. A yellow fever epidemic in 1878 scared a couple thousand residents out of the city and ultimately killed 41 people.

For a few years after the Civil War, riverboats continued to play an important role in Cairo's economy. The nature of the river traffic changed, though. There were some log rafts coming from the northern forests, but most boats ran routes that were local, between Paducah and Memphis, for instance, rather than to New Orleans or St. Louis. Some boats also ferried rail cars across the rivers, at least until 1889 when the Illinois Central Bridge opened. When river traffic finally began to wane around 1880, the railroads kept a lot of folks employed. By the end of the 19th century, seven separate railroads served Cairo.

Cairo continued to draw new residents at the end of the 19th century and into the early part of the 20th century. The city's population peaked in 1920 at 15,000 people. Cairo was a busy regional hub for shopping and entertainment. During Prohibition, Cairo was an easy place to get a drink. In the 1930s, the main industries included warehousing, transshipping (between railroads and the river), lumber milling, and cottonseed processing. Factories turned out egg cases, overalls, and ice cream. Farms in the area grew corn, clover, alfalfa, wheat, vegetables, watermelons, and tobacco, some of which was shipped through Cairo.

But the city's future wasn't as solid as it seemed. The city's population was already declining by 1930. Factories closed or scaled back. And the city's social structure was a powder keg ready to burst.

Cairo was built on a vigilant and virulent foundation of racial oppression. Most of the African American population—about a third of the city in 1940—lived in a segregated neighborhood in the center of town. Cairo had 11 churches for White residents and 11 churches for African American residents. There were four grade schools for White children and three for African American children, and one junior high and high school for each racial group.

As the fight against segregation and Jim Crow grew in neighboring states, life didn't change much in Cairo. Whites and Blacks lived in different social worlds, not by choice but through the force of law and social pressure. Restaurant seating was reserved for White residents only. If you were Black, you had to go to a back door or window and get food to go. Blacks were banned from the public library and the swimming pool. The only hospital in town refused to treat Black residents. And just so there was no confusion about what group you belonged to, the city directory had an asterisk next to the name of every Black resident.

Periodic outbursts of violence enforced the racial status quo. In 1909, William James was accused of killing a White woman named Anna Pelly. As the story spread through the White community, a mob organized to go after him. The police managed to get him into a train car and on his way out of town, but the mob hijacked another train and caught up. They brought James back to Cairo and hanged him from the metal arch that stretched over Commercial Avenue. When the rope broke, rioters shot him dozens of times and set his body on fire, then they dismembered his corpse and planted his head on a stake in the ground. James was never tried in a courtroom.

After World War II, organized efforts by African Americans began to challenge the racial hierarchy. In 1946, African American teachers sued for equal pay. They were represented by Thurgood Marshall, who later served on the US Supreme Court. During the hearing, the judge and defense counsel kept calling Marshall "boy," a derogatory term directed at Black men in that era. The defense counsel tried to undermine Marshall by referencing a similar case in Tennessee. The defendants in that case, the defense asserted, had had excellent counsel, unlike the teachers in Cairo, who were represented by this "boy." Marshall listened patiently, and when it was his turn to address the court, he stood up and thanked the defense counsel, then noted that he—Marshall—had been the attorney in the Tennessee case, too.

In June 1962, four representatives of the Student Non-Violent Coordinating Committee (SNCC)—including civil rights pioneer John Lewis—traveled to Cairo to integrate public accommodations as required by a new Illinois law. Their first target was the Mark Twain Restaurant, where a server told them: "I ain't familiar with no law; what I'm familiar with is you Niggers can't eat here and if you don't get your asses out, I'm going to call the police."

The protests successfully integrated most restaurants in the city, but many of those restaurants responded by charging Blacks higher prices and offering poor service. Other protests didn't end so well. On August 17, 1962, SNCC members protested segregation at the Roller Bowl. Whites responded by beating the protesters with iron rods. In 1963, the city opted to close the public swimming pool rather than integrate it.

The conflict blew wide open four years later. On the night of July 15, 1967, Army private Robert Hunt was riding in a car with friends. The police pulled them over for a defective taillight, a common tactic police used to harass Black motorists. Hunt was accused of arguing with the police, charged with disorderly conduct, and taken to jail. Less than an hour later, Hunt was found hanging in his cell. Police called it suicide, and the coroner agreed without completing an autopsy. Few in the African American community believed that Hunt had killed himself.

Violent protests erupted, and the Governor called in the National Guard to restore order. For the next few years, open and violent conflict was common. White residents formed a vigilante group called the White Hats, who sometimes fired shots from the levee into Pyramid Courts, a housing project with Black residents. In 1969, sniper fire sent residents scrambling for cover an astonishing 170 nights. Residents of Pyramid Courts turned out the lights at night, so snipers wouldn't have an easy target. Black residents organized a group of their own called the United Front and sometimes shot back.

When Black residents won legal victories, Whites resisted. Cairo High School was desegregated in 1968, so White families opened a private school they called Camelot. (It closed in 1986 when it ran out of money.) In 1969, Black residents organized a boycott of White-owned businesses that lasted for three years. During some of their protests, columns of Nazis marched nearby. When the city hired African American police officers, some callers to 911 specifically requested assistance from White officers.

From 1968 to 1972, the high school football team played every game away, because no schools would travel to Cairo. When the Cairo team arrived in a town to play, they almost always needed a police escort. More often than not, the players were bombarded with racial epithets and threats during the games.

In 1980, a court ruled that the city's commission form of government disenfranchised Black voters. Since the system had been adopted in 1913, no African Americans had been elected to city government even though they accounted for nearly 40% of the population. The federal government monitored voting in Alexander County under the Voting Rights Act well into the 1980s—the only county in Illinois subject to oversight.

Reversing decades of racial oppression hasn't fixed the city's underlying economic weaknesses, however. The city's population had peaked in 1920 at just over 15,000. By 1960—well before the protests began—the city had lost 40% of its population. As is the case for most cities in decline, people with means left first, while those with limited resources had to stay. In Cairo, the residents of housing projects and older residents in senior housing (Black and White) have generally stayed put.

Cairo's hospital closed in 1986. Only one railroad is still active in Cairo. Metropolis, a city a few miles up the Ohio River, got a casino license over Cairo. The few remaining jobs in town are at the port, at a seed oil processing plant, at a rice seed company, and at the school and local government. In 2020, the city's population fell to 1,733, a nearly 40% drop just from 2010.

Cairo is still protected by a massive levee, seven miles of which encircle the city. When you enter Cairo from Illinois, you pass under a railroad bridge that turns into a flood gate when the rivers rise. The city is a collection of vacant lots, deteriorating housing, and a few historic buildings that volunteers determinedly take care of.

Many residents continue to fight for their hometown and to hope for an improvement in their economic fortunes, but it's hard to imagine where that's likely to come from. The geography of Cairo—in the bottomlands at the confluence of two great rivers—is a difficult location to build a sustainable city, yet it was nearly inevitable that people would try. The great injustices committed in Cairo, though, weren't inevitable, and the city is still paying for them today.

Explore the West Bank (Missouri)

CAPE GIRARDEAU

Attractions

Tower Rock Natural Area (County Road 460; 573.290.5730) is the best place to get a close look at this Mississippi River landmark. The 60-foot tall remnant of a bluff sits in the river channel, where the tricky currents around its base have confounded river navigators for centuries. There's a decent overlook just above the rock, but if the river is really low, you may be able to walk across the rocky shelf to the rock. The site is nearly an hour's-drive from Cape Girardeau. Take Interstate 55 north to US Highway 61 near Fruitland. Go north, then veer right at County Highway C, then east on County Highway A. When you reach County Road 460 (a gravel road), go south to reach the site.

AUTHOR'S PICK: **Trail of Tears State Park** (429 Moccasin Springs; 573.334.1711) is one of the special places along the Mississippi. Sprawling over 3,400 acres, the park marks one of the sites in the forced exodus known as the Trail of Tears, when the US government removed Cherokee and other Native Americans from the Southeast. Thousands of people died as they walked 800 miles to reservation lands in Oklahoma. Nine of the thirteen groups of refugees who reached the Mississippi River crossed at this site in 1838 and 1839. The visitor center has exhibits on the Trail of Tears and its legacy.

The park is more than a memorial, though. There are miles of hiking trails running through forest and along the top of the hills to overlooks with expansive views of the river and the Illinois floodplain (try the Peewah trail). Fall is an especially good time to visit as colors paint the hillsides. There's also a lake with a swimming beach and two campgrounds, including one next to the Mississippi, and it's a good area for birding and fishing. To get there from Cape Girardeau, follow Main Street north out of town (which becomes Big Bend Road and State Highway 177) for 11 miles to the park entrance.

There's a cluster of wildlife areas next to each other just north of the city limits: **Juden Creek Conservation Area**, **Twin Trees Park**, and **Kelso Sanctuary.** A hiking trail cuts through them all, much of it along a ridge that is popular with birders. Follow Highway 177 north out of town (Spring Street, which becomes Big Bend) until you reach Old Route V, turn right, then right again on Cape Rock Drive; the first right after that takes you into a parking lot at the trailhead.

Cape Rock Park (10 East Cape Rock Dr.; 573.339.6340) has an overlook of the Mississippi River at the spot where Ensign Girardot founded the original trading post.

The **Century Casino Cape Girardeau** (777 Main St.; 573.730.7624) is based near the river just north of downtown. You can pass your time at one of the 900 or so slot machines, 20 gaming tables, or four poker tables.

Check the schedule for the **Show Me Center** (1333 N. Sprigg St.; 573.651.2297), which hosts live performances throughout the year, including many top musicians, plus college basketball games.

Riverfront Park has a concrete terrace where touring boats dock when they visit. Follow a short walking trail along the river. During high water, the flood gates close.

The city side of the flood wall is decorated with **24 murals** over 1,100 feet that depict scenes from the city's long history. They were designed by Chicago artist Thomas Melvin and painted in 2005 with the help of local artists. As you might guess, the city's river history is well represented. The murals continue past Melvin's designs with images of 50 native Missourians who did good.

Built on a prominent rise on the river bank, the **Common Pleas Courthouse** (44 N. Lorimier St.) has stood as a landmark to river travelers since 1854. Walk the grounds and check out the Civil War memorials.

Just east of the downtown, **Capaha Park** (1400 Broadway)—the city's oldest public park—features lovely rose gardens, a scenic pond, a band shell, walking trails, and the home field for the Cape Girardeau Capahas, who have been playing games since 1894.

Cape River Heritage Museum (538 Independence St.; 573.334.0405) hosts exhibits on Native Americans who lived in the area, steamboats, and some of the famous people from the region, as well as a few rotating exhibits. The building began life in 1908 as a police and fire station.

Red House Interpretive Center (128 S. Main St.; 573.339.6340) recreates the French Colonial home and trading post of Louis Lorimier, the city's founder. The exhibits highlight the city's early history. It is usually open on Friday and Saturday (1-4).

The red brick edifice of **Old St. Vincent's Church** (131 S. Main St.) has been watching over the riverfront since 1853. It is one of the oldest churches west of the Mississippi River. The church is primarily English Gothic in style. Twenty-six buttresses shore up the outside walls. The steeple was added in 1903 but was destroyed by lightning twice and rebuilt, the last time in 1912. The pews are original. Under the altar, there are relics of St. Vincent de Paul, St. Peter, St. Paul, and St. Andrew. When a new church was built in the 1970s, old St. Vincent was nearly torn down. Supporters rallied, though, and oversaw a major restoration that began in 1977. Mass is held on Sundays at 10am, so a good time to visit is just before or after mass.

Take a tour of the **Glenn House** (325 S. Spanish St.; 573.579.3290) for a look at the life of an upper middle class family at the end of the 19th century. Built in 1883, the original house was given a Queen Anne-style makeover a decade later. The house is open for tours on Friday and Saturday afternoons from May through October.

During the Civil War, four imposing forts protected Cape Girardeau from attacks by the Confederate Army. The remnants of one of those, **Fort D**, are preserved in a city park by that name (920 W. Fort St.; 573.339.6340). Part of the earthen walls are still visible. During the Depression, men from the Works Progress Administration built a stone house on the site. The park also has a good overlook of the river.

The **River Campus at Southeast Missouri State University** opened in 2007 on the site of the former St. Vincent's College and Seminary. The campus hosts a variety of arts programming throughout the year. Highlights include the **Crisp Museum** (518 S. Fountain St.; 573.651.2260), inside the Cultural Arts Center (the building on the right if you're facing the river), which has exhibits on the broad swath of human and geologic history in the region, plus student art exhibits.

For another pretty view, walk to the **Old Mississippi River Bridge Scenic Overlook** (Morgan Oak at Spanish St.), which preserves part of the approach for Cape's first river bridge. While you're here, take a selfie with the state's largest American beech tree.

Little Egypt

The most southern portion of Illinois has been known as Little Egypt since at least since the 1830s. Many early Euro-American settlers considered the Mississippi River to be America's Nile. When you add in the fact that the area was inhabited by an ancient civilization that built earthen mounds that resembled pyramids, it's not a stretch to imagine a connection to Egypt.

The name may have been cemented in local lore by a crop failure in central Illinois. The winter of 1830-31 was especially harsh, with snow on the ground from September to April. The growing season didn't start until June, then was cut short by a September frost. The only corn that survived grew on the farms in the most southern part of the state. Farmers from central Illinois were forced to travel there to buy corn and other food, just like Jacob went to Egypt for his grain when Canaan was hit by drought. Or so the story goes.

If you lived in northern or central Illinois, "Little Egypt" was an insult, a place associated with slavery and poor, uneducated whites. Today, the nickname is a source of pride.

The first place in southern Illinois with an Egyptian name was Cairo. Investors in the Bank of Cairo and City of Cairo bought land at the Ohio/Mississippi confluence in 1817. Thebes sprang to life in the early 1840s, and a town called Alexandria was proposed between Cairo and Thebes but never developed. Other towns with Egyptian names that survived included Dongola and Karnak.

So where exactly is Little Egypt? It depends on whom you ask. At times it seems to include the entire southern half of the state. Folks today would probably say it's just the bottom third, some 16 or 17 counties.

The name is so well known that it has appeared in popular music, such as the sweet song by James Talley called *Little Egypt Land* (released on his 2008 CD called *Journey: The Second Voyage*).

RANDOM FACT: Cairo-born artist Hale A. Woodruff, was an acclaimed modernist painter, whose work often featured themes about African American life. One of his most acclaimed works was a three-panel mural he completed in 1938 called **Amistad Mutiny**. You can see it Talladega College in Alabama, at the Savery Library.

Cape Girardeau/Southern Illinois Route Map

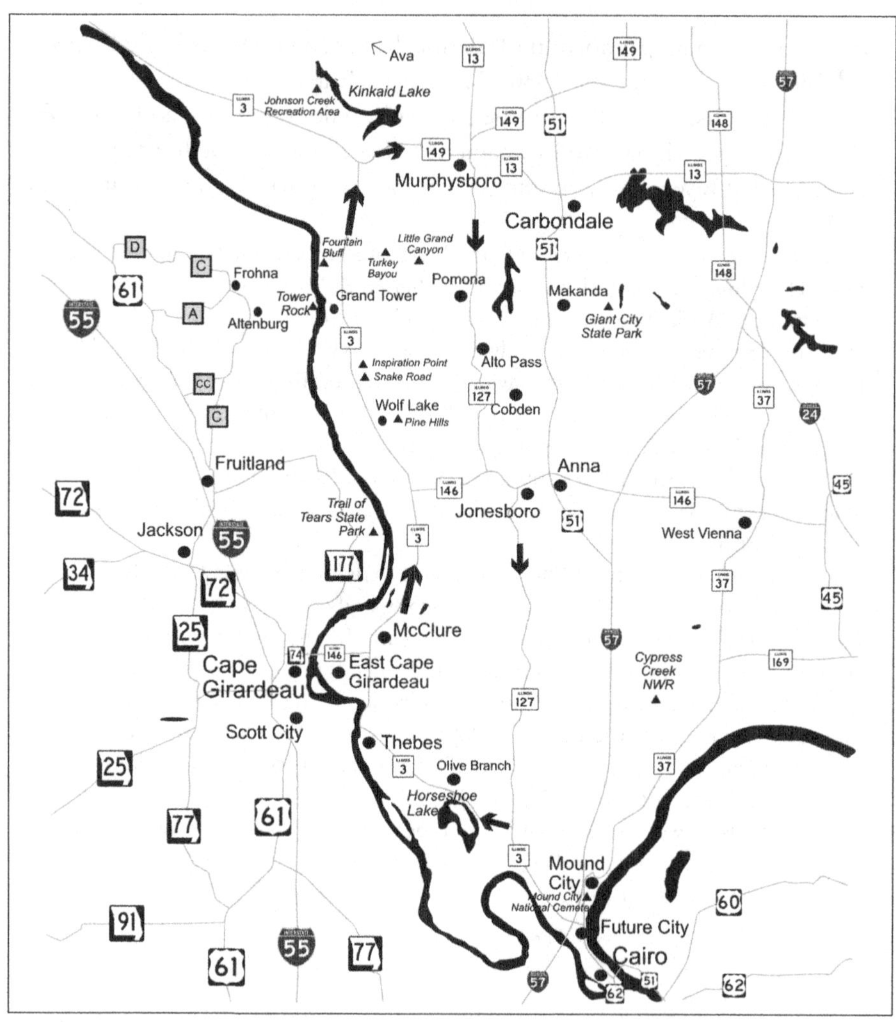

DRIVING DIRECTIONS

From Cape Girardeau, it's easy to drive a circular route through the southern Illinois. Once you've crossed the Bill Emerson Memorial Bridge to the east side of the river, you'll get to Illinois Highway 3. To stick to sites relatively close to the Mississippi River, follow this route (it is about 115 miles long):

- Head north on Highway 3
- Go east on Illinois Highway 149 to Murphysboro
- Go south on Illinois Highway 127 until it intersects with Illinois Highway 3 just west of Mound City
- Detour into Cairo by going south on Illinois Highway 3
- Follow Highway 3 north to get back to Cape Girardeau

Cape Girardeau Map

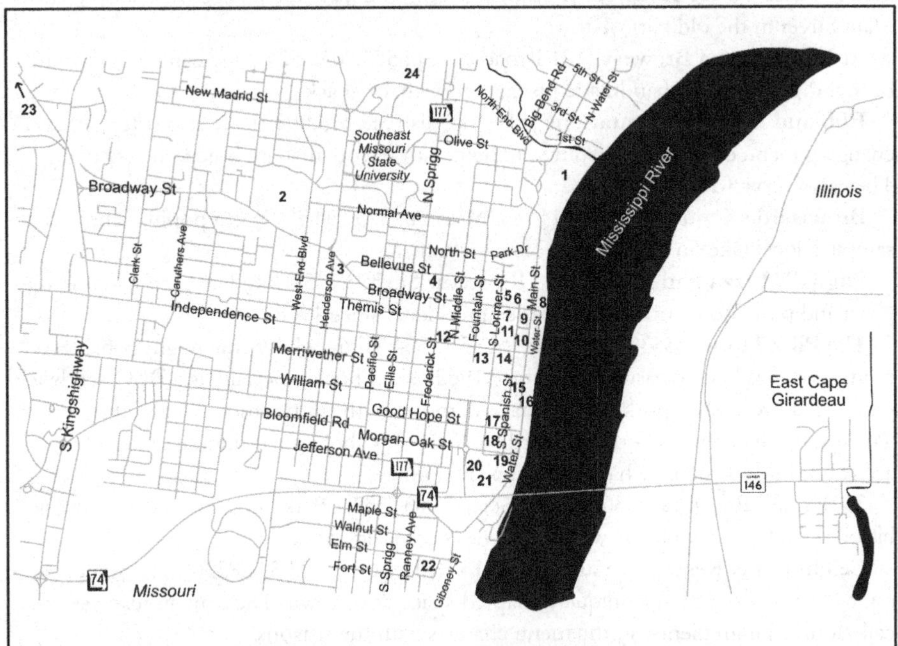

Attractions

2. Capaha Park
12. Cape River Heritage Museum
1. Century Casino Cape Girardeau
11. Common Pleas Courthouse
20. Crisp Museum
22. Fort D
18. Glenn House
19. Old Mississippi River Bridge Scenic Overlook
15. Old St. Vincent's Church
16. Red House Interpretive Center
21. River Campus at Southeast Missouri State University
8. Riverfront Park/Murals
24. Show Me Center

Where to Eat and Drink

10. 36 Bar and Restaurant
9. Broussard's Cajun Cuisine
17. Cape Riverfront Market
4. Celebrations Restaurant and Bar
14. Ebb and Flow Fermentations.
7. Minglewood Brewery
3. Pagliai's Pizza and Pasta
5. Red Banner Coffee Roasters

Where to Stay

23. Cape Camping & RV Park
6. Kage House
13. Neumeyer's B&B

Random Fact: Cairo left such a lasting impression on Dickens that he used the town as inspiration in his novel **Martin Chuzzlewit**. In that book, the title character goes to a place called Eden that was a "hideous swamp… choked with slime and matted growth," a destitute and depressing place run by the corrupt Eden Land Corporation.

Drinking and Dining

Red Banner Coffee Roasters (1 N. Spanish St.) is a pleasant small coffee shop just off Main Street in the old part of town.

At **Minglewood Brewery** (121 Broadway St.; 573.803.0524), you can sip on a craft beer and pair it with a handmade pizza, sandwich, or snack.

Ebb and Flow Fermentations (11 S. Spanish St.; 573.803.1611) also offers an ever-changing menu of craft beer, some of them with flavors that are bold and surprising. They also serve food.

Broussard's Cajun Cuisine (114 N. Main St.; 573.334.7235) is a popular choice to sample a local take on the food of New Orleans.

Pagliai's Pizza and Pasta (1129 Broadway St.; 573.335.0366) has been meeting the pizza and pasta needs of Cape Girardeau residents since 1968.

The **Pilot House** (3532 Perryville Rd.; 573.334.7106), what some might consider a roadhouse, has been pleasing folks since 1962. Their house specialty is a BBQ sandwich on toasted bread. The pork is delicious and moist, with a little smoke and slightly sweet. The rest of the menu is fairly standard bar food. It's about a ten-minute drive. They aren't too big, so you may have a short wait at times.

36 Bar and Restaurant (36 N. Main St.; 573.803.2333) offers a fine dining experience in a historic storefront downtown, with an emphasis on quality steak entrées.

Celebrations Restaurant and Bar (615 Bellevue St.; 573.334.8330) is another fine dining option housed in a uniquely adapted space downtown. Their menu features locally sourced ingredients, so the menu changes with the seasons.

Where to Stay: Camping

There are two main campgrounds at **Trail of Tears State Park** (Jackson: 429 Moccasin Springs; 573.290.5268). The Mississippi River Campground is, as you'd expect, next to the river and has a few sites with full hookups and electric. The Lake Boutin Campground sits atop the bluffs and is heavily shaded but all sites are primitive.

Cape Camping & RV Park (1900 N. Kingshighway; 800.335.1178) has 90 sites with full-hookups, and WiFi throughout the campground; it also has a swimming pool and mini-golf.

Bed and Breakfasts

Neumeyer's Bed and Breakfast (25 S. Lorimier St.; 573.225.5633) offers a two-room suite and a single room in a charming, lushly landscaped, cottage-style home.

Lodging

The **Kage House** (636.399.4020) is a modern one-bedroom apartment in a 19th-century brick rowhouse in downtown Cape Girardeau. The back deck has great views of the river and downtown.

Special Events

The **Cape Riverfront Market** assembles on Saturday mornings from May through October (35 S. Spanish St.; 573.334.8085).

In April, the **Mississippi River Valley Scenic Drive** (573.275.7487) highlights the Great River Road in Cape Girardeau and Perry Counties. Communities roll out the red carpet for visitors, with food and craft vendors and tours of historic sites.

> **Tip:** Sundays in Cape Girardeau are a great time to go for a hike or a swim, because many of the town's attractions, including museums, aren't open.

Southeast Missouri State's **River Campus** hosts live shows, including theatrical performances, dance, and concerts. Check the schedule at rivercampus.org.

The **Southeast Missouri District Fair** has been an off and on regional affair since 1855. It's family-friendly fun, with carnival rides, fried food, livestock judging, tractor pulls, a demolition derby, and live music. Look for it in September at the Fairgrounds at Arena Park (410 Kiwanis Dr.).

Cape Girardeau Heritage Days in October offers a crash course in local history, with free admission to museums and presentations on local history.

Explore the East Bank (Illinois)

GRAND TOWER

Attractions

The **Mississippi River Museum and Interpretive Center** in Grand Tower (606 Front St.; 618.565.2227) goes deep into local river history, with exhibits on the people and boats of the Mississippi. The museum is usually open on Saturday afternoons, but call ahead if you really want to tour it.

There's a good view of **Tower Rock** from the levee at Grand Tower. If you want to get closer, you'll need to access it from the Missouri side (see page 391).

Just north of Grand Tower, **Fountain Bluff** offers spectacular overlooks of the Mississippi River. From Highway 3, go west on Happy Hollow Road and follow it up a steep, narrow gravel road to the top. You'll find a few places to pull over and enjoy the views, which are even better at sunset. (This can be a challenging road for cars with low clearance.)

Where to Stay: Camping

Devil's Backbone Park (1 Brunkhorst Ave.; 618.684.6192) is right next to the Mississippi River, so it's a great place to watch the world flow by. Most sites have electric and water hookups, and there's a shower house.

Special Events

Twice a year, 2.5 miles of LaRue Road (aka **Snake Road**) are closed to vehicle traffic so snakes (there are over 15 species in the area!) can migrate between the bluffs where they winter and the swamp where they spend their summer vacations. You can park at either end and stroll down the road. The walk is best enjoyed at a slow pace. If you see a snake, keep your distance, as some are venomous (cottonmouths are common). The road is typically closed for the migration from mid-March to mid-May and again from September through October. Your chances of seeing snakes are better when the weather is warm. Even if you don't see snakes, the walk between the spring-fed wetlands and bluffs is gorgeous and wildflowers burst in spring. To reach the north access, turn east onto a gravel road just before crossing the Big Muddy River (you'll be five miles south of Grand Tower). When the road ends, turn right to park. The other entrance is from the end of Larue Road, which is a mile south of the Big Muddy River.

MURPHYSBORO

Attractions

As a young Congressman, John Logan defended segregation and embraced the "dirty work" of returning enslaved Blacks to their plantation masters in the South. When he served in the Illinois legislature, the Democrat helped pass a law in 1853 that banned all Blacks from settling in the state, even if they were free. Still, he went on to serve the Union in the Civil War. Like many of his fellow southern Illinoisans, he looked down on abolitionists, but he also strongly opposed secession. Logan rose to the rank of General and fought with Grant at Vicksburg, then served as the city's military governor after Union forces occupied the city. Witnessing the horrendous and dehumanizing conditions that enslaved Blacks endured in the South had a profound effect on him. After the Civil War, he switched political parties and strongly advocated for civil rights (and voting rights) for America's formerly enslaved citizens. Logan is also credited as one of the founders of the Memorial Day holiday. The **General John Logan Museum** in Murphysboro (1613 Edith St.; 618.684.3455) traces his life and fascinating career and is well worth a visit, even if you aren't a Civil War buff. There's also a bronze memorial dedicated to Logan at the middle school (2125 Spruce St.).

Just across the street, the **Jackson County Historical Society** (1616 Edith St.; 618.684.6989; W, F Noon-3) features a collection of textiles and an exhibit on the Tri-State Tornado that devastated the region, killing 234 people in Murphysboro alone.

Drinking and Dining

If you're more in the mood to sit and sample directly from a local brewer, find your way 12 miles northwest of Murphysboro to the **Scratch Brewing Company** near Ava (264 Thompson Rd.; 618.426.1415). They brew beer from ingredients they grow themselves or find in the woods near them, so they create beers with flavor profiles you are unlikely to find anywhere else. They also serve pizza baked in a wood-fired oven, but if you're starving, call ahead to make sure they are available; they sometimes sell out.

Molly's Pint Brewpub (12 N. 13th St.; 618.967.6267) is a local pub that brews their own beer and an ethos of bringing people together.

For a small town, Murphysboro cooks up some good barbecue. **17th Street BBQ** (32 N. 17th St.; 618.684.3722) has earned the devotion of fans of smoked meats and not just from southern Illinois. Their ribs get a lot of love. On the north edge of town, **Pat's BBQ** (111 Tower Rock Lane; 618.687.4227; Th-Sa 10-6) attracts a legion of its own devoted followers.

Where to Stay: Lodging and Cabins

The **Historic Hull House Inn** (1517 Walnut St.; 618.305.5950) rents three rooms in a 19th-century Italianate mansion. Rates include a continental breakfast.

Kinkaid Lake Cabins (1761 Marina Rd.; 618.303.1317) consists of three unique, round units that are located a mile from the namesake Kinkaid Lake northwest of Murphysboro. Each includes 2-3 beds plus a small kitchen. Prices are quite affordable.

Special Events

Murphysboro hosts a **farmers market** on Saturday mornings (1101 Walnut St.).

ALTO PASS

Attractions

Bald Knob Cross of Peace (3630 Bald Knob Rd.) towers over the hills near Alto Pass. The boxy white cross rises 111 feet and consists of insulated metal panels on top of a thick granite base. It was completed in 1963. The views from its perch are spectacular.

Drinking and Dining

Two miles north of Alto Pass, **Rendleman Orchards** (9680 State Highway 127; 618.893.2771) offers fresh produce in season (late June through October), plus locally made jams, jellies, and other ready-to-eat products. A great place to stock up on peaches.

Sip wine with a light snack at **Alto Vineyards** (8515 Highway 127; 618.893.4898) in their spacious tasting room or go outside and enjoy the scenery outside. They make several tasty wines locally and at a sister vineyard in Australia.

Check out the wine, beer, and/or distilled spirits at **Von Jakob Vineyard** (230 Highway 127; 618.893.4600). Grab a bite to eat while you're there, and enjoy it all out on the large deck.

Peachbarn Winery and Café (560 Chestnut St.; 618.893.4923), just south of Alto Pass, offers another wine tasting experience, as well as good, seasonal food.

When you get tired of wine, check out the **Havisham Bourbon Bar** (260 Main St.; 618.893.5910) for something a little stronger that you can savor in a historic storefront.

Where to Stay: Bed and Breakfasts

Von Jakob Winery and Brewery (230 Illinois Highway 127; 618.893.4600) rents five modern rooms in two cottages on the winery grounds. Each room comes with a full breakfast, Jacuzzi tubs, a bottle of wine, and scenic views.

Shawnee Hill B&B (Cobden: 290 Water Valley Rd.; 618.697.0385) rents peace and quiet at its two Victorian-themed suites and a beautiful log cabin five miles southeast of Alto Pass. Rooms can be booked with a full breakfast for an extra fee.

Lodging

The Peachbarn Winery (560 Chestnut St.; 618.893.4923) rents a couple of small vacation homes, plus a suite carved out of a 1940s barn that is thoroughly up-to-date and located in a pastoral setting.

JONESBORO/ANNA

Drinking and Dining

Hebrewz in Jonesboro (300 W. Broad; 618.833.3000) is a friendly little coffee shop that can also make you a sandwich for breakfast or lunch.

Just down the road, **Kiki's Coffeehouse** (326 S. Main St.; 618.833.2023) occupies a historic storefront in Anna where you can get your favorite coffee drink and a snack.

Lodging

Rustic Hideaway Cabins (60 Rustic Hideaway Lane; 618.534.0481) rents two log cabins deep in the woods northwest of Jonesboro. Each has a big outdoor patio, hot tub, and full kitchen.

At the **Davie School Inn** in Anna (300 Freeman St.; 618.833.2377), it's not only OK to sleep in class, it's expected. They rent eight comfortable themed-rooms and three suites in a converted schoolhouse. Rates include a full breakfast served in your room.

Special Events

Anna hosts a **farmers market** on Tuesday mornings downtown.

SHAWNEE NATIONAL FOREST

The rolling terrain and thick forests of the Ozark and Shawnee Hills, untouched by glaciers, offer spectacular scenery with many ways to enjoy it. Humans have been enjoying the area for nearly 12,000 years, just not always wisely. In the 19th century, the old forests were cleared for farming, but the soil was thin and not especially fertile, so most of the farms failed. Farmers eagerly sold their land to the federal government in the late 1930s, which then created Shawnee National Forest. At the end of the Great Depression, armies of men working for the Civilian Conservation Corps planted trees by the tens of thousands as the first step in re-foresting the land. The national forest today spreads out over 280,000 acres and includes a diverse group of ecosystems and landscapes, including hardwood forests, swamps, and canyons.

Whether you're passing through on a day trip or sticking around for a few days, there are many ways to experience the forest. An extensive trail system means you can hike or ride a horse on trails that range from easy to challenging. Lakes and rivers offer good fishing, swimming, and paddling. Birds are abundant and easy to spot all year. Many areas are open to hunting for specific seasons. On top of all that, the national forest offers camping in developed areas, as well as backcountry sites.

The route for this chapter cuts through the **Mississippi Bluffs Ranger District** (the rangers office is in Jonesboro: 521 N. Main St.; 618.833.8576), which includes two designated wilderness areas: Bald Knob and Clear Springs. If you're looking to stretch your legs, the national forest has a trail to match your ambition:

- If you're feeling ambitious, the **River to River Trail** runs 160 miles from the Ohio River (Elizabethtown) to the Mississippi River (Grand Tower) through rugged terrain. You aren't obligated to do the whole trail at once, of course. See www.rivertorivertrail.net for maps and detailed descriptions of the trail.
- If you want a decent challenge but only have an hour or two, the **Little Grand Canyon** offers 2.7 miles of amazing scenery. It's not an easy hike, though, as the footing is slippery in some places, and you have to hike uphill at times. From Murphysboro, go six miles south on Highway 127 to Etherton Road, then go west and north for 2.5 miles. At Poplar Ridge Road, veer west. After one mile, you'll reach a four-way stop. Continue forward. The road becomes Hickory Ridge Road. After 2.3 miles, you'll reach the entrance road.
- The views of the bottomlands and cultivated fields from **Inspiration Point** live up to the name. From Grand Tower, go south on Highway 3. After crossing the Big Muddy River, go east on the gravel road. When the road ends at the bluff, turn left, then take the first right. (Turn right at the bluff to get to Snake Road.) You can park at the base of the bluff and take a strenuous uphill hike or continue driving up the road to the upper parking lot for an easy half-mile walk to the edge of the bluff.

Giant City State Park (Makanda: 235 Giant City Rd.; 618.457.4836) is off the main route but worth a side trip. The park is best known for its towering pillars of eroded sandstone and its hiking trails. The one-mile Giant City Nature Trail is the easiest place to see some of those sandstone pillars. The Stone Fort Nature Trail loops up and around an area where Native Americans built a long stone wall a thousand years ago. The park is a few miles south of Carbondale. From Cape Girardeau, it's an hour's drive.

If you want to go deeper into Shawnee National Forest, here are a few highlights:

- If you have the time, go further east to **Garden of the Gods Recreation Area** and its spectacular scenery. It's a one hour, 20 minute drive from Carbondale.

> **Tip:** Several outfitters arrange horseback riding tours through the National Forest; call or visit the forest office for a current list (Jonesboro: 521 N. Main; 618.833.8576).

- The old Ohio River town of **Metropolis** is worth a stop to take selfies with the Superman statues. Metropolis is about an hour from Carbondale.
- There are several places where you can visit remnants of the swamps that once covered much of Southern Illinois. Most are in the Cache River Watershed. **Cypress Creek National Wildlife Refuge** (www.fws.gov/refuge/cypress_creek; 618.634.2231) has a couple of hiking trails and boat ramps among its 16,000 acres. In addition, look for the **Cache River Auto Tour** brochure that details over a dozen places where you can tour parts of the old swamp, such as the boardwalk at Section 8 Woods (Highway 37 south of the Henry Barkhausen Cache River Wetlands Center) and the paddling opportunities at Lower Cache River Access (Perks Road west of Highway 37).

Tours

Volunteers from the **River-to-River Trail Society** (www.rivertorivertrail.net) lead guided hikes along portions of the River-to-River Trail throughout the year. Fall tours when colors are peaking are a popular option.

Drinking and Dining

Wine! There are a lot of wineries in the hills and valleys of southern Illinois, several just along the route detailed in this book (see Alto Pass). Try them all (in moderation, of course)! Fall is the busiest time to tour, so plan ahead if you want to stay the night in the area. For a complete list, pick up a copy of the Shawnee Hills Wine Trail.

If you're near **Giant City State Park**, stop at the 1930s-era lodge for a tasty home-style meal (Makanda: 460 Giant City Lodge Rd.; 618.457.4921). People go out of their way for the fried chicken.

Where to Stay

Southern Illinois has a lot of good options for camping, although many are basic, non-electric sites. If you feel like backpacking, you can camp just about anywhere in **Shawnee National Forest**.

At the other end of the spectrum, there are a lot of cabins and vacation homes for rent. They are generally best suited for large groups or families traveling together and many require a minimum stay of two nights. My recommendations below focus on places that cater more to individuals or couples, like bed and breakfasts or small inns.

Camping

Giant City State Park (Makanda: 235 Giant City Rd.; 618.457.4836) rents 85 campsites with water and electric in a shady area, plus several basic sites. The campground has a shower house.

There are three developed **campgrounds** in the Mississippi Bluffs Ranger District of Shawnee National Forest (618.833.8576):

- **Johnson Creek Recreation Area** (Highway 151 about four miles north of Highway 3) has 20 basic campsites with water near popular Kinkaid Lake; there are no showers.
- **Pine Hills** (Forest Road 236) has 13 basic sites with water in a shaded area near the village of Wolf Lake; no showers.
- Well off the beaten path, **Turkey Bayou** offers free, basic camping next to a small lake. The campground is about seven miles from Highway 3. It sometimes floods after heavy rains.

Cabins

Giant City State Park (Makanda: 235 Giant City Rd.; 618.457.4836) rents several historic cabins in sizes that range from cozy enough for couples to big enough for a group. The cabins come with plenty of modern amenities.

IN AND AROUND CAIRO

Attractions

At the southern end of the route, **Mound City National Cemetery** (141 State Highway 37; 618.748.9107) is the final resting place for 9,000 veterans of every conflict since the Mexican-American War. Many were killed in the Civil War. Several of the Union Army's **iron clad boats** were built at Mound City; a sign on Walnut Street marks the factory's location.

When Cairo was built, buildings were oriented more to the Ohio River than the Mississippi. The Ohio shoreline grew into a long row of docks for barges and industries. Some of those docks are still active today. The tall **flood wall** along the Ohio River has a few **murals** that depict scenes from the city's history. The old business district was centered around Washington and Commercial Avenues, but there's hardly anything left there today, except for the arch over 8th Street at Washington.

Charles Galigher made a lot of money by selling flour to the federal government during the Civil War. He used part of his fortune to construct the four-story **Magnolia Manor** (2700 Washington; 618.734.0201) in 1872. The red-bricked Italianate mansion has 14 rooms with tall ceilings. Enjoy good views of the town and rivers from the cupola. The museum is currently open daily except for Wednesdays.

Cairo's **A.B. Safford Memorial Library** (1609 Washington Ave.; 618.734.1840) is an architectural gem. The Queen Anne-style building opened in 1883 and has retained most of its original features, including the leaded glass windows.

Another legacy of the boom years, the federal government built the stout **US Custom House** in 1872 to collect tariffs on international products that had not been unloaded before reaching Cairo. Today, the building houses the **Cairo Customs House Museum** (1400 Washington Ave.), which maintains exhibits about the Civil War, floods, and other aspects of Cairo's history. The side facing Washington Avenues still has holes from bullets fired during the city's racial protests. The museum can be toured by appointment; call the library to set one up (618.734.1840).

The Ohio River ends its 981-mile journey at Cairo where it merges with the Mississippi. The Ohio is the bigger river at the confluence, at least in terms of the amount of water it carries. The color of the water in the two rivers is quite distinct, something that artist and naturalist John James Audubon noticed after floating through it in 1820:

> "the Beautiful & Transparent Watter of the Ohio when first entering the Mississipi is taken in Small Drafts and Looks the More agreeable to the Eye as it goes down Surrounded by the Muddy Current, it keep off as much as possible by running down on the Kentucky side for Several Miles but reduces to a Narrow Strip & is Lost."

You can view the confluence from **Fort Defiance State Park** (US Highway 51/US Highway 62), which is sometimes open to vehicle traffic and sometimes isn't. The park isn't the most beautiful place you'll visit, mostly because repeated flooding from the two big rivers makes it tough to maintain. As you are leaving town heading south on US Highway 51, continue driving for half a block after US Highway 51 turns left to Kentucky, then make a left into a parking lot. Miss the turn and you'll end up on the Cairo Mississippi River Bridge heading to Missouri. If the road to the park isn't open, you can park in the lot and walk to the confluence.

Drinking and Dining

Shemwell's (1102 Washington; 618.734.0165) is a small-town restaurant that has been serving barbecue from this location since the 1940s. The meats are tender with a slight smokiness and come with a vinegar-based sauce that has a bit of a peppery spice to it.

NORTH OF CAIRO

Attractions

Horseshoe Lake State Fish and Wildlife Area (Miller City: 21759 Westside Dr.; 618.776.5689) preserves a 2,400-acre cypress swamp in an old oxbow that was once part of the main channel of the Mississippi. It's a popular place for birding and fishing and is a fine place to paddle around in a canoe or kayak. The lake is 11 miles south of Thebes.

The **old courthouse in Thebes** (5th St. at Oak St.; 618.764.2658), a small limestone structure built in 1848 on top of the bluff, has commanding views of the river. If you are determined to get inside, it's best to call ahead to arrange a tour.

The **Thebes Gap** is a narrow channel that runs 12 miles over clusters of rocks that steamboat captains called the Grand Chain. They dreaded navigating through. The Mississippi River began passing through this area relatively recently, about 11,000 years ago. When the water is low, much of the shelf is exposed at Thebes and can be fun to walk across (but it can be quite slippery too, so step carefully). The US Army Corps of Engineers periodically blasts bits from the bottom to help maintain a channel for barges.

Where to Stay: Camping

Horseshoe Lake State Fish and Wildlife Area (Miller City: 21759 Westside Dr.; 618.776.5689) has a campground with sites that range from basic to full hookups. There's a shower house on site.

Getting There

Cape Girardeau Regional Airport (860 Limbaugh Dr.; 573.334.6230) is a few miles southwest of the city center.

For More Information

There are practical limits to how much I can include in a book, but not with a website! Check out the city profiles on my website to see if they include listings that I couldn't fit in this book.

Cape Girardeau: MississippiValleyTraveler.com/Cape-Girardeau
Shawnee National Forest: MississippiValleyTraveler.com/Shawnee-National-Forest
Grand Tower: MississippiValleyTraveler.com/Grand-Tower
Cairo: MississippiValleyTraveler.com/Cairo
Thebes: MississippiValleyTraveler.com/Thebes

MISSISSIPPI RIVER GEOLOGY

Bluffs above the Mississippi River near Reno, Minnesota

The Mississippi River begins in northern Minnesota and travels about 2,350 miles before emptying into the Gulf of Mexico. Measurements of the river's length vary depending upon when they were taken. Before the river was channelized for navigation, the Mississippi regularly cut new paths and abandoned old ones, so its length was always changing. In addition, the US Army Corps of Engineers shortened the river in a few places to make it easier for big boats to navigate.

The river's name—Mississippi—is derived from an Ojibwe (Chippewa) name for the river: Misi-ziibi (long river). The Ojibwe were intimately familiar with the river and had names to mark different spots. The short channel that connects Lakes Irving and Bemidji, for example, was called Wub'-i-gum-ag zi'-bi (the river of the lake that has a constrictive place).

Other Native Americans had their own names for the river, of course:

- The Dakota (Sioux) people knew it as Wakpa Tanka (great river) or Hahawakpa (river of the falls)
- The Cheyenne called it Má'xe-é'ometaa'a (Big Greasy River)
- The Wyandot (Wendat) word was reportedly Yandawezue (Great River)
- The southern Lenape, who encountered the Mississippi after being forced from the east coast, may have called it namesi sipu (fish river)

For the past 10,000 years, the Mississippi River has emerged from an outlet at Lake Itasca in northern Minnesota, a body of water the Ojibwe called O-mush-ko'zo za-gai-i-gun. Early French visitors to the area translated this as *Lac la Biche* or Elk Lake. You'll still find an Elk Lake in the park today, just south of Lake Itasca, but it is a different body of water that the Ojibwe knew it as Man-i-do za'-gai-i-gun (the spirit's lake).

Henry Schoolcraft reached the source of the Mississippi in 1832 thanks to the help of his Ojibwe guide, Ozawindib. Rather than using the lake's Ojibwe name, Schoolcraft asked another companion, the Reverend WT Boutwell if he knew of a phrase in Latin or Greek that meant source or true head. Boutwell suggested the Latin phrase *veritas caput* could be translated as "true head." Schoolcraft then borrowed the middle letters of that phrase to coin the name "Itasca."

The spot where the river emerges from Lake Itasca today looks different than it did before the 1930s, when workers from the Civilian Conservation Corps (CCC), a Depression-era public works program, stabilized the area and prettied it up. Before this project, the area was marshy, so it was hard to tell where the river actually began. The CCC built a 44-foot long, seven-foot wide concrete dam and covered it with rocks to make the remade river outlet look natural. In 2020, the Minnesota Department of Natural Resources redid it again to improve its appearance.

The Mississippi has several distinct segments. Through the 500 miles of the Headwaters area, the Mississippi is a marshy stream that gradually widens into a shallow, rocky-bottomed river. The only gorge along the Mississippi is the narrow passage it cuts through the Twin Cities below the Falls of St. Anthony in Minneapolis.

South of the Falls, the upper Mississippi runs for 750 miles to its confluence with the Missouri River north of St. Louis. (Some folks count the upper Mississippi as running all the way to the Ohio River, but I like the upper, middle, and lower divisions.) A series of dams from Minneapolis to St. Louis constricts the flow of the river. They create slackwater pools that guarantee a minimum depth for barges, but they have also damaged the river's ecosystem.

The upper Mississippi is defined by limestone bluffs that were carved by water from melting glaciers at the end of the last ice age. As the glaciers melted, water stretched from bluff to bluff, forming an immense river known as Glacial River Warren that cut deep into the landscape. The bluffs are composed of layers of easily eroded sandstone at the base and dolostone at the top, a form of limestone that doesn't erode as easily. As water washes away the lower layers of sandstone, chunks of the dolostone cleave off, giving us the dramatic vertical bluff faces we see today along the upper river.

The valley along the upper river is as narrow as 1 ¼ miles at Prescott and as wide as six miles at Trempealeau. The tallest bluffs are around Great River Bluffs State Park near Dakota, Minnesota, and lowest around Prescott, Wisconsin.

The Mississippi River flows over a thin layer of clay, silt, loam, and sand on top of a stratum of glacial outwash that is 150 to 200 feet deep. You have to dig through a lot of sand and silt deposits to reach bedrock. There are several places where natural terraces formed that are well above the river. Most of the village of Pepin (Wisconsin) is on a terrace 45 feet above the river. Trempealeau (Wisconsin) is 60 feet above the river.

The upper Mississippi passes through the heart of the Driftless Area, 15,000 square miles in Minnesota, Wisconsin, Iowa, and Illinois that escaped crushing glacial masses during the most recent Ice Age. The area has no glacial drift (the rocky debris deposited by glaciers), hence the name Driftless Area. While surrounding areas are mostly prairies and forests, the Driftless Area is a landscape of steep cliffs, rolling hills, and deep valleys, carved by water.

> **WANT TO KNOW MORE** about the lock and dam system? Read about what it costs us.. .and who pays for it at StrongTowns.org: bit.ly/STwaterways

The Middle Mississippi River flows for 200 miles from the confluence of the Missouri River near Alton, Illinois, to the Ohio River confluence at Cairo, Illinois. As you travel south of St. Louis, this is the first stretch of river that is not dammed and the volume of water increases thanks to added flow from the Missouri River.

The lower Mississippi River begins at Cairo, Illinois, and ends at the Gulf of Mexico, a distance of nearly a thousand river miles. The river in this section is confined by tall levees on both banks but remains remarkably wild. It meanders through sub-tropical swamps and forests rife with wildlife. The river's natural floodplain extends up to a hundred miles wide in the Delta region of Mississippi and Arkansas (an area geologists call the Mississippi Embayment).

Below New Orleans, the Mississippi fans out into a lush delta of coastal swamps that the Mississippi River built over the past 7,000 years. The river no longer builds land in the delta, however, and Louisiana is losing coastal wetlands at an alarming pace. Much of the wetlands loss has been caused by oil and gas exploration in the area. In addition, the tall levees that line the river create a fast, narrow channel, so the river can no longer deposit the sediment that used to build land. Louisiana is making ambitious efforts to stem the loss of coastal wetlands, but the best-case scenario is to stop or slow the rate of land loss. Land that has already been lost to the Gulf of Mexico is unlikely to be restored.

A Few Facts About the Mississippi River

Ten states border the Mississippi River: Minnesota, Wisconsin, Iowa, Illinois, Missouri, Arkansas, Kentucky, Tennessee, Mississippi, and Louisiana. Here are a few other facts to help you out at that next trivia night.

MAJOR TRIBUTARIES

- Minnesota River
- St. Croix River
- Chippewa River
- Wisconsin River
- Iowa River
- Illinois River
- Missouri River
- Ohio River
- Arkansas River
- Yazoo River

WATER VOLUME (DISCHARGE)

The Mississippi River grows from a small prairie stream in northern Minnesota to a watery behemoth along the latter part of its course. At Lake Itasca, the Mississippi River's average discharge is about six cubic feet/second (cfs) or roughly 45 gallons of water. By the time the river reaches Saint Paul (Minnesota), its average flow has increased to about 12,000 cfs or 90,000 gallons of water. At Clinton (Iowa), just upstream from the Quad Cities, the average flow increases four-fold to about 49,000 cfs.

The average flow of the Mississippi River at Grafton (Illinois) jumps to 112,000 cfs after adding water from the Illinois River, then increases to 187,000 cfs at St. Louis after the Mississippi joins with the Missouri River. At Hickman (Kentucky), the average flow is 489,000 cfs or 2 ½ times the flow at St. Louis, thanks to the added flow from the

Ohio River. You'll generally find the highest volume of water in the Mississippi from Vicksburg to Red River Landing. At Vicksburg, the average flow of the Mississippi River is 679,000 cfs, which is over 100,000 times greater than the flow at Lake Itasca!

At Red River Landing, the Army Corps of Engineers diverts nearly one-third of the river's volume down the Atchafalaya River, so the average flow at Baton Rouge (576,000 cfs) is less than places upstream. The flow of the Mississippi River spreads out even more as it spiderwebs its way through the Louisiana Delta to the Gulf of Mexico.

The numbers above, though, only speak to the average volume of water in the river. Rivers are dynamic and rise and fall continually. At the extreme ends, the river can run up to ten times as high as the average flow or as low as one-tenth of it.

Still, the increased capacity in the river as it flows south is awe-inspiring. The record flow at St. Louis, for example, is roughly one million cubic feet per second (in 1844 and 1993), which is only twice the average flow at Memphis. While folks at Memphis would probably notice the extra water, they wouldn't be stuffing sandbags. On the other hand, the highest flow ever recorded was nearly 3,000,000 cfs during the 1927 flood, a volume that got everyone's attention.

Here's a table showing the average flow at five locations, plus record high and low flows at each spot, for the hundred or so years in which we've been keeping records.

Location	Average Flow in ft^3/second	Record High Flow in ft^3/second (year)	Record Low Flow in ft^3/second (year)
Bemidji	234	1,820 (1997)	16 (1998)
Saint Paul	12, 211	171,000 (1965)	632 (1934)
St. Louis	186,750	1,080,000 (1993)	27,800 (1937)
Vicksburg	678,700	2,272,000 (2011)	100,000 (1939)
New Orleans	577,167	1,320,000 (2011)	121,000 (2010)

LENGTH

The combined Mississippi-Missouri River system is 3,710 miles long (5,970 km), which makes it the fourth longest in the world after the Nile (4,160 miles/6,693 km), Amazon (4,000 miles/6,436 km), and Yangtze (3,964 miles/6,378 km) Rivers. The Mississippi River alone runs about 2,350 miles from northern Minnesota to the Gulf of Mexico.

In *Life on the Mississippi*, Mark Twain had a unique take on the river's dynamic length:

> "Therefore, the Mississippi between Cairo and New Orleans was twelve hundred and fifteen miles long one hundred and seventy-six years ago. It was eleven hundred and eighty after the cut-off of 1722. It was one thousand and forty after the American Bend cut-off. It has lost sixty-seven miles since. Consequently its length is only nine hundred and seventy-three miles at present...
>
> In the space of one hundred and seventy-six years the Lower Mississippi has shortened itself two hundred and forty-two miles. That is an average of a trifle over one mile and a third per year. Therefore, any calm person, who is not blind or idiotic, can see that in the Old Oolitic Silurian Period,' just a million years ago next November, the Lower Mississippi River was upwards

of one million three hundred thousand miles long, and stuck out over the Gulf of Mexico like a fishing-rod. And by the same token any person can see that seven hundred and forty-two years from now the Lower Mississippi will be only a mile and three-quarters long, and Cairo and New Orleans will have joined their streets together, and be plodding comfortably along under a single mayor and a mutual board of aldermen. There is something fascinating about science. One gets such wholesale returns of conjecture out of such a trifling investment of fact."

WIDTH

At its source, the Mississippi River is 20 feet wide. You'll hear many claims from folks stating that this part or that part of the river is the widest. The river is, in fact, much wider in most places today than it was before the lock and dam system was built on the upper river. The widest spot today is just north of Clinton, Iowa, where the river spans three miles. When the river ran naturally, the widest part was at Lake Pepin, which has a maximum width of 2 ½ miles. If you include the lakes in northern Minnesota that the river passes through, then the widest spot is actually Lake Winnibigoshish, which stretches up to 11 miles wide.

SPEED

At the headwaters, the river's surface speed is just over one mile per hour, while at New Orleans it is usually around three miles per hour. When the river is high, the current flows much faster, though. On the lakes in northern Minnesota and on Lake Pepin, there is little current. Just ask the folks who've tried canoeing there.

DEPTH

When the Mississippi River leaves Lake Itasca, it is only two to three feet deep. You can walk from one side to the other without getting your knees wet! Through Lake Pepin, the river depth averages 20-32 feet. Before the lock and dam system was built, sections of the upper Mississippi south of Lake Pepin were sometimes shallow enough in late summer that people could walk from one bank to the other.

Today the US Army Corps of Engineers maintains navigation structures (dams) and dredges to ensure a deep enough channel for barges. Although it is called the "nine-foot channel," the average depth in the main channel is typically closer to 12 feet. Away from the main channel, however, the water can still be very shallow. South of Cairo (Illinois), where the Ohio River joins the Mississippi, the river is often 20 to 50 feet deep. The deepest spot in the river is at New Orleans (near Algiers Point) where you'd have to submerge 200 feet to find the bottom.

DRAINAGE BASIN

The entire Mississippi River watershed covers 1.25 million square miles, which is the third largest in the world. The river drains 41% (1.25 million square miles) of the US (excluding Alaska and Hawaii), including parts of 32 states and two Canadian provinces. A drop of water from as far away as New York or Montana will end up in the Mississippi River.

The State of the River

The Mississippi River is in much better shape today than it was 50 years ago, but that's a pretty low bar. The river has much less of the stinky, visible pollution that it once had, at least in most places, which is great! Many cities still dump large volumes of untreated sewage into the river when their systems are overwhelmed, but it doesn't happen routinely.

Still, there are still significant issues that impair the health of the river. Agricultural pollution is a major problem. Many of the chemicals used to fertilize corn and soybean crops—nitrogen and phosphorus, in particular—wash into the Mississippi River and flow downriver where they settle into the Gulf of Mexico at the mouth of the Mississippi. This creates a large dead zone—6,000 square miles or so—where algae go crazy and devour all the dissolved oxygen so no other organisms can survive. That fertilizer runoff also sometimes accumulates in lakes and ponds leading to dangerous algal blooms that poison the water.

We've also disrupted the river's natural system of transporting sediment. There's too much of it accumulating in the upper Mississippi and not enough of it in the lower Mississippi. The navigation dams on the upper Mississippi trap sediment, causing the rich backwater habitats to slowly fill in. If we allow this to continue, the river will support less and less life over time.

In contrast, there's not enough sediment at the end of the river. The dams we built on the Missouri River trap a large proportion of the sediment that used to reach the Gulf of Mexico. In addition, the levees that line the river today have narrowed the channel and sped up its flow. As a result, the silt that the river still carries speeds into the deep water of the Gulf instead of building land at the delta. Levees, which cut off the river from its historic floodplains, force more water into the main channel and cause the river to reach higher stages more often than it used to. Our attempts to confine the river between walls of levees are actually causing more frequent—and bigger—floods.

There's also much we just don't know, because we haven't built the systems to monitor the quality of the water in the Mississippi. After all, if we knew the details of what's in the water, we'd feel obligated to do something about it and to hold accountable the people and the companies that foul the river.

Nearly everyone I talk to wants to know if it's safe to swim in the Mississippi. The short answer is yes! I've been swimming in the Mississippi in many places, and all six of my toes are still fine. Along the upper Mississippi, I am cautious about swimming in the river just below a major city after heavy rain, but that's the only time. On the lower Mississippi, I wouldn't swim in most of the river from Baton Rouge to New Orleans, although I have been swimming downriver of the Big Easy.

So yes, there are plenty of threats to the river's health but there are also plenty of places where it's perfectly safe to swim, fish, and enjoy the river without worry.

Go deeper into the world of the Mississippi with my other guide: *The Wild Mississippi: A State-by-State Guide to the River's Natural Wonders*. The *Wild Mississippi* describes the river's main ecosystems, the plant and animal life supported in them, and lists 166 places (public lands) to be near the river.

FLOODS

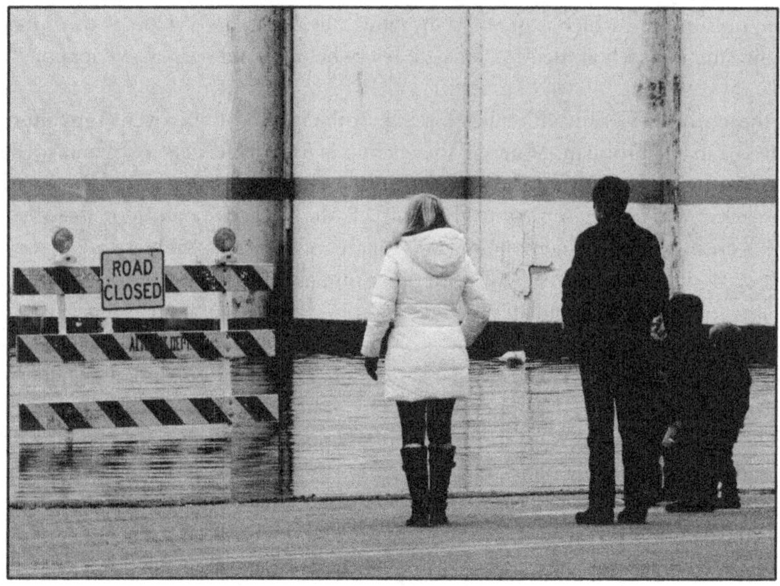

Flooding at Alton, Illinois

Rivers naturally rise and fall, a cycle that sustains the variety and abundance of life in their ecosystems. Some plants need high water to do well, while others won't grow until the ground dries out. Periods of high water also replenish ground water, as long as the water is allowed to seep in and isn't funneled away by concrete roads and drainage tunnels. In most years, river levels peak in spring with runoff from melting snow and early spring rains, but rain-induced rises in June and October aren't unusual.

We've tried to control the river by forcing it into a narrow channel with tall levees and floodwalls, but these efforts have ironically shot the river up to higher levels than it reached before our interventions. Water levels in the Mississippi and its tributaries are also more variable because of increased development in the watershed, draining of wetlands, and forcing runoff into concrete-lined drainage ditches.

The impact of development on river levels has been understood since at least 1852 when Charles Ellet wrote a report ahead of its time. He argued that higher water levels on the lower river were caused by: 1) increased farming in the floodplain; 2) the construction of levees; 3) building cutoffs that straighten the river and increase the surface speed of the water; and 4) the continued deposits at the delta that were extending the land mass further into the sea, which decreased the slope of the river and caused more water to back up into the land.

So we shouldn't be surprised that the Mississippi floods more often and more severely. These conditions threaten our levees and flood barriers, but the cost of raising them over and over again is prohibitive and doesn't solve the core problem. We need to re-examine our policies about what we build in floodplains and how we manage water.

Folks in the media like to throw around the phrase "100-year flood" to describe major floods because it makes for a nice sound bite, but the term is widely misunderstood.

It does not mean the type of flood that one would expect to happen only once a century. It just means there is only a 1% chance that the river would reach that specific height in any given year. There is the same 1% chance of that happening every year. Incidentally, the records we use to calculate those odds are only based on a century's worth of data, so today's 100-year flood could be tomorrow's 25-year flood as more data are collected and we continue to change the river.

We also believe common misconceptions about how flooding in one part of the river impacts the rest of the river. Flooding along the upper Mississippi River has little impact on river levels on the lower Mississippi (look again at the average and highest water volumes in the previous chapter). The volume of water in the Mississippi increases dramatically after the confluences with the Missouri and Ohio Rivers, so high water from the upper Mississippi—even record amounts—can be absorbed with minimal impact south of Cairo, Illinois. Record floods along the upper Mississippi River in 1993 did not push the lower Mississippi River above flood stage because the Ohio River—which contributes half of the volume of the Mississippi River south of Cairo—wasn't high.

Below is a summary of the big floods along the Mississippi since Euro-Americans began record keeping. (For more on Mississippi River floods, check out my book, *Mississippi River Mayhem: Disasters, Tragedy, and Murder on Ol' Man River.*)

1844

The year of the greatest flood along the middle Mississippi River—at least in terms of water volume—it had a small economic impact because few people lived near the river. No one had expected severe spring floods, but by early May, the river had spread 2 ½ miles across the floodplain. By June 7, the river was back in its banks, but it proved to be a brief reprieve.

The river rose again after more heavy rain and high water flowed down the Missouri River. At St. Louis, the river peaked again on June 27 at just over 41 feet, with an estimated flow of around one million cubic feet per second. Steamboats ran across corn fields. Water rose to the rooftops of houses in East St. Louis. The flooding convinced a lot of people to move out of the floodplain, at least for a while, and it put Kaskaskia, the former commercial and administrative center of Illinois, on a path to irrelevance.

1882

Heavy rains early in the year ushered in high water along the lower Mississippi from January to March. At New Orleans, the river was above flood stage for 91 days. Levees, most of them built by local and state governments, were breached from Memphis south. Water spread nearly 20 feet wide in places, inundating homes and washing out rail lines. The attic (or roof) became the primary living space for folks in flooded areas. This flood triggered the first major effort from the federal government to coordinate and build levees along the lower river.

Random Fact: When you hear that the Mississippi River hit 40 feet at St. Louis, that's not the actual depth of the river but an arbitrary measure of the river's elevation. In 1864, the Mississippi was extremely low. River levels observed in that year became the standard reference point for subsequent years. A river level of 0 therefore does not mean that there's

1927

Persistent heavy rain in the basin from the Illinois River south began in the winter of 1926 and pushed the Mississippi to record levels that peaked in April and May, creating one of the worst disasters in modern history. The Mississippi River overwhelmed levees and reclaimed 27,000 square miles of floodplain. The river stretched over 70 miles wide and covered the land up to 30 feet deep. The flood waters displaced 900,000 people; hundreds died.

The flood led to a major change in policy for flood management. Previous to 1927, the US Army Corps of Engineers had pursued a flood control policy that relied on levees at the expense of everything else. In 1928, Congress passed the Flood Control Act, and the Corps was forced to use a more varied approach to flood control by supplementing levees with floodways, outlet channels, channel stabilization, and tributary basins. This was quite possibly the largest flood control project in the world, at least at that time.

1937

Just ten years after the Big One, heavy rains in the Ohio River basin pushed the Ohio and lower Mississippi Rivers to near-record levels again. This time, unusually heavy rain in January raced off the frozen ground and into the rivers. The US Army Corps of Engineers blasted a hole in a levee to divert water down the newly designated Birds Point-New Madrid Floodway. Water had overtopped the levee but not enough to erode a big hole, so the Corps blew it open with dynamite. Thousands of migrant farmers and sharecroppers evacuated, especially in Missouri south of Cape Girardeau.

1965

The most destructive flood along the upper Mississippi north of the Quad Cities occurred in April 1965. Almost every river town recorded their highest water levels in that year. The early part of 1965 was unusually wet and cold. Ice on the river formed dams that, when they finally broke, sent torrents of water cascading downriver. Thousands of volunteers piled sandbags on top of makeshift levees to try to contain the Mississippi. At Winona, the river peaked on April 20 at a record 20.75 feet (flood stage was 12 feet) but the sandbag wall—up to 20 feet tall and nine miles long—held. The crest reached La Crosse on April 21, reaching a record 17.9 feet (flood stage is 12 feet). About 200 homes were flooded. Downriver at Prairie du Chien, a quarter of the city's homes were evacuated as the river peaked at a record 25.57 feet (seven feet above flood stage).

In the end, nineteen people died from the flooding, 40,000 people were displaced from their homes, and flooding caused an estimated $200 million in damages. This "100-year flood" was followed by another "100-year flood" just four years later.

1993

This was the record-breaking flood for communities along the central Mississippi valley from the Quad Cities to Cairo, Illinois (as well as for many communities along the Missouri River). The primary cause was heavy, persistent rain in the Upper Midwest. Already saturated soils could not absorb any more water, so rainwater ran directly to streams and rivers. At St. Louis, the river was above flood stage from April 1 to September 30—a total of 144 days. The river peaked on August 1 at 49.58 feet or just 2 ½ feet below the top of the city's flood walls. Flood stage is 30 feet. The Missouri River also reached record crests around the same time. High water wiped out 80% of the levees along the Mississippi and flooded 17,000 square miles. Flooding displaced 74,000 people and destroyed 50,000 homes. The disaster killed 52 people, most of whom died when they tried to drive over flooded roads. While the Mississippi reached record crests in 1993, the peak volume was probably lower than the 1844 flood.

In the aftermath, there was much public debate about the causes, including the relative contribution of development along the river and human interventions to control the river for navigation. A few communities decided to move out of the floodplain, including the small town of Valmeyer, Illinois, which relocated to the top of nearby bluffs. Some communities, though, insisted on building new, taller levees instead. At Chesterfield, Missouri, areas that were submerged under ten feet of water from the Missouri River are now flooded with strip malls and shopping centers.

2008

Some communities on the Mississippi River near its confluence with the Des Moines River saw levels that surpassed the 1993 records, although water levels did not stay high nearly as long. Flooding along tributaries was especially severe in Iowa. The Cedar River reached a record height and jumped its banks, devastating downtown Cedar Rapids. In Iowa City, the Iowa River rampaged through the middle of town.

2011

Another big year for flooding, especially along the lower Mississippi River. Early in the year, it seemed likely that the upper river was going to be hit hard. River levels stayed unusually high through the winter after a wet fall. In addition, the northern sections of the watershed had a lot of snow and much of it was still on the ground in early March. However, the snowpack melted gradually, and spring rains weren't especially heavy. Although water levels stayed high for weeks, flooding along the upper river was minor. It was a different story for the lower river, though.

The Ohio River watershed also had a deep snowpack. Relentless heavy rain in the spring in the Ohio and Missouri River basins dumped torrents of water into the Mississippi. The river gauge at Cairo, Illinois, reached a record high on May 2 at 61.72 feet.

On May 3, the US Army Corps of Engineers blasted a hole in the Birds Point Levee again, which sent water pouring into the 210-square mile Birds Point-New Madrid Floodway. Two hundred residents were flooded out and 130,000 acres of land was submerged, most of it farmland.

The high water crested at Memphis on May 10, just one foot shy of the record. Some tributaries backed up and flooded Memphis neighborhoods. The casinos in Tunica County closed for weeks. Many of them got wet. At Vicksburg, the river crested on May 18 at a new record high of 57.17 feet and didn't fall below flood stage (43 feet) until June 16.

On May 14, the Corps began opening gates of the Morganza Spillway to protect Baton Rouge and New Orleans. The spillway hadn't been used since 1973. That still wasn't enough to protect New Orleans, though, so on May 23 the Corps also opened gates on the Bonnet Carre Spillway, which diverted water to Lake Pontchartrain and the Gulf.

The Corps' flood protection system essentially worked as intended, but flood damages were still estimated at $5 billion. And the Corps spent hundreds of millions of dollars to rebuild the flood control system that was damaged in 2011.

2015/2016

One of the most unusual floods in memory took place at the end of 2015. In early November, the Mississippi River had dropped to just two feet on the St. Louis gauge and looked like it was headed toward its typical winter slumber, but heavy rains sent the river rising 12 feet in two days. More big storms drove the river up five feet on December 16 and another five feet three days later. Cold air holds less moisture, so heavy rains in winter are rare, which made the next downpour even more astonishing. Up to ten inches of rain fell over hundreds of square miles over three days around Christmas.

The Meramec River in suburban St. Louis roared out of its banks and forced the closure of two major interstate highways in St. Louis. At St. Louis, the Mississippi crested on New Year's Day at the third highest level in recorded history, although the amount of water in the river didn't even reach the top ten. Levees burst or were overtopped, and there were anxious moments for a whole bunch of people. Then the rains stopped, and the river fell as quickly as it had risen, leaving us all to wonder how much of the flooding was "natural" and how much we had caused it by altering the river so dramatically.

2019

And the floods keep coming. A wet spring followed a soggy winter over much of the central US. Steady rains drove rivers out of their banks. Water spilled out of the Ohio and Tennessee Rivers. The Missouri River raged out of its banks in Iowa, Nebraska, Kansas, and Missouri. The Arkansas River reached new heights. High water forced the closure of barge traffic on the Mississippi for weeks. In July, Hurricane Barry struck the Mississippi Delta when the river was still high, a co-occurrence that rarely happens.

In the end, the flood of 2019 was remarkable for the amount of time that the river stayed high. The Mississippi didn't set any records for crests or the volume of water it carried, but it pestered folks by refusing to go down for months. At Dubuque, Iowa, the Mississippi River stayed above flood stage for 85 consecutive days (the previous record was 34 days in 2011). At Baton Rouge, the Mississippi remained high for 211 days.

The river's managers, the US Army Corps of Engineers, opened the Bonnet Carre Spillway in February to divert water away from New Orleans. It was the first time on record they had opened it in back-to-back years. They had to open the gates again in May, which marked the first time they had used the Spillway twice in a single year.

A FOOTNOTE

In May 2011, I was in Grand Rapids, Minnesota, in the Headwaters region, and the river was high enough to flood a few low-lying roads. In St. Louis, the river was expected to peak a few feet above flood stage over the weekend. Meanwhile, record or near-record flood levels were rolling down the lower Mississippi. What was so remarkable to me at that moment was that each of these sections is really a different river. Flooding on one stretch has only minimal impact on the water levels in other stretches. Yet there we were in spring 2011, with flooding along these very different parts of the Mississippi River. I don't know what that means, but it sure was interesting.

PLANT AND ANIMAL LIFE

Bald Eagle

The Mississippi River cuts a thousand-mile path through the middle of the US and passes through several climates and micro-climates. In January, you'll need a parka in Minneapolis, but shorts may be fine in New Orleans. In spite of the differences, there's a lot of similarity in the types of plants and animals that live in or near the river. While you may not see Spanish moss in Minnesota, for example, you'll find catfish just about anywhere along the Mississippi. (For a deeper dive into the river's natural world, check out my book, *The Wild Mississippi: A State-by-State Guide to the River's Natural Wonders.*)

Plants

The Mississippi River is lined with dense forests that run most of its length (although less dense than they were a century ago). Close to the river, hardwood trees reach up toward the sky, providing cover for shade-loving plants. The flora in the floodplain forest are uniquely adapted to tolerate periods that are sometimes wet and sometimes dry.

Along the upper Mississippi, the trees in the floodplain forest consist mostly of silver maple, river birch, bur oak, green ash, hackberry, cottonwood, and swamp white oak. Below the canopy, you'll find buttonbush, plus plants such as nettles, gray-headed coneflower, ostrich fern, and cardinal flowers. As you travel south, cottonwood, hackberry, pecan, elm, and willow dominate the floodplain forests.

The bluffs along the upper river are lined with trees such as oak, hickory, and walnut. You can still find a few remnants of the prairies that used to be common atop the bluffs (sometimes called "goat prairies"), including the ones with impressive views at Maiden Rock Bluff State Natural Area near Stockholm, Wisconsin.

Along some sections of the upper Mississippi River, you can even find a few examples of a rare and fragile ecosystem called algific talus slope. A throwback to the Ice

Age, this ecosystem still exists today near the base of north- or east-facing bluffs. Sinkholes and underground ice caves vent cold air well into the summer months through cracks in the rocks. This uncommon ecosystem supports rare plants and animals, including the northern monkshood wildflower, cherrystone drop snail, and Pleistocene vertigo snails. In some places, this ecosystem also produces features nicknamed petrified waterfalls, which are basically above-ground stalactites that form when algae interact with certain minerals. A few examples of algific talus slope survive in the Driftless Area National Wildlife Area.

In the backwaters, you'll find plants that grow well in shallow water, such as wild rice, cattails, bulltongue arrowhead, American lotus, and waterlily. (What's the difference between lotus and water lily? Lotuses bloom in August and the flower stands upright; lily blooms float on the water. You can thank me later.)

The river also sustains a variety of wetlands. Fens and bogs (two types of peatlands) are common in the Headwaters Region of northern Minnesota. Fens have a high water table, peat up to six feet thick, and a current moving through them. They attract a wide range of plant life. Bogs are highly acidic and lack water movement, with a peat layer that can be as much as 30 feet thick.

The bogs—the Ojibwe's pharmacy, as Louise Erdrich wrote in *Books and Islands in Ojibwe Country*—have several unique plants, including tamarack, a deciduous conifer that turns bright gold in fall. You'll also find Labrador tea (*Ledum groenlandicum*)—and yes, those leaves do make a pretty good beverage. Orchids also thrive in the bogs, including the showy lady's slipper, a stunning blue orchid that is Minnesota's state flower. It blooms from early June to mid-July, along with a few other orchids.

Swamps also abound along the Mississippi. In the river's southern reaches, you'll find swamps dominated by bald cypress, with tupelo gum, swamp blackgum, swamp red maple, and green ash mixed in. These swamps also include unique plants called epiphytes, which includes bromeliads (like Spanish moss) and orchids. These plants wrap themselves around the trunks and branches of the trees and get most of their nutrients directly from the air instead of through the soil or from the host; they are not parasites.

Coastal marshes form at the mouth of the Mississippi River, where it meets the Gulf of Mexico. In these areas, fresh water mixes with salt water and the land is relatively new, as it is composed of sediments deposited by the Mississippi River over the last few centuries. Grasses such as roseau cane are common in the coastal marshes.

Animals

There is a much greater range of animal life along the Mississippi River than you might think. Deer are ubiquitous; it is the animal (other than squirrels) that you are most likely to see (or hit with your car).

If you are paying attention and have some luck, you may also catch sight of beaver, muskrat, otter, raccoons, turtles (maybe even a large snapping turtle), and fox. If you are really lucky, you might spot mink, a timber rattlesnake, or a massasauga rattlesnake. Rattlesnakes are timid and most likely will flee if you come anywhere near them, but they will strike out of self-defense if they are cornered or surprised. The timber rattlesnake is listed as a threatened species under the Endangered Species Act.

Animals you might hear but probably won't see include coyotes and bobcats. Black bear are increasingly common in some areas, including the forests of Minnesota, Wisconsin, Mississippi, and Arkansas.

If you are a birder, you probably already know about the Mississippi River flyway. Forty percent of all North American waterfowl migrate along the Mississippi River; 326 species of birds—one-third of all birds on the continent—migrate through in the spring and fall. That's a lot of birds!

Bald eagles move south in winter, while song birds and pelicans migrate along the river in spring and fall. Tundra swans make a pit stop along the river in late fall. Hawks, turkey, peregrine falcons, great blue heron, egrets, geese, ducks, cormorants, and turkey vultures are common and easy to see. While the number of bald eagles along the Mississippi increases dramatically in winter (they like to fish in the open waters around the dams), many bald eagles now nest along the Mississippi River, so in many places you can see bald eagles any time of year.

Even with the dramatic man-made changes to the ecology of the Mississippi River, fish still abound—260 species live in the river, which is one-quarter of all fish species in North America. Many species are threatened (pallid sturgeon and several species of mussel such as the Higgins' eye pearly mussel), but anglers' favorites like crappie, largemouth bass, striped bass, sunfish, walleye, catfish, white bass, and bluegill are still common. The river also abounds with carp, suckers, and buffalo fish.

The river is also home to four ancient species of fish: the bowfin, sturgeon, paddlefish, and alligator gar. The latter three are threatened or endangered. And of course, there are plenty of turtles and mussels. All of these are under pressure from invasive species like zebra mussels and the invasive silver and bighead carp, some of which jump high out of the water when disturbed (as seen on YouTube!).

Ticks and Mosquitoes

Mosquitoes and ticks are a fact of life along the Mississippi River. They can be annoying, but a few also spread diseases that can make you feel miserable, ticks especially. If you're going to spend time outside, you have to be ready to deal with them. It's not difficult, but it takes a little preparation.

Cover up. That's the easiest solution, and the one I follow 99.9% of the time. There's no substitute for wearing a hat, long sleeves, and long pants and checking your body for ticks after being outside (or having someone else check your body—wink, wink).

If you prefer to cover yourself with bug spray, here are a few tips. According to the US Centers for Disease Control and Prevention, there are only four chemicals that are proven mosquito and tick repellents:

- Picaridin (works against mosquitoes, ticks, chiggers, gnats, fleas): It irritates skin less than DEET but needs to be reapplied often; it doesn't have a scent. It's in products such as Avon Skin-so-Soft Bug Guard and Cutter Advanced.
- Lemon-eucalyptus oil: Is now widely available in the US. I'm a fan of Repel Lemon Eucalyptus; don't use lemon-eucalyptus oil on children under four years of age.
- DEET: The most widely used repellent, it comes in different concentrations: 5% will last about 90 minutes, while 100% will last ten hours; 20% will also keep the ticks away. It is oily and concentrations of 30% or greater should not be used on children.
- Citronella: Not as effective as DEET; at 10% concentration, citronella will only keep the bugs away for 20 minutes.

INDEX

A

Alexandria (Missouri) 270
Alma (Wisconsin) 115, 138, 140, 158–159
Alto Pass (Illinois) 399
Alton (Illinois) 7, 265, 315–317, 320–324, 326, 330, 334, 342, 406, 410
Amtrak 299, 314, 330, 367
Anna (Illinois) 399
Arsenal Island (Illinois) 7, 232–233, 251
Audubon, John James 370
Author's Picks 20, 35, 81, 86, 106–107, 121, 125, 144, 152, 172, 191, 194, 196–197, 205, 254, 305, 312, 324–325, 350, 357, 362–364, 379, 391

B

Bakeries/Pastries 20, 60, 65, 68, 87, 105–106, 118, 125, 145, 152, 172, 203, 220, 292, 296, 307, 313, 325, 368, 377
Baxter (Minnesota) 45, 60
Bay City (Wisconsin) 116–117, 125
Beiderbecke, Bix 240, 242, 245
Bellevue (Iowa) 5, 209, 217–218
Bemidji (Minnesota) 6, 12, 15, 17–18, 22, 24–26, 29, 41, 59, 407
Best of the Great River Roads Lists 6
    Festivals 6
    Museums 6
    Native American Historic Sites 6
    Park and Public Lands 6
Bettendorf (Iowa) 226, 229, 231, 235, 238–239, 241, 244, 253, 256
Bettendorf, Joseph 231, 238
Bike Trails 16, 29, 59, 80, 89, 150, 202, 220, 323, 345, 347
    Mississippi River Trail 8
Birch Bark Scrolls (Wiigwaasabakoon) 12
Black Hawk (Sauk leader) 161, 170, 227–228, 240, 267–268, 273
Black Hawk War 161, 186, 188–190, 209, 216, 233, 268, 270, 273
Bog 17, 416
Boone, Daniel 216, 382, 384
Brainerd 42, 44–45, 47, 56, 59
Breweries/Brewpubs 6, 20, 38, 40, 58, 60, 64, 66, 86, 105, 119, 121, 152, 180, 194, 196, 203, 206, 218, 238–239, 244, 250, 254, 289, 294, 313, 324, 351, 361, 377, 379, 396, 398–399
Brice Prairie (Wisconsin) 154
Brooklyn (Illinois) 342
Buffalo City (Wisconsin) 138, 157
Bunyan, Paul 17, 35, 40, 45, 59, 70
Burlington (Iowa) 260, 263, 265–267, 275, 290–292, 299

C

Cache River 401
Cahokia (Illinois) 332–333, 337–338, 356, 364, 369
Cahokia Mounds State Historic Site 6, 332, 365, 385
Cairo (Illinois) 7, 341, 384–391, 393, 402, 406–408

Calumet (Minnesota) 39
Camanche (Iowa) 211, 214, 221
Camp Lacupolis (Minnesota) 113, 120
Camp Ripley (Minnesota) 47, 61
Canoe Rentals. See Outfitters
Canoeing/Kayaking. See Paddling, Tips
Cape Girardeau (Missouri) 6, 381–383, 391–392, 394, 396
Casinos 117, 178, 191, 239, 241, 250, 291, 321, 361, 365, 391
Cassville (Wisconsin) 179, 182
Centerville (Wisconsin) 155, 330
Chautauqua (Illinois) 319–320
Cherokee Indians 391
Chester (Illinois) 372–373, 376, 378
Chickasaw Indians 385
Chippewa Indians. See Ojibwe Indians
Chippewa National Forest 27–30
Chisholm (Minnesota) 32, 39
Civil War 50, 75, 77, 79, 158, 186, 189, 201, 223, 233, 251, 266, 271–272, 286, 293, 302–304, 316, 323, 356, 383, 388, 392, 402
Clemens, Andrew (Artist) 171, 178
Clemens, Samuel. See Twain, Mark
Clinton (Iowa) 210–212, 214, 219–221, 258, 406
Cobden (Illinois) 399
Cochrane (Wisconsin) 156–157
Collinsville (Illinois) 366–367
County Fairs 200, 205, 397
Crane Meadows National Wildlife Refuge 64
Crosby (Minnesota) 53
Crow Wing (Minnesota) 44, 46, 60
Curling 25, 31, 155, 319
Cuyuna Iron Range. See Iron Range, Cuyuna
Cypress Creek National Wildlife Refuge 401

D

Dakota (Minnesota) 149, 405
Dakota Indians 13, 23, 46–47, 54, 71, 74–78, 82–83, 92–93, 102–103, 109, 111, 114, 118, 130–131, 161, 228, 273, 338, 404
Davenport (Iowa) 226, 228–232, 235–236, 239–241, 243–244, 246, 253, 256
Davenport, Colonel George 209, 230, 232–233, 247, 251, 257, 270
De Soto (Wisconsin) 163, 166, 174–175
Deere, John 187, 194, 228, 236–237, 244, 253, 312
Deerwood (Minnesota) 53
Dickens, Charles 387, 395
Distilleries 152, 203, 238, 399
Dodge, Frank (Mystery Series) 129, 206, 248, 255, 427
Driftless Area 129, 175, 202, 208, 405, 416
Driftless Area National Wildlife Area 416
Dubuque (Iowa) 6, 165–166, 171, 183–184, 186, 190–191, 194, 196–197, 199–200, 206, 237

Dubuque, Julien 184–186, 194
Dupo (Illinois) 338
Dylan, Bob 39

E

Eagles 6, 9, 15, 29, 118, 121, 140, 247, 415, 417
East Alton (Illinois) 326
East Carondelet (Illinois) 337, 364
East Dubuque (Illinois) 186–187, 190, 200
East Moline (Illinois) 194, 226, 229, 236–237, 244, 254, 256
East St. Louis (Illinois) 326, 339–341, 345, 359, 365, 367, 386–387
Effigy Mounds National Monument (Iowa) 6, 177
Elkader (Iowa) 169, 181
Elsah (Illinois) 315, 319, 328
Erdrich, Louise 48, 82, 416
Eveleth (Minnesota) 40

F

Farmers Markets 10, 21, 39, 65, 68, 88, 107, 119–120, 123, 148, 153, 173–174, 178–179, 182, 197, 205, 207, 218, 221, 225, 245, 290, 292, 294, 296–297, 308, 313, 324, 363–364, 378, 396, 398–399
Ferries. See Mississippi River, Ferries
Ferryville (Wisconsin) 162–163, 173–174
Fish Shops (Fresh Fish) 172, 177, 222, 224, 294, 329
Fishing 25–26, 35, 55, 59, 64, 127, 141, 176, 181, 194, 206, 223, 391, 400, 403, 409
Floods. See Mississippi River, Floods
Floyd, George 91
Fort Madison (Iowa) 183, 260–261, 263, 267–269, 274, 293–294, 296, 299, 305
Fort Ripley, Village (Minnesota) 46–47
Forts (Historic) 33, 46–47, 49, 56, 73–79, 83, 92–94, 102, 112, 134, 161, 170, 172, 183, 189, 201, 228, 233, 253, 267–269, 293, 371, 373–374, 379, 383, 385, 388, 392
Fountain City (Wisconsin) 138–139, 157–158
Fox Indians. See Meskwaki Indians
Frank Dodge. See Dodge, Frank (Mystery Series)
Frontenac Station (Minnesota) 112, 126
Frontenac, Old (Minnesota) 112, 120
Fulton (Illinois) 208, 211–212, 215, 221–222
Fur Trade 13, 38, 47, 50, 54, 74–78, 83, 92, 94, 102, 137, 160–161, 163, 170, 183, 230, 263, 270, 278, 317, 333, 348–349, 351

G

Galena (Ilinois) 163, 183–184, 188–190, 199–206, 212, 215–216, 237, 301
Garland, Judy 38
Glaciers 14, 61, 129, 222, 399, 405
Glen Haven (Wisconsin) 169
Godfrey (Illinois) 315, 317–319, 325
Grafton (Illinois) 7, 315, 319–322, 328–330, 406
Grand Rapids (Minnesota) 6, 30, 32–33, 35, 37, 41
Grand Tower (Illinois) 384, 397, 400
Granite City (Illinois) 343, 345, 366–367

Great River Road 5, 7–9, 17–18, 25, 37, 73, 99, 166, 235, 260, 309, 311, 315, 319, 322–323, 332, 344–345
History 5
Most scenic drives 7
Without a car 8
Grey Cloud Island (Minnesota) 102–103
Guttenberg (Iowa) 166, 168–169, 180–182

H

Hager City (Wisconsin) 110, 117, 125
Hamilton (Illinois) 261, 270–272, 275–277, 297
Hampton (Illinois) 226, 232, 237, 243, 254
Hannibal (Missouri) 6, 270, 300–302, 304–307, 311, 327
Hanover (Illinois) 212, 216–217, 225
Harpers Ferry (Iowa) 164, 176–177
Hartford (Illinois) 323–324, 327, 366
Headwaters. See Mississippi River, Headwaters
Hibbing (Minnesota) 34, 39–40
Hickman, Rev. Robert 95
Hiking Trails 16, 29, 35, 55, 59, 81, 120, 149, 155, 172, 177–178, 194, 204, 217, 254, 288, 297, 328–329, 346, 378, 380, 391, 400–401
Ho Chunk Indians 150, 188, 277
Homer (Minnesota) 148

I

Illini Indians 371
Illinois River 320–322, 328, 330, 371, 406
Iron Range
Cuyuna 34, 43–45, 52–53, 56, 58
Mesabi 32, 34, 37, 39
Ironton (Minnesota) 53
Itasca State Park 6, 10, 12, 14–16, 18, 21, 24, 26, 41

J

John Deere Company. See Deere, John
Joliet, Louis 323
Jonesboro (Illinois) 399–400
Joplin, Scott 336, 351

K

Kaskaskia (Illinois) 333, 356, 370–373, 378–379
Kaskaskia River 371–372
Kayak Rentals. See Outfitters
Keller, Helen 264
Kellogg (Minnesota) 140–141
Keokuk (Chief) 161, 227, 273, 295
Keokuk (Iowa) 138, 257, 260–261, 263, 269–272, 274–277, 285, 288, 293, 295–296
Kickapoo Indians 369
Kimmswick (Missouri) 368

L

La Crescent (Minnesota) 7, 133, 149
La Crosse (Wisconsin) 7, 107, 116, 129, 131, 133–136, 139, 149, 151–154

La Guillannée 374, 378, 380
La Moille (Minnesota) 149
Lacrosse (the sport) 134
Lake City (Minnesota) 47, 113, 120
Lake Pepin 108–110, 113, 115, 117, 121, 124–125, 408
Lansing (Iowa) 127, 162–164, 166, 175
LeClaire (Iowa) 7, 226, 228, 230, 235, 237–238, 241
LeClaire, Antoine 228, 230, 236, 240
Leopold, Aldo 267
Lilydale (Minnesota) 73, 99, 102
Lincoln, Abraham 51, 186, 204, 303, 308–309, 316, 321, 346, 388
Lindbergh, Charles 48, 61, 64–65, 106, 325
Little Crow 76, 131, 161
Little Egypt 381, 393
Little Falls (Minnesota) 46–48, 56, 61, 64
Logging Industry 15, 17, 28–30, 33–35, 41, 46, 55, 59, 113, 115, 121, 135, 137, 139–140, 158, 162, 164, 211, 219, 228, 230, 240, 279, 301, 383, 388
Looney, John 233, 250, 255
Lovejoy (Illinois). See Brooklyn (Illinois)
Lovejoy, Elijah 265, 315–317, 321, 342
Lynxville (Wisconsin) 7, 162, 173

M

Madison (Illinois) 343, 366–367
Maiden Rock (Wisconsin) 108, 116, 125
Makanda (Illinois) 400–402
Marquette (Iowa) 165–166, 177–178, 180
Marquette, Father Jacques 165, 179, 323
Marshall, Thurgood 389
Mazzuchelli, Father Samuel 170, 183, 201, 240, 280, 289, 291, 293
McGill, Pearl 262, 264
McGregor (Iowa) 160, 165–166, 171, 178, 180
Meachum, John Berry 334
Meachum, Mary 347
Meat Markets/Butcher Shops 10, 58, 64, 102, 141, 155, 172, 222, 377
Mendota (Minnesota) 74, 76–77, 83, 93–94
Mesabi Iron Range. See Iron Range, Mesabi
Meskwaki Indians 161, 168, 184–186, 190, 208, 214, 216, 227, 233, 247, 263, 267–268, 273, 277, 338
Metropolis (Illinois) 390, 401
Miller City (Illinois) 403
Mining
  Coal 236, 272, 343, 384
  Iron Ore 34, 39, 42, 370, 385
  Lead 168, 183–184, 186, 188–190, 201, 204–205, 237, 371, 375
  Sand 116
Minneapolis (Minnesota) 6, 41, 49–50, 71, 73, 75, 77–83, 87–89, 92, 94, 99, 107, 170, 233, 405, 415
Minnehaha Falls 78, 82

Minneiska (Minnesota) 141

Minnesota City (Minnesota) 130, 141

Mississippi River 8
- Animal Life 416
- Books/Essential Reads 7
- Cruises, Day/Sightseeing 83, 102, 105, 151, 178, 194, 221, 253, 307, 329, 357
- Cruises, Overnight 8, 237
- Depth 408
- Drainage Basin 408
- Ferries 166, 182, 322, 330, 376, 380
- Floods 47, 95–96, 109, 131, 161, 165, 178, 188, 210, 214, 231, 252, 269, 274–275, 301–302, 317, 319, 321, 338, 340, 342, 346, 358, 370–372, 374, 378, 384–385, 387, 401–402, 409–410, 413
- Geology 404–406
- Headwaters 16, 24, 54, 169, 267, 405, 408
- Headwaters Dam Project 27, 55
- Length 407
- Locks and Dams 81, 97, 109, 127, 135, 138–140, 158, 169, 187, 214, 219, 229, 252, 272, 274, 295, 321, 405, 408
  - Visiting 7
- Names, Native American 404
- Plant Life 415
- Rapids 32, 45, 49, 59, 188, 228–230, 237, 252, 269–270, 272, 274–275, 277–278, 366, 382
- Seasonal travel 8
- Speed of the Current 408
- State of the River 409
- Tributaries 406
- Water Volume (Discharge) 406
- Width 408

Mississippi River Parkway Commission. See Great River Road

Missouri River 307, 332–333, 346, 366, 385, 405–406, 409

Moline (Illinois) 115, 201, 226, 228, 233, 235–236, 239, 244, 251–254, 256

Montrose (Iowa) 261, 272, 274

Mosquitoes 8, 47, 386, 417

Mound City (Illinois) 388, 394, 402

Murphysboro (Illinois) 394

Muscatine (Iowa) 6, 257–264, 288–290

N

National City (Illinois) 326, 341

Nauvoo (Illinois) 6–7, 134, 257, 260–261, 263, 268, 274, 276–279, 281–283, 285–287, 297–298, 303

Nelson (Wisconsin) 110, 114, 123

O

Ohio River 386, 390, 400, 402, 405–408

Ojibwe Indians 12–14, 21–23, 27–29, 33, 46, 49, 54–55, 74–75, 83, 404, 416

Onalaska (Wisconsin) 136, 150, 154

Orchids 17, 416

Outfitters 8, 20, 38, 53, 60, 177, 221, 291, 357, 400

Overlooks 6, 59, 149–150, 158, 174, 177–179, 181, 217, 219, 223, 254, 273, 288, 290, 307, 312, 323, 365, 378, 391–392, 397

Oxcarts. See Red River Trail

P

Paddling, Tips 8, 27, 35, 59, 83, 105, 121, 129, 357, 400
Paddle Share Stations 81, 83, 105
Paul Bunyan. See Bunyan, Paul
Pepin (Wisconsin) 115, 123, 405
Popeye 373, 379
Port Byron (Illinois) 7, 226
Port Louisa National Wildlife Refuge 291
Potosi (Wisconsin) 189–190, 199, 205–206
Powwows 6, 21–22
Prairie du Chien (Wisconsin) 6, 74, 134, 137, 160–161, 163–166, 168, 170, 172, 183, 185, 188, 228
Prairie du Rocher (Illinois) 370, 374, 376, 379–380
Prairie Island Indian Community (Minnesota) 6, 76, 109, 111, 117
Prescott (Wisconsin) 405
Pyles, Charlotta 271–272

Q

Quad Cities 127, 226, 228–229, 231, 233, 235, 239–240, 243–244, 252–253
Quimby, Mildred 168
Quincy (Illinois) 274–275, 278, 280, 284, 300–304, 309, 312–314

R

Reads Landing (Minnesota) 113, 121
Red River Trail 51, 94
Red Wing (Dakota Indian Leader) 111, 131, 161
Red Wing (Minnesota) 7, 107–108, 110–112, 118–119, 126, 137, 139, 154
Revolutionary War 161, 169, 382
Rice, Wild 9, 12, 14, 22–23, 27–28, 54–55, 60, 74, 86, 416
Tips for Buying 23
Robinson, Harriet 75
Robinson, Jane Muckle 97
Rock Island (Illinois) 127, 209, 221, 226–229, 232–233, 235–237, 247, 250–252, 255, 271, 273, 287
Rock Island Arsenal. See Arsenal Island (Illinois)
Russell, Lillian 219–220

S

Sabula (Iowa) 210, 212, 216, 219
Saint John's Bible 67
Saint Paul (Minnesota) 6, 9, 27, 44, 51, 73, 75, 77–80, 87–89, 92–95, 97, 99, 104–107, 112–114, 116, 137, 154, 162, 170, 406–407
Sainte Genevieve (Missouri) 6, 369–370, 372, 374, 376–377
Sandy Lake (Minnesota) 54–55
Sartell (Minnesota) 48–49
Sauget (Illinois) 339, 365
Sauk Indians 49, 161, 168, 208, 216, 227–228, 233, 247, 263, 267–268, 270, 273, 277
Sauk Rapids (Minnesota) 49–50
Saukenuk 227, 273
Savanna (Illinois) 210, 215–216, 221–222, 224, 256

Schultz, Charles 98
Scott, Dred 75, 350, 355
Shawnee Indians 369, 382
Shawnee National Forest 399–401
Sinsinawa (Wisconsin) 183
Sioux Indians. See Dakota Indians
Sliced Bread 231
Smith, Joseph 275, 278, 280–281, 283, 288, 297–298
South Saint Paul (Minnesota) 96, 99, 107
Sporting Events
  Baseball 87, 104, 220, 241, 291, 361, 365
  Basketball 87
  Football 87
  Soccer 87, 361
St. Anthony Falls 77–78, 81, 83
St. Cloud (Minnesota) 42, 49–51, 56, 64, 66–67, 78, 107, 154
St. Donatus (Iowa) 208–209, 217
St. Louis (Missouri) 5–8, 41, 74–75, 79, 162, 176, 185, 228, 253, 262, 264–265, 267, 269, 274, 277, 285–286, 300–301, 305, 307, 315–316, 319–320, 325–326, 329–330, 333–338, 340, 343–351, 356–357, 359–364, 366–374, 376, 382, 387–388, 405–407
Stacy, Jess 383
Stockholm (Wisconsin) 108, 115–116, 124, 415
Swisshelm, Jane Grey 51

T

Thebes (Illinois) 385, 393, 403
Thebes Gap 403
Thomson (Illinois) 215, 221–223
Thoreau, Henry David 111
Ticks 417
Tower Rock 384, 391, 397
Trail of Tears 391
Trempealeau (Wisconsin) 137, 154–156, 405
Trempealeau National Wildlife Refuge 155
Trenton (Wisconsin) 117
Tugfest 7
Twain, Mark 6, 116, 180, 205, 258, 270, 272, 300–301, 305–306, 308, 314, 407
Two Rivers National Wildlife Refuge 328

U

Upper Mississippi River National Wildlife and Fish Refuge 127, 154, 223–224

V

Venice (Illinois) 342, 345
Virginia (Minnesota) 40

W

Wabasha (Minnesota) 6, 110, 114–115, 121, 127, 133
Wadlow, Robert 317, 323, 331
Warsaw (Illinois) 269–270, 272, 274, 277, 279, 281–282
Water Trails 8, 16, 83, 105, 141, 155, 176, 179, 291, 307, 401, 403

Weaver (Minnesota) 141
Wexford (Iowa) 176
Weyerhaeuser, Charles 48, 61, 64
Weyerhaeuser, Frederick 47, 140, 228, 247, 258
Wild Rice. See Rice, Wild
Wilder, Laura Ingalls 123
Wineries 124–126, 155, 157, 159, 196, 203, 206, 220, 225, 298, 308, 328, 377, 399
Winnebago Indians. See Ho Chunk Indians
Winona (Minnesota) 6, 107, 129, 131, 137, 141, 144
Winter Travel/Activities 6, 8–9, 17, 24–26, 29, 39, 55, 59–60, 83, 102, 107, 109, 141, 149–150, 155, 200, 202, 218, 221, 247, 313, 417
Wolf Lake (Illinois) 401
Wood River (Illinois) 326–327

Y

Young, Joe 5

About the Author

Dean Klinkenberg, the Mississippi Valley Traveler, is on a mission to explore the complex history, diverse cultures, and rich world of the Mississippi River Valley, from the Headwaters in northern Minnesota to the Gulf of Mexico. He's driven over 140,000 miles along the Great River Road, hiked to the tops of bluffs, paddled on the Mississippi River in canoes, and floated in luxury for a few days as a guest lecturer on the *American Queen*. He is the author of the Mississippi Valley Traveler guides, The Wild Mississippi, and the Frank Dodge mystery series.

Looking for more photos and information about the Mississippi River? Head to his website: MississippiValleyTraveler.com.

You can find out more about the Frank Dodge mysteries at DeanKlinkenberg.com or claim a FREE copy of one of the books at: deanklinkenberg.com/free-book

Thanks!

You can't do work like this for a lot of years and not have a whole bunch of people to thank. I'm deeply grateful to all the folks who took the time to chat with me about where they live and/or to extend a helping hand. As always, I am especially grateful to the dedicated volunteers and staff at historical societies, museums, and libraries who work with little fanfare to watch over our cultural artifacts, so we can all learn a little something about our communities. And thanks to my husband, John, for his on-going support and love in this road trip through life with the Mississippi River as our companion.